14 $\frac{75}{=}$

# Garrie L. Tufford

MAY 26 1966

*Regional Geomorphology of the United States*

*By the same author*

PRINCIPLES OF GEOMORPHOLOGY

# Regional Geomorphology
## of the United States

WILLIAM D. THORNBURY

*Department of Geology*
*Indiana University*

John Wiley & Sons, Inc.
New York · London · Sydney

*To the memory of the illustrious
Evans, Lesley, Powell, Bowman, and Fenneman,
each a pioneer in regional geomorphology
in his own day and way*

# *Preface*

For many years, in the United States, the study of the origins of land forms has been called geomorphology, whereas discussion of the regional distribution and the geomorphic histories of landscapes has been called physiography. It seems to me that this inconsistency should be eliminated, and with this idea in mind the present book is entitled *Regional Geomorphology of the United States*. Since work on this book began, Hawaii and Alaska have been added to the United States; therefore chapters on Hawaii and Alaska have been added despite my lack of firsthand knowledge of the land forms of these states.

For many years Fenneman's two volumes have served as the main sources of information on the regional geomorphology of the United States. Despite their many excellent qualities, parts of these books have become out-of-date, and a need has arisen for a treatment of the subject that incorporates the knowledge that has been acquired during the past three decades. I hope that the present volume to some degree meets this need.

I have had two primary goals in mind during the writing of this book. The first and major objective has been to provide a book that may serve satisfactorily as a text for courses dealing with the regional geomorphology of the United States. I have made no attempt to cover all aspects of this subject; rather it has been my goal to provide a book which may serve as the core of a course in regional geomorphology around which each teacher may pattern a course to fit his particular preferences. A second objective has been to provide a book that may serve as a useful reference for persons who are not special-

ists in regional geomorphology but who wish to familiarize themselves with the regional geomorphology of our country.

I have made no attempt to provide an exhaustive bibliography. In the main, the references cited are those that have proven most useful, and I believe that they provide a fairly satisfactory reference framework from which it is possible to extend readings in as much detail as desired.

Restriction of discussion to one volume has limited treatment of most topics and necessitated the omission of some that might logically have been included. I hope, however, that this has not lead to superficiality. Choice of topics and length of discussions inevitably reflect my interests and competence. Variation in the quality of discussion in part reflects the degree of my familiarity with different parts of our country, but it also is an indication of the amount of up-to-date information available for various parts of the United States. For many areas the only geomorphic information obtainable is to be found in papers that treat geomorphology only incidentally, and for some parts of the country few modern geomorphic studies have been made.

To do justice to the regional geomorphology of an area as large as the United States presupposes a knowledge of petrology, structure, stratigraphy, and geologic and geomorphic history which no person likely possesses. Dependence on the geologic literature necessitates an evaluation of it and consequent acceptance of some ideas and rejection of others. Doubtless I have been guilty of numerous mistakes of judgment, but I hope that I have presented fairly the varying viewpoints. Some readers may feel that controversial ideas have not been given enough attention. Some have been discussed at length, but to have developed all of these as fully as they might have been would have resulted in a book of excessive size and cost. Much more attention could well have been given to the rocks and structures of each province, but here also space was limited.

I have assumed that the reader is familiar with the Fenneman regional classification of the United States, and with two exceptions I have followed it. Although this classification could doubtless be improved in certain areas, it was beyond the scope of this book to attempt such a revision.

It is impossible to give credit to all the individuals who have contributed in major or minor ways to development of the ideas expressed. First of all, indebtedness should be acknowledged to the innumerable authors of books and articles which I have drawn on so freely. Without the information provided by them the book could not have been written. I have attempted to cite the major sources of information, but not all could be so identified without unduly breaking the continuity of reading with excessive references. Most of the articles listed under "Additional References" have been drawn on to some degree.

I wish to extend my sincere thanks to the many individuals and organizations that have so generously provided illustrative materials. Particular thanks is due John S. Shelton for the many excellent aerial photos which he made available to me. Several of the photos provided by him were obtained on special flights made for the purpose of obtaining a desired photo. John Peace worked long and conscientiously on the line drawings and diagrams, under trying conditions during part of the time, and I am deeply indebted to him.

Since much of my philosophy of geomorphology was obtained from the late C. A. Malott, some of his ideas appear consciously and doubtless others unconsciously. A. O. Woodford, J. Hoover Mackin, H. T. Stearns, and Troy Péwé read parts of the manuscript and offered many helpful suggestions, as did F. A. Melton, who read the entire manuscript. Clyde Wahrhaftig very kindly made available an open-file report on Alaska which aided greatly in writing what was probably the most difficult chapter.

I would be unappreciative indeed if I did not express my thanks to Indiana University for two sabbatical leaves during which I worked on the text; without them the book would never have been completed. Finally, to my wife, Doris, I am grateful for her encouragement at times when completion of the manuscript seemed remote indeed and especially for her assistance in typing and proofreading.

To all these people and the many unnamed persons to whom I am indebted I extend my deepest thanks, with the hope that they may find in the book a slight reward for their efforts without feeling in any way responsible for shortcomings attributable to my inability to make the most of their suggestions.

WILLIAM D. THORNBURY

*Bloomington, Indiana*
*November 1964*

# Contents

# Backgrounds of Regional Geomorphology

## DAWN OF THE REGIONAL CONCEPT

The birth of a science or subscience is usually difficult to date. Most sciences do not have clear-cut origins but rather emerge slowly as the result of many contributions, often made by persons long forgotten. Such has been true in that field of geology that has long been called regional physiography but that now, it seems to the writer, may more appropriately be designated as regional geomorphology. Probably not long after scientists (they were not yet even called geologists) began to observe land forms and speculate about their origin, they also noted that there were regional variations in the character of landscapes. This observation, by whomever it was first made, marks the birth of the concept of regional geomorphology.

As a distinct branch of geology regional geomorphology was late in emerging. As a recognizable branch of geology it can hardly be dated earlier than the latter part of the 19th century. However, there were persons who thought in terms of regional geomorphology much earlier than this. Just as the recognition of the evidence of former more extensive glaciation in the Alps started with the observations of the Alpine peasants, so very likely the beginnings of regional geomorphology started with men who were by no means to be considered scientists. White (1953) has pointed out that Robert Beverley, an early Virginia planter, in 1705, in a publication entitled "History and present State of Virginia," recognized the geomorphic differences between the areas of Virginia which we now designate

as the Coastal Plain, Piedmont, and Folded Appalachians. If any single individual deserves credit for being the first to grasp the concept of regional geomorphology in the United States, it is, according to White (1951), Lewis Evans, who in 1755 published his "Map of the Middle British Colonies" and "An Analysis of a general map of the middle British colonies." In the "Analysis" is a clear recognition of several of the major geomorphic provinces of the eastern United States. This description appears to be the first attempt to delineate geomorphic regions as we think of them today. The following extract from Evans' "An Analysis of a general map of the middle British colonies" gives an idea of how modern his differentiation of the geomorphic regions was:

The land, South Westward of Hudson's River, is more regularly divided, and into a greater Number of Stages than the other. The first Object worthy Regard, in this Part, is a Rief or Vein of Rocks, of the Talky or Isinglassy Kind, some two or three, or Half a Dozen Miles broad; rising generally some small Matter higher than the adjoining Land; and extending from New-York City South Westerly by the Lower Falls of Delaware, Schuylkill, Susquehanna, Gun-Powder, Patapsco, Potomack, Rapahannock, James River and Ronoak. This was the antient maritime Boundary of America, and forms a very regular Curve. The Land between this Rief and the Sea, and from the Navesink Hills South Westward as far as this Map extends, and probably to the extremity of Georgia, may be denominated the *Lower Plains* [Coastal Plain], and consists of Soil washt down from above, and Sand accumulated from the Ocean . . . .

From this Rief of Rocks, over which all the Rivers fall [Fall Line], to that Chain of broken Hills, called South Mountain [Blue Ridge], there is the Distance of 50, 60 or 70 miles of very uneven Ground, rising sensibly as you advance further inland; and may be denominated the *Upland* [Piedmont Plateau]. This consists of Veins of different Kinds of Soil and Substrata, some Scores of Miles in Length; and in some Places overlaid with little Ridges and Chaines of Hills. The Declivity of the whole gives great Rapidity to the Streams; and our violent Gusts of Rain have washt it all into Gullies, and carried down the Soil to enrich the Borders of the Rivers in the *Lower Plains* [Coastal Plain]. These Inequalities render half the Country not easily capable of Culture; and impoverishes it, where torne up with the Plough, by daily washing away the richer Mould that covers the Surface.

The *South* Mountain is not in Ridges like the *Endless* Mountains [Folded Appalachians], but in small, broken, steep, stony Hills; nor does it run with so much Regularity. In some Places it gradually degenerates to Nothing, not to appear again for some Miles, and in others spreads several Miles in Breadth. Between the South Mountain and the higher Chain of the Endless Mountains (often for Distinction called the North Mountain and in some Places the Kittatinni, and Pequilin,) there is a Valley of pretty even, good Land, some 8, 10 or 20 miles wide, and is the most considerable Quantity of valuable Land that the English are possesst of; and runs through New-Jersey, Pensilvania, Mariland and Virginia. It has yet obtained no general Name, but may properly enough be called Piedmont, from it situation. Besides Conveniences always attending good Land, this Valley [Great Valley] is every where enriched with Limestone.

The *Endless Mountains* [Folded Appalachians], so called from a Translation of the Indian Name, bearing the Signification, comes next in Order. They are not confusedly scattered, and in lofty Peaks overtopping one another, but stretch in long uniform Ridges, scarce Half a Mile perpendicular in any Place above the intermediate Vallies. Their Name is expressive of their Extent, though no Doubt, not in a literal Sense.

There are several Chains of the Endless Mountains which have not come to my Knowledge, and had they been so, might have filled several Places which lie vacant in the Map. But so far as we are acquainted with them, we observe that each Chain consists of a particular Kind of Stone, and each different from the rest; and these Differences continue for their whole Extent, as far as I can learn.

To the North Westward of the Endless Mountains is a Country of vast Extent, and in a Manner as high as the Mountains themselves. To look at the abrupt Termination of it, near the Sea Level, as is Case on the West Side of Hudson's River, below Albany, it looks as a vast high Mountain; for the Kaats Kills, though of more lofty Stature than other Mountains in these Parts of America, are but the Continuation of the Plains on the Top; and the Cliffs of them, in the Front they present towards Kinderhook. These UPPER PLAINS [Appalachian Plateau] are of extraordinary rich level Land, and extend from the Mohocks River, through the country of the Confederates. Their Termination Northward is a little Distance from Lake Ontario, but what it is Westward is not known. . . .

This description written more than 200 years ago seems remarkably modern and certainly displays a recognition of geomorphic regions as we think of them today. However, development of anything that approached a science of regional geomorphology was still a long way off.

Regional geomorphology as a distinct subscience could hardly develop until widespread observations of geology and associated land forms had been made, and these were not made systematically in the United States until the era of geological surveys. Even then concepts of regional geomorphology were to a large degree incidental by-products. The first state geological survey was organized in Massachusetts in 1830. In the decade between 1830 and 1840 fifteen such organizations came into existence. Merill (1924) designated the 50 years between 1830 and 1880 as "the era of state geological surveys." The United States Geological Survey was not organized until 1879; it was an outgrowth of the so-called Hayden, King, Powell, and Wheeler Surveys of the West, which were inaugurated between 1867 and 1869 and continued for a period of about 10 years.

Not many men connected with the state or federal surveys were particularly interested in land forms per se. Emphasis was on discovery of valuable mineral resources, and most attention was given to such aspects of geology as stratigraphy, structure, petrology, and paleontology. Two men might be singled out from this era whose interests were broad enough that they gave considerable attention to the regional aspects of the landscapes of the areas in which they worked: J. P. Lesley and Major J. W. Powell.

J. P. Lesley was an assistant to H. D. Rogers, who headed the first state geological survey of Pennsylvania, organized in 1836, and was himself head of the second state geological survey of Pennsylvania, organized in 1874. To a considerable degree he was what we would today call a geomorphologist. At least he had an interest in land forms and their regional variations as related to geologic controls. One of the first maps that attempted to correlate configuration of the mountains in eastern Pennsylvania with the geology and structure of the area appeared in 1856 in Lesley's *Manual of Coal and Its Topography* (see Fig. 1.1). Lesley claimed that this map, which was completed in 1841 but

not published until 1856, was the first American map to show the characteristics of the topography of part of the eastern United States.

More significant and comprehensive was a map of the United States 15 feet square on which Lesley placed his interpretation of all the available information dealing with the topography of various states. Figure 1.2 shows a part of this 15-foot map as shown in a paper presented in 1869 entitled "Notes on a map intended to illustrate five types of earth-surface in the United States between Cincinnati and the Atlantic seaboard." In reading Lesley's discussion of this map one is impressed with the fact that he fully appreciated the regional variations in topography that today represent the bases for recognition of physiographic or geomorphic provinces. In discussion of the map he stated:

The result was very striking. Familiar as I have been for years with the topography of every part of the United States, and of Canada, east of the Mississippi River, I was surprised at the beauty of the whole representation now for the

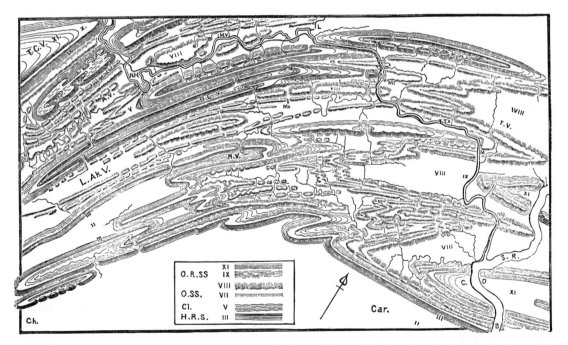

FIG. 1.1   Map of topography on folded strata in Pennsylvania.   (*After J. P. Lesley, Manual of Coal and Its Topography, J. B. Lippincott and Co.*)

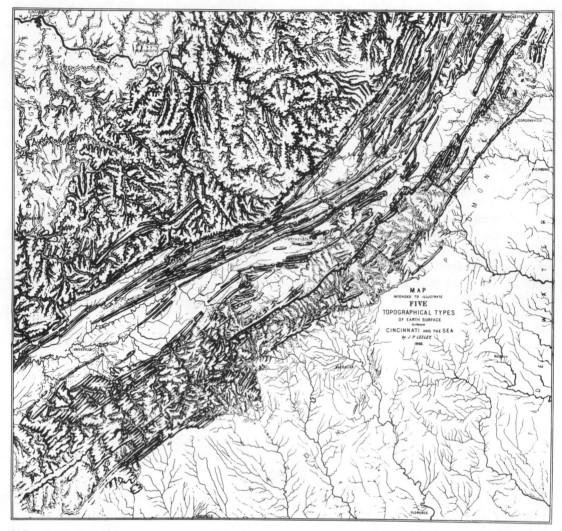

FIG. 1.2    Portion of a map prepared by J. P. Lesley to show various types of topography between the Atlantic seaboard and Cincinnati, Ohio.    (*Trans. Am. Phil. Soc.*, **13**.)

first time made to the eye. The correlation of parts was very fine, in a geological sense. The plateau of the coal, commencing in Alabama and cut off square by the Hudson, contrasted strongly with the essentially unbroken run of the Quebec Group and Laurentian System, from Georgia to the extreme east end of Canada; while the open valley of the Lower Silurians, everywhere keeping the two systems apart, was most remarkable. The sweep of the Lower Devonian and Upper Silurian escarpments around the end of the Catskill, with their long straight lines through New York and their curve through western Canada, was likewise beautiful. But the charm of the map lay in its unmistakable utterances respecting different topographical types of earth-surface or strongly contrasted systems of erosion, lying in masses side by side, or running for long distances in parallel belts.

Thus, for instance, the eye takes in at a glance the whole Blue Ridge, Highland, and Green Mountain belt, but in echelon arrangement, with irregular summit lines, rising with knobs and peaks from 3000 to 7000 feet above the sea.

Behind it runs the belt of the Appalachians, composed of interminably long and narrow barrow-mountains, with level summits, seldom 1000 feet in height, looped and gophered in an intricate and artificial style, with lens-shaped covers in the northern part; and on the other hand, in the Southern States, terminating in pairs of perfectly straight ridges, cut off short by faults.

Behind these lies the Great Cumberland-Alleghany-Catskill Plateau, with its horizontal geology and its quaquaversal, arborescent drainage-system, boldly contrasting with the Appalachian topography in front of it, and settling the questions of mode and agency in favor of slow aerial denudation.

Still further west, the low finger-shaped bounding ridges and central plains of the Blue Grass Country of Kentucky and Ohio shows another allied type.

And in the east, the wide belt of low sand-hills, southeast of the Blue Ridge, and the immense cretaceous and tertiary flats of the tidewater country, crenulated with bays and covered with dismal swamps, presents a fifth, differing from all the rest.

It might be argued that Lesley was fortunate in that much of his work was done in Pennsylvania, a state with strongly marked geomorphic regions, but numerous other geologists had worked in the same area without seemingly having been impressed with the marked topographic contrasts present in the state; at least they gave them only passing notice.

Major Joseph Wesley Powell was a man of many accomplishments, but we are here interested in his contributions to the development of a science of regional geomorphology. His work in the western United States, particularly in the Uinta Mountains and Colorado Plateaus, led to numerous significant contributions to the science of what is now called geomorphology. Powell not only made significant contributions to an understanding of land form evolution, but he also grasped the concept of geomorphic regions. A paper published by Powell in 1895 entitled "Physiographic regions of the United States" represents the first attempt to divide the entire United States into geomorphic regions as we conceive them today. Regarding this attempt Powell stated:

It will be noticed that an old custom of describing great physiographic regions in units of basins has not been followed. Against that plan are insuperable objections. Where there are large rivers, there are large basins, and such are again subdivided into ever smaller and smaller basins; and where there are oceans and gulfs, there are many small disconnected basins; so that the basin unit divided the country into very unequal parts, and fails to exhibit the association of great features that are intimately connected in physiographic history. Gradually as the new science of physiography has grown, physiographic regions have come to be recognized; and an attempt is here made, by map and verbal description, to define the principal regions of the United States, exclusive of Alaska.

The regions here delineated are held to be natural divisions, because in every case the several parts are involved in a common history by which the present physiographic features have been developed. They have been characterized by the more prominent features used in the name.

In dividing the United States into a few great physiographic regions, it is not found possible always to draw lines with exactness. Often one region blends with another, the transformation in general characteristics being marked by a general change. There are some lines of division clearly drawn by nature within narrow limits; other divisions are imperfectly marked by a low gradation from one to the other.

Powell's map of physiographic regions of the United States (Fig. 1.3) broadly resembles our present mapping of physiographic regions. Rather interesting departures from present usage are seen in the area that now encompasses the Southern Rocky Mountains province and in the western part of the Central Lowlands province. Powell called the Southern Rocky Mountain region the Park Mountains. It is surprising that major emphasis was placed upon the intermontane parks present in this area as a distinguishing feature of this region rather than upon the geology and topography of the mountains. In the western part of the Central Lowlands region emphasis is placed upon the major agency responsible for the topography through the use of the terms "Ice Plains" and "Water Plains."

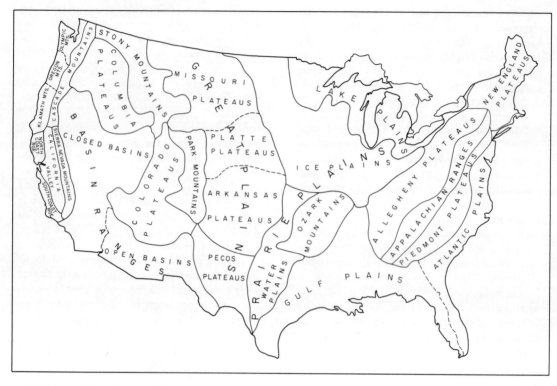

FIG. 1.3    Map of geomorphic regions in the United States.    (*After J. W. Powell, Nat. Geog. Soc., Mon.* 3.)

## PERIOD OF STATE PHYSIOGRAPHIES

Powell's work apparently had considerable influence on workers in the field of regional geomorphology, for during the next 30 years some ten state physiographies were published. These were as follows.

| Date | Author | State |
|------|--------|-------|
| 1896 | C. F. Marbut | Missouri |
| 1898 | R. D. Salisbury | New Jersey |
| 1899 | Cleveland Abbe, Jr. | Maryland |
| 1900 | R. T. Hill | Texas |
| 1902 | R. S. Tarr | New York |
| 1916 | Lawrence Martin | Wisconsin |
| 1907 | L. G. Snider | Oklahoma |
| 1918 | W. B. Clark | Maryland |
| 1922 | C. A. Malott | Indiana |
| 1925 | L. LaForce et al. | Georgia |

Interest in the regional geomorphology of individual states seems to have lagged since 1925. Only one state physiography has been published since then, "Evolution of the California landscape," by N. E. A. Hinds, published in 1952.

## FIRST REGIONAL MAPS

Following publication of Powell's 1896 map of the physiographic regions of the United States there appeared during the next 20 years a number of maps that were attempts at regional classification of the United States. Among such maps were those by Davis in 1899, Gannett in 1902, Brooks in 1906, Bowman in 1911, Blackwelder and Dryer in 1912, and Tarr and Von Engeln in 1913. These maps varied as to their bases of classification: some were physiographic in nature; some were based upon combinations of physiography, soils, climate, vegetation, or other factors. But they were significant, in that they pointed up the possibility of dividing the country into regions having similarity in various geographic or geologic characteristics.

## FIRST REGIONAL TEXT

Publication in 1911 of *Forest Physiography*, by Isaiah Bowman, marked an important milestone in the development of regional geomorphology. Although Bowman did not quite break away from the geographer's concept of natural regions and as a consequence devoted considerable space to discussion of the climate, soils, and vegetation, the book was essentially a regional geomorphology of the United States. Approximately three-fourths of its pages were devoted to what we would today call regional geomorphology, and the remaining one-fourth to a discussion of climate, soils, and vegetation. Considering the time of its publication, this was an excellent book and undoubtedly did much to stimulate interest in regional geomorphology.

## ORIGIN OF THE FENNEMAN CLASSIFICATION

At the 1913 meeting of the Association of American Geographers papers were presented by W. L. G. Joerg and N. M. Fenneman dealing with the possibility of dividing the United States into natural subdivisions. Joerg's paper considered natural subdivisions as having a physical basis dependent on structure, relief, climate, and vegetation; Fenneman's suggested subdivisions that were essentially geomorphic in nature. Fenneman's paper, which was published in 1914 in the *Annals* of the Association of American Geographers, appears to have been the first attempt to define the boundaries of suggested physiographic units. At the next meeting of the Association of American Geographers, in Chicago in 1914, a committee was appointed to devise a systematic division of the United States into physiographic units. This committee consisted of M. R. Campbell and F. E. Matthes of the United States Geological Survey, Douglas Johnson of Columbia University, Eliot Blackwelder, then of the University

of Illinois, and N. M. Fenneman of the University of Cincinnati, who was appointed chairman.

The detailed work on this project was delegated to a subcommittee consisting of Campbell, Matthes, and Fenneman. The results of this committee's work were incorporated in a map of the United States showing physiographic units of three orders, major divisions, provinces, and sections. This map, along with the naming and classification of the various units, constituted the report of the committee made at the 1916 meeting of the Association of American Geographers. At this same meeting Fenneman presented a paper entitled "Physiographic divisions of the United States," which appeared in print in the spring of 1917. This paper was not an official part of the committee's report, but in general it agreed with the committee's judgments. The map nomenclature and classification suggested by the 1916 committee report were officially accepted and put to use by the United States Geological Survey. The 700 reprints of Fenneman's 1917 paper were soon exhausted, and in 1921 a second edition of 600 copies was run off. In 1928, a revised and enlarged third edition was published.

In none of the three editions of Fenneman's papers was there much description of the topography of the various geomorphic units. There remained a need for such descriptions, along with background discussion of their geology and geomorphic histories. This gap was largely filled with publication of Fenneman's *Physiography of Western United States* in 1931 and *Physiography of Eastern United States* in 1938. These two volumes have long served as the standard references on the regional geomorphology of the United States.

Loomis' *Physiography of the United States*, published in 1937, combines a discussion of the origin of land forms with a regional description and as a consequence treats most of the physiographic subdivisions rather briefly. Atwood's *The Physiographic Provinces of North America*, published in 1940, has many good features, but it was written more from the viewpoint of the geographer than from that of the geologist; its treatment of most geomorphic units is rather brief, and it departs somewhat from the classification system set up by the Fenneman committee.

## THE NATURE OF GEOMORPHIC REGIONS

*Criteria for Recognition of Geomorphic Units*

Development of a system whereby the United States is divided in geomorphic regions of varying degrees of magnitude implies that there are available criteria for recognition of such regions. Recognition of geomorphic regions involves a consideration of the questions of what is a geomorphic unit and what are the fundamental bases for establishment of such units.

Some of the early subdivisions made of the United States, such as that of Joerg (1914), recognized so-called natural regions. These regions were hardly geomorphic units, for they were based mainly on such controls as climate and vegetation. Today such divisions, if used by geographers, are commonly called geographic regions. To a large degree Atwood's *The Physiographic Provinces of North America* makes use of such units as a basis for discussion. It is true that there may be a marked resemblance between some geographic and some geomorphic regions, but they are not necessarily the same; particularly when the geographer deals with areas in terms of dominant activities within them, he may depart considerably from a geomorphic definition of regions.

Bowman (1911) defined a physiographic (geomorphic) region as "a tract in which the topographic expression is in the main uniform." So far as the writer has been able to determine, Fenneman in none of his writings ever formally defined a physiographic or geomorphic unit. Hinds (1952), in the latest of the state physiographies, rather indirectly defined a geomorphic unit when he stated "California may be divided into a number of units called geomorphic provinces . . . , each of which is characterized by a distinguishing geological record, particularly in the later part of earth history, and by more or less uniform relief features or combination of features throughout its area." A definition that

the writer learned from his college teacher, C. A. Malott, and has used over the years is as follows: "A physiographic [geomorphic] unit is an area or division of the land in which the topographic elements of altitude, relief, and type of land forms are characteristic throughout and as such is set apart or contrasted with other areas or units with different sets of characteristic topographic elements."

Definitions are man-made things and in themselves are important only in so far as they convey a basic idea or concept. The concept of a geomorphic unit is certainly important in the science of regional geomorphology and needs to be thoroughly understood, not only as to what it implies but also as to what the bases are for recognition of such units. Only then can the problems that are encountered in attempting to divide any large segment of the earth's surface into geomorphic units be fully appreciated and dealt with consistently.

Fenneman (1928) stated that "all orders of [geomorphic] divisions rest ultimately on existing differences in topography and elevation." He pointed out that the dominant features of topography may be explained in terms of three control factors, structure, process, and stage, as taught by W. M. Davis. Davis' influence upon geomorphic thinking is not as strong today as it was in 1928, and there are those who would certainly question the importance, if not the reality, of stage as a determining topographic condition. It is difficult, however, for the writer to see how any geomorphologist can question the importance of structure and process in the determination of topographic characteristics. Dietz (1952) suggested that the topography of any area can be defined in terms of (*a*) formative tectonics, (*b*) internal structure, (*c*) erosional and sedimentational processes acting on the land, and (*d*) the intensity of the above processes and the length of time that they have been operating. Except for the substitution of "length of time" for "stage" (there are many who would contend that this is a significant change), this is saying pretty much the same thing that Davis taught.

That there is no uniformity in thinking as to what constitutes the proper bases for distinguishing geomorphic units may be demonstrated by looking at the criteria used in the various state physiographies listed above for dividing the particular states into geomorphic units.

| Date | Author | State | Stated Bases for Divisions of State |
|------|--------|-------|-------------------------------------|
| 1896 | Marbut | Missouri | Principally geologic structure |
| 1898 | Salisbury | New Jersey | Geologic structure, altitude, and topography |
| 1899 | Abbe | Maryland | Geology, altitude, relief and topography |
| 1900 | Hill | Texas | Soil, climate, geologic structure, drainage, human culture |
| 1902 | Tarr | New York | No clear statement |
| 1916 | Martin | Wisconsin | Contrasting altitude, relief, and topographic forms |
| 1922 | Malott | Indiana | Altitude, relief, and type and relationships of land forms |
| 1925 | LaForce et al | Georgia | Altitude and relief, grouping of the features or relief pattern, size and scale of features, nature of surface |
| 1952 | Hinds | California | Geologic history and uniformity of relief features |

### Bases for Recognition of Geomorphic Units

Two things stand out in the above classifications: (*a*) the great variety of criteria used and (*b*) the need for clearly distinguishing between physiographic (geomorphic) and geographic units. Most geologists would agree that in the simplest analysis a geomorphic unit has an individual topographic expression which may be related to certain control factors such as the geology (including geologic structure in the narrow sense of the word) and the geomorphic processes that have operated in the area through certain periods of geologic time. Some may like to think that the geomorphic processes have attained a certain stage of landscape evolution; others may prefer to think only that they have been at work for a certain length of geologic time.

We may well ask what is implied by the term "topographic expression." In its simplest analysis it probably involves the four topographic factors of altitude, relief, form, and interrelationships of the landscape features. Regardless of how complex the geologic structure of the area may be, how involved its geomorphic history has been, and whatever its stage of development in a presumed geomorphic cycle may be, its individuality can be most simply and directly expressed in terms of altitude, relief, and type of

land forms present. Thus the explanatory description that was so much emphasized by W. M. Davis and his followers is not necessary to setting up bases for division of a land surface into geomorphic units. However, division of land areas into such units and description of these units solely in terms of altitude, relief, and land forms would make rather dull reading and throw little light on the geologic or geomorphic history of the units.

It will probably be granted by most geomorphologists that the topographic expression or condition of any area can be adequately explained in terms of the three control factors of structure, process, and stage (in the broad sense of this last term). This is equivalent to saying that a certain region possessed an initial geologic framework, as determined by the kind and arrangement of its rocks; this geologic structure has been subjected to gradational processes which have produced a certain assemblage of land forms; and the characteristics of these land forms are to a certain degree related to the length of time that the geomorphic processes have been at work. This amounts to saying that given a certain geologic framework, the topographic condition or expression of an area is largely determined by its geomorphic history.

The geomorphic history may have been simple or complex; it may have been brief or long; but whatever the circumstances, the influence of geologic structure persists and is strongly reflected in the landscape characteristics. It is thus not surprising that there is commonly a close correlation between geomorphic and geologic units, for in most areas the geology is one thing that is essentially unchanging, at least in terms of the period of time during which our present topography developed. However, there are geomorphic units whose distinctive characteristics show little correlation with bedrock geology. This is particularly true in the areas of later Pleistocene glaciation. Here process has been the all important control factor in the development of the existing topography. Even here, however, bedrock geology cannot be ignored completely. In varying degrees the thickness, lithology, and topographic expression of the glacial drift was influenced by the kind of rocks over which the glaciers moved. Furthermore, postglacial erosion has already begun to remove the glacial cover and exhume the bedrock geology; before long it will again have significant expression in the landscape. This has already happened in varying degrees in the areas of pre-Wisconsin glaciation in central United States.

*Boundary Line Problems*

The distinctive nature of a particular geomorphic unit usually stands out rather clearly. In such areas, for example, as the Appalachian Highlands the contrasts in geology and landscape characteristics are so marked that the differences between the Piedmont Plateau, Blue Ridge, Valley and Ridge, and Appalachian Plateaus provinces are readily seen and appreciated. However, in that section of the Piedmont province known as the Piedmont Lowland, a lowland area because it is developed on relatively weak Triassic sedimentary rocks, the topographic contrast between it and the adjoining Coastal Plain province is not sharp at all. Basically there is little difference between the topographic expression of the two areas, but there are marked differences in rock types and ages and in their geomorphic histories which justify recognition of two different geomorphic units. The topography of southwestern Ohio and southeastern Indiana is little different in general appearance from the adjacent area across the Ohio River in Kentucky, yet the area north of the river is mapped as a part of the Till Plains section of the Central Lowlands province and the area south of the Ohio River as a part of the Lexington Plain section of the Interior Low Plateaus province. Grounds for this division are found in their different geomorphic histories: one area has been glaciated, the other has not.

Conversely, we may have within a major geomorphic unit areas that have distinctly different topographic expression. This constitutes grounds for subdivision of the region into smaller units so as to have a minimum of anomalous topography within each unit. Thus geomorphic provinces are divided into sections, and sections are divided into what may be called districts or regions. Division of the country into smaller and smaller units would eventually result in geomorphic units with reasonably homogeneous topography throughout. However, unless exceedingly small subdivisions are established, which would result in classifications exceedingly detailed and tedious, we are likely to have within most geomorphic units areas that depart in some degree from the characteristic topographic expression. Our goal in setting up geomorphic subdivisions should be, as Fenneman (1928) stated, that "each division to be described should be as homogeneous as possible; that is, it should admit of the largest number of general statements before details and exceptions become necessary."

For much of the United States regional subdivision has not extended beyond sections or provinces. In those states for which state geomorphologies have been written subdivision has been carried further, but as yet there is no general agreement on the names given to the units of lower ranks than sections. Several of the Western provinces have not yet been subdivided into sections. The classification proposed by the Fenneman committee marked important progress in regional geomorphology, but there remains a need for further refinement.

Classifications of any sort are to a considerable degree artificial. They represent man's attempt to pigeonhole natural phenomena into distinct compartments with sharply drawn boundaries between them. In nature, clear-cut boundaries are the exception rather than the rule; most geomorphic boundaries are transitional in nature. An escarpment comes as near as any topographic feature to representing a sharp change from one topographic area to another; but even escarpments become irregular in plan and may have outliers associated with them. The distinctiveness of the boundaries of the various geomorphic provinces and subdivisions of the Fenneman classification therefore varies greatly. Many natural boundaries exist that can be recognized with little difficulty, but in some areas there are no natural boundaries, and artificial lines must be drawn to separate two geomorphic units.

It is entirely possible to have two strongly individualized geomorphic units separated by indefinite boundaries. This is true of the boundary between the northern part of the Basin and Range province and the adjacent Columbia Plateau province as well as for the boundary between the Floridian section of the Coastal Plain province and the adjacent East Gulf Coastal Plain and Sea Island sections. Sometimes, as Fenneman (1928) pointed out, geomorphic regions, instead of having a transitional zone between them, may interfinger. This is true where the Western Young Drift section of the Central Lowlands province abuts against the extension of the Laurentian Highland of Canada into the United States known as the Superior Upland.

The problem of outliers is a common one, sometimes on a small scale, sometimes on a large scale. The general principle followed is that outliers belong to the geomorphic unit of which they are geographically a part rather than to the area to which they are more closely akin geologically and geomorphically. Thus the numerous mountain uplifts east of the northern Rocky Mountain front, such as the Bearpaws, Judith, Little Rocky, and other mountains, belong with the Great Plains province even though geologically and geomorphically they resemble the Rocky Mountain province. The Black Hills represent an outlier of Rocky Mountain geology and landscape that is large enough and distinctive enough to merit being recognized as a separate section of the Great Plains Province.

## Work to Be Done

It should be recognized that although the report of the Fenneman committee marked an important step in the division of the United States into geomorphic units, there remains a need for further refinement of this classification. As our knowledge of the regional geomorphology of the country improves, refinements of boundaries will become possible, and resectioning of some of the provinces may prove desirable. At the time the committee report was made the Rocky Mountains provinces were not even divided into sections, presumably for lack of sufficient information; this needs to be done. For most of the provinces it will ultimately be possible to divide sections into units of lesser magnitude with resulting greater homogeneity of topography within each area.

Discussions in the following chapters mainly follow the classification set up by the Fenneman committee, and it is largely taken for granted that the reader is familiar with this classification. For the Columbia Plateau province and the Californian portion of the Pacific Border province other classifications are followed, because they seem better suited to effective discussion of the regional geomorphology of these areas.

## REFERENCES CITED

Atwood, W. W. (1940). *The Physiographic Provinces of North America*, Ginn and Co., New York, 536 pp.

Bowman, Isaiah (1911). *Forest Physiography*, John Wiley and Sons, New York, 759 pp.

Dietz, R. S. (1952). Geomorphic evolution of the continental terrace (continental shelf and slope), *Am. Assoc. Petroleum Geologists Bull.*, **36,** 1802–1819.

Fenneman, N. M. (1914). Physiographic boundaries within the United States, Assoc. Am. Geog., *Annals*, **4,** 84–134.

——— (1917). Physiographic divisions of the United States, Assoc. Am. Geog., *Annals*, **6,** 19–98.

——— (1928). Physiographic divisions of the United States, Assoc. Am. Geog., *Annals*, **18,** 261–353.

——— (1931). *Physiography of Western United States*, McGraw-Hill Book Co., New York, 534 pp.

——— (1938). *Physiography of Eastern United States*, McGraw-Hill Book Co., New York, 714 pp.

Hinds, N. E. A. (1925). Evolution of the California landscape, Calif. Dept. Nat. Resources, Div. Mines, *Bull.* 158, 240 pp.

Joerg, W. L. G. (1914). The subdivision of North America into natural regions: a preliminary inquiry, Assoc. Am. Geog., *Annals*, **4**, 55–83.

Lesley, J. P. (1856). *Manual of Coal and Its Topography*, J. B. Lippincott and Co., Philadelphia, 224 pp.

—— (1869). Notes on a map intended to illustrate five types of earth-surface in the United States, between Cincinnati and the Atlantic seaboard, Amer. Philos. Soc., *Trans.*, N.S. 13, pp. 305–312.

Loomis, F. K. (1937). *Physiography of the United States*, Doubleday, Doran and Co., New York, 350 pp.

Merrill, G. P. (1924). *The First One Hundred Years of American Geology*, Yale University Press, New Haven, 772 pp.

Powell, J. W. (1895). Physiographic regions of the United States, Nat. Geog. Soc., *Monograph* 3, pp. 65–100.

White, G. W. (1951). Lewis Evan's contributions to early American geology, Ill. Acad. Sci., *Trans.*, **44**, 152–158.

—— (1953). Early American geology, *Scientific Monthly*, **76**, 134–141.

ADDITIONAL REFERENCES

Davis, W. M. (1915). Biographical memoir of John Wesley Powell, Nat. Acad. Sci., *Biograph. Memoir*, **8**, 11–83.

—— (1915). Biographical memoir of Peter Lesley, Nat. Acad. Sci., *Biograph. Memoir*, **8**, 155–240.

# 2

# *The Continental Margins*

Most discussions of the regional geomorphology of the United States have ignored the continental margins.[1] Justification for this omission may

have existed in the past, when knowledge of the continental margins was meagre, but this excuse can no longer be offered. The continental margins are a part of the continental platform, and their geologic history has been more intimately associated with the continents than with the ocean basins. Along much of the coast of the United States the land forms seen above sea level extend seaward onto the continental shelf. Much of the presently submerged continental

[1] The term continental margin as here used includes the transitional zone between the continents and the ocean basins and commonly consists of three recognizable parts, the continental shelf, the continental slope, and the continental rise. In this chapter we are concerned primarily with the continental shelf and to a lesser degree with the continental slope.

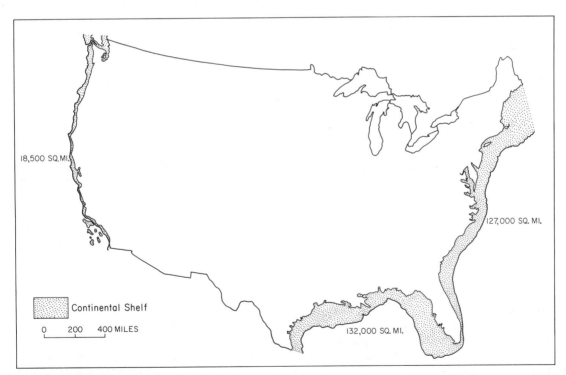

FIG. 2.1   Map showing extent of continental shelves around conterminous United States.   (*After J. B. Carsey, Am. Assoc. Petroleum Geologists Bull.*, **34**.)

shelf was land during part of either Tertiary or Pleistocene time, during which subaerial erosion shaped the major relief features. It therefore seems logical that a treatment of the continental shelves should be included in a discussion of the regional geomorphology of the United States, particularly in view of the fact that the shelves display regional topographic variations comparable to those found on land. These topographic variations are distinctive enough that it would be entirely possible to divide the shelf areas into geomorphic divisions comparable to those recognized on land.

## EXTENT OF SHELF AREA

The continental shelf off conterminous United States varies in width from as little as 10 miles along some parts of the Pacific coast to as much as 250 miles along the northern Atlantic coast, where the entire coastal plain is submerged. According to Thomasson (1958) the average width of the continental shelf is 80 miles along the Atlantic coast, 65 miles along the Gulf of Mexico, and 20 miles along the Pacific coast. The total area of the continental shelf adjoining conterminous United States is between 275,000 and 290,000 square miles (see Fig. 2.1).

## CONTINENTAL MARGIN ALONG ATLANTIC COAST

Topographically the continental shelf off the eastern United States can be divided into three sections: (1) the area from the Bay of Fundy southward to Cape Cod, (2) the part from Cape Cod southward to Cape Hatteras, and (3) from Cape Hatteras to the tip of Florida (Shepard, 1948).

### Bay of Fundy–Cape Cod Section

*Topography.* The continental shelf north of Cape Cod is marked by irregular topography with rows of banks and shallow water on the outer margin and deeper water inshore from the banks. The southernmost of the banks, Georges Bank, lies southeast of Cape Cod. Detailed mapping of the Gulf of Maine area (Murray,

1947, Drake et al., 1954) has shown that the submarine topography here is extremely irregular and complex. Innumerable knolls, ridges, swells, and basins give relief to the sea floor. Cashe Ledge, the highest ridge in the area, rises to within 25 feet of sea level. Numerous basins are present that are broad and shallow but beneath 500 to 1000 feet of water. The larger ridges are probably bedrock, but a strong probability exists that many of the minor knolls are of glacial origin and represent preserved parts of end moraines or glacial sediments that were dumped onto the ocean floor. How far into the ocean the ice moved and whether it was grounded or floating ice at its terminus are unknown. Minor depressions on the floor of the Gulf of Maine may be partially products of glacial scouring.

*Geology.* Geophysical data (Drake et al., 1954) indicate that the wedge of Coastal Plain sediments south of the Gulf of Maine is largely lacking in the Gulf of Maine except for a few scattered remnants. The data seem to confirm the existence in the Gulf of Maine of Triassic sediments as postulated by Johnson (1925). The western edge of the Triassic rocks seems to be about Cashe Ledge. Johnson interpreted the Gulf of Maine as an inner lowland bounded on the seaward side by a cuesta of Coastal Plain sediments similar to that seen on land in New Jersey. Thus, according to him, the Gulf of Maine was produced largely by subaerial stream erosion. Shepard and associates (1934) concluded, however, that glacial more than stream erosion contributed to the development of the lowland that now forms the Gulf of Maine. Geophysical work by Stetson (1936) and Drake and associates (1954) seems to indicate that Cretaceous and Tertiary sediments are present in Georges Bank, but their data do not preclude a cover of glacial deposits over the Coastal Plain sediments. The thickness of Triassic rocks in the Gulf of Maine seems to be about 1600 feet. This is considerably less than is found in the Acadian area (3300–6500) but compares favorably with the 1550 feet of Triassic rocks in the Quaco section, New Brunswick.

*Origin of Gulf of Maine.* Chadwick (1948) regarded the floor of the Gulf of Maine as being essentially a resurrected Jurassic or early Cretaceous peneplain, presumably the equivalent of the Fall Zone peneplain of Renner (see p. 92). He believed that this peneplain extended inland as far as the White Mountains and Mount Katahdin and that it was subsequently buried beneath Cretaceous and probably Pliocene sediments as far inland as Mt. Katahdin. After the peneplain and its sedimentary cover were tilted eastward, in late Mesozoic time, it was resurrected as the seaward receding cuesta inface on the Tertiary sediments receded to its present position at Georges Bank. The lowland developed by resurrection of the peneplain presumably was further expanded by glacial erosion before becoming the site of the present Gulf of Maine.

## Cape Cod–Cape Hatteras Section

*Topography.* The continental shelf from Cape Cod and Georges Bank southward to Cape Hatteras is one of the best-explored shelf areas in the world. Its topography is distinctly different from that north of Cape Cod. The inner deeps, outer banks, and lesser topographic irregularities that are found in the Gulf of Maine are lacking. In contrast, the surface of the shelf is smooth and remarkably uniform in its topographic characteristics, and it slopes gently seaward (Heezen et al., 1959). The shelf narrows southward as the coastal plain widens, and in the latitude of Cape Hatteras almost disappears. Reduction in width of the continental shelf near Cape Hatteras is produced by a prominent cuspate foreland which has been built seaward across the shelf. The greater smoothness of the Cape Cod–Cape Hatteras section of the continental shelf may be explained by the fact that this part of the shelf has not been as recently subjected to subaerial erosion as the part north of Cape Cod, nor has its surface been modified by glacial erosion.

*Submarine Canyons.* Submarine canyons, long one of geology's puzzling geomorphic problems, are particularly well developed at the edge of the continental shelf between Cape Cod and Cape

Hatteras. Here are found such canyons as the Oceanographer, Hydrographer, Hudson, Wilmington, Baltimore, Washington, and Norfolk. Most famous of these canyons is Hudson Canyon. This canyon is some 23 miles long and 5 miles wide, and cuts more than 500 fathoms into the continental slope. It continues as a shallow valley not over 50 fathoms deep for more than 150 miles beyond the base of the continental shelf and ends in a deep-sea fan or delta (Heezen et al., 1959). Not to be confused with the Hudson Canyon is the submerged Hudson Valley cut into the surface of the continental shelf. This drowned valley can be traced seaward for nearly 100 miles and at its easternmost extremity is only about 250 feet below sea level. Drowning of the Hudson Valley was largely a result of late-glacial and postglacial rise of sea level. An even more striking example of the drowning of a river system by recent rise of sea level is to be found in the Chesapeake Bay region, where the lower part of a major river system has been dismembered by drowning. Streams such as the Potomac, Rappahannock, and James were formerly tributaries of the now drowned lower Susquehanna River.

## Cape Hatteras–Florida Section

*Nature of Shelf.* South of Cape Hatteras the continental shelf widens gradually until off the coast of Georgia it attains a width of 75 miles; from here it narrows again until in the latitude of Miami, Florida, the shelf almost disappears. Lying seaward about 60 miles along the Cape Hatteras–Florida section of the continental shelf is an area intermediate in altitude between the shelf and the sea floor known as the Blake Plateau. This submarine plateau is as much as 170 miles wide and is 300 to 400 fathoms below the level of the inner continental shelf; much of its surface is as flat as that of the continental shelf. The Blake Escarpment, at the eastern edge of the Blake Plateau, presents a sharp drop of 2000 fathoms to the floor of the ocean basin. The origin of the Blake Plateau is not clear. It may represent a down-faulted part of the continental shelf, but Shepard (1948) and Prouty (1946) considered it a part of the continental shelf that had been deeply eroded by the powerful Gulf Stream during periods of Pleistocene low sea levels. This explanation does not seem as unlikely today as it once did when we take into account the fact that current ripples have been reported on the floor of the ocean bottom at depths as great as 15,000 feet. Prouty further suggested that the narrowness of the continental shelf in the Cape Hatteras area may also be attributable to erosion of the shelf by the Gulf Stream.

*Influence of Faults.* Support is given to the idea that major faults may bound the continental shelf off the southeastern United States by the topography in the Straits of Florida. Here four contiguous belts of submarine topography have been reported (Jordan, 1954): (1) a belt of smooth topography about 5 miles wide just off-shore from the Florida reefs, (2) a terrace belt of irregular relief including numerous sink holes as much as one-half mile wide and 500 feet deep, (3) a 600-foot escarpment immediately east of the sink hole belt which is at least 70 miles long, and (4) an apron at the base of this escarpment which blends gradually into a smooth outer slope similar to that in the inner belt.

The sink holes suggest that the part of the submerged shelf where they are may have stood above sea level at one time. The upper rims of the sink holes are beneath as much as 800 to 900 feet of water, which is too great a depth to be explained as the result of postglacial rise of sea level. The escarpment bounding the sink hole zone on the east is not nearly so high as the one present off the west coast of Florida (see p. 17), but it is equally steep. Pressler (1947), from a study of the configuration of the submarine topography off Florida, came to the conclusion that Florida is bounded on both the east and the west by major fault zones.

*Geology of the Continental Shelf.* The continental shelf off the middle Atlantic coast has been the site of numerous seismic profiles over the past two decades, and fairly good information is at hand regarding the nature of the basement surface upon which Cretaceous and younger rocks were deposited. Basement rocks appear to be mainly schists, gneisses, diabase, and porphyritic granites similar to those found in the adjacent Piedmont and New England provinces. The idea once held that the Cretaceous and Tertiary strata on the continental shelf dipped seaward in regular homoclinal fashion is only partially true. Seismic profiles have shown that in places there is a reverse slope of the basement floor which gives a basin effect to the shelf. A profile off Cape May, New Jersey (Ewing et al., 1950) showed that the sediments on the continental shelf increased from a thickness of about 5000 feet near shore to a maximum of 17,200 feet, but this maximum thickness rather than being at the edge of the continental shelf lies inland from it.

Superposed on the continental shelf and slope are numerous small benches or terraces. Some can be traced for hundreds of miles; others are discontinuous or only present locally. Four possible explanations have been suggested for them: (1) they represent ancient shorelines, (2) they are structural or rock benches, (3) they are the result of block faulting, and (4) they are landslide or slump scars. Doubtless all these causes have contributed to the development of the benches, but Heezen and associates (1959) concluded that most of them are structural benches that represent the edges of resistant rock layers in the Cretaceous and Tertiary strata which underlie the continental shelf. They viewed the continental slope as similar to an erosional escarpment bounding a high plateau or mesa which is underlain by a series of sedimentary strata.

Seismic profiles indicate that relief on the basement floor varies considerably but is generally slight to moderate. In most places the maximum relief is less than 300 feet, but it may be as much as 500 feet. This amount of relief does not preclude the possibility that the floor of the basement complex may be an old erosion surface, but it does throw some doubt on whether it may properly be considered a peneplain surface.

# CONTINENTAL SHELF IN GULF OF MEXICO

## *General Description*

West of Florida the continental shelf widens notably and becomes as much as 150 miles wide. Off the coast of Alabama and Mississippi the shelf narrows again and at the Mississippi delta nearly disappears, because the Mississippi River has built its delta almost to the edge of the continental shelf. Shepard (1956) has called the submarine delta extension of the Mississippi River a delta-front platform. At its forward edge is a rather sharp break in slope and descent to the floor of the Gulf of Mexico. West of the Mississippi delta the continental shelf widens again and along the Louisiana-Texas coast it is as much as 115 miles wide.

*Major Escarpments.* Three major escarpments— the West Florida Escarpment on the east, the Sigsbee Scarp on the northwest, and the Campeche Escarpment on the south—form the walls, so to speak, of the Gulf of Mexico. The West Florida Escarpment (Jordan, 1951) is at least 350 miles long and has a height of 3000 to 6000 feet. The Sigsbee Scarp (Gealy, 1955) is comparable in height and length with the West Florida Escarpment. The Campeche Escarpment (see U. S. Coast and Geodetic Survey Chart No. 1007, Gulf of Mexico, 1927) is as much as 8000 feet high and forms the northern margin of the Campeche Bank (see profile *B-B'* of Fig. 2.2). The West Florida and Campeche escarpments are more precipitous than the Sigsbee Scarp because they are on limestone, whereas the Sigsbee Scarp is on argillaceous sediments.

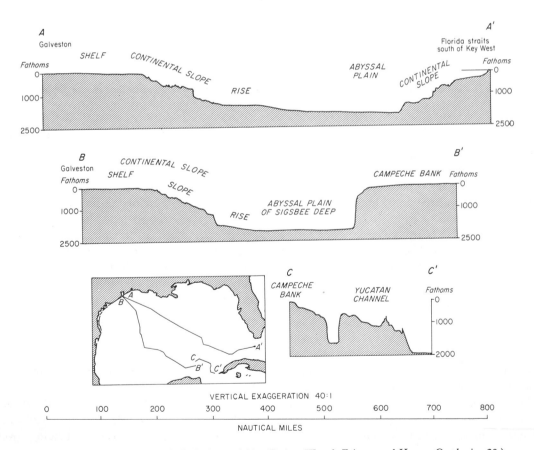

FIG. 2.2    Profiles across Gulf of Mexico.    (*After Ewing, Worzel, Ericson, and Heezen, Geophysics,* **20.**)

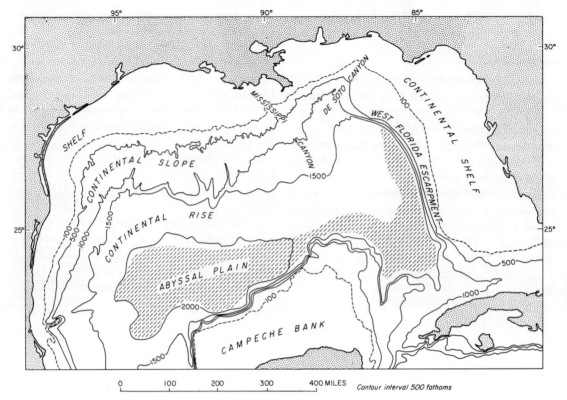

FIG. 2.3    Topography of the floor of the Gulf of Mexico.    (*After Ewing, Worzel, Ericson, and Heezen, Geophysics,* **20.**)

These scarps on three sides of the Gulf of Mexico seem to lend support to Weaver's (1950) theory that the Gulf of Mexico as a deep sea is relatively young and is the result of downfaulting localized most intensely off Florida and Yucatan. The Sigsbee Deep (see Figs. 2.2 and 2.3) at the base of the Sigsbee Scarp is a basin which reaches to depths of 2200 fathoms, but the details of its topography are not well known.

*Submarine Troughs.* Two major features of the edge of the continental shelf and the continental slope in the Gulf of Mexico are Desoto Canyon and the Mississippi Trough. However, neither of these is comparable in size with the larger canyons off the Atlantic and Pacific coasts. Desoto Canyon, which lies offshore northwestern Florida, is about 25 miles long, 2 miles wide, and 600 feet deep and apparently is not connected with any present stream on land. It is

rapidly undergoing filling rather than being in a state of active enlargement.

The ancient valley of the Mississippi River, or what is called the Mississippi Trough, lies about 35 miles west of the present Mississippi delta. It is nearly 80 miles long, has a broad flat floor as much as 10 miles wide, and is as much as 1800 feet deep where it crosses the edge of the continental shelf. It, like the Desoto Canyon, seems to be filling up rather than being deepened and extended.

*Mississippi Submarine Platform.* The birdfoot portion of the Mississippi River deltaic plain is the surface expression of a broad submarine platform that has been built out onto the continental shelf. This 50-mile wide protuberance covers some 700 square miles (Fisk et al., 1954) and nearly reaches to the edge of the continental shelf. Hydrographic surveys extending over more than a hundred years have made possible estimates of the rate of growth seaward of the delta (see Fig. 2.4). The annual increment of deposition has been estimated at 0.06 cubic mile or 495 million tons of sediment.

Ewing and associates (1958) have designated the large mass of sediments which have been deposited by the Mississippi River in the Gulf of Mexico as the Mississippi Cone. Its apex lies a few hundred feet below sea level near the head of the submarine canyon known as the Mississippi Trough rather than at the head of the Birdfoot Delta. The base of the Mississippi Cone extends onto the floor of the Sigsbee Deep. The radius of the cone averages about 300 miles, and its area is approximately 30,000 square miles. It is Ewing's belief that this great pile of sediments was deposited largely by turbidity currents, most of which postdate the latest deformation of the Gulf of Mexico basin and predate the Recent.

*Delta-Front Valleys.* Along the forward edge of the delta are numerous small trenches which Shepard (1955) has called delta-front valleys. Most of them are from one-third to two-thirds of a mile wide and 1 to 4 miles long. They are

especially abundant off South Pass. Shepard favors the idea that they were formed as the result of movement of sediments down the seaward front of the delta as earthflows, but some geologists have considered them more likely the work of turbidity currents.

*Mud Lumps.* Near the mouths of the Mississippi River passes are found the rather unique features known as mud lumps. This name has been given to small dome-like upswellings which form small islands that vary in size from small pinnacles to as much as 20 acres in area. They rarely rise more than 5 or 10 feet above the water and their positions are subject to frequent changes. Submarine mud lumps are more common than islands. Some of the mud lumps have vents through which fluid mud is discharged as from a "mud volcano." Although relatively unimportant geomorphically, the mud lumps do present transportation hazards.

The mud lumps seem to be genetically associated with the bars which are built seaward along each delta distributary (see Fig. 2.5). Morgan (1952) has offered an explanation for the growth of the mud lumps which recognizes three stages of development (see Fig. 2.6).

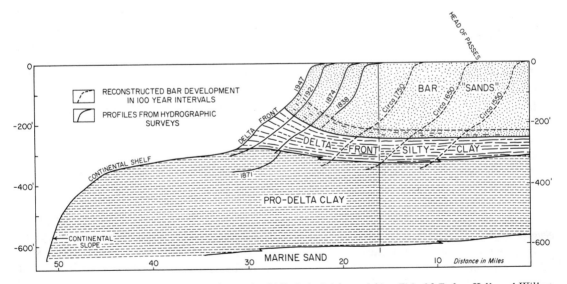

FIG. 2.4  Profile showing estimated rate of growth of Mississippi delta.  (*After Fisk, McFarlan, Kolb, and Wilbert, Jour. Sed. Petrology,* **24.**)

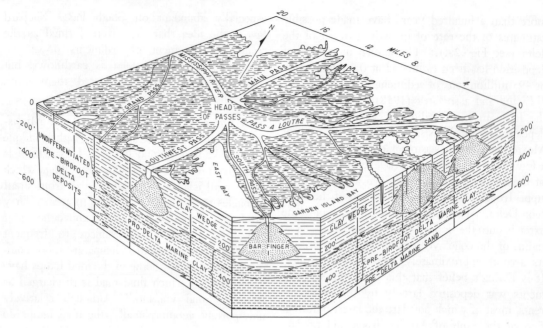

FIG. 2.5   Diagram showing major features of Mississippi delta.   (*After Fisk, McFarlan, Kolb, and Wilbert, Jour. Sed. Petrology,* **24.**)

*Stage A*

a. A near-shore massive bar composed chiefly of sand and silt is built seaward by the river.

b. Beyond this bar silty clays are deposited on the sea floor.

c. Still farther seaward are deposits that are primarily clay.

*Stage B*

a. The river mouth is extended seaward until bar materials are being deposited where formerly plastic clay accumulated.

b. Static pressure of the bar deposits on the plastic clay causes it to be thinned and squeezed toward the forward edge of the bar.

c. At the forward edge of the bar the load pressure is suddenly reduced, causing the plastic clay to break through and initiate upward growth of a mud lump.

*Stage C*

a. Further forward building of the bar surrounds the plastic material of the incipient mud lump, causing it to become stabilized in position, and forces growth upward.

b. With increased static pressure and a sufficient supply of plastic clay, growth of the mud lump may reach the surface.

Mud lumps are confined to the ends of those passes which terminate in deep water and thus approach the edge of the continental shelf. The reason for this seems to be that only in deep water does sufficient static pressure develop to cause flowage of the plastic clay beneath the bar.

Mud lumps seem to be restricted to the delta of the Mississippi River, as they have not been reported from other deltaic areas. Morgan (1952) suggested three possible reasons as to why this may be: (1) the Mississippi River discharges only fine-grained materials, mainly of silt and clay size; (2) the Mississippi River discharges its load into relatively still water, and consequently longshore currents are not present to prevent growth of the river bar into the Gulf of Mexico; and (3) the mouths of the Mississippi River distributary system are much closer to the edge of the continental shelf than those of most rivers, and the steep slope at the front of the delta favors formation of a bar thick enough to exert the static pressure necessary to force the plastic clays upward.

*Submarine Mounds.*　The continental shelf in the Gulf of Mexico, particularly west of the Mississippi delta, is characterized by a great number of minor relief features ranging in height from less than 10 feet to a few hundred feet (see Fig. 2.7). Apparently no other part of the continental shelf off the United States has such features in anything like the number that is found here. They have been variously called ridges, banks, reefs, mounds, coral heads, and pinnacles. Undoubtedly they have diverse origins. Shepard (1937) interpreted the larger ones as submarine salt domes, but Carsey (1950) has suggested that some of the larger forms may be igneous plugs. Offshore drilling in recent years has established the existence of numerous salt domes on the continental shelf, and it has been estimated that at least 200 such features exist (see Fig. 3.24).

The forms that have been called pinnacles, mounds, and coral heads are probably mainly biohermal in origin. Stetson (1953) and Parker and Curray (1957) considered this origin most likely for most of the pinnacle-like forms. The pinnacles are commonly steep-sided, 40 to 50 feet high, and only a few hundred feet across.

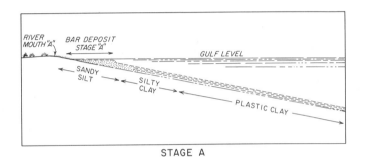

STAGE A
DEPOSITION AT RIVER MOUTH

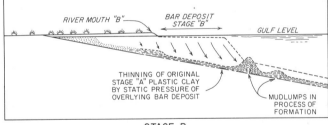

STAGE B
RIVER MOUTH HAS MOVED SEAWARD BY NORMAL DELTAIC GROWTH

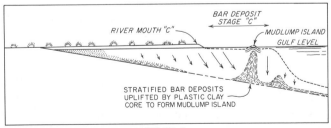

STAGE C
RIVER MOUTH HAS EXTENDED FARTHER SEAWARD

FIG. 2.6　Diagrams suggesting stages in growth of mud lumps.　(*After J. P. Morgan, Proc., 2nd conf. on coastal engineering, Engineering Foundation, Univ. Calif.*)

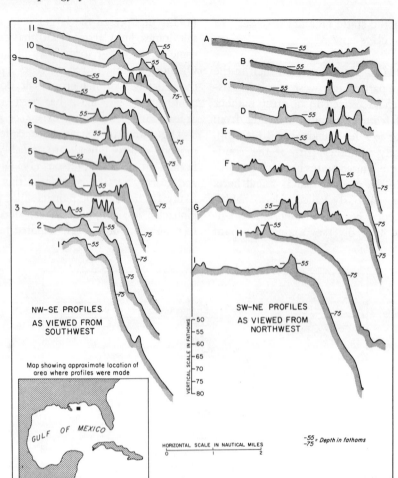

NW-SE PROFILES
AS VIEWED FROM
SOUTHWEST

Map showing approximate location of
area where profiles were made

GULF OF MEXICO

SW-NE PROFILES
AS VIEWED FROM
NORTHWEST

VERTICAL SCALE IN FATHOMS
50
55
60
65
70
75
80

HORIZONTAL SCALE IN NAUTICAL MILES
0    1    2

$-55 \atop -75$ = Depth in fathoms

FIG. 2.7    Profiles of pinnacles in Gulf of Mexico.    (*After Ludwick and Walton, Am. Assoc. Petroleum Geologists Bull.* **41.**)

## CONTINENTAL MARGIN ALONG PACIFIC COAST

### General Description

The continental shelf off the Pacific coast of conterminous United States includes areas of shelf that are well known and other tracts that are poorly known. An area of some 30,000 square miles off the coast of southern California ranks with the shelf area between Cape Cod and Cape Hatteras as one of the best-known continental shelf areas in the world, but even here the amount of unknown geology far exceeds the known. The continental shelf off the western conterminous United States in general is narrow, with its maximum width ranging from 10 to 25 miles. The broader features are fairly well known along the California coast, but not nearly so much information is available for the shelf area off Oregon and Washington. Most of the discussion in this section will therefore be limited to the continental margins off California.

Six "submarine geomorphic provinces" have been recognized by Shepard and Emery (1941) off the California coast between San Francisco and the Mexican border. Each of these has certain distinctive features that sets it off from the rest. Possibly the most interesting, certainly the most explored, of these provinces is

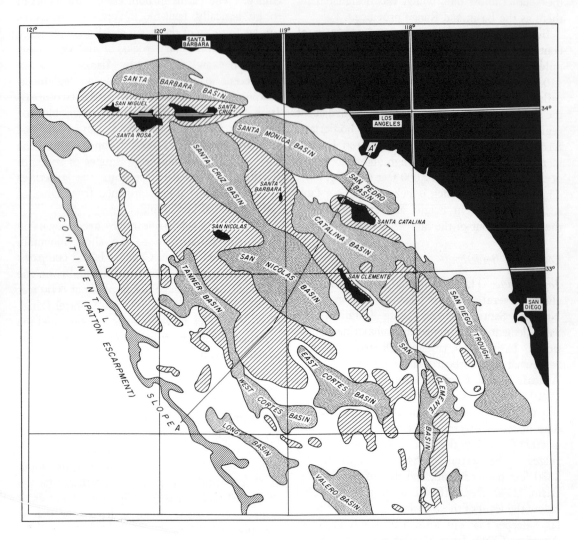

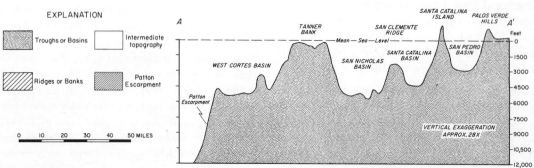

FIG. 2.8   Major features of sea floor off southern California.   (*After F. P. Shepard and K. O. Emery, Geol. Soc. Am., Spec. Paper* 31.)

the southernmost one, which was designated by them as the Basin and Range province.

Bordering the mainland is a narrow strip of continental shelf ranging in width from 1 to 15 miles; seaward from this strip is a tract 35 to 150 miles wide which Shepard and Emery have called the "continental borderland" because of the similarity of its topography to that of adjacent regions on land. The continental borderland terminates seaward at the steep Patton Escarpment, which is 10,000 feet high and descends to ocean depths of around 12,000 feet (see Fig. 2.8). This escarpment, which is believed to be a fault scarp, compares in height and steepness with the eastern front of the Sierra Nevada.

### Continental Borderland

*Topography.* The continental borderland includes several offshore islands, such as Santa Nicolas, Santa Barbara, Santa Catalina, and San Clemente, and numerous submarine banks, ridges, basins, and troughs, all arranged in a somewhat checkerboard fashion (see Fig. 2.8), At least 18 basins are known in the area (Emery. 1960), ranging in size from a little over 100 square miles to more than 1000 square miles. The floors of several of the basins are as much as 6000 feet below the tops of adjacent banks and ridges. The bottom of Santa Cruz Basin lies 2880 feet below its sill, and that of San Nicolas Basin, 2370 feet. If sea level were lowered below the level of these basin sills, it would leave lakes deeper than any known anywhere in North America (Crater Lake, the deepest lake in North America, is 2000 feet deep). Saline Basin between Owens Lake and Death Valley is probably the deepest basin on land without a lake in it; its floor is 3900 feet below its sill.

*Comparison with Topography on Land.* Four basins on land that are essentially similar to the submarine basins of the continental borderland are the nearby Ventura, San Fernando, Los Angeles, and San Gabriel basins. The essential difference between the submarine basins and those on land is that those on land are partially filled with debris from adjacent mountains, whereas those beneath the sea are essentially

empty. The basins in both environments seem to be basically fault-block type of structures similar to those of the Basin and Range province on land. Sedimentary rocks of the two areas are similar and range from Triassic to Plio-Pleistocene in age. Similar volcanic and metamorphic rocks are also found in the two areas. It is believed that the faulting which blocked out the continental borderland began in Miocene time and continued recurrently until Pleistocene time. Only the Transverse Ranges of southern California (see p. 545) separate the structures of the Basin and Range province from those of the continental borderland.

Most of the submarine ridges are elongate in shape and comparable to the short mountain ranges on land. Santa Catalina Island compares in height with the Santa Ana Mountains on the mainland, each having a height of about 6000 feet above adjacent lowlands; the San Gabriel Range rises 10,000 feet above its adjacent plain, and the San Juan Seamount rises 10,000 feet above the adjacent ocean floor. The steep fronts of the submarine ridges suggest fault scarp faces even more strikingly than the fronts of some of the ranges on land because features analogous to the pediment and bajada slopes that develop on land are sparingly present.

San Clemente Island is a fault block that stands one mile above the ocean floor and about 2000 feet above sea level. Its northeast face is an eroded fault scarp (see Fig. 2.9). The fault is probably a right lateral fault, a type that is common in California.

At the bases of some of the submarine ridges are minor depressions parallel to the ridge fronts that may be analogous in origin to the range front grabens that are found along the fronts of some of the ranges in the Basin and Range province (see p. 489). Faults can be inferred from the pattern made by the topography (see Fig. 2.10), and Shepard and Emery (1941) thought that strike-slip faulting similar to that found on land best explained the topographic relationships between San Clemente Island and nearby Twentymile and Fortymile Banks.

Emery (1960), from precision echo sounding of the basins, showed that they have two rather

distinct parts, aprons or sub-sea fans, adjacent to the bases of the ridges or plateaus, and flat basin floors. He believed that there is a striking similarity of these depositional surfaces to alluvial fans and playa surfaces on land. The main difference is that on land streams carry debris into the basins, whereas in the ocean turbidity currents are the main transporting agent.

*Submarine Canyons.* Submarine canyons are present in the continental borderland. Names have been given to 13 of them; 19 more are known to exist (Emery, 1960); and undoubtedly numerous others are present that have not yet been discovered. Of the 32 known canyons, 20 border the mainland, 10 border islands, and 2 are off submarine banks. This seems to indicate that turbidity currents are largely generated from material derived above sea level.

Some of the finest submarine canyons off the California coast are found in the area between Lucia and Monterey Bay. Probably the greatest and best known of these canyons is Monterey Canyon, one of the world's great submarine canyons. Monterey Canyon is about 50 miles long and extends from near the coast in Monterey Bay to the base of the continental slope. Work by Dill and associates (1954) has shown that this Canyon, like the Hudson Canyon, has a

deep sea extension with an associated deep-sea fan or delta extending seaward from the mouth of the canyon. This delta can be identified down to a depth of 2100 fathoms and is at least 60 miles long and equally wide.

*Punta Gorda–Mendicino Escarpments.* One striking feature of the submarine topography off the California coast is a prominent submarine escarpment that extends westward from Punta Borda, a minor promontory south of Cape Mendicino. This scarp was named the Punta Gorda escarpment (Shepard and Emery, 1941). It is a north-facing scarp that can be traced to sea for 70 to 80 miles, where it becomes subdued and is replaced, or continued, by a south-facing escarpment which lies south of the Punta Gorda escarpment, to which the name Mendocino escarpment has been given (Menard and Dietz, 1952). The south-facing Mendocino escarpment can be traced some 1100 miles out into the Pacific Basin. Although the two escarpments may be separate, it appears likely that they are related to each other and are a part of the same structures. Menard (1955) believed that these two escarpments represented one of the major structural features of the Pacific basin; certainly they merit such consideration, for the Punta Gorda escarpment attains a height of 6000 feet

FIG. 2.9   Fault scarp along northeast side of San Clemente Island, viewed from the southeast.   (*Photo by Navy Fleet Air Wing* 14.   *Courtesy K. O. Emery.*)

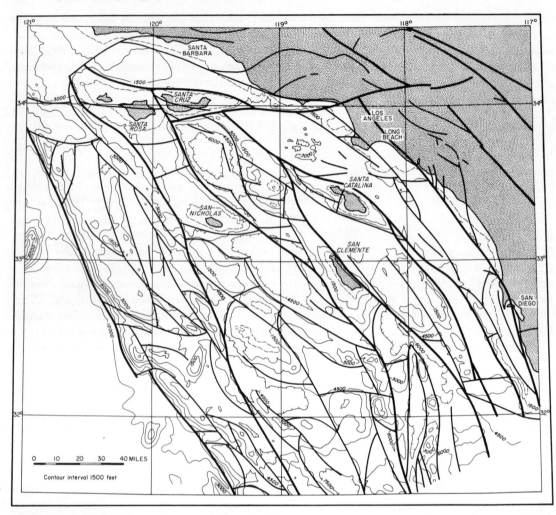

FIG. 2.10    Map of inferred fault pattern off coast of southern California.    (*After K. O. Emery in The Sea off Southern California, John Wiley and Sons, Inc.*)

and the Mendocino escarpment a height of 10,000 feet.   Whether or not this major fault zone is related to the San Andreas fault (see p. 538) on land is questionable.   The trend is different from that of the San Andreas fault, and such evidence as exists seems to favor the view that they are two different fault systems.

### Continental Margin off Oregon and Washington

Information regarding the nature of the continental shelf and slope of this area is rather meager.   The shelf narrows noticeably north of San Francisco and is no greater than 10 miles in width at the California-Oregon state line. From here it widens somewhat and attains a width of 20 miles or more (Shepard, 1948).   North of Eureka, California, there is a repetition of topography somewhat similar to that found off the southern California coast, with numerous terraces and hills, but the submarine canyons which are so common along the California coast are notably inconspicuous until the latitude of the Columbia River is reached.   North of here they become more common.   A broad submerged glacial trough extends through the Strait of Juan de

Fuca and extends seaward across the continental shelf to connect with a submarine canyon. South of the Strait of Juan de Fuca there is no evidence of glacial deposits on the shelf, but north from here such deposits become common.

## CONTINENTAL MARGINS AROUND ALASKA

### Continental Margin off Southern Alaska

Southern Alaska begins with the Alexander Archipelago, which is a part of so-called Fiordland (Peacock, 1935). The continental shelf is only a few miles wide at the southern end of the Alexander Archipelago, but it widens northward and attains a width of 50 miles at the northwest side of Cross Sound. This stretch of the shelf is notched by a large number of submarine valleys. Between the Queen Charlotte Range and the Alexander Archipelago is a broad submarine trough called Dixon Entrance, which is undoubtedly a glacial trough. Numerous other submarine valleys representing seaward extensions of fiords extend across the continental shelf westward from the Alexander Archipelago.

Westward around the Gulf of Alaska the continental shelf widens notably and attains a maximum width of 120 miles near Kodiak Island. Numerous islands rise above the shelf in this area, and four submerged banks extend off Kodiak Island nearly to the edge of the shelf (Murray, 1945). Between these banks are broad depressions 10 miles or so wide which appear to be glacially scoured troughs. Similar troughs extend onto the shelf from the Kenai Peninsula, and these connect landward with bays which have glaciers extending into them; however, no glaciers exist today on Kodiak Island. It thus appears that the continental shelf around the Gulf of Alaska was extensively modified by glaciers which extended onto it from the mainland.

The continental shelf south of the Aleutian Islands chain has a relatively smooth southward slope out to about 100 fathoms; here begins the sharp drop into the Aleutian Trench to maximum depths in excess of 24,000 feet. The upper part of the continental slope here is cut by numerous valleys. These submarine valleys are not canyon-like, as are those along the northeast and west coasts of the United States (Shepard, 1959), but are trough-like in nature and much like the basins in the continental borderland off California, except that the troughs are open at their seaward ends and have a continuous seaward slope. Their steep sides are suggestive of fault scarps, and this, along with the fact that this area is one of the most seismically active regions in the world, lends support to the belief that these valleys are essentially fault-controlled.

### Continental Margin West of Alaska

The continental shelf in the Bering Sea west of Alaska is remarkably smooth, as it is also in the Chukchi Sea north of Bering Strait. Several submarine valleys are known to be present in this area. One in the Chukchi Sea, the Ogotoruk Sea Valley, heads in water 30 feet deep off the mouth of Ogotoruk Creek (Scholl and Sainsbury, 1961) and extends seaward for a distance of 15 miles and to a depth of 135 feet. It has a maximum relief of only 15 feet and is believed to be a drowned valley of subaerial origin formed during Pleistocene time and drowned by the postglacial rise of sea level.

### Continental Margin North of Alaska

In the Beaufort Sea north of Alaska most of the shelf is smooth, and the depth of water is less than 35 fathoms (Carsola et al., 1961). Exploration during 1950 and 1951 (Carsola, 1954a) of some 35,000 square miles of the sea floor north of Alaska has thrown considerable light on the details of the topography of this area. Numerous submarine canyons are known to be present; two of these are particularly well known, the Barrow Sea Valley, north of Point Barrow, and the MacKenzie Sea Valley, off the mouth of the MacKenzie River. These valleys are broad and shallow across the continental shelf but become narrow and canyon-like when they reach the continental slope. According to Carsola (1954b) the continental shelf north of

Alaska lacks topographic irregularities resulting from deposition or erosion by Pleistocene glacial ice. He placed the westward limits of ice extension into the Beaufort Sea at Herschel Island a short distance east of the Canadian border.

## REFERENCES CITED

Carsey, J. B. (1950). Geology of the Gulf coastal area and continental shelf, *Am. Assoc. Petroleum Geologists Bull.*, **34**, 361–385.

Carsola, A. J. (1954a). Submarine canyons on the Arctic slope, *Jour. Geol.*, **62**, 605–610.

—— (1954b). Extent of glaciation on the continental shelf in the Beaufort Sea, *Am. Jour. Sci.*, **252**, 366–371.

——, R. L. Fisher, C. J. Shipek, and G. Shumway (1961). Bathymetry of the Beaufort Sea, *in Geology of the Arctic*, G. O. Raasch, Editor, University of Toronto Press, 678–689.

Chadwick, G. H. (1948). Peneplains in Maine, *Geol. Soc. Am. Bull.*, **59**, 1315–1316 (abs.).

Dill, R. F., R. S. Dietz, and S. Harris (1954). Deep-sea channels and delta of the Monterey submarine canyon, *Geol. Soc. Am. Bull.*, **65**, 191–193.

Drake, C. L., J. L. Worzel, and W. C. Beckman (1954). Geophysical investigations in the emerged and submerged Atlantic Coastal Plain, Part IX, Gulf of Maine, *Geol. Soc. Am. Bull.*, **65**, 957–970.

Emery, K. O. (1960). *The Sea of Southern California*, John Wiley and Sons, New York, 366 pp.

Ewing, Maurice, J. L. Worzel, N. C. Steenland, and F. Press (1950). Geophysical investigations in the emerged and submerged Atlantic Coastal Plain: Part V; Woods Hole, New York, and Cape May sections, *Geol. Soc. Am. Bull.*, **61**, 877–892.

Fisk, H. N., E. McFarlan, Jr., C. R. Kolb, and L. J. Wilbert, Jr. (1954). Sedimentary framework of the modern Mississippi delta, *Jour. Sed. Petrology*, **24**, 76–99.

Gealy, B. L. (1955). Topography of the continental slope in northwest Gulf of Mexico, *Geol. Soc. Am. Bull.*, **66**, 203–228.

Heezen, B. C., M. Tharp, and M. Ewing (1959). The floors of the ocean, I, The North Atlantic, *Geol. Soc. Am. Spec. Paper* 65, 122 pp.

Johnson, Douglas (1925). *The New England–Acadian Shoreline*, John Wiley and Sons, New York, 591 pp.

Jordan, G. F. (1951). Continental slope off Apalachicola River, Florida, *Am. Assoc. Petroleum Geologists Bull.*, **35**, 1978–1993.

—— (1954). Large sink holes in Straits of Florida, *Am. Assoc. Petroleum Geologists Bull.*, **38**, 1810–1817.

Menard, H. W. (1955). Deformation of the northeastern Pacific basin and the west coast of North America, *Geol. Soc. Am. Bull.*, **66**, 1149–1198.

—— and R. S. Dietz (1952). Mendocino submarine escarpment, *Jour. Geol.*, **60**, 266–278.

Morgan, J. P. (1952). Mudlumps at the mouths of the Mississippi River, *Proc. second conference on coastal engineering*, Engineering Foundation, Univ. Calif., 130–140.

Murray, H. W. (1945). Profiles of the Aleutian Trench, *Geol. Soc. Am. Bull.*, **56**, 757–782.

—— (1947). Topography of the Gulf of Maine, *Geol. Soc. Am. Bull.*, **58**, 153–196.

Parker, R. H., and J. R. Curray (1955). Macrofauna and bathymetry of calcareous banks on the continental shelf of the northern Gulf of Mexico, *Geol. Soc. Am. Bull.*, **66**, 1604–1605 (abs.).

Peacock, M. A. (1935). Fiord-land of British Columbia, *Geol. Soc. Am. Bull.*, **46**, 633–696.

Pressler, E. D. (1947). Geology and occurrence of oil in Florida, *Am. Assoc. Petroleum Geologists Bull.*, **31**, 1851–1862.

Prouty, W. F. (1946). Atlantic coastal plain floor and continental slope of North Carolina, *Am. Assoc. Petroleum Geologists Bull.*, **30**, 1917–1920.

Scholl, D. W., and C. L. Sainsbury (1961). Marine geology and bathymetry of the Chukchi shelf off the Ogotoruk Creek area, Northwest Alaska, *in Geology of the Arctic*, G. O. Raasch, Editor, Univ. of Toronto Press, 718–732.

Shepard, F. P. (1937). "Salt" domes related to Mississippi submarine trough, *Geol. Soc. Am. Bull.*, **48**, 1349–1362.

—— (1948). *Submarine Geology*, Harper and Brothers, New York, 348 pp.

—— (1955). Delta-front valleys bordering the Mississippi distributaries, *Geol. Soc. Am. Bull.*, **66**, 1489–1498.

—— (1956). Marginal sediments of Mississippi delta, *Am. Assoc. Petroleum Geologists Bull.*, **40**, 2537–2623.

—— (1959). *The Earth beneath the Sea*, The Johns Hopkins Press, Baltimore, 275 pp.

——, J. M. Trefethen, and G. V. Cohee (1934). Origin of Georges Bank, *Geol. Soc. Am. Bull.*, **45**, 281–302.

—— and K. O. Emery (1941). Submarine topography off the California coast, Geol. Soc. Am., *Spec. Paper* 31, 171 pp.

Stetson, H. C. (1936). Geology and paleontology of the Georges Banks canyons, *Geol. Soc. Am. Bull.*, **47**, 339–366.

—— (1953). The continental terrace of the western Gulf of Mexico: its surface sediments, origin, and development, *Massachusetts Inst. Technology and Woods Hole Oceanographic Inst. Papers in Phys. Oceanography*, **12**, 1–45.

Thomasson, E. M. (1958). Problems of petroleum production on the continental shelf of the Gulf of Mexico, *U. S. Geol. Survey Bull.* 1067, pp. 67–90.

Weaver, Paul, (1950). Variations in history of continental shelves, *Am. Assoc. Petroleum Geologists Bull.*, **34**, 351–360.

ADDITIONAL REFERENCES

Brown, M. V., J. Northrop, R. Frasetto, and L. H. Grabner (1961). Seismic refraction profiles on the continental shelf south of Bellport, Long Island, New York, *Geol. Soc. Am. Bull.*, **72**, 1693–1706.

Uchupi, Elazar, and K. O. Emery (1963). The continental slope between San Francisco, California, and Cedros Island, Mexico, *Deep-Sea Research*, **10**, 397–447.

Emery, K. O. (1954). General geology of the offshore area, southern California, Calif. Div. Mines, *Bull.*, **170**, Chapter 2, pp. 107–111.

Ewing, Maurice, D. B. Ericson, and B. C. Heezen (1958). Sediments and topography of the Gulf of Mexico, in *Habitat of Oil*, L. Weeks, Editor, Am. Assoc. Petroleum Geologists, pp. 995–1053, Tulsa.

Goedicke, T. R. (1955). Origin of the pinnacles on the continental shelf and slope of the Gulf of Mexico, *Texas Jour. Sci.*, **7**, 149–159.

Jordan, G. F., and H. B. Stewart, Jr. (1959). Continental slope off southwest Florida, *Am. Assoc. Petroleum Geologists Bull.*, **43**, 974–991.

——— (1961). Submarine topography of the western Straits of Florida, *Geol. Soc. Am. Bull.*, **72**, 1051–1058.

Murray, H. W. (1941). Submarine mountains in the Gulf of Alaska, *Geol. Soc. Am. Bull.*, **52**, 333–362.

Shepard, F. P. (1963). *Submarine Geology*, 2nd ed., Harper and Row, New York, 557 pp.

Torphy, S. R., and J. M. Zeigler (1957). Submarine topography of eastern channel, Gulf of Maine, *Jour. Geology*, **65**, 433–441.

Veatch, A. C., and P. A. Smith (1939). Atlantic submarine valleys of the United States and the Congo submarine valley, *Geol. Soc. Am. Spec. Paper* 7, 101 pp.

Woodford, A. O. (1951). Stream gradients and Monterey sea valley, *Geol. Soc. Am. Bull.*, **62**, 799–852.

# 3

# The Coastal Plain Province

Along the eastern and southeastern margins of the United States is an extensive seaward-sloping plain which from Cape Cod to the Mexican border measures 2200 miles in length. This plain, however, does not end at the Mexican border, but extends an additional 1000 miles into Mexico. Northward from Cape Cod it is completely submerged. That part of the plain above sea level we call coastal plain, that below sea level, continental shelf.

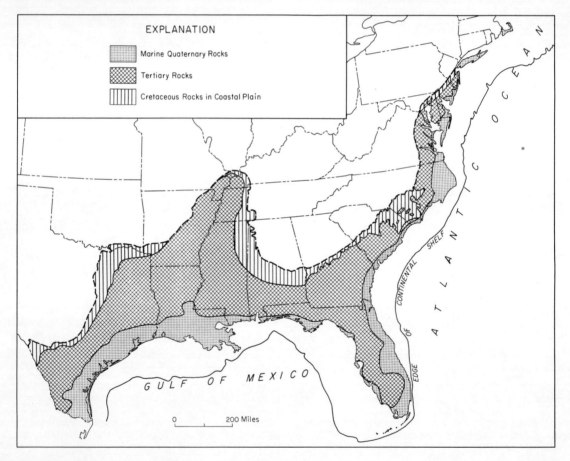

EXPLANATION

Marine Quaternary Rocks

Tertiary Rocks

Cretaceous Rocks in Coastal Plain

0    200 Miles

FIG. 3.1   Map showing ages of rocks underlying different parts of Coastal Plain.   (*After W. H. Monroe, Ky. Geol. Surv., Spec. Pub.* 1.)

Lack of agreement exists about the location of the northern edge of the Coastal Plain province. If we adhere strictly to Fenneman's (1928) definition of the Coastal Plain as "that portion of the former continental shelf which has been raised above sea level without essential deformation," we might exclude Cape Cod and such offshore islands as Martha's Vineyard, Nantucket, and Block Island, for they consist primarily of glacial materials and not coastal plain sediments. However, they are underlain by coastal plain sediments. Two wells drilled on Cape Cod (Zeigler et al., 1960) penetrated Eocene sediments, and beds of Miocene and Cretaceous age crop out at Gay Head on Martha's Vineyard. If the glacial materials were removed from Long Island, it would be much smaller than at present, but part of it would still stand above sea level. We shall consider Cape Cod and the offshore islands as part of the Coastal Plain mainly because their geology and topography seem to fit in better with the Coastal Plain province than with New England and because before the postglacial rise of sea level they were in reality a part of the Coastal Plain.

## GEOLOGY OF COASTAL PLAIN

The Atlantic Coastal Plain is underlain by relatively unconsolidated sediments which range in age from early Cretaceous to Recent (see Fig. 3.1). Some of the sediments are of marine and some of terrestrial origin; the terrestrial deposits are partly fluviatile and partly deltaic in origin.

### Thickness of Sediments

The sediments underlying the Coastal Plain province and adjacent continental shelf vary in thickness from a few hundred feet at the inner margin of the Coastal Plain to many thousands of feet on the continental shelf. A seismic traverse off Cape May, New Jersey (Ewing et al., 1950) indicated that the sediments above the basement rocks attained a maximum thickness of 17,210 feet. The sediments of the Gulf Coastal Plain are estimated to exceed 30,000 feet

in thickness (Waters, et al, 1955). A well near the tip of Florida penetrated 11,600 feet of sedimentary rocks (Applin and Applin, 1944) above the basement rocks.

### Nature of Basement Rocks

The so-called basement rocks on which the Cretaceous and younger rocks rest vary in nature. Along the Atlantic coast they appear to be essentially the same rocks that crop out to the west in the igneous and metamorphic terrain of the Piedmont Plateau; some are Precambrian and some are Paleozoic in age (see p. 90). Downfaulted blocks of Triassic rocks are part of the basement complex in the north and as far south as Florida (Murray, 1961). Diabase dikes thought likely to be of Triassic age have been encountered in wells. Fossils from well cuttings indicate that over a considerable area in southern Georgia, northern Florida, and southeastern Alabama Paleozoic sedimentary rocks form the basement floor on which the coastal plain sediments rest.

The idea long held that the basement surface has a continuous gentle seaward slope has been disproved, for some areas at least. Prouty (1946) and Berry (1948) have shown that the basement surface beneath the coastal plain of North Carolina has an inner slope of 10 to 14 feet per mile, as compared with an outer slope of 122 to 124 feet per mile. Prouty considered these two slopes to represent facets of two erosional surfaces. The inner, more gently sloping surface he correlated with the Schooley peneplain, and the outer, more steeply sloping surface, with the Fall Zone peneplain (see p. 92). Ewing and associates (1950) found from a seismic profile off New York City that the basement floor slopes gently seaward for about 20 miles south of Long Island and then sharply steepens and attains a depth below sea level of 13,260 feet in 28 miles. It then rises and at the edge of the continental shelf is only 11,500 feet below sea level.

It may be questionable whether the surface of the buried basement complex has low enough relief to be thought of as having peneplain characteristics. Seismic profiles that have been made along various parts of the Atlantic coast by various workers from the Lamont Geophysical Laboratory indicate that relief ranging from 200 to 500 feet exists on the surface of the basement complex.

## DISTINCTIVE CHARACTERISTICS OF SECTIONS

A coastal plain might seem to lack the variety of topography necessary for subdivision into smaller geomorphic units, but significant differences in both geology and topography exist within the Coastal Plain province to justify its division into six sections. These sections with their major distinguishing characteristics are:

1. Embayed section. Estuarine embayments divide the coastal plain into a number of broad peninsular tracts; an inner lowland on the lower Cretaceous Raritan clays extends as far south as Virginia; a series of terraces reaches back almost to the Fall Line; offshore bars are particularly common along the northern part.
2. Sea Island section. This section is youthful to mature terraced coastal plain with a submerged margin that is bordered by low-lying islands; drowning of valleys is less marked than in the embayed section, and the terraces do not reach back to its inner border; here instead is found a belt of dissected hills.
3. Floridian section. This section is a very youthful and recently emergent terraced coastal plain; karst features are extensively developed; much marshy and swampy land exists at the south; offshore bars or limestone keys border much of the eastern coast.
4. East Gulf Coastal Plain section. This section may be described as youthfully to maturely dissected belted coastal plain; a series of alternating cuestas and lowlands comprise its most striking features; coastwise terraces are present along the outer margin.
5. Mississippi Alluvial Plain section. Alluvial and deltaic plains characterize this section; alluvial terraces are found inland and coastwise deltaic terraces along its seaward margin.

6. West Gulf Coastal Plain section. The inner portion of this section is belted coastal plain, but the cuestas are not as conspicuously developed as are those of the East Gulf Coastal Plain section; deltaic coastal plain forms its seaward margin.

## HISTORY OF ATLANTIC COASTAL PLAIN

The Atlantic Coastal Plain, particularly north of Florida, has shared enough of a common history that certain major events in its development may be suggested in summary form. Difference of opinion may exist regarding the early history, but the later history of the province is reasonably clear. The major episodes in coastal plain history seem to have been:

1. By the close of the Paleozoic era an erosion surface of low relief developed that may have extended from the Piedmont as far east as the present edge of the continental shelf (Spangler and Peterson, 1950). This phase is somewhat conjectural and is postulated on rather meager evidence.
2. Triassic continental sediments were deposited, accompanied by block-faulting and intrusion of diabase dikes and sills.
3. Peneplanation of the area occurred during Jurassic time, with the development of the so-called Fall Zone peneplain (Renner, 1927; see p. 92). There is better evidence for this erosion surface than for a late Paleozoic erosion surface, but in view of the amount of relief that has been shown to exist on the floor of the basement complex, it is doubtful whether it merits being called a peneplain. Most of the Triassic sediments were removed during the development of the Fall Zone erosion surface, but some are preserved in downfolded and downfaulted areas in the Piedmont and also beneath the coastal plain sediments, as shown by wells drilled into these sediments.
4. The Fall Zone erosion surface was depressed, and the Cretaceous sea invaded to an unknown distance west of the present inner margin of Cretaceous sediments. The Cre-

taceous and Tertiary sediments of the present coastal plain accumulated during a series of emergences and submergences, with resulting hiatuses in the sequence of sediments. However, rocks of early and late Cretaceous age are present, and all epochs of the Tertiary are represented.

5. Uplift of the continental shelf exposed the seaward-dipping Cretaceous and Tertiary sediments and brought into being the Atlantic Coastal Plain. The inner margin of the Coastal Plain was elevated several hundred feet, particularly in the Carolinas and Georgia. It is not to be assumed that all this uplift took place at one time or contemporaneously over the whole Atlantic Coastal Plain. Uplift was probably distributed over much of Tertiary time, and some parts of the Coastal Plain were submerged as late as Pliocene and Pleistocene time.

6. Erosion occurred on the uplifted Coastal Plain, and consequently a system of seaward-extending streams developed, with broad open valleys along their seaward parts. At the north an inner lowland was developed paralleling the contact of the coastal plain sediments and the oldland.

7. Complete drowning of Atlantic Coastal Plain northward from Long Island took place; south of Long Island partial drowning created the Embayed section. This submergence was largely the result of the load imposed on the earth's crust by the Pleistocene ice sheets and probably was not completed until late Pleistocene time.

8. The northern part of the Coastal Plain was modified by glaciation. This effect extends as far south as New Jersey. From Cape Cod southward the effects of glaciation consist largely of end moraines and outwash plains. Farther north, in such areas as the Gulf of Maine, the effects of glacial erosion may also be recognized.

9. Concomitant with depression and glaciation at the north, south of Long Island a set of coastal terraces developed which at their northern limits embrace all of the Coastal Plain; at the south, however, the terraces do not extend to the inner margin of the Coastal Plain.

10. The coastal plain terraces were eroded in varying degrees, with the inner and older terraces being more eroded than the outer and lower ones.

11. The present shoreline features, such as beaches, offshore bars, and coastal dunes, developed.

## COASTAL PLAIN TERRACES

One of the most controversial problems encountered in the Coastal Plain province concerns the number, nature, and age of the coastal terraces. Although by no means restricted to the Atlantic coast, they are particularly well developed here and have been studied here more than along the Gulf coast. Ideally each coastal terrace should be represented by a scarp at its landward edge, a tread of variable width extending seaward from this scarp, and a mantle on the tread of the terrace consisting mainly of gravel, sand, and silt. Practically nowhere is there a complete sequence of terraces, for development of the younger terraces may have cut away some of the older terraces. The correlation chart on page 34 represents various terrace sequences that have been described in various parts of the Atlantic Coastal Plain.

Cooke (1936, 1943a, 1945) has steadfastly maintained that the terraces are marine and were cut during former high sea levels of interglacial or intraglacial time. For many years he maintained that seven marine terraces could be identified along one part or another of the Coastal Plain. The following terrace sequence and age correlation was long defended by Cooke:

| Name of Terrace | Characteristic Altitude | Presumed Age |
|---|---|---|
| Brandywine | 270 | Aftonian |
| Coharie | 215 | Yarmouth |
| Sunderland | 170 | |
| Wicomico | 100 | |
| Penholoway | 70 | Sangamon |
| Talbot | 42 | |
| Pamlico | 25 | Mid-Wisconsin |

Terrace Correlation Chart

| Characteristic Altitude | Florida | Georgia | South Carolina North Carolina | Delaware Maryland Virginia | New Jersey |
|---|---|---|---|---|---|
| 270 feet | | Hazelhurst | | Brandywine | |
| 215 | Coharie | Coharie Claxton | Coharie | Coharie | |
| 170 | Okefenokee | Sunderland | Sunderland | Sunderland | Bridgeton |
| 100 | Wicomico Newberry | Wicomico | Wicomico | Wicomico | Pensauken |
| 42 | Talbot Tsala Apopka | Talbot Penholoway | Talbot Chowan | Talbot Chowan | |
| 25 | Pamlico Pensacola | Pamlico Saltilla | Pamlico | Pamlico Dismal Swamp | Cape May |
| 8 | Silver Bluff | | Princess Ann | Princess Ann | |

Cooke later admitted (1952, 1954) that evidence in the northern part of the Atlantic Coastal Plain seemed to indicate that the Brandywine gravels are nonmarine, and therefore the highest marine terrace here may be the Coharie. Cooke admitted that the Brandywine formation in its type locality in southern Maryland appears to be an alluvial fan deposit of probable Pliocene age. He argued, however, that along the southern part of the Atlantic Coastal Plain there is a 270-foot marine terrace, for which he revived the name Hazelhurst, a name originally applied by him to a terrace at this altitude in Georgia but later abandoned when it appeared that the name Brandywine had priority.

Hack (1955) has shown that the Brandywine formation, in southern Maryland, is divisible into three parts, a lower gravel member, a middle loam member, and an upper eolian silt member. He considered the formation to be partly marine and partly nonmarine in origin. The basal gravels were believed to represent near-shore deltaic deposits laid down in a Miocene sea. Hack concluded that no evidence exists in Maryland for marine terraces above an altitude of 100 feet. Hack's views were thus essentially similar to those of Campbell (1931), who held that the Brandywine and Sunderland formations are alluvial fan materials brought by the Potomac River from the Piedmont area to the west, and that no real basis exists for separating the

Brandywine from the Sunderland. Hack concluded, however, that the marine terrace hypothesis may be valid for the lower terraces in Maryland and elsewhere.

MacNeil (1950), working in northern Florida and Georgia, found what he considered evidence of four marine terraces in that area. These are the Okefenokee at 150 feet, the Wicomico at 100 feet, the Pamlico at 25–35 feet, and the Silver Bluff at 8–10 feet.

Flint (1940, 1941, 1957) has questioned the existence of as many marine terraces as postulated by Cooke and others. He saw evidence for only two marine strandlines, the Suffolk and Surry scarps. The Suffolk scarp (see Fig. 3.2) is about 20–30 feet above sea level and extends from New Jersey southward to the Gulf coast. The marine plain seaward from it is covered with what in New Jersey is called the Cape May formation, which is believed to correlate with the Pamlico formation farther south. Landward from the Suffolk scarp is the Surry scarp; this scarp was recognized by Flint only south of the James River in Virginia. The Surry scarp's characteristic altitude is 90–100 feet, and it presumably is the equivalent of what has been called by many the Wicomico scarp. Flint considered it likely that both the Suffolk and Surrey scarps are Sangamon in age. He believed all the sediments in the northern part of the coastal plain between the Pamlico terrace and the high-level

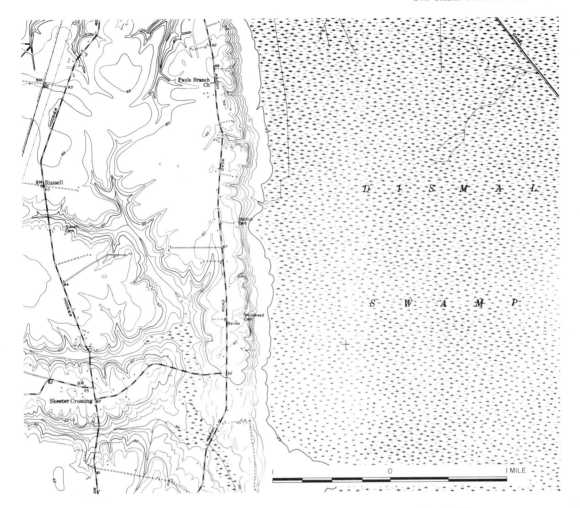

FIG. 3.2   Portion of Suffolk, Virginia, topographic sheet, showing part of the Suffolk scarp.

Brandywine gravels to be of fluvial origin. He did admit the possible existence of marine deposits above the Pamlico terrace in the southern states, but he considered them to be mainly marine bars, spits, and thin sediments. He considered the area between the Suffolk and Surrey scarps too broad to be appropriately called a terrace.

Oaks and Coch (1963) have presented results of a detailed study of the post-Miocene stratigraphy of a narrow strip of land lying between the Suffolk scarp and the coast in southeastern Virginia. They reached the following conclusions.   (1) The Suffolk scarp is an impor-

tant stratigraphic as well as morphological boundary, in that it separates older and deeply weathered nonmarine post-Miocene sediments from younger and less weathered late Miocene–pre-Recent dominantly marine sediments.   (2) Six post-Miocene submergences are reflected in seven marine and marine-lagoonal formations east of the Suffolk scarp.   (3) The submergences during which the sediments were deposited were attributed to glacio-eustatic rises of sea level. (4) The term "terrace" as it has been applied to topographic surfaces along the Atlantic Coastal Plain is inappropriate, first because it has come to have a genetic implication which is invalid, and second, because the topographic surfaces called "terraces" are too broad to be properly called terraces. (5) The concept held by many geologists that each terrace tread has over it a veneer representing a single geological formation deposited during a single marine submergence is untenable.

It is perhaps too early to form a firm conclusion regarding the Atlantic coastal plain terraces. Many more detailed field studies are needed, and it would be particularly helpful in these studies if topographic maps made with a 5-foot contour interval rather than the 10- and 20-foot intervals used on most of the maps of the coastal plain were available. The preponderance of opinion seems to be that in the northern area (Maryland and New Jersey) the Pamlico terrace is a truly marine terrace, but that the deposits above the Pamlico-Cape May formation are largely fluvial, deltaic, or estuarine. Both marine and fluvial deposits exist in Virginia, and most of the persons who have worked in the Carolinas, Georgia, Florida, and Alabama seem to believe in the existence of extensive marine terraces in these states, although they differ in their opinions as to how many there are. General agreement seems to have been reached that the Brandywine formation is not a marine deposit and that therefore the Brandywine terrace should be dropped from the marine terrace category. It may be that the upper terraces are not marine in origin, but it is difficult to look at maps of these surfaces in the Carolinas and Georgia, even where they are notably dissected, without coming to the conclusion that they represent successive topographic surfaces which are not too inappropriately termed terraces.

One thing that has led some geologists to be skeptical of the theory of marine terracing along the Atlantic Coastal Plain is the fact that the postulated topographic and time sequences are in the same order. It would represent a most remarkable coincidence to have each successive high sea level fall short of the preceding one. This would indeed seem highly unlikely if the land were stationary during all the time that Pleistocene sea levels rose and fell, but it would not be unreasonable if during Pleistocene time

this part of the Atlantic coast was slowly but continuously rising. This, in fact, seems to have been true along the Gulf coast (see p. 59).

## DESCRIPTION OF SECTIONS OF COASTAL PLAIN PROVINCE

### *Embayed Section*

*Cause and Extent of Submergence.* The Embayed section of the Coastal Plain extends from a little south of the Neuse River, in North Carolina, northward to a somewhat debatable boundary at the north, which is here taken to be Cape Cod. The most outstanding geomorphic characteristics of this section are related directly or indirectly to fairly recent submergence of the Atlantic Coastal Plain. From Long Island Sound southward as far as the James River, in Virginia, this submergence reaches inland as far as the contact of the coastal plain sediments with the older rocks of the New England and Piedmont provinces, or the so-called Fall Line. The submergence was the combined result of the weighting down of northeastern North America under the Pleistocene ice load and the postglacial rise of sea level attendant upon return of large volumes of water to the oceans. Submergence was greater at the north than at the south, as evidenced by decrease northward in the width of the Coastal Plain and in the altitude of its inner edge. North of Cape Cod the Coastal Plain is completely submerged and has become a part of the continental shelf.

*Cape Cod.* Cape Cod consists mainly of glacial, glacio-fluviatile, and glacio-lacustrine materials of Wisconsin age. A belt of hummocky topography known locally as "the backbone of the Cape" is formed by the Sandwich moraine (Mather et al., 1942). Extending southwestward from the western end of the Sandwich moraine is the Buzzards Bay moraine. The two moraines mark minor readvances of two sublobes of the Labrador ice sheet known as the Cape Cod and Buzzards Bay sublobes. The reentrant between the two moraines is filled with the glacial outwash of the Mashpee pitted outwash plain (see Fig. 3.3).

FIG. 3.3    Pitted outwash plain, looking northwest toward Plymouth, Mass.    (*From* Geology Illustrated, *by John S. Shelton, copyright by W. H. Freeman and Company.*)

*Long Island.* Basement rocks beneath Long Island consist of Paleozoic gneisses and schists intruded by pegmatites and granites (Oliver and Drake, 1951). Apparently the Triassic rocks found in New Jersey do not continue beneath Long Island Sound, as has been believed by some geologists. The Cretaceous Raritan and Magothy (?) formations rest on the basement rocks and form the core of the island. The Manetto gravels at the western end of the island are generally considered to be of Pliocene age and correlative with the Brandywine and Citronelle formations farther south.

The outline of Long Island is largely determined by two end moraines, the Ronkonkoma at the south and the Harbor Hill at the north.

These moraines are responsible for the flukes at the eastern end of Long Island. The moraines are probably of early Wisconsin age, but it is uncertain to which substage of the Wisconsin glaciation they belong. South of the Ronkonkoma moraine is an outwash plain that makes up a considerable part of the island. The highest point on Long Island is near its western end and slightly exceeds 400 feet in altitude. If the glacial materials were removed from Long Island its area would probably be not much more than one-fourth what it now is and its maximum altitude not over 250 feet. Most of the eastern part of the island would disappear.

Long Island Sound is part of an inner lowland that lies along the boundary of the Coastal Plain and the oldland back of it. This lowland lies back of a cuesta whose scarp is responsible for Long Island, Block Island, Martha's Vineyard, and Nantucket Island. This submerged inner lowland can be traced northeastward at least as far as the Gulf of Maine (Murray, 1947). From Raritan Bay, New Jersey, southward the inner lowland is mainly land and can be traced as far south as northeastern Virginia. This part of the lowland is developed on the lower Cretaceous Raritan formation and the rocks of the Potomac group below the Raritan. Where the Delaware River enters the lowland west of Trenton, New Jersey, it makes a sharp right-angled turn to the southwest and follows the lowland to Delaware Bay. In New Jersey, minor cuestas developed on Upper Cretaceous and Miocene formations lie eastward from the lowland.

*Chesapeake Bay Area.* Along the Maryland-Virginia part of the Embayed section submergence is not as great as at the north part, but it is enough that a large number of broad estuaries have been formed by drowning of the lower courses of the Delaware and Susquehanna Rivers. Submergence here has broken the coastal plain into a number of peninsular tracts separated by broad estuaries, many of which extend inland to the Fall Line. The Chesapeake Bay region is thus a striking example of a dismembered river system. The original drainage of this area consisted of the Susquehanna River and its tributaries. These tributaries were such rivers as the present James, Rappahannock, Potomac, and Patuxent. Farther south in North Carolina, where submergence was not as great, we find several estuaries and broad sounds such as Albemarle Sound and Pamlico Sound but not extensive dismemberment of drainage systems.

*Embayed Section South of Chesapeake Bay.* Pleistocene terraces are prominent in the Embayed section of the Coastal Plain. At the north end they extend across the entire coastal plain, but beginning in Virginia and widening to the south is an inner belt of nonterraced coastal plain. Here, as elsewhere, difference of opinion exists as to the nature of the terraces. Several geologists have favored the idea that the higher terraces in

this area are nonmarine. Wentworth (1930) concluded that the Brandywine, Sunderland, and Wicomico terraces are fluviatile terraces; Campbell (1931) interpreted the terraces around Washington, D. C., as remnants of a large alluvial fan; and, as stated above, Hack (1955) considered all the terraces above the 100-foot level nonmarine.

Present on the surfaces of the terraces of the Embayed section are numerous depressions similar to those in the Carolinas that go by the name of "bays." Discussion of these features will be found under the Sea Island section (see p. 41). Certain small basins in New Jersey have been interpreted by Wolfe (1953) as thaw sinks resulting from the melting of ice wedges formed under periglacial conditions. The basins are oval to irregular in shape and are developed on formations as young as Cape May, the New Jersey equivalent of the Pamlico formation. Wolfe concluded that the depressions are thaw sinks rather than bays because of the presence in them of involutions and other structures that suggest strong frost action.

*Shoreline Features.* The most youthful topographic features of the Embayed section are the wave-cut cliffs, beaches, coastal dunes, and various types of bars. Although present along much of the coastline, offshore bars are particularly conspicuous along the New Jersey coast and south of Chesapeake Bay. The shoreline from Cape Henry, Virginia, southward to Cape Fear, North Carolina, is an example of a compound cuspate foreland probably not excelled anywhere in the world. Albemarle Sound and Pamlico Sound are almost completely enclosed by cuspate bars; in time the whole area back of these bars will be filled and the coastline prograded to the site of the present offshore bars.

## Sea Island Section

The Sea Island section is a good example of the principle that a geomorphic unit may lack strongly defined boundaries but still possess individuality. Only at the west along the Fall Line is the boundary of the Sea Island section readily recognizable; its boundaries at both the north and south are rather arbitrarily drawn.

*Distinguishing Characteristics.* Five noticeable topographic differences set this section off from the Embayed section to the north. (1) The amount of submergence is less, and although the rivers are drowned in their lower parts, they have not been converted into large estuaries. (2) Offshore bars, which are so conspicuous in the Embayed section, are in general lacking. (3) In place of the offshore bars is a chain of coastal islands known as sea islands. (4) There is a sizeable nonterraced zone inland which is dissected enough to make the inner Coastal Plain here notably hilly. (5) The shallow depressions commonly known as the "Carolina Bays" are most extensively developed in the section, although they are by no means restricted to it.

*Geology of Section.* The geology of the Sea Island section is with one exception essentially similar to that of the Embayed section. The one major change in geology encountered in the Sea Island section is that Miocene rocks do not extend to the inner margin of the Coastal Plain; here, rocks of Eocene and Cretaceous age are found instead. These rocks are not weak, as are the Miocene rocks; consequently, a belt of hills is found in place of the inner lowland of New Jersey, Maryland, and Virginia. Such information as exists indicates that the Piedmont rock complex extends beneath the Coastal Plain. Topographic relief on the basement complex is of the order of 200 feet. It was in this area that Prouty (1946) and Berry (1948) thought that well data suggested two distinct slopes of the basement floor, which they believed could be correlated with the Fall Zone and the Schooley peneplains (see p. 31).

*Topographic Belts.* The Sea Island section can be divided into five rather distinct topographic belts. From the inner margin to the coast, these are: (1) the Fall Line Hills, a strip of maturely dissected hills cut out of the oldest coastal plain deposits; (2) the Tifton Upland, an area of submaturely dissected coastal plain; (3) a belt of older coastal terraces which show a moderate degree of erosion; (4) a tract of younger terraces which are largely unmodified by stream erosion and have extensive swampy areas on them; and (5) the offshore line of sea islands.

FALL LINE HILLS. A belt 20 to 40 miles wide known as the Fall Line Hills coincides with the outcrop areas of Cretaceous and Eocene rocks. Maximum relief is from 100 to more than 300 feet, and dissection has advanced enough that the terrain has largely lost its original plain-like character. Sand is so abundant in the Cretaceous and Eocene formations that the hills are locally known as the Sand Hills. The name Red Hills is often applied to the area underlain by rocks of Eocene age, because of the red soils here. In Georgia this belt is known as the Louisville Plateau.

TIFTON UPLAND. The Tifton Upland is a strip of land in Georgia, 30 to 50 miles wide, which lies between the Red Hills and the belt of older terraces. This area has a cover of Miocene sediments and is largely rolling hills, not as maturely dissected as the Red Hills and Fall Line Hills, but noticeably more dissected than the belt of older marine terraces seaward from it. Relief is commonly of the order of 50 to 100 feet, but it may exceed this along major valleys.

TERRACE BELTS. The terraces above the Wicomico in general are notably dissected; the higher ones, such as the Brandywine (Hazelhurst) and Coharie (Claxton), are so dissected that they have to a large degree lost their terrace-like characteristics, although the elevation contrasts between them are still evident. From the Wicomico terrace downward, dissection is either very slight or lacking, and swampy areas are common.

SEA ISLANDS. The Sea Islands are a chain of islands parallel to the mainland and separated from it by salt marshes, passes, sounds, or lagoons (see Fig. 3.4). Fenneman (1938) interpreted them as parts of the Pamlico terrace which had been isolated from the mainland by a slight submergence. In those places where the Sea Islands rise above the altitude of the Pamlico terrace, the additional height was attributed to dunes. The passageways between the islands presumably represented courses of former streams that have been deepened somewhat by tidal scour accompanying and following submergence.

Zeigler (1959) concluded that there are three types of islands present along the coast, erosion

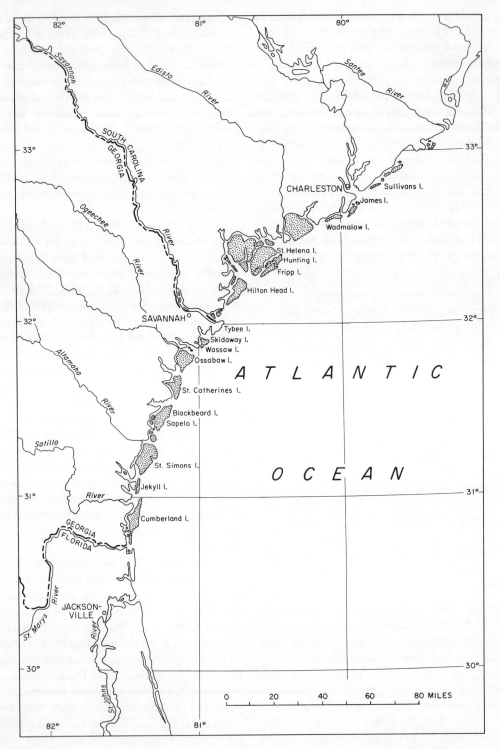

FIG. 3.4   Map of the sea islands.   (*After J. M. Zeigler, Geog. Rev.,* **49,**   *Courtesy American Geographical Society.*)

remnant islands, marsh islands, and beach ridge islands. The erosion remnant islands represent parts of the eroded Pamlico terrace that were not destroyed during a low stand of sea level because they were composed of more resistant sediments. The marsh islands developed on mud flats and in protected water bodies and represent accumulations of clay, silt, and marsh plants. The beach ridge islands are still in the process of growth. Zeigler pointed out that there are distinct differences in the topographies of the three types of islands. The erosion remnant islands are sand covered and irregular in outline, but they lack dunal topography; the marsh islands are lower in altitude and are composed of a mixture of rock detritus and vegetation; the beach ridge islands are still different, in that their topography consists of subparallel, arcuate sand ridges.

Zeigler thought that two generations of rivers could be recognized along this part of the Coastal Plain, pre-Wisconsin and post-Wisconsin rivers. The pre-Wisconsin rivers are those such as the Santee, Edisto, Savannah, Saltilla, and others, which drain from the Piedmont across the coastal plain. The post-Wisconsin rivers are rivers like the Midway, Newport, and Turtle, which head near the scarp that forms the inner boundary of the Pamlico terrace.

### The Carolina Bays

The term "bay" has long been applied in the middle Atlantic Coastal Plain to shallow depressions that are commonly oval or elliptical in outline (see Fig. 3.5). This name was apparently given to the depressions because of the common occurrence in them of the evergreen bay tree. For many years these features attracted little more than local attention. Their striking characteristics did not become readily apparent until the days of aerial photography. Melton and Schriever in a paper presented in 1933 suggested that they represent scars produced by the impact of a shower of meteorites. Since then much has been written about them and numerous theories of origin proposed.

Bays are particularly abundant in the coastal plain regions of Virginia, in the two Carolinas, and in Georgia. Features that have been considered to be similar in origin, although somewhat different in appearance, have been described as far south as Alabama and as far north as New Jersey.

*Physical Characteristics.* The following are some of the significant facts about the bays listed by Prouty (1952), which any theory of origin must be able to explain:

1. They are restricted to the Coastal Plain and are particularly abundant in the two Carolinas and northeastern Georgia (see Fig. 3.6).
2. The bays are notably irregular in size and distribution.
3. No correlation between the distribution of the bays and rock types, rock age, or specific type of topography has been established. They are found on interstream uplands, valley sides, terraces, and even floodplains.
4. The number of bays may be as great as one half million.
5. A pronounced tendency toward elongation in a northwest-southeast direction is apparent.
6. Sand rims are characteristic features of the bays and these rims are best developed on the southeast sides of the bays and most poorly developed on the northwest sides.
7. Numerous bays have multiple rims.
8. The deepest part of a bay is commonly found toward its southeast end and somewhat to the west of an axial line through the bay.
9. Similarity in development and state of preservation of the bays suggests that they are nearly the same age.
10. Overlapping bays and rims suggest multiple periods of bay formation of slightly different ages.
11. All the bays are developed on the sandy Pleistocene terraces and are younger than any of the beach ridges with which they are associated.
12. The bays are in general nearly filled with peat varying in thickness from 15 to 30 feet.
13. A few bays have lake bottom springs in them, located usually near the southeast ends of the bays.

FIG. 3.5   Vertical photograph of some of the Carolina "bays," Horry County, South Carolina.   (*Production and Marketing Administration photo.*)

*Theories of Origin.* The meteoritic theory has been supported in a somewhat modified form by Prouty (1935, 1952) and MacCarthy (1937), who suggested that the bays were the result of "shock waves" in the form of cones of compressed air ahead of the meteorites rather than of the direct impact of the meteorites. Melton (1950) has modified the original meteoritic hypothesis to the extent that he is willing to admit that the bays could have been produced by a number of meteorite falls rather than by one shower. He considered it possible that the showers had begun as far back as late Cretaceous time and that at least eight or nine times between Cretaceous time and the present the Coastal Plain was

emergent and could have received showers of meteorites. He thought it possible that the depressions had been formed long before the bay rim features, which he considered largely of Recent origin. This seems difficult to visualize in view of the fact that the bays are present on terrace surfaces that are generally considered to be of Pleistocene age.

Cooke (1934, 1943b, 1954) has maintained that the bays represent the basins of extinct lakes or lagoons that formed on the Coastal Plain as it began to emerge from the sea. Their elliptical shapes were attributed by him to eddy currents developed under the gyroscopic effect of the earth's rotation.

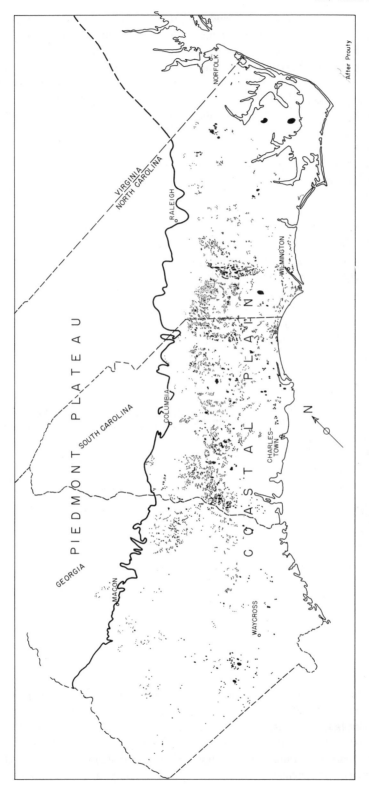

FIG. 3.6   Map showing distribution of Carolina "bays."   (*After W. F. Prouty, Geol. Soc. Am. Bull., 63.*)

Johnson (1942) proposed a composite theory of origin designated as the "artesian-lacustrine-eolian" theory. He believed that the bays were initiated by thousands of artesian springs that rose to the surface of the Coastal Plain through joint systems in the rocks. The springs were supposed to have enlarged their openings by solution until small lakes came into existence over the sites of the artesian springs. The bay rims were interpreted as beach ridges around the lakes, some of which have been enlarged considerably by the construction of dune ridges.

LeGrand (1953) has proposed a modification of Johnson's theory which he called "the streamline theory." He postulated solution in a near-surface limestone or marl aquifer, with resulting subsidence of overlying clays. This was followed by streamlined groundwater flow around the clay obstruction in the depressed area, which caused more solution and subsidence, leading finally to an ellipsoidal or oval-shaped bay. His hypothesis differs from Johnson's in that he does not postulate the presence of thousands of artesian springs. He considered massive limestones beneath the surface as unfavorable to the development of bays and pointed out that in Georgia and Florida, where massive limestone underlies the surface, sinkholes rather than bays develop. He observed that even in South Carolina, where the Tertiary limestone is thick, bays are not prominent.

Rasmussen (1953) thought that Wolfe had not made a convincing case for the small basins in New Jersey described by him as being periglacial thaw sinks (see p. 38). Rasmussen thought that the basins in New Jersey might well be bays that were close enough to the ice front to have been modified in form and structure by freeze and thaw. This he thought would account for the irregularity in shape of some.

We probably are not yet in a position to come to a firm conclusion as to the origin of the Carolina Bays. Certain facts that are sometimes overlooked or given scant consideration should be taken into account before we attempt to arrive at a preferred hypothesis of origin. It should be emphasized, as Johnson maintained, that not all of the bays are as symmetrical as those that are commonly pictured; many irregular-shaped depressions are found in association with the symmetrical bays. Secondly, similar depressions are present in parts of the Coastal Plain other than the Carolinas, even as far west as Texas. The possibility cannot be ignored that these more irregular depressions represent the less mature stages of bay development. The solutional theories of Johnson and LeGrand encounter numerous difficulties, but possibly fewer than do the meteoritic and eddy theories. It seems too remarkable a coincidence that a meteoritic shower should just happen to hit the Coastal Plain and not the Piedmont Plateau, Blue Ridge, or Ridge and Valley provinces to the west. Restriction of the bays to a particular geologic province seems to lend support to the belief that whatever the origin of the bays was, it had a geologic basis rather than an astronomical one.

### Floridian Section

*Distinctive Features.* Despite the fact that the Floridian section must be delimited at the north by an artificial boundary, the section possesses several distinguishing topographic characteristics which justify its recognition as a separate geomorphic unit. The major distinctive features of the Floridian section are: (1) the presence of various phenomena attesting to a recent emergence, (2) widespread distribution of carbonate rocks with associated karst features, (3) the Florida keys along the southern tip of the peninsula, (4) much swampy land, particularly at the southwest, and (5) extensive marine terraces on the east, south, and west around a higher central area where terraces are either lacking or obscure.

*Geology of Florida.* The peninsula of Florida is a recently emergent part of a southward projection of the continental mass of North America known as the Floridian Plateau, the submerged portion of which still greatly exceeds the emergent part. The emergent part is rather asymmetrically distributed with respect to the entire Floridian Plateau. The edge of the continental shelf is only a few miles off the east coast, whereas off the west coast the continental slope lies many miles offshore. The Floridian Plateau has probably long been a part of the North American continental platform, but Florida has very recently been added to the continent.

Exposed rocks in Florida range in age from Eocene to Pleistocene. The Eocene Avon Park formation is the oldest rock that crops out. In addition to it, rocks of Miocene, Oligocene, possibly Pliocene, and Pleistocene age are exposed. The sedimentary section of Florida has a known thickness in excess of 18,000 feet (Vernon, 1951) and includes rocks as old as Cambrian, Ordovician, Silurian, and possibly Devonian. The greater part of the sedimentary section, however, consists of rocks of Mesozoic and Cenozoic age (see Fig. 3.7). A well near the tip of southern Florida penetrated more than 15,000 feet of limestone, dolomite, and anhydrites of Tertiary, Cretaceous, and possibly Jurassic age.

Several hundred oil and gas wells have been drilled in Florida, and although the majority of these penetrated only Cenozoic and Mesozoic rocks, a considerable number were drilled through these rocks into what is called the basement complex. These wells encountered granites, diorites, various types of metamorphic rocks, diabases, basalts, rhyolites, and pyroclastic rocks (Applin, 1951). It thus appears that the basement rocks of Florida are essentially the same types found to the north in the Piedmont, Blue Ridge, and Ridge and Valley provinces.

The major structural feature of the Florida peninsula is the Ocala Uplift in north central Florida (see Fig. 3.8). This is a gentle flexure developed in Tertiary sediments that is approximately 230 miles long and 70 miles wide. At the crest of the Ocala Uplift, the Eocene Ocala limestone is 150 feet above sea level; 250 miles to the south it is 1200 feet below sea level, giving to the formation an average regional dip of 5 feet per mile. Uplift of the Ocala arch began before late Eocene time and continued into late Miocene time, as indicated by the fact that the Miocene Hawthorn formation is involved in the uplift (Cooke, 1945).

Much of the surface of Florida consists of marine terraces. In one part or another of the state as many as seven terraces have been described (see Fig. 3.9), ranging from the uppermost Hazelhurst at altitudes of 250 to 270 feet to the Silver Bluff at 8 to 10 feet. The parts of Florida that reach the levels of the highest terraces constitute a small part of the state. A striking feature associated with the marine terraces is Trail Ridge in northern Florida and southern Georgia. This large bar has a length of 130 miles and rises conspicuously above its surroundings. Its construction probably began during the Hazelhurst high sea level and was continued through the Coharie and Sunderland high sea levels.

*Floridian Karst Features.* Karst features are abundant in Florida, as might be expected in a state which is largely underlain by carbonate rocks. It is, however, in the central lake district that they are most excellently displayed; south of Lake Okeechobee karst features are few. Floridian karst differs from that of most other karst regions of the United States in that it has developed under conditions of a high water table, and as a consequence most underground passageways are filled with water. Only in the higher parts of northern Florida are air-filled caverns found. Florida has an extensively developed artesian system, with water flowing through open passageways that may be thousands of feet below the surface of the land. Several of these deep artesian systems discharge on the sea bottom many miles offshore. A typical freshwater "boil" of this origin exists about 3 miles offshore from Crescent Beach near St. Augustine (Jordan, 1950). By far the most important aquifer in this artesian system is the Eocene Ocala limestone. The most common sealing rocks above the Ocala limestone are the clays, dense marls, and limestones of the Miocene Hawthorn formation. Aquifers of secondary importance are the Eocene Avon Park formation, the Oligocene Suwannee limestone, and the Tampa and Hawthorn formations of Miocene age.

The geological conditions which exist in Florida naturally favor the development of numerous artesian springs. Of the 75 first magnitude

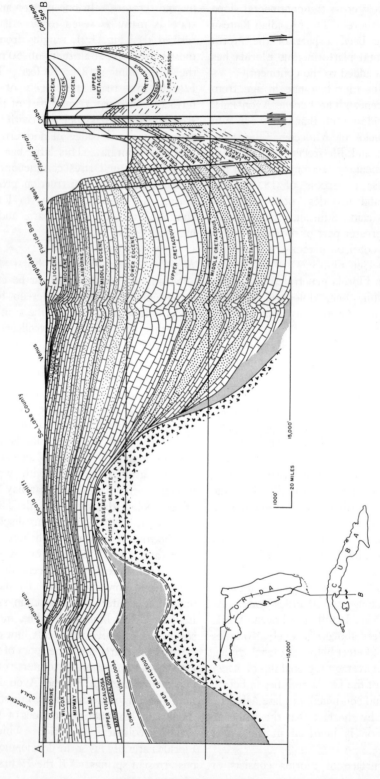

FIG. 3.7   Structure section across Florida to Cuba.   (*After E. D. Pressler, Am. Assoc. Petroleum Geologists Bull.,* 31.)

springs (average flow of 100 second-feet or more) in the United States, 17 are in Florida (Ferguson et al., 1947). Silver Springs, the largest of the artesian springs, has an average flow of 808 second-feet per day (a second-foot equals 646,000 gallons), which gives it an average daily discharge of approximately 500,000,000 gallons.

Openings of many of the artesian springs are tube-like; Bugg Spring, at Okahumpka, emerges from a nearly vertical-walled opening which has a depth of 176 feet. Many spring bottoms are below sea level and may be related to Pleistocene low sea levels. Drillers may encounter cavities in the limestones at depths of several thousand feet. Florida seems to be honeycombed with subsurface passageways that extend far below any 300- to 400-foot lowering of sea level that might be attributed to lower Pleistocene sea levels.

Floridian karst has much in common with other karst regions, but differences related to

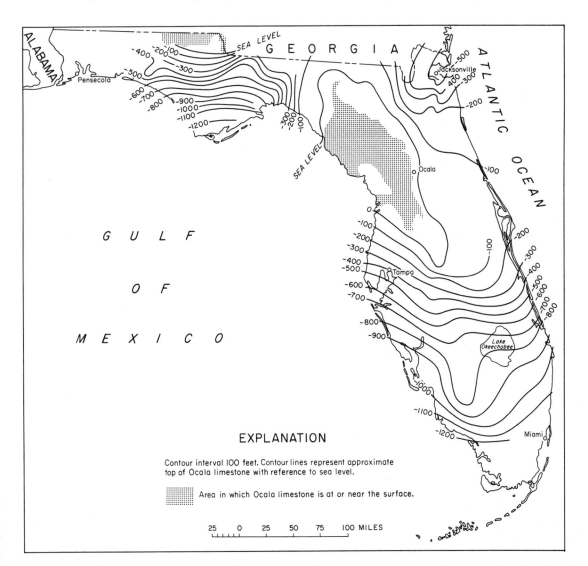

FIG. 3.8    Structural map of Florida based on top of Ocala limestone.    (*After R. C. Heath and W. E. Clark, Fla. Geol. Surv. Rept., Invest.* 7.)

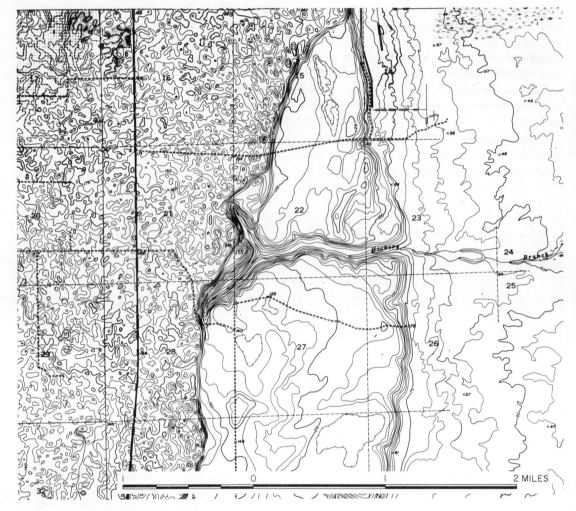

FIG. 3.9   Portion of Childs, Florida topographic sheet showing two marine scarps and terraces with low dunes covering upper terrace.

the particular geological conditions exist. Sinkholes are common (see Fig. 3.10). Most of them are similar to the shallow sinkholes found in other karst regions, but we do find in Florida more of the deep, steep-sided sinkholes known as ponors. Dismal Sink, about 10 miles southeast of Tallahasse, is such a feature. It is 60 feet in diameter, and its rim stands 100 feet above the level of the water in it; the water in the ponor has a depth of 75 feet, giving to the ponor a total depth of 175 feet. The Devil's Mill Hopper, a similar feature 6 miles northwest of

Gainesville, is over 100 feet deep. Nearness of the water table to the surface in much of Florida results in the sinkholes' having ponds or lakes in them more commonly than elsewhere in the United States.

At numerous localities in Florida are features known locally as steepheads. These are what are elsewhere called spring alcoves. They form where karst springs emerging from the bases of the walls of sinkholes have by sapping extended themselves headward into the surrounding upland and developed steep-walled recesses.

Variation in the character of the karst topography can be related to whether the Ocala limestone immediately underlies the land surface or is overlain by another formation such as the Hawthorn.   Where the Hawthorn or some other formation covers the Ocala limestone, the sinkholes are generally more shallow, and the ponor type is less commonly encountered.   This difference has served as a basis for dividing the karst region of Florida into the lime-sink district, where the Ocala is covered, and the lake district, where it is not.   The karst of the lime-sink district is to some degree comparable to that found elsewhere in the United States.   A few karst springs and natural bridges are found here, but sinking creeks and associated phenomena are largely lacking.   The altitudes in Florida do not favor the valley entrenchment necessary for diversion of surface streams to underground routes, and the permeability of the widespread Hawthorn formation favors mass penetration of surface waters rather than runoff into streams that later sink in swallow holes.   .

*Southern Florida.*   Southern Florida has very little land that could be called "high" even as that term is used in Florida : much of it lies below an altitude of 20 feet.   This low altitude, along with an annual rainfall in excess of 60 inches, produces extensive areas of poorly drained land. It has commonly been assumed that Florida recently underwent downtilting to the west. Arguments cited in favor of this assumption are: (1) Tampa Bay, Charlotte Harbor, and the 10,000 Islands off the southwest coast suggest recent coastal drowning; (2) drowned sinkholes are present off the west coast; and (3) the submerged portion of the Floridian Plateau on the west is much wider than that on the east coast. White (1958), however, has maintained that the evidence commonly cited in support of the idea of westward tilting is really only evidence of recent submergence.   He believed that the conclusion that no westward tilting has taken place is supported by the following evidence: (1) drowning is not confined to the west coast, as extensive lagoonal areas exist along the east

FIG. 3.10   Sinkholes in central Florida.   *(Photo by U. S. Geological Survey.)*

FIG. 3.11   The Everglades in Dade County, Florida, looking north from Tamiami Trail.   (*Photo by Groundwater Branch, U. S. Geological Survey.*)

coast; (2) drowned sinks merely indicate submergence, and these are found off the southeast coast of Florida as well as the west coast (see p. 16); (3) drainage of the Everglades is to the to the east as well as to the west (see Fig. 3.12); and (4) the Pamlico terrace has the same altitudes on the east as on the west.   White admitted that the fact that the Floridian Plateau is higher on the east than on the west may have resulted from tilting, but he believed that the tilting took place so long ago that it has not affected the present topography.

*Atlantic Coastal Ridge.*   Between the Everglades and the coast of southern Florida is a strip of dry land called the Atlantic Coastal Ridge.   To call it a ridge is somewhat misleading, for nowhere is it more than 50 feet above sea level, and most of it is considerably less.   The coastal ridge almost everywhere has a rock foundation on which lie dune sands or sands of the Pamlico formation.   The ridge disappears south of Florida City in a series of low islands called the "Everglade Keys" but reappears in the lower Florida Keys.   The coastal ridge was probably built at the same time as the Talbot terrace (late Sangamon time) as an irregular limey bar under conditions similar to those represented in the present Bay of Florida–Florida Keys area.

*Lagoonal Rivers.*   Almost the entire east coast of Florida is bordered by a line of offshore bars back of which lie lagoonal tracts.   Some of these are marshy; some are occupied by what are called lagoonal rivers.   Indian River, a 130-mile-long body of brackish water, is an example. The term river, however, is hardly applicable to this type of water body, as there is no stream-like flow of its water.

*Everglades.*   The Everglades is a region of organic soils about 100 miles long and 40 miles wide which merges at the south with Florida Bay and the Gulf of Mexico in an area of saltwater marshes and mangrove swamps (Parker and Cooke, 1944).   Large areas in the eastern and western parts of the Everglades are practically treeless, and here sawgrass 10 to 12 feet high is found (see Fig. 3.11).   Trees grow only where there is enough height above water level to permit aeration of their roots.   The floor of the Everglades consists mainly of the Pleistocene Fort Thompson freshwater limestone and marl, except at the south, where the Miami oölite is found.   The gently sloping basin of the Everglades was sea bottom in Pliocene time, but during Pleistocene time its floor was subjected to some erosion plus deposition of a succession of Pleistocene formations, the youngest of which is the Pamlico sand.   In late Wisconsin time the sea withdrew, exposing a large area of fresh-water lakes and swamps in which for a time solutional erosion was prevalent.   More recently deposition has produced a thin veneer of peat and muck.

In the Everglades are numerous "tree-islands" or hammocks, which are separated from each other by water areas variously called swales, sloughs, or runs, the pattern of which indicates the general direction of drainage of the Ever-glades (see Fig. 3.12).   It is possible that the

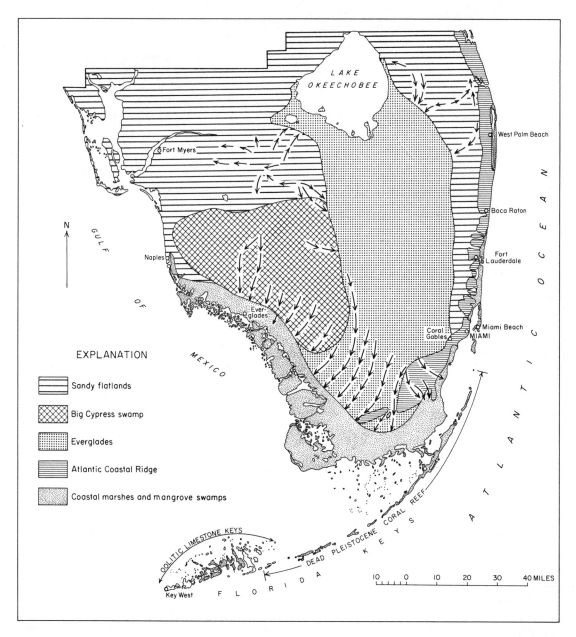

FIG. 3.12   Topographic-ecologic map of southern Florida, showing directions of drainage.   (*After G. G. Parker, U. S. Geol. Surv. W.S.P.* 1255.)

FIG. 3.13   Part of Overseas Highway across Florida Keys.   (*Florida State News Bureau photo.*)

present drainage pattern is related to the ocean currents that prevailed over the Everglades during Pamlico time.

*Big Cypress Swamp.*   The name Big Cypress Swamp is applied to a somewhat indefinite area lying west of the Everglades.   In it are large areas of solutionally-riddled limestone and solution pockets containing marl.   It is an area of alternating swampland and hammocks, with the higher areas supporting grasses, palmettos, and pines and the lower areas having cypress, willows, reeds, sedges, and other marsh vegetation.

*Lake Okeechobee.*   North of the Everglades lies Lake Okeechobee, which, like the Everglades, was originally a depression on the Pliocene sea floor.   Its floor has since been modified slightly by solution and deposition of sediments.   Lake Okeechobee is about 30 miles wide and at its maximum depth covers over 700 square miles. Most of the lake has a depth of less than 20 feet; its deepest part lies near sea level.   Overflow from Lake Okeechobee goes eastward through the St. Lucie canal and westward through the

Caloosahatchee canal-river.   During part of the year it drains through several canals that terminate on the east coast between West Palm Beach and Miami.   Because of its bowl shape and shallowness Lake Okeechobee is subject to severe wind-generated waves.   During the 1928 hurricane wind velocities of 135 miles per hour produced "tidal waves" on Lake Okeechobee better than 13 feet high.

*Florida Keys.*   South of Miami Beach, the Florida Keys extend in a curve for 150 miles to Key West and separate the shallow waters of Biscayne Bay, Card Sound, Barnes Sound, and Florida Bay from the deeper waters of the Straits of Florida (see Fig. 3.13).   The limestone floor of the Everglades continues southward beneath the shallow waters of Florida Bay and emerges again in the Florida Keys.   Islands comprising the keys are of two types (Cooke, 1939).   The eastern keys, which terminate at Loggerhead Key, are long narrow islands composed of the Key Largo limestone; apparently they formed as coral reefs in the Pamlico Sea.   The western keys, which lie back of the eastern keys and extend beyond them to as far as Key West, were merely a shoal in the Pamlico sea. They are similar in origin to the Everglades and composed of the same limestone, the Caloosahatchee marl and associated deposits.

The main line of keys begins south of Safety Valve entrance and curves southwestward to Loggerhead Key in a broad arc almost 110 miles long. The highest point on the eastern keys is only 18 feet above sea level. These keys are long, narrow islands covered with a dense jungle of low trees and shrubs. The Key Largo limestone apparently developed as a submerged coral reef in the Pamlico sea when sea level was about 25 feet higher than now.

The western keys form a compact group extending more than 40 miles, from East Bahia Honda Key to Key West. The maximum width of this group is about 14 miles. These keys rise from a tongue-like bank that underlies Florida Bay and projects westward near the southern edge of the Floridian Plateau. The bank stands only 10 to 20 feet higher than the surrounding sea bottom and appears to have formed as a shoal during Pamlico time as a result of rapid accumulation of limy oölitic ooze. The keys and subjacent bank are composed of oölitic limestone which is a continuation of the Miami oölite of the mainland.

## East Gulf Coastal Plain

*Distinctive Features.* Although no sharp topographic boundary exists between the Sea Island section and the East Gulf Coastal Plain, a short distance west of the Georgia–South Carolina boundary a sufficient change in topographic characteristics takes place to constitute grounds for differentiating the two sections. Increase westward in number and thickness of the Cretaceous and Eocene formations and a greater variability in their lithological characteristics are responsible for the change in topography. The greater thickness and number of the Cretaceous and Eocene formations results in a widening of the coastal plain, and the increased variability of lithology produces notable variation in the erosi-

bility of the rocks. As a consequence the East Gulf Coastal Plain exhibits a series of lowlands and cuestas with infacing escarpments which justify its designation as a belted coastal plain.

The term Fall Line is used along the Atlantic Coastal Plain to refer to the contact between the Cretaceous and Tertiary sediments and the rocks of the oldland. It is also used in the East Gulf Coastal Plain, but the term hardly has the same implication here that it does along the Atlantic Coastal Plain. Only as far west as central Alabama do the coastal plain sediments come into contact with igneous or metamorphic rocks, as they do along the contact of the Atlantic Coastal Plain and the Piedmont Plateau. North of central Alabama coastal plain rocks abut against Paleozoic sedimentary rocks, and the differences in lithology are not great enough to produce the rapids and waterfalls that are common along the eastern part of the Fall Line. The Coosa and Tallapoosa rivers in eastern Alabama and the Chattahoochee River in Georgia have rapids along them (Fenneman, 1938), but few of the other streams that come from the oldland onto the Coastal Plain do.

The East Gulf Coastal Plain can be divided into two distinct types of topography. The greater part of it is belted coastal plain, including a series of lowlands developed on weak rock, commonly limestones or clays (shales), bounded seaward by cuesta scarps and dip slopes on the stronger rocks, commonly sandstones. Adjacent to the coast, however, is a narrow strip of coastwise terraces similar to those described for the Atlantic Coastal Plain and Florida. The succession of topographic belts that would be crossed in going across the East Gulf Coastal Plain would vary somewhat according to where the traverse was made (see Fig. 3.14). A traverse made along a line connecting Birmingham, Alabama, and New Orleans, Louisiana, would be fairly typical and would cross the following topographic belts, going from northeast to southwest: the Fall Line Hills, Black Belt, Ripley cuesta, the Flatwoods, Red Hills, Buhrstone cuesta, Jackson Prairie, Southern Pine Hills, and the Pine Meadows (see Fig. 3.15).

FALL LINE HILLS. The Fall Line Hills form

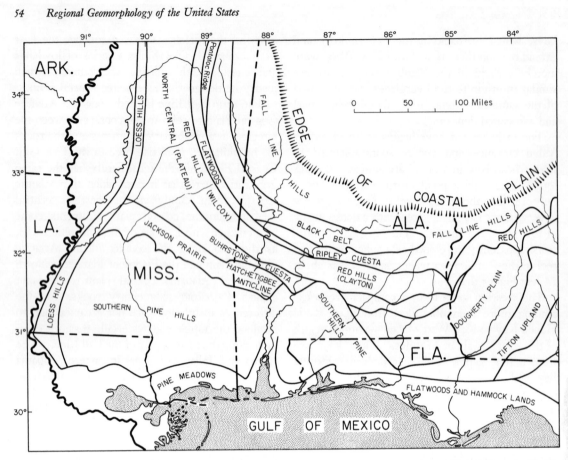

FIG. 3.14   Geomorphic units of the East Gulf Coastal Plain.   (*From Physiography of Eastern United States, by N. M. Fenneman, 1938; used by permission of the McGraw-Hill Book Company.*)

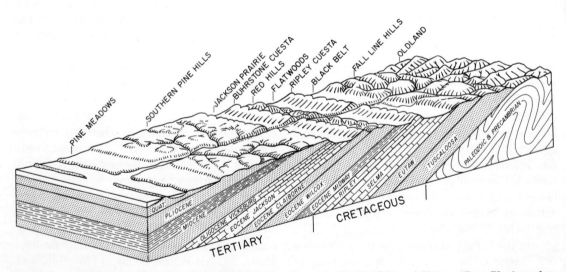

FIG. 3.15   Relations of topograpic belts to lithology and structure in East Gulf Coastal Plain.   (*From Physiography of Eastern United States, by N. M. Fenneman; used by permission of the McGraw-Hill Book Company.*)

the innermost belt of the East Gulf Coastal Plain and are developed on rocks belonging to the Cretaceous Tuscaloosa and Eutaw formations. This belt attains a maximum width of about 50 miles. In general the texture of the topography is coarser on the Tuscaloosa than on the Eutaw formation; local relief may be as great as 200 to 250 feet. The soils developed from the Tuscaloosa sands are generally poor, and much of the area is wooded rather than cultivated. The Tennessee River follows fairly close to the boundary between the Fall Line Hills and the oldland, but there are areas where rocks of Paleozoic age lie west of the Tennessee River and others where rocks of Cretaceous age lie east of the river.

BLACK BELT. The Fall Line Hills are bordered on the south by one of the most famous areas of the Old South. The Black Belt, also called the Black Prairie, at one time was widely famous for its rich soils, large cotton production, attractive ante-bellum mansions, and other evidences of wealth. The name derives from the black soils that have developed from weathering of the Cretaceous Selma chalk (once called the Rotten limestone). The Black Belt extends across northeastern Mississippi and into Alabama to a little beyond Montgomery, where it looses its distinctive characteristics. Most of the topography of this belt would be described as gently undulating; some areas are so lacking in relief that railways and highways have straight stretches of as much as 10 or 12 miles. The average width of the Black Belt is between 20 and 25 miles, and it lies from 200 to 300 feet below the uplands to the north and south of it. Cleland (1920) interpreted the surface of the Black Belt as a local Pleistocene peneplain or what today we would call a strath. The grounds for attributing a Pleistocene age to the erosion surface are that "Lafayette gravels" (see p. 192) cap the uplands to either side of the Black Belt, leading to the assumption that they once extended across the area and were removed during the development of the present surface of the Black Belt. Since the "Lafayette gravels" are most commonly regarded as being late Pliocene in age, it was thought that development of the Black

Belt strath likely took place in early Pleistocene time. Streams at the present time are incised about 60 feet below the surface of the Black Belt.

RIPLEY CUESTA. Overlying the Selma chalk is the predominantly sandy Ripley formation, of Late Cretaceous age, which is responsible locally for a prominent escarpment. In northern Mississippi an escarpment formed by the Ripley formation is known as Pontotoc Ridge; this ridge stands 200 to 300 feet above the Black Belt east of it. About 90 miles south of the Tennessee line this escarpment dies out because of the thinning of the Ripley formation, and for a stretch the Black Belt and the Flatwoods are contiguous. A short distance east of the Mississippi-Alabama line the Ripley Escarpment reappears and continues eastward as what is known as the Chunnennuggee Hills.

THE FLATWOODS. The lowland known as the Flatwoods is developed on the Eocene Midway formation. It extends in an arcuate pattern from near the Tennessee-Mississippi boundary nearly to central Alabama. In some respects this lowland is similar to the Black Belt, but it is not so wide; its surface does not possess as low relief, and the soils derived from the Midway clays are not so fertile as those of the Black Belt.

THE RED HILLS. The sands of the Eocene Wilcox formation are responsible for the Red Hills escarpment. This hilly belt can be recognized from Tennessee to Georgia; although it goes by various local names, the belt stands out because of the yellow, orange, or reddish color of its soils. The belt is high enough above adjacent lowlands that it has commonly undergone appreciable dissection, but locally extensive tracts such as the North Central Plateau of Mississippi are still undissected and present surfaces of low relief which are essentially dip slopes.

BUHRSTONE CUESTA. The term Buhrstone cuesta is applied to a belt along the south side of the Red Hills about half of which is in Mississippi and half in Alabama. This cuesta is caused by the very resistant Tallahatta formation of the Clairborne group which is commonly called the Buhrstone formation. The local name of Buhrstone (burrstone) derives from the presence in the formation of siliceous rock suitable for use as millstones. The hills of this cuesta are the most rugged found in any part of the coastal plain.

JACKSON PRAIRIE. The Jackson Prairie is developed mainly on the clays of the Eocene Jackson formation. It is confined mainly to Mississippi, where it is as much as 40 miles wide. The belt narrows eastward and terminates near the Alabama line. Near the Alabama line the terrain of the Jackson Prairie undergoes a marked change in character, becoming notably more hilly. This change is due partly to change in the lithology of the Jackson formation from clay to limestone, but more to the presence in this area of a marked flexure known as the Hatchetigbee anticline. This structure is an asymmetrical northwest-southeast-extending structure with which are associated a number of faults that are responsible for two systems of strike grabens arranged *en echelon* on the northeast side and southeast end of the structure (Murray, 1961). Surface displacement of beds along these faults is as much as 500 feet.

SOUTHERN PINE HILLS. Lying south of the Jackson Prairie and the hilly terrain of the Hatchetigbee anticline is the outermost of the various cuestas of the East Gulf Coastal Plain, which is known as the Southern Pine Hills. The rocks here are Miocene and Pliocene in age, with the Pliocene Citronelle formation forming the caprock over much of the area. The Southern Pine Hills cuesta slopes southward from altitudes of 400 or 500 feet to the level of the Pleistocene coastwise terraces, which begin at 200 to 250 feet.

PLEISTOCENE COASTWISE TERRACES. The strip of coastal terraces around the East Gulf Coast section is not as wide as it is along the middle Atlantic coast, but several terrace levels have been identified. Carlston (1950) thought that he saw evidence of five terraces in coastal Alabama. These were identified by him as the Coharie, at 190–210 feet; the Sunderland, at 150–160 feet; the Wicomico, at 90–110 feet; the Penholoway, at 60–70 feet; and the Pamlico, at 20–30 feet. He also observed terraces along the Mobile River valley at elevations that seemed to suggest that they might correlate with the Coharie, Penholoway, and Pamlico marine terraces.

Vernon (1942), working in northwestern Florida, described five coastwise terraces (presumably marine) and four fluvial terraces. The coastwise terraces were identified by him as the Brandywine-Citronelle, at 250–320 feet; the Coharie, at 120–170 feet; the Sunderland, at 115–150 feet; the Wicocomico, at 60–105 feet; and the Pamlico, at 5–30 feet.

## Mississippi Alluvial Plain Section

*Description.* The alluvial valley of the Mississippi River (see Fig. 3.16) begins near Cape Girardeau, Missouri, and extends southward as far as the head of the Atchafalaya River, where the deltaic plain begins. The alluvial valley varies in width from 25 miles near Natchez, Mississippi, to 125 miles near Helena, Arkansas. The alluvial valley is bounded by prominent valley walls which in places rise as much as 200 feet above the valley floor. In general, the valley walls decrease in height southward. A thick veneer of loess overlies the bedrock of the valley walls, particularly on the east side of the valley.

*Intravalley Ridges.* Within the alluvial valley are several ridges that break the continuity of the valley floor. The northernmost and longest of these ridges is Crowley's Ridge. This ridge extends for about 200 miles, from near Commerce, Missouri, to Helena, Arkansas, although it is broken at several places by gaps through it. Crowley's Ridge rises as much as 200 feet above the valley floor. Its bedrock core consists mainly of rocks of Eocene age plus some small patches of Cretaceous rocks; above the bedrock is a cover of Pliocene gravels (so-called Lafayette) and loess.

At the south are three upland remnants in the alluvial valley, Macon Ridge, the Bastrop Hills, and Sicily Island. Macon Ridge extends from Eudora, Arkansas, to Sicily Island, Louisiana—about 100 miles. Most of it is older alluvium of the Arkansas River fan that was built into the Mississippi Valley, but there are small island-like tracts, varying in width from 0.5 to 2.5 miles and having a maximum length of 18 miles, that are composed of Pleistocene alluvial deposits of the Prairie formation (see p. 59). The Bastrop Hills, to the west of Macon Ridge, consist of this same Pleistocene formation. Sicily Island, just to the south of the southern tip of Macon Ridge, is composed of rocks of Tertiary age and is mantled with Pleistocene loess.

Sikeston Ridge, to the east of Crowley's

Ridge, extends from the southern end of the Commerce Hills to New Madrid. It rises as much as 40 feet above the floodplain at its north end but decreases in altitude southward. It too is composed of older alluvium.

*Pleistocene Changes in Mississippi River Course.* Fisk (1944) has presented a detailed history of the changes in the course of the Mississippi River from Thebes Gap at the north to its delta.

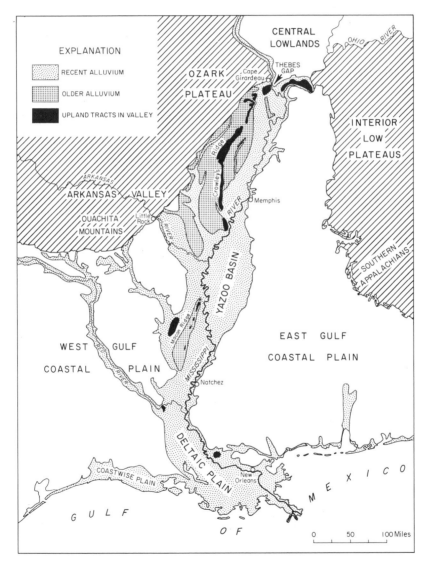

FIG. 3.16 Types of materials in Mississippi alluvial valley. (*After H. N. Fisk, Geological Investigation of the Alluvial Valley of the Lower Mississippi River, Mississippi River Commission, Vicksburg.*)

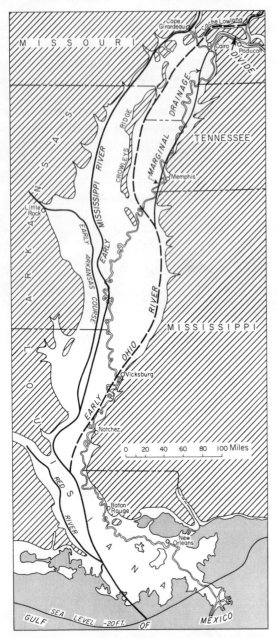

FIG. 3.17 Early stage relationships between Mississippi and Ohio rivers. (*After H. N. Fisk, Geological Investigation of the Alluvial Valley of the Lower Mississippi River, Mississippi River Commission, Vicksburg.*)

Only a few of the more important of these changes can be discussed. What Fisk called the $A_1$ stage (see Fig. 3.17) is believed to closely approximate the initial stage of the Mississippi River. It will be noted that at this stage (1) the Mississippi River's course lay well to the west side of the alluvial valley, and that the river, where it left the area of Paleozoic rocks and entered the upper end of the alluvial valley, followed the Drum Lowland route to the west of Crowley's Ridge; (2) the Ohio River followed the Cache Valley route across southern Illinois some 50 miles or so north of its present route (see Fig. 3.18), and instead of joining the Mississippi near the head of the alluvial valley, as it does now, followed a route at the east side of the alluvial valley for a distance of about 400 miles before effecting a junction with the Mississippi River near Simmesport, Louisiana. The present junction of the Ohio and Mississippi rivers near Cairo, Illinois, was not established until rather late in the history of the Mississippi River.

Figure 3.18 shows the successive changes in position of the Mississippi River near the head of the alluvial valley that finally culminated in establishment of the present route of the Mississippi River through Thebes Gap and a junction with the Ohio near Cairo, Illinois. Diversion of the Mississippi River from its western route through the Drum Lowland came about as a result of aggradation of this route with glacial outwash, following which the Mississippi River spilled over into the lower route east of Hickory Ridge known as the Advance Lowland. In similar fashion the river's course was diverted to the Moorehouse Lowland and still later to the present Thebes Gap route through the Commerce Hills.

*Change in the Ohio River's Course.* Analogous circumstances resulted in diversion of the Ohio River from its Cache Valley route to the more southerly route through the Metropolis Lowland (see Fig. 11.15). According to Fisk (1944), the abandonment of the Cache Lowland route by the Ohio River took place before diversion of the Mississippi River to the Morehouse Lowland route. Change of the route of the Ohio River from the Cache Valley to the Metropolis Lowland did not affect the place of junction of the Ohio with the Mississippi River, which was still far south in the alluvial valley. Establishment of the Ohio-Mississippi junction near Cairo, Illinois, was not effected until the Mississippi River had occupied the Thebes Gap route.

*Origin of Mississippi Valley Terraces.* The lower Mississippi Valley has been the subject of intensive study by Fisk (1938, 1944, 1951), Russell (1940a, 1940b), and associates. From their work there has emerged the basic philosophy that the major events in lower Mississippi Valley history are to be interpreted in terms of fluctuating Pleistocene sea levels. According to this viewpoint, the basic valley history has been an alternation between alluviation or valley filling during times of high sea level and valley erosion or trenching during times of low sea level. During each interglacial age sea level rose; as a result the lower Mississippi valley was drowned and valley filling ensued. Each period of high sea level is represented by a valley fill, deposited in an entrenched valley which had been excavated during the preceding low sea level. Each valley fill is given the rank of a geologic formation and consists of a basal graveliferous facies which grades upward through sand into a silt and clay facies.

During each glacial age when sea level was lowered, valley trenching caused removal of a good part, but not all, of the previously deposited valley fill; thus part of the valley fill was left as terraces along the valley. The terraces carry the names of the valley fills beneath them, and are from oldest and highest to youngest and lowest the Williana, Bentley, Montgomery, and Prairie. According to Fisk and McFarlan (1955), the Williana terrace is Aftonian in age; the Bentley, Yarmouth; the Montgomery, Sangamon; and the Prairie, mid-Wisconsin. The fact that the topographic sequence and chronological sequence are in the same order is explained as the consequence of continuing uplift of the lower Mississippi Valley region during Pleistocene time to compensate for subsidence of the Gulf geosyncline under the increasing deltaic load. The alluvial terraces along the Mississippi Valley merge gulfward with a corresponding series of coastwise deltaic plain terraces to both the east and the west of the Mississippi delta. The five cycles of valley evolution as controlled by oscillating sea level are indicated in Figure 3.19. Each cycle was initiated by a presumed drop of sea level of 300 or 400 feet. It is claimed that the basal gravel of the Williana valley fill can be

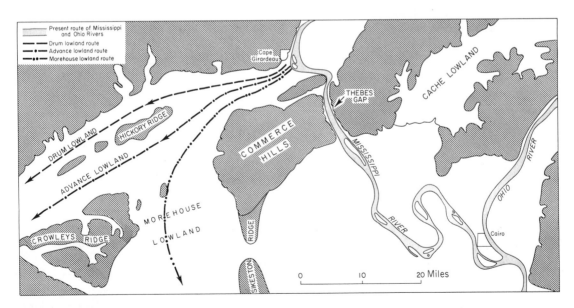

FIG. 3.18  Successive changes in the position of Mississippi River near head of its alluvial valley.  (*After H. N. Fisk, Geological Investigation of the Alluvial Valley of the Lower Mississippi River, Mississippi River Commission, Vicksburg.*)

| GLACIATED AREA | | LOWER MISSISSIPPI VALLEY |
|---|---|---|
| GLACIAL STAGES | INTERGLACIAL STAGES | INTERGLACIAL TERRACE DEPOSITS |
| Each glacial stage characterized by accumulation of ice upon continents and lowering of sea level with resultant entrenchment of streams and valley cutting. | Each interglacial stage characterized by retreat of ice sheets from continents and rise of sea level with alluviation of valleys cut during previous glacial stage. | Each terrace deposit is of interglacial age, fills valleys cut during preceeding glacial stage, and constitutes a geologic formation. Continued uplift during Quaternary Period has raised terrace deposits above level of present floodplain. |

| QUATERNARY PERIOD | PLEISTOCENE OR GLACIAL EPOCH | RECENT EPOCH | | | |
|---|---|---|---|---|---|
| | | | | | RECENT ALLUVIUM (RA) |
| | | Late Wisconsin (youngest) | | | Valley cutting VC-5 |
| | | | | Bradyan | PRAIRIE FORMATION (PF) |
| | | Early Wisconsin | | | Valley cutting VC-4 |
| | | | | Sangamon | MONTGOMERY FORMATION (MF) |
| | | Illinoian | | | Valley cutting VC-3 |
| | | | | Yarmouth | BENTLEY FORMATION (BF) |
| | | Kansan | | | Valley cutting VC-2 |
| | | | | Aftonian | WILLIANA FORMATION (WF) |
| | | Nebraskan (oldest) | | | Valley cutting VC-1 |

IDEALIZED RELATIONSHIP OF TERRACES

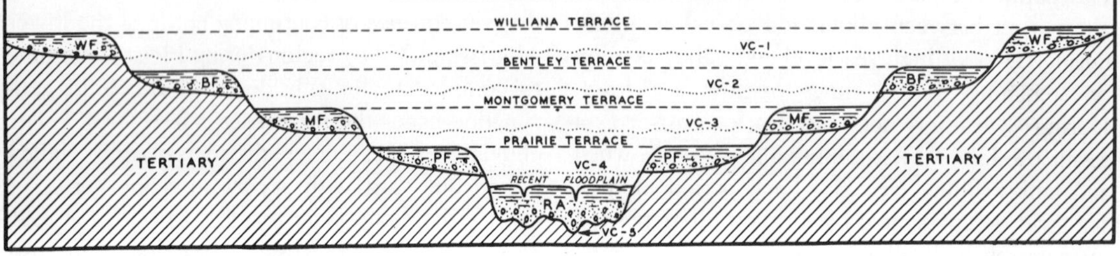

FIG. 3.19    An interpretation of the Pleistocene history of the lower Mississippi valley.    (*After H. N. Fisk, Geological Investigation of the Alluvial Valley of the Lower Mississippi River, Mississippi River Commission, Vicksburg.*)

recognized beneath the younger deposits at a depth of approximately 3000 feet near the present shoreline in Terrebonne Parish, Louisiana.

It is believed that the fluviatile terraces can be recognized on both sides of the Mississippi Valley, as paired terraces, as far up the Mississippi Valley as the Cache River Lowland in southern Illinois. The apex of the Williana deltaic plain lies in the latitude of Jackson, Mississippi, and younger deltaic plains apex progressively farther down the valley.

*Alternative Terrace Interpretation.* Leighton and Willman (1949) disagreed markedly with the Fisk and Russell interpretation of Mississippi Valley history. They believed that valley filling characterized glacial time and valley trenching interglacial time. They recognized the existence of terraces along the Mississippi Valley, but in their opinion only the Prairie terrace is as young as Pleistocene in age. The other terraces were considered to be Tertiary in age and were correlated with certain erosional surfaces found in the

Central Lowlands and adjacent regions (see p. 216). Leighton and Willman's correlation of the terraces in the lower Mississippi Valley was as follows:

Williana terrace...... Lancaster peneplain
Bentley terrace....... Central Illinois peneplain
Montgomery terrace.. Havana strath
Prairie terrace........ Mankato in age

At first thought these two contrasting interpretations seem completely irreconcilable, but perhaps this is not so true as it seems. The effects of glaciation and deglaciation were different in the upper and lower Mississippi Valley because of their varying distances from the sea. The lower Mississippi Valley region felt strongly the effects of changing sea levels, whereas in the upper Mississippi Valley, because of its remoteness from the sea, the significant changes were alternation between periods when large quantities of glacial outwash were being dumped into valleys, with resulting aggradation, and periods of reduced stream loads during interglacial time, when valley trenching was dominant.

The question of whether or not the Tertiary erosional surfaces of the upper Mississippi Valley region have correlatives in the terraces of the lower Mississippi Valley region can not be definitely answered until more work has been done on this problem in a more unbiased fashion than has characterized the controversy so far. It would appear that the really critical area in

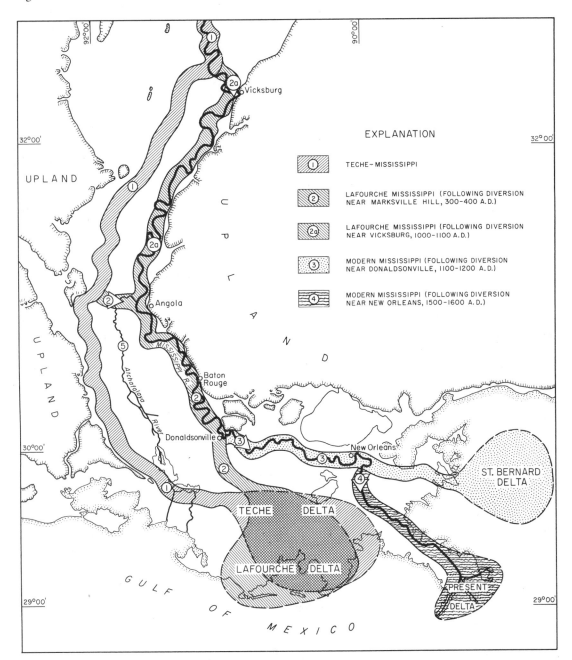

FIG. 3.20  Subdeltas of the Mississippi delta.  (*After H. N. Fisk, Geological Investigation of the Atchafalaya Basin and the Problem of Mississippi River Diversion, Mississippi River Commission, Vicksburg.*)

this controversial problem is at the head of the Mississippi alluvial valley, where the effects of glacio-eustatically rising and falling sea levels merge with alternating periods of heavy and light stream loads associated with alternating glaciation and deglaciation. Detailed work here might possibly reconcile the two contrasting interpretations of Mississippi Valley history.

*Mississippi Deltaic Plain.* Several distinct courses of the Mississippi River in its terminal zone have been recognized and traced along the alluvial valley into deltas which mark former termini of the river (Fisk, 1944, 1952). These changes in the stream routes are believed to have taken place within the past 2000 years. What is commonly called the Mississippi delta heads near the source of the Atchafalaya River and consists of a number of subdeltas which were built when the lower Mississippi River had different routes from its present one. Figure 3.20 shows the major subdeltas that comprise the present Mississippi delta. The oldest subdelta is the Teche delta; it was estimated by Fisk (1952) that the Mississippi River abandoned the Teche delta about A.D. 300–400 for the LaFourche route. The diversion which led to the construction of the St. Bernard delta is believed to have occurred between A.D. 1100 and A.D. 1200. Abandonment of the St. Bernard delta took place about A.D. 1500–1600; this initiated the construction of the modern Birdsfoot delta.

Conditions exist at the present time which, if allowed to continue unhindered by man, would lead soon to abandonment of the present delta course of the Mississippi River for a more westerly route via the Atchafalaya River. The Atchafalaya River at present is the principal distributary of the Mississippi River. Discharge through it averages 25 per cent of the volume of the Mississippi above the point of likely diversion, and Fisk (1952) estimated that between 1965 and 1975 the critical period for diversion would be reached. Fundamentally this diversion is imminent because the gradient of the Atchafalaya is steeper than that of the Mississippi River route; the distance to the Gulf of Mexico is 140 miles via the Atchafalaya, compared with 300 miles by the present Mississippi route.

## West Gulf Coastal Plain

*Contrasts with East Gulf Coastal Plain.* The West Gulf Coastal Plain section in its broader aspects is very similar to the East Gulf Coastal Plain. Several of the same geologic and topographic belts are found in the two sections, although differently named (see Fig. 3.21). However, some significant differences can be noted between the two sections. The West Gulf Coastal Plain section is considerably wider than the East Gulf Coastal Plain, as a result of which its streams have larger drainage basins and have brought more sediments into the Gulf of Mexico and thereby built more extensive deltas than any of the streams of the East Gulf Coastal Plain. A second difference is the presence along the western margin of the West Gulf Coastal Plain of a series of fault systems, the westernmost of which has notable topographic expression. Numerous igneous intrusions are found in association with this fault zone, and several of them stand up as prominent topographic features. Salt domes are far more numerous west of the Mississippi alluvial valley than east of it, and, although these features do not usually have pronounced topographic expression, some do stand out conspicuously.

*Western Boundary.* The western boundary of the Coastal Plain logically should follow the boundary between Cretaceous and older rocks. This is true across Arkansas and Oklahoma and in Texas as far south as Waco, on the Brazos River. South of the Brazos River, however, the province boundary changes in its geological relationships, and an area of Lower Cretaceous rocks is assigned to the Great Plains. The outcrop belt of Lower Cretaceous rocks between the Brazos and Colorado Rivers is placed in the Central Texas section of the Great Plains because its dissected plateau type of topography resembles more the Great Plains than the Coastal Plain. South of Austin, on the Colorado River, the Lower Cretaceous terrain is a part of the Edwards Plateau section of the Great Plains because of uplift along the Balcones fault system.

*Fault Zones.* Three fault zones are recognizable in Texas: from west to east, the Balcones,

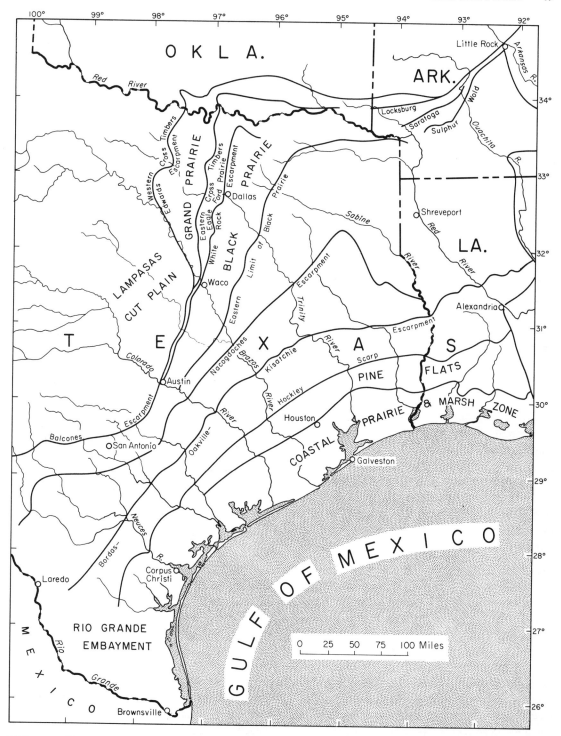

FIG. 3.21  Topographic belts and escarpments of the West Gulf Coastal Plain.  (*From Physiography of Eastern United States, by N. M. Fenneman, 1938; used by permission of the McGraw-Hill Book Company.*)

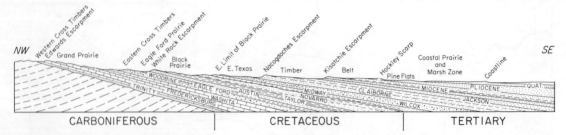

**FIG. 3.22** Relations of topographic belts and escarpments of West Gulf Coastal Plain to lithology and structure. (*From Physiography of Eastern United States, by N. M. Fenneman, 1938; used by permission of the McGraw-Hill Book Company.*)

Luling, and Mexia. Only the Balcones fault zone has major topographic expression. What is commonly called the Balcones fault zone is actually a complex of faults (Weeks, 1945; Deussen, 1924) near the boundary between Cretaceous sediments of the Edwards Plateau and Tertiary strata of the Coastal Plain. It is marked by a prominent scarp, the Balcones Escarpment, which forms the boundary between the Edwards Plateau and the West Gulf Coastal Plain.

*Contrast between Inner and Outer Parts of the West Gulf Coastal Plain.* As Doering (1935) has emphasized, the West Gulf Coastal Plain displays two contrasting types of topography, an inner zone of erosional cuestas and an outer zone of coastwise, terraced, deltaic plain. The boundary between these two types of topography lies somewhat east of a northeast-southwest-extending escarpment known as the Bordas-Oakville-Kisatchie Escarpment.

*Cuesta Scarps or Wolds.* The inner part of the Coastal Plain owes its major features to the fact that erosion on Tertiary and Cretaceous formations has developed a series of lowlands on the weak rocks and low west-facing scarps or wolds, as they are locally called, on the stronger rocks. Four escarpments have been recognized (Deussen, 1914); in Texas, these are known from northwest to southeast as the Edwards, White Rock, Nacogdoches, and Bordas-Oakville-Kishatchie escarpments (see Fig. 3.22). The equivalent of the Edwards Escarpment north of the Red River in Oklahoma and Arkansas is known as the Lockesburg Wold, and the equiva-

lent of the White Rock Escarpment is the Saratoga Wold. These escarpments are on rocks of Cretaceous age. Escarpments on rocks of Tertiary age are the Sulphur Wold of northeast Texas and southwestern Arkansas and the Nacogdoches and Bordas-Oakville-Kistahchie escarpments in Texas and Louisiana. These escarpments or wolds are not everywhere present or equally conspicuous; locally other escarpments may be present on resistant strata.

*Coastwise Terraces.* The Quaternary coastwise plain consists of a series of coalescing deltaic and alluvial plains (Barton, 1930, 1936) built by the nine rivers which flow southeastward across the Coastal Plain. These rivers are, from east to west, the Sabine, Neches, Trinity, Brazos, Colorado, Lavaca, Guadalupe, Nueces, and Rio Grande. Topographically the deltaic plain can be divided into five terrace levels, four of Pleistocene and one of Recent age (Bernard et al., 1962). The Pleistocene terraces decrease in age and altitude in going seaward, and in this order are the Willis (200–400 feet), Lissie (100–160 feet), an unnamed terrace (70–100 feet), and the Beaumont (a few feet to 70 feet). Doering (1956) had previously recognized a sequence of five Pleistocene terraces, which from oldest to youngest were named the Citronelle, Lissie, Oberlin, Eunice, and Holloway Prairie and a Recent terrace called the Sicily Island.

Each terrace is presumed to have developed during a high sea level, and they are all underlain by similar materials: basal sands and gravels which grade upward into silts and clays. The terraces have undergone tilting, as is indicated by the fact that the upper Willis terrace has the steepest seaward slope and the Beaumont terrace the lowest slope. It is evident that this interpretation of the coastwise terraces of the West Gulf Coastal Plain is the same as that applied to the terraces in the Mississippi Valley. Table 3.1 suggests possible correlations of the terraces of the two areas.

In contrast to the cuesta scarps of the inner coastal plain, which face inland and updip, the scarps which bound the Pleistocene terraces face seaward. Most prominent of the terrace scarps is the Hockley Scarp, between the Willis and Lissie terraces. This scarp does not continue west of the Brazos River, but it is a prominent feature in the southeastern part of the coastwise plain. Although at one time it was regarded as a fault scarp, it is now more commonly considered to be an erosional scarp between the Willis and Lissie terraces.

*Outer Coastal Features.* The outer coastal features of the West Gulf Coastal Plain can be grouped into three categories: (1) alluvial valleys and associated deltaic plains, (2) estuaries and lagoons, and (3) barrier islands and chenier plains (LeBlanc and Hodgson, 1959). Each stream which enters the Gulf of Mexico flows in an alluvial valley cut a few feet below the flanking Pleistocene terrace surface. In general the size of the alluvial valley and deltaic plain for each stream is proportionate to the size of the stream; large streams, such as the Brazos and Rio Grande, flow directly into the Gulf of Mexico and have broad valleys and deltaic plains; lesser streams have narrower valleys and commonly empty into estuaries or lagoons back of barrier islands. The estuary type of bay, such as Galveston Bay, is elongated normal to the coastline, whereas the lagoonal type of bays, such as Laguna Madre, are elongated parallel to the coast. Both types are shallow, and none of the estuarine type has multiple arms like those of Chesapeake Bay.

The West Gulf Coastal Plain from Galveston Bay southwestward has what may be called an inner and an outer coastline. The outer coastline is formed by an almost continuous line of barrier islands or offshore bars. Padre Island (Fisk, 1959), the longest link in this island chain, extends for 110 miles from Corpus Christi Bay nearly to the mouth of the Rio Grande; it varies in width from $\frac{1}{2}$ mile to nearly 2 miles. Back of it lies the Laguna Madre depression, a string of elongate shallow basins separated from each other by sand or mud flats. Dunes are common on the surfaces of the barrier islands and may attain heights as great as 50 feet. The barrier islands commonly have on them abandoned beach ridges aligned parallel to the seaward edges of the islands.

Along the coast of southwestern Louisiana and adjacent Texas is a stretch of coastal plain characterized by relict beach ridges. These ridges are known in Louisiana as cheniers (Russell and Howe, 1935), from the French word *chene*, in reference to the live oaks which are common on them. This type of coastal plain was given the name chenier plain by Price (1955). The cheniers are part of a thin wedge of Recent

T A B L E 3.1   Correlation of Coastal Terraces

|  | *Bernard et al.* (1962) | *Doering* (1956) | *Fisk* (1944) |
|---|---|---|---|
| RECENT | Recent | Recent<br>Sicily Island | Recent<br>"A" Series |
| PLEISTOCENE | Beaumont<br>Unnamed second terrace<br>Lissie<br>Willis | Holloway Prairie<br>Eunice<br>Oberlin<br>Lissie<br>Citronelle | Prairie<br>Montgomery<br>Bentley<br>Williana |

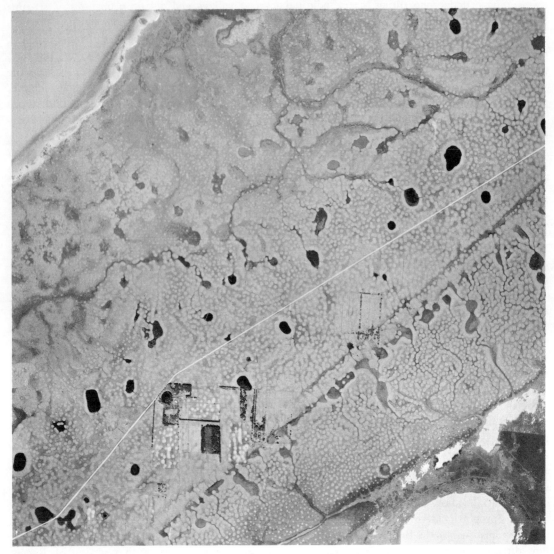

FIG. 3.23    Vertical photo of pimpled ground, Chambers County, Texas.    (*Production and Marketing Administration photo.*)

sediments which thins landward and thickens sea-ward.    The lower part of the sedimentary wedge was deposited by the postglacial transgressing sea on the weathered and eroded surface of the Prairie formation, and the uppermost sediments were deposited as the shoreline was prograded to its present position (Gould and McFarlan, 1959). Surficially the chenier plain consists of numerous beach ridges separated from each other by a complex of tidal marshes, freshwater and brackish lakes, and mud flats.    The cheniers themselves

are essentially lenticular sand bodies much like shoestring sands.    They are commonly parallel to the present shoreline, but may recurve inland adjacent to tidal inlets or even lie at right angles to the shore.    Individual cheniers are as much as 30 miles long and vary in height from a few to more than 10 feet.

*Pimpled Ground.*    In various parts of the West Gulf Coastal Plain are certain features that have been designated by such terms as "pimpled ground," "pimpled mounds," and "soil mottling." When seen on aerial photographs (see Fig. 3.23) these features produce an air photo pattern that is in some respects even more striking than that of the Carolina Bays. Pimple mounds exist by the hundreds of thousands in the Gulf Coast area of Texas and Louisiana. The mounds of the Gulf Coast area average between 30 and 35 feet in diameter and 2 or 3 feet in height, but their diameters may exceed 100 feet, and they may be as much as 5 feet high (Krinitzsky, 1949). They typically show no regularity of distribution, but in places there may be a suggestion of a polygonal pattern. The material of which they are composed commonly is fine sandy or silty loam. They may develop on alluvial deposits, eolian sand on coastal beaches, and spits and bars along coasts.

Origin of pimpled ground has been the cause for much speculation. It has been attributed to (1) erosion by a network of rivulets, (2) wind erosion, (3) the work of burrowing animals such as ants and pocket gophers, (4) eolian deposition, (5) hydrostatic pressure by groundwater, (6) frost action in a periglacial environment, (7) gas blowouts, and other causes. None of these theories of origin seems to fit all conditions; it may be that they form in different ways, but the uniformity of pattern makes this seem unlikely. Several recent observers have been inclined to regard them as erosional features of some sort that, rather than being thought of as a complex system of mounds, might equally well be interpreted as uneroded areas within a complicated network of interconnecting furrows made by some erosional process.

### Salt Domes

Salt domes are found from western Alabama westward across Mississippi, Louisiana, and Texas to near the Mexican border. They are

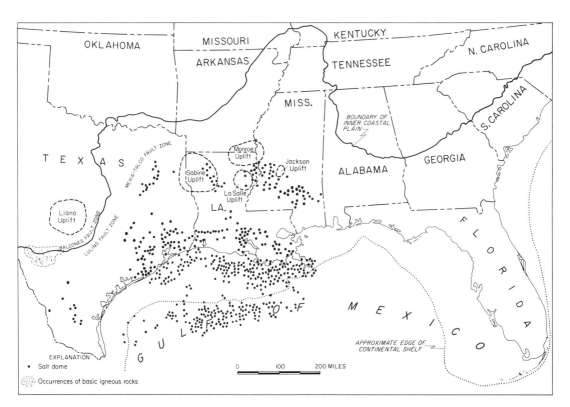

FIG. 3.24　Distribution of salt domes, uplifts, and igneous intrusions in the Coastal Plain. (*After Grover Murray, Trans. Gulf Coast Assoc. Geol. Soc.,* **7**; *Max Bornhauser, Am. Assoc. Petroleum Geologists Bull.,* **42**; *and J. T. Lonsdale, Bureau Econ. Geol. Univ. Texas Bull.,* **2744**.)

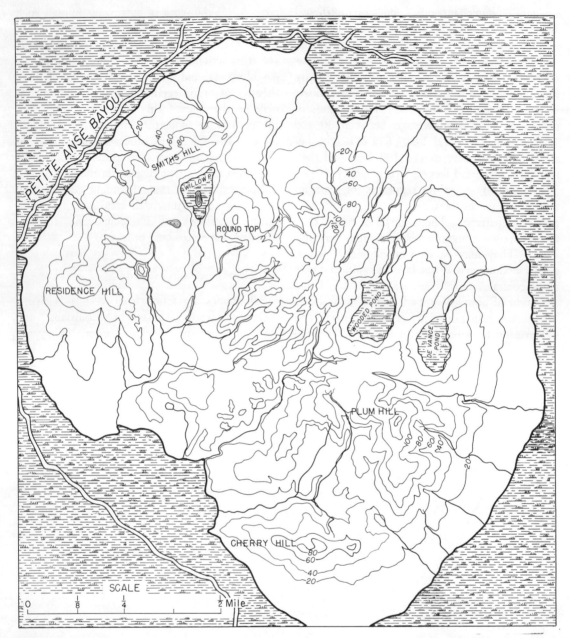

FIG. 3.25    Topographic expression of Avery Island salt dome.    (*After A. C. Veatch, La. State Experiment Station Spec. Rept.* 3.)

particularly abundant (see Fig. 3.24) in south-eastern Texas, Louisiana, and Mississippi. In the 60 some years since the Spindletop oil field was discovered on a salt dome, in 1901, over 300 salt domes have been found in the Gulf Coast area of Texas, Louisiana, Mississippi, and Alabama, and they are being discovered in comparable numbers beneath the waters of the Gulf of Mexico. An excellent description of these structures, along with a discussion of the various theories as to their origin, has been given by Murray (1961). Two possible source beds for the salt exist in the 1500-foot thick Louann salt and the thinner Haynesville salt beds. Views as to the age of the Louann salt vary from Permian to Jurassic, but it is more commonly regarded as of probable Jurassic age; the Haynesville salt is definitely of late Jurassic age. It is generally believed that the more likely source of the salt is the Louann beds.

*Topographic Expression.* A typical salt dome, if such may be imagined, is a stock-like structure with a salt core, which may or may not have a cap of gypsum, anhydrite, limestone, or dolomite. The surface structures produced by the salt intrusions vary in form from circular or lobate to quadrate or triangular. Their diameters range from about 1 to 4 miles. Topographically there may be either a positive or negative correlation with structure; but more commonly the domes are represented by topographic highs that stand from a few feet to a hundred feet or more above their environs (see Fig. 3.25). The domes are marked by such features as salt licks or salt prairies near their centers, circular lake basins with or without outlets, and radial or annular drainage. Generally the sharpness of topographic expression of the dome depends on the nearness of the salt to the surface and the amount of uplift there has been of the near-surface rock formations.

Perhaps the most famous of the hundreds of salt domes in the Gulf region is the group in Louisiana known as "The Five Islands" (Vaughn, 1925). They extend in a northwest-southeast line from near the mouth of the Atchafalaya River, to about 9 miles west of New Iberia, Louisiana. They acquired the name "islands" because they stand 75 to 150 feet above their coastal plain environs. These five salt domes, from southeast to northwest, are Belle Isle, Côte Blanche, Weeks Island, Avery Island, and Jefferson Island. The last three are the best known; Avery Island was the first American salt dome to be seen from within when, in 1886, a salt mine was opened in it.

# REFERENCES CITED

Applin, P. L. (1951). Possible future petroleum provinces of North America—Florida, *Am. Assoc. Petroleum Geologists Bull.*, **35**, 405–408.

——— and E. R. Applin (1944). Regional subsurface stratigraphy and structure of Florida and southern Georgia, *Am. Assoc. Petroleum Geologists Bull.*, **28**, 1673–1753.

Barton, D. C. (1930). Deltaic coastal plain of southeastern Texas, *Geol. Soc. Am. Bull.*, **41**, 359–382.

——— (1936). Post-Recent plains and shorelines of south Texas and southwestern Louisiana, *Geol. Soc. Am. Proc.*, 63–64 (abs.).

Bernard, H. A., R. J. LeBlanc, and C. F. Major (1962). Recent and Pleistocene geology of southeast Texas, in *Geology of the Gulf Coast and Central Texas and Guidebook of Excursions*, E. H. Rainwater and R. P. Zingula, Editors, Houston Geol. Soc., 175–224.

Berry, Willard (1948). North Carolina coastal plain floor, *Geol. Soc. Am. Bull.*, **59**, 87–90.

Campbell, M. R. (1931). Alluvial fan of the Potomac River, *Geol. Soc. Am. Bull.*, **42**, 825–852.

Carlston, C. W. (1950). Pleistocene history of coastal Alabama, *Geol. Soc. Am. Bull.*, **61**, 1119–1130.

Cleland, H. F. (1920). A Pleistocene peneplain in the Coastal Plain, *Jour. Geol.*, **28**, 702–706.

Cooke, C. W. (1934). Discussion of the origin of supposed meteorite scars of South Carolina, *Jour. Geol.*, **42**, 88–104.

——— (1936). Geology of the coastal plain of South Carolina, *U. S. Geol. Survey Bull.* 867, 196 pp.

——— (1939). Scenery of Florida interpreted by a geologist, *Fla. Geol. Surv. Bull.* 17, 118 pp.

——— (1934a). Geology of the Coastal Plain of Georgia, *U. S. Geol. Survey Bull.* 941, 122 pp.

——— (1943b). Elliptical bays, *Jour. Geol.*, **51**, 419–427.

——— (1945). The geology of Florida, *Fla. Geol. Surv. Bull.* 29, 339 pp.

——— (1952). Geology and water resources of Prince Georges County, Maryland, *Maryland Geol. Surv. Bull.* 10, 1–53.

——— (1954). Carolina bays and shapes of eddies, *U. S. Geol. Survey Profess. Paper* 254-I, 195–206.

Deussen, Alexander (1914). Geology and underground waters of the southeastern part of the Texas coastal plain, *U. S. Geol. Survey Water Supply Paper* 335, 365 pp.

——— (1924). Geology of the coastal plain of Texas west of the Brazos River, *U. S. Geol. Survey Profess. Paper* 126, 139 pp.

Doering, J. A. (1935). Post-Fleming surface formations of coastal southeast Texas and south Louisiana, *Am. Assoc. Petroleum Geologists Bull.*, **19**, 651–688.

——— (1956). Review of Quaternary surface formations of Gulf Coast region, *Am. Assoc. Petroleum Geologists Bull.*, **40**, 1816–1862.

Ewing, Maurice, J. L.Worzel, N. C. Steenland, and Frank Press (1950). Geophysical investigations in the emerged and submerged Atlantic Coastal Plain: Part V; Woods Hole, New York, and Cape May sections, *Geol. Soc. Am. Bull.*, **61**, 877–892.

Fenneman, N. M. (1928). Physiographic divisions of the United States, Assoc. Am. Geog., *Anns.*, **18**, 261–353.

—— (1938). *Physiography of Eastern United States*, McGraw-Hill Book Company, New York, 714 pp.

Ferguson, G. E., C. W. Lingham, S. K. Love, and R. O. Vernon (1947). Springs of Florida, *Fla. Geol. Surv. Bull.* 31, 196 pp.

Fisk, H. N. (1938). Geology of Grant and Lasalle parishes, *Louisiana Geol. Surv. Bull.* 10, 246 pp.

—— (1944). *Geological Investigation of the Alluvial Valley of the Lower Mississippi River*, Mississippi River Commission, Vicksburg, 78 pp.

—— (1951). Loess and Quaternary geology of the lower Mississippi Valley, *Jour. Geol.*, **59**, 333–356.

—— (1952). *Geological Investigation of the Atchafalaya Basin and the Problem of Mississippi River Diversion*, Mississippi River Commission, Vicksburg, 145 pp.

—— (1959). Padre Island and the Laguna Madre flats, coastal South Texas, *Proceedings*, 2nd Coastal Geography Conference, Coastal Studies Institute, Louisiana State Univ., pp. 103–151.

—— and E. McFarlan, Jr. (1955). Late Quaternary deltaic deposits of the Mississippi River, *Geol. Soc. Am. Spec. Paper* 62, 279–302.

Flint, R. F. (1940). Pleistocene features of the Atlantic Coastal Plain, *Am. Jour. Sci.*, **238**, 757–787.

—— (1941). Pleistocene strand lines: A rejoiner, *Am. Jour. Sci.*, **239**, 459–462.

—— (1957). *Glacial and Pleistocene Geology*, John Wiley and Sons, New York, 553 pp.

Gould, H. R., and E. McFarlan, Jr. (1959). Geologic history of the chenier plain, southwestern Louisiana, Gulf. Assoc. Geol. Socs., *Trans.*, **9**, 261–270.

Hack, J. T. (1955). Geology of the Brandywine area and origin of the upland of southern Maryland, *U. S. Geol. Survey Profess. Paper* 267-A, 43 pp.

Johnson, D. W. (1942). *The Origin of the Carolina Bays*, Columbia University Press, New York, 341 pp.

Jordan, R. H. (1950). An interpretation of Floridian karst, *Jour. Geol.*, **58**, 261–268.

Krinitzsky, E. L. (1949). Origin of pimple mounds, *Am. Jour. Sci.*, **247**, 706–714.

LeBlanc, R. J., and W. D. Hodgson (1959). Origin and development of the Texas shoreline, *Proceedings*, Second Coastal Geography Conference, Office Naval Research–National Academy Science–National Research Council, 57–101.

Leighton, M. M., and H. B. Willman (1949). *Itinerary of field conference—late Cenozoic geology of Mississippi Valley, southeastern Iowa to central Louisiana*, auspices of State Geologists, Urbana, Illinois Geol. Surv., 86 pp.

MacNeil, F. S. (1950). Pleistocene shorelines in Florida and Georgia, *U. S. Geol. Survey Profess. Paper* 221-F, 95–107.

Mather, K. F., and L. R. Thiesmeyer (1942). Pleistocene geology of western Cape Cod, Massachusetts, *Geol. Soc. Am. Bull.*, **53**, 1127–1174.

MacCarthy, G. R. (1937). The Carolina bays, *Geol. Soc. Am. Bull.*, **48**, pp. 1211–1225.

Melton, F. A. (1950). The Carolina "Bays," *Jour. Geol.*, **58**, 128–134.

—— and W. Schriever (1933). The Carolina "Bays" —Are they meteorite scars? *Jour. Geol.*, **41**, 52–62.

Murray, G. E. (1961). *Geology of the Atlantic and Gulf Provinces of North America*, Harper and Brothers, Publishers, New York, 692 pp.

Murray, H. W. (1947). Topography of the Gulf of Maine, *Geol. Soc. Am. Bull.*, **58**, 153–196.

Oaks, R. Q., Jr., and N. K. Coch (1963). Pleistocene sea levels, southeastern Virginia, *Science*, **140**, pp. 979–983.

Oliver, J. A., and C. L. Drake (1951). Geophysical investigations in the emerged and submerged Atlantic Coastal Plain, Part VI: The Long Island area, *Geol. Soc. Am. Bull.*, **62**, 1287–1296.

Parker, G. G., and C. W. Cooke (1944). Late Cenozoic geology of southern Florida, with a discussion of ground water, *Fla. Geol. Surv. Bull.* 27, 119 pp.

Price, W. A. (1955). Environment and formation of chenier plain, *Quaternaria*, **2**, 75–86.

Prouty, W. F. (1935). "Carolina Bays" and elliptical lake basins, *Jour. Geol.*, **43**, 200–207.

—— (1946). Atlantic Coastal Plain and continental slope, *Am. Assoc. Petroleum Geologists Bull.*, **30**, 1917–1920.

—— (1952). Carolina bays and their origin, *Geol. Soc. Am. Bull.*, **63**, 167–224.

Rasmussen, W. C. (1953). Periglacial frost-thaw basins in New Jersey: a discussion, *Jour. Geol.*, **61**, 473–474.

Renner, G. T. (1927). The physiographic interpretation of the Fall Line, *Geog. Rev.*, **17**, 276–286.

Russell, R. J. (1940a). Quaternary history of Louisiana, *Geol. Soc. Am. Bull.*, **51**, 1199–1234.

—— (1940b). Lower Mississippi Valley loess, *Geol. Soc. Am. Bull.*, **55**, 1–40.

—— and H. V. Howe (1935). Cheniers of southwestern Louisiana, *Geog. Rev.*, **25**, 449–461.

Spangler, W. B., and J. J. Peterson (1950). Geology of Atlantic Coastal Plain in New Jersey, Delaware, Maryland, and Virginia, *Am. Assoc. Petroleum Geologists Bull.*, **34**, 1–99.

Vaughn, F. E. (1925). The Five Islands, *Am. Assoc. Petroleum Geologists Bull.*, **9**, 756–797.

Vernon, R. O. (1942). Geology of Holmes and Washington counties, Florida, *Fla. Geol. Surv. Bull.* 21, 161 pp.

—— (1951). Geology of Citrus and Levy counties, Florida, *Fla. Geol. Surv. Bull.* 33, pp. 14–52.

Waters, J. A., P. W. McFarland, and J. W. Lea (1955). Geologic framework of Gulf Coastal Plain of Texas, *Am. Assoc. Petroleum Geologists Bull.*, **39**, 1821–1850.

Weeks, A. W. (1945). Balcones, Luling, and Mexia fault zones in Texas, *Am. Assoc. Petroleum Geologists, Bull.*, **29**, 1733–1737.

Wentworth, C. K. (1930). Sand and gravel resources of the Coastal Plain of Virginia, *Va. Geol. Surv. Bull.* 32, 146 pp.

White, W. A. (1958). Some geomorphic features of central peninsular Florida, *Fla. Geol. Surv. Bull.* 41, 92 pp.

Wolfe, P. E. (1953). Periglacial frost-thaw basins in New Jersey, *Jour. Geol.*, **61**, 133–141.

Zeigler, J. M. (1959). Origin of the sea islands of southeastern United States, *Georg. Rev.*, **49**, 222–237.

——, W. S. Hoffmeister, G. Geiese, and H. Tasha, (1960). Discovery of Eocene sediments in subsurface of Cape Cod, *Science*, **132**, 1397–1398.

ADDITIONAL REFERENCES

Bonini, W. E., and G. P. Woollard (1960). Subsurface geology of North Carolina-South Carolina coastal plain from seismic data, *Am. Assoc. Petroleum Geologists Bull.*, **44**, 298–315.

Byrne, J. V., D. O. Leroy, and C. M. Riley (1959). The chenier plain and its stratigraphy, southwestern Louisiana, *Gulf Coast Assoc. Geol. Socs., Trans.*, **9**, 237–259.

Doering, J. A. (1960). Quaternary surface formations of southern part of Atlantic Coastal Plain, *Jour. Geol.*, **68**, 182–202.

Fleming, W. L. S. (1935). Glacial geology of Long Island, *Am. Jour. Sci.*, **230**, 216–238.

LaMoreaux, Philip (1946). Geology and ground-water resources of the Coastal Plain of east central Georgia, *Ga. Geol., Surv. Bull.* 52, *Pt.* 1, 173 pp.

Lonsdale, J. T. (1927). Igneous rocks of the Balcones fault region of Texas, *Univ. Texas Bureau Econ. Geol. Bull.* 2744, 178 pp.

McFarlan, E., Jr. (1961). Radiocarbon dating of the late Quaternary deposits, south Louisiana, *Geol. Soc. Am. Bull.*, **72**, 129–158.

Powers, Sidney (1920). The Butler salt dome, Freestone County, Texas, *Am. Jour. Sci.*, **199**, 127–142.

Price, W. A. (1958). *Sedimentology and Quaternary Geomorphology of South Texas*, Supplement to field trip manual, Sedimentology of South Texas, Corpus Christi Geol. Soc. Field Trip, 1958, 41–75.

Rich, J. L. (1934). Soil mottlings and mounds in northeastern Texas as seen from the air, *Geog. Rev.*, **24**, 576–583.

Richards, H. G. (1945). Subsurface stratigraphy of Atlantic Coastal Plain between New Jersey and Georgia, *Am. Assoc. Petroleum Geologists Bull.*, **29**, 885–955.

Robertson, E. C. (1962). The Carolina Bays and emergence of the Coastal Plain of the Carolinas and Georgia, *U. S. Geol. Survey Profess. Paper* 450-C, pp. C87–C90.

Schlee, John (1957). Upland gravels of southern Maryland, *Geol. Soc. Am. Bull.*, **68**, 1371–1410.

Schriever, William (1951). On the origin of the Carolina Bays, *Am. Geophys. Union, Trans.*, **32**, 87–95.

Shepard, F. P. (1956). Late Pleistocene and Recent history of the central Texas coast, *Jour. Geol.*, **64**, 56–69.

—— (1960). Mississippi delta; marginal environments, sediments, and growth, in *Recent Sediments, Northwest Gulf of Mexico*, Am. Assoc. Petroleum Geol., 56–81.

Trowbridge, A. C. (1954). Mississippi River and Gulf Coast terraces and sediments as related to Pleistocene history—a problem, *Geol. Soc. Am. Bull.*, **65**, 793–812.

Weeks, A. W. (1945). Quaternary deposits of Texas Coastal Plain between Brazos River and Rio Grande, *Am. Assoc. Petroleum Geologists Bull.*, **29**, 1693–1720.

Wharton, J. B., Jr. (1960). Jefferson Island salt dome, *Am. Assoc. Petroleum Geologists Bull.*, **37**, 433–443.

# 4

# Appalachian Highlands

## GENERAL DISCUSSION

What has been called the Appalachian Highlands division of North America (Fenneman, 1928) includes seven provinces, the New England, Adirondacks, St. Lawrence Valley, Piedmont, Blue Ridge, Ridge and Valley, and Appalachian Plateaus provinces. Use of the term Appalachian Highlands in this inclusive sense differs somewhat from its more common connotation. Generally the term Appalachian Highlands is more likely to suggest only three of these seven provinces, the Blue Ridge, Ridge and Valley, and Appalachian Plateaus provinces, and perhaps parts of the Piedmont Plateau. This portion of the United States is sometimes designated by geographers as Appalachia, but modern Appalachia is not to be confused with the often-postulated ancient landmass of the same name. The present chapter deals primarily with the four last-named provinces (see Fig. 4.1), although certain aspects of the following discussion might apply equally well to the New England, Adirondacks, and St. Lawrence Valley provinces.

The Appalachian Highlands do not terminate at the Hudson Valley but continue northeastward into New England, where counterparts of the Piedmont and Blue Ridge can be recognized; however, true equivalents of the Ridge and Valley and Appalachian Plateaus provinces are lacking east of the Hudson-St. Lawrence lowlands. There is good reason to believe that the belt of rocks characterized by what is commonly termed "Appalachian type of structure," as well as the metamorphic and plutonic rocks of the Blue Ridge and Piedmont provinces, continues southwestward beneath the sediments of the Gulf Coastal Plain to reappear in the Ouachita Mountains of Arkansas and Oklahoma and in the Marathon Uplift of Texas (see p. 498).

Not all of the region under discussion is "highland"; much of the Piedmont and Ridge and Valley provinces is not. Yet enough is highland that application of this term to the whole region is not inappropriate. Despite differences in rock types, geologic structures, and topography the four provinces have shared a common geomorphic history to such a degree that it would be repetitious to discuss the geomorphic history of each province separately, if indeed this could be done.

The Piedmont and Blue Ridge provinces were formerly called the "Older Appalachians," and the Ridge and Valley and Appalachian Plateaus provinces, the "Newer Appalachians." This differentiation was made when it was believed that there were significant age differences between the rocks of the two western and two eastern provinces. To a certain degree this is true, but as geologic work continues it is becoming more and more evident that this difference is not so fundamental as once thought. Many of the intrusive bodies in the Piedmont that were once believed to be Precambrian are now known to be Paleozoic in age. Furthermore, the youngest rocks in the Appalachian Highlands are the Triassic rocks in the Piedmont Plateau province. It would be more appropriate to divide the region into areas of sedimentary and crystalline rocks, for, as King (1955) has stated,

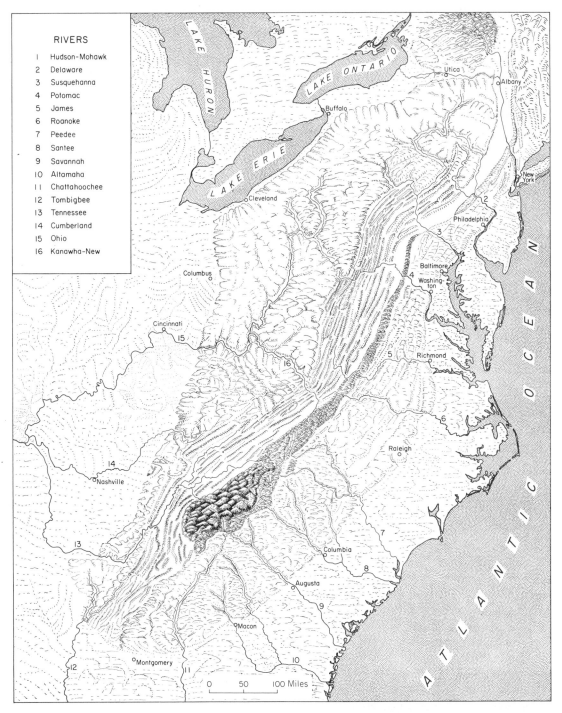

**RIVERS**

1 Hudson-Mohawk
2 Delaware
3 Susquehanna
4 Potomac
5 James
6 Roanoke
7 Peedee
8 Santee
9 Savannah
10 Altamaha
11 Chattahoochee
12 Tombigbee
13 Tennessee
14 Cumberland
15 Ohio
16 Kanawha-New

FIG. 4.1 Geomorphic map of Appalachian Highlands and adjacent areas.

Differentiation into a sedimentary and a crystalline area expresses differences in both rock character and structure. Rocks of one area [the Appalachian Plateaus and Ridge and Valley provinces] are dominantly sedimentary and of Paleozoic age, possess a sequence that can be established by ordinary stratigraphic methods, and have responded to deformation by faulting and folding. Rocks of the other area [the Blue Ridge and Piedmont provinces] are dominantly metamorphic and plutonic, and although they probably include large volumes of what were originally sedimentary and volcanic rocks, they have been largely changed and reconstituted. Their sequences and ages are poorly established, and their structure is largely undeciphered but appears to differ greatly from that of the sedimentary area.

## GEOLOGIC CONTRASTS BETWEEN PROVINCES

Despite the fact that the four provinces have shared somewhat similar geomorphic histories, there are striking differences in their topographies which are comprehended only if the geology of each province is known.

The Piedmont Plateau is primarily a belt of metamorphic and plutonic rocks. According to King (1959) the maximum degree of metamorphism in the Appalachian Highlands is found in about the middle of the Piedmont province; from here the metamorphic rank decreases both southeastward and northwestward. Plutonic bodies are widespread in the Piedmont; some are small bodies of ultrabasic rocks, but the larger intrusive rock masses are granitic in type. The structures of metamorphic and igneous rocks of the Piedmont are highly complex. Locally, there are tracts of downfolded or downfaulted Triassic sedimentary rocks, associated with which are numerous basic dikes and sills. The Piedmont has the greatest variety of rock types of any of the four provinces under discussion.

The rocks of the Blue Ridge are mainly Precambrian metamorphic and igneous rocks and early Paleozoic sedimentary rocks (mainly Cambrian), which are all strongly folded, faulted, and more or less metamorphosed. Several great

shear thrusts are present along the western border of the province.

Rocks of the Ridge and Valley province are largely sedimentary in nature and range in age from lower to upper Paleozoic; their age in general increases from west to east. Closed folding is especially characteristic of the northern part of the province, and thrust faulting of the southern part. It is to this province that the term "Appalachian type of structure," which has been so widely used in American geologic literature, is appropriately applied. Carbonate rocks are particularly plentiful, but certain sandstone formations are prominent topographically.

The Appalachian Plateaus province, commonly called the Cumberland Plateau at the south and the Allegheny Plateau at the north, is essentially a broad syncline in rocks of upper Paleozoic age. Toward the eastern edge of the province are local folds that are open, in contrast to the closed folds in the Ridge and Valley province. Surficial rocks are mainly Mississippian and Pennsylvanian in age, but there is an area of Permian rocks in northern West Virginia and adjacent parts of southwestern Pennsylvania and southeastern Ohio. Clastic rocks predominate throughout the province.

## DIVISIONAL BOUNDARIES

The Appalachian Highlands division of the United States, despite great variety in relief and topographic form, stands out rather sharply from adjoining provinces. The boundary on the east is the Fall Line, and, although this is by no means a bold topographic feature, it is readily enough recognizable from the steepening of stream gradients at it or a few miles back of it, as well as from soil and vegetation contrasts between the Piedmont and the Coastal Plain. Only where the Coastal Plain abuts against the area of Triassic rock within the Piedmont, the so-called Piedmont Lowland section, is there little difference in the altitude or relief of the two areas. Here change in geology and associated soil differences mark the boundary. A west-facing escarpment forms the boundary between the Appalachian Highlands and adjacent provinces on the west. This escarpment is very conspicuous in Tennessee and Kentucky, less so across Ohio, and again prominent across Pennsylvania and New York. At the south the crystalline rocks of the Piedmont abut against the younger sedimentary rocks of the Coastal Plain. At the north the boundary is between the sedimentary rocks of the Appalachian Plateaus province and the crystalline rocks of the Adirondack province.

## PROVINCE BOUNDARIES

The interprovince boundaries are generally readily recognizable as sharp changes in rock types, altitude, relief, or characteristic land forms. Usually a sharp topographic break marks the boundary between the Piedmont and Blue Ridge provinces. This is particularly true at the south, where there is a bold escarpment, the Blue Ridge frontal scarp. Only where numerous monadnocks are present in the Piedmont adjacent to the Blue Ridge can there be doubt as to where the province boundary should be drawn. Although the Blue Ridge is not nearly so high at the north as at the south, there is usually a sharp topographic break along the zone of contact of a belt of weak Triassic rocks in the Piedmont and the stronger Cambrian and Precambrian rocks of the Blue Ridge province.

The boundary between the Blue Ridge province and the Ridge and Valley province to the west follows fairly closely the geological contacts between Precambrian or Early Cambrian rocks and Late Cambrian or Ordovician rocks. This boundary is conspicuously reflected in different types of topography. The parallel ridges and valleys on the west contrast sharply with the more sprawling and higher (particularly at the south) mountainous terrain of the Blue Ridge province. The eastern portion of the Valley and Ridge province consists of a chain of lowlands, developed on limestones and dolomites, known collectively as the Great Valley. The marked difference in altitude between the Great Valley and the Blue Ridge makes the two provinces stand out sharply.

The boundary between the Valley and Ridge

province and the Appalachian Plateaus province is probably the most continuous and readily recognizable interprovince boundary in the Appalachian Highlands. Although the term "The Endless Mountains" was applied by early colonists to the numerous ridges of the Valley and Ridge province, the bold front which marks the eastern margin of the Appalachian Plateaus and the deeply dissected plateau terrain back of it (locally known as mountains) were more of a hindrance to migration into the interior of the United States than were the ridges of the Valley and Ridge province. The bold escarpments which form the fronts of the Catskill, Pocono, Allegheny, and Cumberland mountains is probably the longest and most nearly continuous topographic feature in the United States.

## INTERPRETATION OF APPALACHIAN LAND FORMS

### *General Discussion*

Despite diversities in geology, structure, and topography, the Appalachian provinces to a large degree have shared a common geomorphic history. This is not entirely true, because part of the area drains to the Gulf of Mexico and part to the Atlantic Ocean, and it is perhaps too much to assume that the geomorphic histories of the two drainage basins were completely similar.

The great diversity of topography in the four provinces is due to a variety of factors. Chief among these are: (1) structural differences, (2) differences in lithology, (3) varying diastrophic histories and associated differential uplift, (4) unequal distances from the sea, related to whether the drainage was to the Atlantic Ocean or the Gulf of Mexico, (5) different degrees of baseleveling, and (6) varying states of preservation of old erosional surfaces.

Basic to an interpretation of the land forms is an understanding of their erosional history. Much that has been written regarding the geomorphic history involves arguments regarding how many, if any, periods of peneplanation the region has undergone and remnants of how many peneplains[1] may be recognized in the present landscape. On this point there are almost as many opinions as there are writers on the subject. Despite the fact that there are those who deny the existence of peneplains, a large number of competent observers have concluded that remains of former erosion surfaces (not necessarily all peneplains) can be recognized in the present-day Appalachian landscape.

Originally the Appalachian Mountains were believed to be direct products of diastrophism. Modern ideas can perhaps be dated from two papers, one written by W. M. Davis in 1891 entitled "The geological dates of origin of certain topographic forms on the Atlantic slope of the United States" and one by C. W. Hayes and M. R. Campbell, in 1894, entitled "Geomorphology of the Southern Appalachians." The change to the viewpoint that the present topography of the Appalachians is largely a product of denudation rather than diastrophism opened the way to a more logical interpretation of the topography. Davis expressed the concept of the denudational origin of the topography in his 1891 paper as follows:

In the first place, it is too often tacitly assumed that the mountain ridges of the Appalachians are simply the unconsumed residuals of the original post-Carboniferous folding and upheaval . . . . The Appalachians in Pennsylvania at least have been rubbed out once certainly, and perhaps twice; and what we now see may be truly likened to a cameo; a plateau and a series of ridges wrought

---

[1] In view of the fact that the term peneplain will be used more frequently in this chapter than in any succeeding one, this is probably an appropriate place to comment on the use of this term throughout the book. The writer sometimes thinks that the science of geomorphology might be better off if use of the word were abandoned. This view is prompted not so much from disbelief in peneplains as from the fact that the concept has been so abused, misapplied, and misunderstood that it has almost as many connotations as it has users. As much as possible we shall use the less specific term erosion surface in discussing the erosional history of a region unless more specific terms such as peneplain or pediplain seem justified. However, when trying to present the views of others we shall use their terminology even though we may not share their viewpoints.

out of a low, even surface by the wasting of its weaker parts after it had been moderately uplifted . . . . Our mountains . . . are essentially the products of Tertiary erosion on an uplifted Cretaceous peneplain of moderate relief. The pre-Cretaceous forms are in nearly all parts lost; the post-Tertiary work is in nearly all places insignificant. Our topography is, for the most part, a Tertiary product.

### Theories of Appalachian Geomorphic History

In the following historical sketch the discussion is divided into two parts, one part dealing with that part of the Appalachian Highlands which drains to the Atlantic Ocean and the other part dealing with the area that drains to the Gulf of Mexico. This is necessary because the terminology applied to erosion surfaces in the two drainage areas is somewhat different.

The eastern area includes a considerable part of the Appalachian Plateaus at the north, most of the Blue Ridge and Ridge and Valley provinces, the Piedmont, and New England, but discussion of New England is deferred to a later chapter. The western area includes much of the Appalachian Plateaus province plus parts of the Ridge and Valley and Blue Ridge provinces at the south. To a considerable degree the terminology developed for the Gulf of Mexico drainage area has been carried westward into the Interior Low Plateaus province.

*Early View of Davis.* The first suggestion of baseleveling in this region occurs in Davis' famous 1889 paper, "The Rivers and Valleys of Pennsylvania." In this paper he stated:

The extraordinarily level crest of the mountain [Blue or Kittatinny Mountain] preserves record of the Cretaceous baselevel lowland; since the elevation of this ancient lowland, its softer rocks have, as it were, been etched out, leaving the harder ones in relief; thus the present valley lowland is to be explained. In consequence of the still later elevation of less amount, the Delaware has cut a trench in the present lowland . . . .

Thus the idea of a Cretaceous peneplain and two later partial cycles is introduced. In a paper published in 1891 Davis recognized the following topographic categories in the Appalachians:

1. Even-crested uplands and ridges considered to be remnants of a peneplain resulting from extended erosion during late Jurassic and Cretaceous time. This erosion surface was referred to as the Cretaceous peneplain.[2]
2. Occasional hills or submountainous areas that rise above this peneplain level and reach truly mountainous proportions in the White Mountains of New Hampshire and the Unakas and Great Smokies of North Carolina.
3. Slopes, valleys, and local open lowlands developed below the Cretaceous peneplain after its elevation in early Tertiary time. The locally baseleveled areas developed adjacent to major streams on belts of weak rock marked an advance toward baseleveling in late Tertiary time.
4. Post-Tertiary narrow young valleys cut a few hundred feet below the level of the Tertiary valleys and lowlands of category 3.

*Views of Other Early Workers.* Keith, in a paper published in 1894 entitled "Geology of the Catoctin belt," gave evidence for what he considered six baselevels of erosion. These were, in order from highest and oldest to lowest and youngest, the Catoctin or Allegheny, Weverton, Upper Tertiary, Lower Tertiary, Upper Pleistocene, and Lower Pleistocene. The Catoctin and Weverton baselevels were interpreted by Keith as being of Cretaceous age. The name Catoctin never caught on and soon disappeared from the literature, but Weverton was in common use for a while and still occasionally appears in the literature.

Bailey Willis, in 1895, introduced the terms Shenandoah baselevel or plain and Kittatinny baselevel or plain into the literature as follows:

[2] It would appear that Davis' 1891 paper may have been written earlier but published later than one by Davis and Wood, in 1890, entitled "The geographic development of northern New Jersey," for in the 1890 paper the term Schooley peneplain was introduced and applied to the erosion surface which Davis in his 1891 paper called the Cretaceous peneplain.

Let us again look over the Appalachian landscape. It has certainly been sculptured by flowing water, to which the deep channels of the streams are due. Could some Titan fill these channels level with the hilltops of the Greater Valley, he would restore a plain which would extend over the area of soft rocks between the ridges of hard rocks. This is the character of a base-level, and we cannot doubt that such a plain was developed by the streams before they began to cut their present channels. Let us call this plain, which is well preserved in the Shenandoah Valley, the Shenandoah base-level.

Above this base-level the valley ridges rise 200 to 1,800 feet. Neighboring ridges are usually of nearly the same height, and their crests are often level lines, but slightly broken. Such lines are elements of a plain, and, with our eyes opened by suggestion, we may see that they do represent one. But it is only through the extensive landscape studies of Professor Davis and Messrs. Hayes and Campbell that we are assured that the ridge tops were once even with the surface of a base-level which was much older than the Shenandoah Plain. Let us call this older plain the Kittatinny base-level, because it is well preserved in the even crest of the long mountain of that name.

Willis gave no reason for preferring the name Kittatinny over the previously proposed Schooley. Kittatinny has persisted in the literature, but the name Shenandoah Plain did not catch on. Instead the name Harrisburg, introduced by M. R. Campbell in 1903, has come to be most widely applied to the erosion surface next below the Schooley or Kittatinny, if they be one and the same surface.

Willis, in an article in 1899 entitled "Round about Asheville," described the broad uplands that are found among the mountains of North Carolina and are known as "balds" and suggested that they may represent remnants of an erosion surface of even older age than the Kittatinny peneplain; he suggested a possible Triassic age for it. Most workers have been reluctant to accept this erosion surface on such meager evidence.

Davis and Wood, in their 1890 paper, had suggested the name Somerville for what was considered to be a local peneplain on weak Triassic rocks in New Jersey. The subcycle which produced this erosion surface was presumed to have been later than that which produced the Harrisburg peneplain. Hayes, in 1899, in a paper entitled "Physiography of the Chattanooga district," introduced the name Coosa peneplain as follows:

> In describing the topography of the district a series of lowland valleys was noted only a short distance above the present channels and flood plains of the streams. These valleys constitute the third and lowest peneplain which can be distinguished in this region . . . . The Coosa peneplain is confined to areas of easily erodible rocks, though not all areas of such rocks have been reduced to this level, but only such as were favorably located with reference to drainage lines. The Coosa "Flatwoods" constitute the largest area of this peneplain.

It thus appears that the Coosa "peneplain" in the south is essentially equivalent to the Somerville "peneplain" at the north and, like the Somerville, is developed only locally on belts of weak rock. Both today would be called straths, not peneplains. The question may be raised, however, whether these erosion surfaces are actually younger than the Harrisburg surface. It may be argued that they are actually the same age as the Harrisburg and are lower because of their development on belts of weak rocks.

*Complex Interpretations.* Much more complex interpretations of the geomorphic history of the Appalachian Highlands have been given, particularly by Bascom, Knopf, Hickok, and Barrell. Bascom (1921), from studies made in the Piedmont province of Pennsylvania, concluded that the erosional history of this region was not to be explained in terms of two major erosional cycles but rather as the product of a complex series of erosional episodes; she was not certain, however, whether the erosional surfaces were of subaerial or marine origin. Five so-called peneplains were recognized (see Table 4.1), and below these four Pleistocene terraces, which were correlated with the Brandywine, Sunderland, Wicomico, and Talbot terraces

of the Coastal Plain. E. B. Knopf (1924), from a study of the area between the Delaware and Susquehanna rivers, came to somewhat similar conclusions. She thought she saw evidence in the topography of 10 terrace-like levels, which were attributed to continuing intermittent uplift (see Table 4.1). She, too, in the absence of conclusive marine deposits and sea cliffs, was uncertain as to whether the surfaces were of subaerial or marine origin.

CONCEPT OF MARINE TERRACING. The suggestions that the erosional surfaces of the Appalachian region might be of marine origin undoubtedly reflected the influence of three papers by Barrell (1913, 1920a, and 1920b) in which he proposed the theory that Appalachian erosion surfaces could be better interpreted as the product of marine terracing than as that of subaerial erosion. Construction of many projected profiles, particularly in New England, led him to conclude that marine terraces were discernible in the topography from New England as far south as the Potomac River. Since Barrell's work dealt mainly with New England, further discussion of it is deferred until the chapter on the New England province.

THEORY OF CONTINUING INTERMITTENT UPLIFT. Hickok (1933), from a study of profiles along the major rivers of south central Pennsylvania, concluded that these profiles gave evidence of a large number of knickpoints along all the streams; these knickpoints he associated with an equal number of partial peneplains in the interstream areas. From 14 to 18 such erosional surfaces were suggested, ranging in altitude from 320 to 1660 feet. Thus it seemed to him that the erosional history of the area could be more logically interpreted in terms of continuing intermittent uplift rather than in terms of periods of long stillstand during which a few peneplain surfaces developed.

It may well be that as many facets of topography as postulated by Hickok can be identified, but to consider them representative of peneplains (straths) seems a highly questionable interpretation. Possibly a more likely explanation is that they reflect control of resistant rock units.

VIEWS OF ASHLEY. Some geologists share the

**T A B L E** 4.1   Correlation of Appalachian Erosion Surfaces

| Hayes-Campbell (1895) | Keith (1894) | Bascom (1921) | Knopf (1924) | Fridley-Nölting (1931) | Ver Steeg (1940) | Cole (1941) | Shaffer (1947) |
|---|---|---|---|---|---|---|---|
| | Catoctin-Allegheny | Kittatinny | Kittatinny | Kittatinny | Kittatinny-Schooley | Upland | Upland |
| Cretaceous peneplain | | Schooley | Schooley | Allegheny | | Schooley | Cumberland-Allegheny |
| | Weverton | Honeybrook | Mine Ridge Honeybrook | | | | |
| | Upper Tertiary baselevel | | Sunbury | | Harrisburg-Worthington-Lexington | Harrisburg | Valley-Lexington-Worthington |
| | | Harrisburg-Bryn Mawr | Harrisburg | | | | |
| Tertiary peneplain | Lower Tertiary baselevel | Lancaster Early Brandy-wine Late Brandy-wine | Lancaster | | Parker Strath-Somerville | Somerville | Coosa-Somerville-Parker Strath |
| | Upper Pleistocene baselevel | Sunderland | Sunderland | | | | |
| | | Wicomico | Wicomico | | | | |
| | Lower Pleistocene baselevel | Talbot | Talbot | | | | |

opinions of G. H. Ashley (1935), long a student of Appalachian geology and geomorphology, whose views were as follows:

1. Topographic features do reflect to some degree the former existence of a peneplain in the Appalachian Highlands. However, actual remnants of this peneplain no longer exist, for it has been differentially lowered as much as 100 feet on hard rock areas and several hundred feet on weak rock areas for each million years since it came into being.
2. Except for the area near the Atlantic Coast, all actual or imaginary surfaces implied by accordant ridge tops can be accounted for by:
   a. Local baseleveling
   b. Stripping of flat-lying or nearly flat-lying rocks
   c. Parallel lowering of rocks of uniform structure
3. Not enough attention has been given to geologic control of topographic surfaces.
4. Most of the geomorphic features are much younger than commonly assumed. The oldest peneplain was probably developed as recently as in Pliocene time.

*Summary of Conventional Views.* Despite continuing diversity of opinion regarding the geomorphic history of the Appalachians, some progress has been made toward reconciling varying viewpoints. Most of the persons who believe that there is evidence of multiple erosion cycles and their concomitant erosion surfaces (peneplains as interpreted by most workers) now agree that the oldest surface is not of Cretaceous age, as was once thought, but rather Tertiary. Whether this oldest erosion surface should be called Kittatinny or Schooley is still in dispute. Some consider the Kittatinny peneplain older than the Schooley; others consider them equivalent surfaces (see Table 4.1). The age of the oldest erosion surface is now variously placed between early and middle Tertiary time.

The name Harrisburg has come to be applied rather generally to the erosion surface which is next below the Schooley and is particularly well displayed in the Piedmont province. This erosion surface is less extensively developed in the Valley and Ridge province, where it is sometimes referred to as the Valley-floor peneplain (Wright, 1925). In the Piedmont province, the Harrisburg surface exhibits rather well the undulating topography expectable in a peneplain. In the Ridge and Valley province, however, the Harrisburg surface is confined largely to valleys and is here probably better considered a strath.

### Erosional History West of the Drainage Divide

It cannot be assumed that the geomorphic history of the portion of the Appalachian Highlands that drains to the Gulf of Mexico was in all respects similar to that of the area draining to the Atlantic; yet considerable evidence suggests that in their broad aspects the erosional histories of the two drainage basins were very similar. However, the greater remoteness from the sea of the headwater areas of the westward-draining streams must be taken into account. As a result of this difference it is to be expected that the more advanced phases of an erosion cycle (the peneplain or near-peneplain stage) may not be as well displayed in the areas remote from the sea as in areas nearer the sea unless baselevel was stable for a very long time. Specifically, evidence of subcycles such as the Coosa and Somerville, if they were such, might not be expected to be present along the headwater portions of westward-draining streams.

As stated above, the names applied to erosion surfaces in the Appalachian Plateau and areas adjacent westward are somewhat different from those used in the Ridge and Valley, Blue Ridge,

and Piedmont provinces. At first an attempt was made to use the same names in both areas, but in later years a more or less distinct terminology has developed for the western area.

*Development of Terminology.* Hayes, in 1899, applied the name Cumberland peneplain to an erosion surface in the Cumberland Plateau which he considered Cretaceous in age. This name for the erosion surface is still encountered occasionally in the literature, although it is now generally held to be younger than Cretaceous. The names Kittatinny and Schooley have been applied to the oldest erosion surface in the westward-draining Appalachian Plateaus. However, considerable confusion exists as to the relationship of the Kittatinny and Schooley erosion surfaces. Some workers (Bascom, 1921; Fridley and Nölting, 1931) considered the Kittatinny older than the Schooley, whereas others, such as Ver Steeg (1931, 1940) considered them equivalent surfaces. To avoid the confusion likely to result from attempting to apply Kittatinny or Schooley to an erosion surface in the Appalachian Plateaus region, Cole, in 1935, suggested that the uppermost erosion surface in the Appalachian Plateaus be called the Upland peneplain.

Fridley and Nölting, in 1931, described two peneplains in the eastern Appalachian Plateau of West Virginia and Pennsylvania, an upper one called Kittatinny and a lower one called Allegheny, neither of which was believed to be older than Tertiary in age. The name Allegheny was intended to replace the name Schooley, which had been applied by Fridley in 1929 to an erosion surface lower than that which he called Kittatinny. Although they were the first to propose formal use of the name Allegheny, they stated that the name had been suggested to them by G. H. Ashley. Fridley and Nölting concluded that the Allegheny peneplain is essentially equivalent to what Keith in 1894 had called the Weverton peneplain. The question of the reality and position of the Allegheny peneplain is a confusing one and will be discussed in more detail in the chapter dealing with the Appalachian Plateaus province (see p. 149).

The name Lexington peneplain was introduced

by Campbell in 1898.   In the description of the Richmond, Kentucky, folio he stated:

> The most striking topographic feature of the Richmond quadrangle is the great plain of central Kentucky . . . which is named from the city of Lexington, situated a few miles to the northeast . . . .  This feature will be regarded as of sub-aerial origin, and it will be referred to as the Lexington peneplain.

Usage of the term Lexington is mainly confined to the Interior Low Plateaus province, but it may occasionally be encountered in papers dealing with the western part of the Appalachian Plateaus.

The name Highland Rim peneplain was introduced by Hayes, in 1899, as follows:

> In the foregoing description of the topography of the district [Chattanooga district], a broad area of level country was noted lying west of the Cumberland Plateau. Its surface is scarcely trenched by stream channels except near its western margin, which borders on the lowlands of middle Tennessee. This Highland Rim is the best preserved portion of the next peneplain below the already described Cumberland, and is regarded as the type locality from which the whole is named.

As with the term Lexington peneplain, usage of Highland Rim as a peneplain name is largely restricted to the Interior Low Plateaus province, but it has been carried over to some extent to the western part of the Appalachian Plateaus province.  There seems to be little question about the Lexington and Highland Rim peneplains being essentially equivalent erosion surfaces, for they can be traced into each other.  Most commonly the name Lexington peneplain is used in the area from Kentucky northward, and Highland Rim in the southern parts of the Interior Low Plateaus and adjacent Appalachian Plateaus province.

The Worthington peneplain was named by Butts, in 1904, in his description of the topography of the Kittanning quadrangle in the plateau area of west central Pennsylvania.  It was considered by him to be an erosion surface about 100 feet below the Harrisburg peneplain.  Al-though there is lack of agreement on this point, there is a tendency nowadays to consider the Worthington peneplain as equivalent to the Lexington rather than a different and slightly lower and younger erosion surface (see Ver Steeg, 1940).

In the Kittanning folio Butts also introduced the term Parker strath, as follows:

> At a number of points on both sides of the [Allegheny] river are deposits of silts and gravels the tops of which form well-marked terraces about 250 feet above the river and about 1050 feet above sea level.  These gravels lie upon rock shelves that are about 200 to 250 feet above the river and from 980 to 1000 feet above the sea.  They are remnants of a former broad valley floor bounded by high steep walls . . . .  It has been customary to call such a broad valley floor a gradation plain, but the propriety of using the word plain for so limited a feature is questionable, and on that account, as well as for the sake of brevity, the term strath is here introduced . . . .  The name Parker is adopted because the strath is well preserved at Parker on the Allegheny. . . .

Parker strath has come into wide use as the name for a baseleveled valley flat produced during the subcycle that followed development of the Lexington-Highland Rim peneplain.

*Evolution of Topography without Peneplanation.*  In view of the large amount of space that has been devoted to discussion of real or alleged peneplains, it should be emphasized that there are those such as Hack (1960) who doubt the reality of cyclical development of landscapes and therefore would question the existence of any peneplain remnants in the Appalachian region.  He would be inclined to believe that "in a landscape like that of the Appalachian region in which large areas are mutually adjusted, the diversity of form is largely the result of differential erosion of rocks that yield to weathering in different ways."   In further arguing that the concept of cyclical peneplanation is untenable Hack stated:

> We have also accepted the idea that many highland areas like the Appalachians eroded in steps or cycles and that the orogenies that deformed the rocks of such highland belts were followed by

long periods of vertical uplift of a cyclical nature involving repeated changes in the rates of deformation. Having abandoned the peneplain we must reexamine the history of such areas and apply areal studies of erosional process and form to the interpretation of their past history. In the Appalachian Highlands, for example, the general outlines of the present drainage may be inherited in part from conditions that existed as early as Permian or Triassic time. The present landscape may have formed through one continuous period of dying orogeny or isostatic adjustment. Differences in relief and form in different areas are explainable partly by the reaction of various erosive processes on a complex bedrock, and partly by what is probably a long history of complicated diastrophic movements.

*Conclusions.* The preceding discussion, although by no means comprehensive, will at least give some idea of the diversity of opinion regarding the number of possible erosion cycles or subcycles that are reflected in the present topography of the Appalachian Highlands. Obviously this question cannot be answered categorically, for there are many and diverse views regarding the geomorphic history of the Appalachians. Table 4.1 attempts to summarize some of the interpretations that have been made as to peneplains represented in the region.

If we accept the premise that there is considerable evidence for the existence of former erosion surfaces in the Appalachian Highlands, a viewpoint with which probably the majority of workers in this region will agree, we are then confronted with two questions: how many erosion surfaces are there and when were they formed? Agreement on the answer to the latter question is more likely than to the first question. Most geomorphologists today would probably agree that these erosion surfaces are mainly Tertiary in age, although they might differ as to when in the Tertiary a particular surface evolved. Probably some of the straths such as the Parker, Somerville, and Coosa are early Pleistocene in age.

On the question as to how many erosion surfaces may be recognized there is wide divergence of opinion. However, there does seem to be a preponderance of belief in two major Tertiary

erosion cycles, in recent years most commonly designated as the Schooley and Harrisburg cycles. This is the terminology most used for those portions of the Appalachian Highlands exclusive of the Appalachian Plateaus. Whether either the so-called Schooley or the Harrisburg peneplain was a peneplain in the Davisian sense of the word, except locally, may be questionable, but these two erosion cycles do seem to have been far enough advanced that geomorphic surfaces were produced whose remnants are still recognizable in the present-day topography. The Harrisburg cycle was probably the shorter of the two, but east of the Blue Ridge, in the Piedmont, the Harrisburg cycle is represented by an extensive area of undulating topography having peneplain-like characteristics. Whether or not the so-called Somerville and Coosa "peneplains" have any real cyclical significance may be reasonably questioned. As stated above, they can just as logically be interpreted in terms of weak rock belts; but the Parker strath does seem to reflect a former baselevel control, for it is developed across a variety of rock types.

## DRAINAGE RELATIONSHIPS AND PROBLEMS

The geomorphic history of a region, particularly one in a humid climate like that of the Appalachian Highlands, is to a certain extent a history of the work of its rivers and the changes which they undergo. Several of the geomorphic problems encountered in the Appalachians are linked with unusual drainage relationships or changes that have presumably taken place.

*Unusual Drainage Divide Relationships.* One striking feature of the drainage of the Appalachians is that the divide which separates the drainage to the Atlantic Ocean and to the Gulf of Mexico cuts obliquely across parts of three provinces. At the north this divide lies well back in the Appalachian Plateaus province and most of this province drains to the Atlantic via such streams as the Delaware and Susquehanna. In the latitude of the Potomac River the divide has shifted eastward until it is very near the eastern edge of the Plateau; farther south the Roanoke River heads at the western edge of the Ridge and Valley province. At the New River and from there on southward the drainage divide is in the Blue Ridge.

This change in position of the Atlantic-Gulf of Mexico divide has long been a cause for speculation. It has usually been assumed that drainage of the whole region formerly was to the west and that at the north there has been a reversal. Attempts to explain this assumed reversal of drainage have produced numerous theories.

## Theories Assuming Reversal of Drainage

*Theory of Davis.* Davis (1889), in his classical paper "The rivers and valleys of Pennsylvania," made the first attempt to explain a presumed reversal of drainage in the northern Appalachians. He assumed that in late Permian time there was drainage to the northwest across the many folds that had previously developed. The major northwestward-flowing stream of the region he called the Anthracite River. Reversal of the headwaters of this river to a southeasterly course was thought to have become possible as a result of warping and faulting during Triassic time. Davis postulated a series of captures of the headwater portions of the Anthracite River by the steeper-gradient streams that flowed into the downwarped and downfaulted Triassic lowland at the east. The present middle portion of the Susquehanna River and the upper parts of the Schuylkill and Lehigh rivers are presumably reversed descendants of northwest-flowing Permian rivers. The lower parts of these rivers, however, were thought to be much younger in age than the middle portions and were considered by Davis to be consequent stream courses initiated on a former and more westerly extension of the Cretaceous rocks of the Coastal Plain and later superposed on the complex structures which they cross. The present westward-flowing streams in the Appalachian Plateau area were viewed as direct lineal descendants of Permian drainage lines which had suffered some loss of their headwater portions from stream piracy by the shorter and steeper eastward flowing streams. One of the great difficulties encountered by Davis' theory is, as Johnson (1931) has pointed out, that having created the hypothetical Anthracite River he must get rid of it somehow, for today there is no vestige of it, unless part of the Schuylkill be considered such. Stream capture is appealed to as a means of accounting for its disappearance, but capture of a major stream by minor streams would seem to demand very special conditions.

*Progressive Stream Piracy Theory of Thompson.* Thompson (1939), from studies made mainly south of the Potomac River, agreed that the presumed reversal of drainage could be explained as the result of progressive stream piracy. He believed that the divide between drainage to the Atlantic Ocean and drainage to the Gulf of Mexico following the Appalachian revolution was in the region of the Blue Ridge. Because of shorter courses and steeper gradients the eastward-flowing streams had an advantage over the westward-flowing streams. He thought that the divide shifted westward in this manner as much as 100 miles at the north and 10 to 20 miles at the south. The greater shifting at the north he attributed to the fact that the belt of resistant rocks of the Blue Ridge is much narrower here than at the south.

The greatest difficulty faced by such a theory as either that of Davis or that of Thompson is the need to explain how streams can effect capture through ridges of resistant rocks. Thompson did not consider this an insurmountable handicap, provided that there was sufficient difference in elevation between the streams on the two sides of a drainage divide. He believed that there was a marked difference in altitudes on the two sides of the divide because of the unequal lengths of streams' courses to the Atlantic and Gulf. He cited the condition which exists today along the Blue Ridge scarp southward from Roanoke, Virginia, as an example of this. Stream piracy has taken place there and seems likely to continue (see p. 105). Thompson did not envisage the piracies as involving spectacular reversals of major streams at one time, but thought rather that they represented many minor reversals that may have begun as early as Jurassic time. His idea as to the nature of the piracies was stated as follows: "Foot by foot the little tributaries of the southeast-flowing streams undercut the little tributaries of their opponents. Each capture strengthened and lengthened the pirate and weakened and shortened the victim. No doubt many captures were simply reversals in valleys partly made by the victims; other captures were made by flank attack." He believed that in areas where limestones are present diversion may have come about by subterranean stream piracy. Thompson estimated that to bring about the amount of divide shifting that he postulated an average divide migration of $\frac{7}{10}$ of a mile per million years was all that was necessary.

Although Davis' and Thompson's theories are similar in that they attribute reversal of drainage to stream piracy, there is a difference in the emphasis given to the conditions which favored the piracies. Davis stressed the importance of Triassic downfolding and downfaulting in the Piedmont area as the major cause for the unequal stream gradients and altitudes on the two sides of the drainage divide, whereas Thompson attributed the asymmetry of drainage conditions to the marked unequal stream lengths plus repeated eastward downtilting on the Atlantic slope.

*Superposition Theory of Johnson.* The two theories outlined above and the postulation of reversal of drainage make the assumption that present streams have a direct lineal connection with Permian rivers, although there may have been considerable modification in position and direction of some of the streams. Johnson (1931) has tried to avoid some of the difficulties encountered by the above theories by assuming that much of the original drainage was obliterated by trangression of a Cretaceous sea and deposition of a marine cover mass over the area. Present southeast-flowing streams are thus interpreted as superposed descendants of consequent streams that developed on the Cretaceous cover mass after withdrawal of the Cretaceous sea. Many difficulties are thus avoided, particularly explanation of the transverse nature of the drain-

age; however, the theory has a weakness in that there is no field evidence that a Cretaceous cover mass ever extended as far west as must be assumed in order to explain the regional reversal of drainage that has been postulated. It was argued that any Cretaceous rocks that once may have been present would necessarily have been eroded during post-Cretaceous time, because if the Cretaceous sediments of the Coastal Plain were projected westward, they would lie far above the summits of the present highest mountains. This is logical enough reasoning, but it does not necessarily follow that Cretaceous rocks were once present west of the Coastal Plain.

Groot (1955) from a petrological study (especially a study of the heavy minerals) of the Cretaceous formations of Delaware concluded that his findings did not support belief in the Cretaceous marine trangression postulated by Johnson. Reasons for this conclusion were: (1) No marine Cretaceous sediments have been found in the Piedmont area of Delaware. (2) The petrology of the Cretaceous rocks in Delaware suggests strongly that the sediments came from the Piedmont region, indicating that this area must have been exposed to subaerial weathering and erosion. (3) Upper Cretaceous rocks have in them an increasing proportion of sediments from the folded Appalachians, which suggests that the streams by late Cretaceous time had extended themselves farther westward.

Johnson proposed the following sequence of events in his interpretation of the geomorphic evolution of the present Appalachian topography.

a. Extended denudation during Jurassic time, leading to the development of an extensive erosion surface called the Fall Zone peneplain.
b. Encroachment of the Cretaceous sea, accompanied by deposition of a cover of coastal plain sediments, resulting in obliteration of all former drainage lines.
c. Arching of the Fall Zone peneplain and its Cretaceous cover mass, with accompanying initiation on this cover mass of a system of southeastward-flowing consequent streams.
d. Superposition on the buried structures of the newly established southeasterly drainage lines.

e. Development in probable mid-Tertiary time of the Schooley peneplain.

f. Uplift of the Schooley peneplain and initiation of a later Tertiary erosion cycle which produced the Harrisburg peneplain.

g. Uplift of the Harrisburg peneplain and subsequent development of local straths, such as the Somerville, on belts of weak rock.

h. Renewal of uplift and inauguration of the present cycle.

i. Glacial modification at the north, particularly in the Appalachian Plateaus.

It perhaps should be pointed out that Johnson's theory was developed not entirely to explain the reversal of drainage that has been presumed to have taken place, but also to account for the numerous southeast drainage lines that characterize much of the Appalachian region. This rectilinear arrangement of stream courses has attracted the attention of numerous geologists. Hobbs (1904) attempted to explain it as the result of control by a number of "lineaments" or fractures that extend in a northwest-southeast direction. Johnson felt that the parallelism of the many stream courses precluded the possibility that they are relicts of an ancient northwest-flowing drainage system which had been reversed to a southeast direction by headwater growth of what were originally short southeastward-flowing streams, or by tilting of the land to the southeast. Superposition from a coastal plain cover of a system of southeast consequent streams seemed to him a more logical explanation for the many aligned streams.

## Theory Assuming No Reversal of Drainage: Meyerhoff-Olmsted Theory

Meyerhoff and Olmsted (1936) have contended that there is no need to postulate a reversal of drainage. They argued that the present streams are lineal descendants of a system of southeast-flowing consequent Permian streams whose courses were controlled by the slopes and surfaces produced by Appalachian folding. They believed that the Permian southeastward drainage was established on great low-angle thrust sheets or overturned folds, and that the drainage divide in Triassic time lay west or northwest of the Great Valley. Trunk streams were assumed to have established southeastward courses, making use of structural sags and transverse faults, before Newark time and to have persisted essentially in these courses despite late Triassic and post-Triassic diastrophism. The fact that each of the major streams of the northern Appalachians crosses a belt of Triassic rocks suggested to them that the streams have had their present courses since Triassic time. Mackin (1938) has pointed out the following weaknesses in this theory: reconstruction of the Permian topography from present structure is impossible, and it cannot be said whether this drainage was to the northwest or to the southeast; it is uncertain whether the Newark series was deposited by streams from the northwest or from the southeast; and suggested relationships of stream courses to Permian structures are not supported by field evidence.

## Conclusions Regarding Drainage History

It is evident that none of the theories proposed to account for the presumed reversal of drainage in the northern Appalachians is without weakness. Johnson's theory of superposition is attractive in its simplicity and logical sequence of events, but the apparent complete lack of any sediments in the Piedmont, Blue Ridge, and Ridge and Valley provinces that might be interpreted as of Cretaceous age is a major weakness. If Groot's conclusion is correct that the petrology of the Cretaceous sediments in the coastal plain area of Delaware indicates an increasingly western source during Cretaceous time, further doubt is cast on the concept of a transgressing Cretaceous sea.

Perhaps the idea of the persistence of Appalachia to the east of the Appalachian geosyncline throughout Paleozoic time and into Mesozoic time needs to be reexamined in view of King's (1955, 1959) idea that the clastic rocks in the Appalachians could have come from fold ridges in the Appalachian geosyncline. It may well be that Appalachia was not continuously present as a highland, but it certainly does appear to be true that numerous Paleozoic conglomerates ranging in age from Cambrian to Pennsylvanian had an eastern source area. But this still may not necessarily mean that drainage at the beginning of Mesozoic time was from east to west.

## REFERENCES CITED

Ashley, G. H. (1935). Studies in Appalachian mountain structure, *Geol. Soc. Am. Bull.*, **46**, 1395–1436.

Barrell, Joseph (1913). Piedmont terraces of the northern Appalachians and their mode of origin, *Geol. Soc. Am. Bull.*, **24**, 688–690 (abs.).

—— (1920a). Post-Jurassic history of the northern Appalachians, *Geol. Soc. Am. Bull.*, **24**, 690–691 (abs.).

—— (1920b). The Piedmont terraces of the northern Appalachians, edited by H. H. Robinson, *Am. Jour. Sci.*, **199**, 227–258, 327–361, and 407–428.

Bascom, Florence (1921). Cycles of erosion in the Piedmont province of Pennsylvania, *Jour. Geol.*, **29**, 540–559.

Butts, Charles (1904). Description of the Kittanning quadrangle, *U. S. Geol. Survey Folio* 115, 2–3.

Campbell, M. R. (1898). Description of the Richmond quadrangle, *U. S. Geol. Survey Folio* 46, 1.

—— (1903). Geographic development of northern Pennsylvania and southern New York, *Geol. Soc. Am. Bull.*, **14**, 277–296.

Cole, W. S. (1935). Rock resistance and peneplain expression, *Jour. Geol.*, **43**, 1049–1062.

Davis, W. M. (1889). The rivers and valleys of Pennsylvania. *Nat. Geog. Mag.*, **1**, 183–253. Also in Davis, W. M. (1909). *Geographical Essays*, 413–484.

—— (1891). The geological dates of origin of certain topographic forms on the Atlantic slope of the United States, *Geol. Soc. Am. Bull.*, **2**, 545–584.

—— and J. W. Wood, Jr. (1890). The geographic development of northern New Jersey, Boston Soc. Nat. Hist., *Proc.*, **24**, 365–423.

Fenneman, N. M. (1928). Physiographic divisions of the United States, Assoc. Am. Geog., *Anns.*, **18**, 261–353.

Fridley, H. M. (1929). Identification of erosion surfaces in south central New York, *Jour. Geol.*, **37**, 113–134.

—— and J. P. Nölting (1931). Peneplains of the Appalachian Plateau, *Jour. Geol.*, **39**, 749–755.

Groot, J. J. (1955). Sedimentary petrology of the Cretaceous sediments of northern Delaware in relation to paleogeographic problems, *Del. Geol. Surv. Bull.* 5, 157 pp.

Hack, J. T. (1960). Interpretation of erosional topography in humid temperate regions, *Am. Jour. Sci.*, **258-A**, 80–97.

Hayes, C. W. (1899). Physiography of the Chattanooga district, *U. S. Geol. Survey 19th Ann. Rept.*, Pt. 2, 1–58.

—— and M. R. Campbell (1894). Geomorphology of the southern Appalachians, *Nat. Geog. Mag.*, **6**, 63–126.

Hickok, W. O. (1933). Erosion surfaces in south-central Pennsylvania, *Am. Jour. Sci.*, **225**, 101–122.

Hobbs, W. H. (1904). Lineaments of the Atlantic border regions, *Geol. Soc. Am. Bull.*, **15**, 483–506.

Johnson, D. W. (1931). *Stream Sculpture on the Atlantic Slope, A Study in the Evolution of Appalachian Rivers*, Columbia Univ. Press, New York, 142 pp.

Keith, Arthur (1894). Geology of the Catoctin belt, *U. S. Geol. Survey 14th Ann. Rept.*, Pt. 2, 285–395.

King, P. B. (1955). A geologic section across the southern Appalachians: an outline of the geology in the segment in Tennessee, North Carolina, and South Carolina, in *Guides to Southeastern Geology*, Geol. Soc. Am., pp. 338–411.

—— (1959). *The Evolution of North America*, Princeton Univ. Press, Princeton, 190 pp.

Knopf, E. B. (1924). Correlation of residual erosion surfaces in the eastern Appalachian Highlands, *Geol. Soc. Am. Bull.*, **35**, 633–668.

Mackin, J. H. (1938). The origin of Appalachian drainage—a reply. *Am. Jour. Sci.*, **236**, 27–53.

Meyerhoff, H. A., and E. W. Olmsted (1936). The origins of Appalachian drainage, *Am. Jour. Sci.*, **232**, 21–42.

Thompson, H. D. (1939). Drainage evolution in the southern Appalachians, *Geol. Soc. Am. Bull.*, **50**, 1323–1356.

Ver Steeg, Karl (1931). Warping of Appalachian peneplains, *Jour. Geol.*, **39**, 386–392.

—— (1940). Correlation of Appalachian peneplains, *Pan-Am. Geol.*, **73**, 203–210.

Willis, Bailey (1895). The northern Appalachians, *Nat. Geog. Soc. Monograph* 1, 169–202.

—— (1899). Round about Asheville, *Nat. Geog. Mag.*, **1**, 291–300.

Wright, Frank (1925). The physiography of the upper James River basin in Virginia, *Va. Geol. Surv. Bull.* 11, 67 pp.

ADDITIONAL REFERENCES

Ashley, G. H. (1930). Age of the Appalachian peneplains, *Geol. Soc. Am. Bull.*, **41**, 695–700.

Bethune, Pierre de (1948). Geomorphic studies in the Appalachians of Pennsylvania, *Am. Jour. Sci.*, **246**, 1–22.

Bryan, Kirk, A. B. Cleaves, and H. T. U. Smith (1933). The present status of the Appalachian problem, *Zeitschrift für Geomorphologie*, Band 7, Heft 6, 312–320.

Cole, W. S. (1941).   Nomenclature and correlation of Appalachian erosion surfaces, *Jour. Geol.*, **49,** 129–148.

Shaffer, P. R. (1947).   Correlation of erosion surfaces of the southern Appalachians, *Jour. Geol.*, **55,** 343–352.

Stose, G. W. (1940).   Age of the Schooley peneplain, *Am. Jour. Sci.*, **238,** 461–476.

Strahler, A. N. (1945).   Hypotheses of stream develop-ment in the folded Appalachians of Pennsylvania, *Geol. Soc. Am. Bull.*, **56,** 45–88.

Thompson, H. D. (1949).   Drainage evolution in the Appalachians of Pennsylvania, N. Y. Acad. Sci., *Anns.*, **52,** 31–62.

Ver Steeg, K. (1933).   Windgaps and erosion surfaces, *Am. Jour. Sci.*, **226,** 507–511.

Wright, Frank (1942).   Erosional history of the southern Appalachians, *Jour. Geomorph.*, **5,** 151–161.

# 5

# *Piedmont Province*

## GENERAL DESCRIPTION

The Piedmont province extends from the Hudson River at the north to Alabama at the south. It is hardly more than 10 miles wide at its narrowest and about 125 miles at its widest portion, near the Virginia-North Carolina boundary. The Piedmont is the least mountainous part of the Appalachian Highlands. Such mountains as exist are mainly near its western margin and are outliers of the Blue Ridge. However, a few isolated mountains, such as Stone Mountain, Georgia, are erosion remnants that rise above the general level of the erosion surface that bevels Piedmont rocks and structures.

Regional slopes in the Piedmont Plateau are to the east at an average rate of roughly 20 feet to the mile. General altitudes along the inner boundary of the Piedmont Plateau increase from 200 or 300 feet in New Jersey to as much as 1800 feet in the Dahlonega Plateau of Georgia. This increase in altitude southward is largely a result of the widening of the Piedmont toward the south, as a result of which the inner border is much farther from the sea than at the north.

The upland portion of the Piedmont province is often called the Piedmont Plateau, but it is a plateau only in the sense that it stands above the Coastal Plain to the east of it. In places the Piedmont lies as much as 1800 feet below the Blue Ridge to the west. Much of the surface of the Piedmont Plateau would be most appropriately described as broadly undulating or rolling topography whose relief is increased locally by low knobs or ridges and valleys 50 to 300

feet deep. Subequality of altitudes is obviously not the result of rock control, for the Piedmont Plateau surface truncates rocks of various types. The surface of the Piedmont has long been exposed to weathering processes, as shown by the presence over much of it of a deep saprolitic soil cover which at places is as much as 100 feet thick (Crickmay, 1935). Pedestal rocks are particularly common in the southern Piedmont in areas of granite, granite-porphyry, and granite-gneiss. Stone Mountain, Delkalb County, Georgia, is the best-known example of several granite domes that rise above the undulating surface of the Piedmont (White, 1945). This granite dome is about 1½ miles long and stands about 650 feet above its surroundings.

Although most of the Piedmont can be aptly described as upland of moderate altitude, several lowland areas are scattered through the province. These lowlands are developed on rocks of Triassic age (see Fig. 5.1) and one area in New Jersey-Pennsylvania-Virginia is extensive enough to be given sectional rank. Farther south in Virginia and in North Carolina other areas of Triassic rocks give rise to local lowland tracts, but they are too small to merit recognition as sections.

Structural or lithologic control of drainage in the Piedmont Province may be observed locally, but regionally it is either lacking or too obscure to be recognized. Lack of such control may be a consequence of structural and geological patterns too complex to be followed by the streams or an inheritance from a former surface of such low relief that stream courses were not influenced by lithologic or structural conditions.

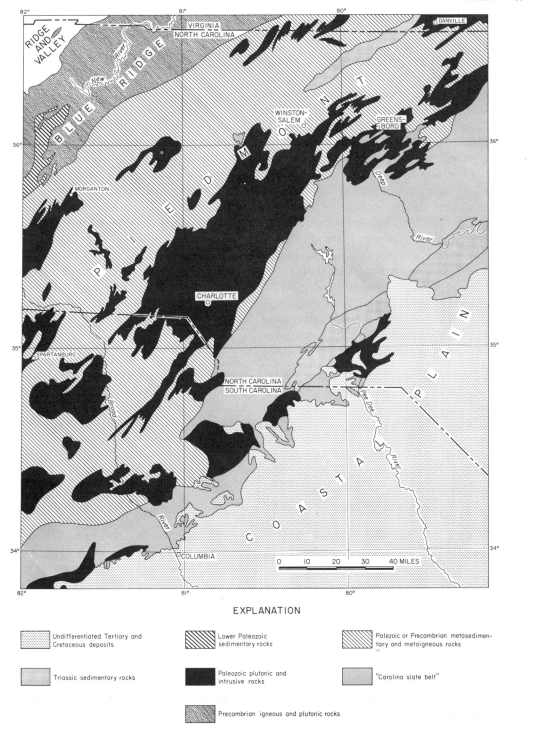

FIG. 5.1  Geologic map of southern Piedmont and adjacent areas.  *(After P. B. King, Guides to Southeastern Geology,*
*Geol. Soc. Am.)*

## GEOLOGY OF PIEDMONT

It was long believed that most of the rocks of the Piedmont Plateau, Triassic areas excepted, were Precambrian in age and belonged to a still unfoundered part of the ancient land mass of Appalachia. As stated above (see p. 85), the existence of this borderland has been seriously questioned in recent years, and it is now more common practice to consider the Piedmont area as having been a part of the Appalachian geosyncline rather than a source region of the sediments that accumulated during Paleozoic time in this geosyncline. The "Crystalline Appalachians," which consist of the Piedmont Plateau and Blue Ridge, are made up mainly of metamorphic rocks (schists, gneisses, quartzites, and slates) and plutonic rocks (granites, granite-diorites, gabbros, peridotites, and dunites). These metamorphic and plutonic rocks have a highly complex structure which on a geologic map often gives the appearance of great knots or swirls.

*Varying Degrees of Metamorphism.* The degree of metamorphism increases progressively eastward from the Ridge and Valley province across the Blue Ridge into the Piedmont Plateau, but surprisingly does not reach its climax in the sillimanite zone at the far eastern edge of the Piedmont but about midway between the Blue Ridge and the inner edge of the Coastal Plain (King, 1959). Between the sillimanite zone and the eastern edge of the Coastal Plain is the Carolina slate belt (see Fig. 5.2), an area of slates, graywackes, pyroclastics, and lavas that have been only moderately metamorphosed except along the margins of occasional granite intrusions. The age of these rocks is uncertain, but they are believed to be of Paleozoic age. It is not entirely clear what kinds of rocks underlie the Coastal Plain, but rocks of undoubted Paleozoic age have been encountered in wells drilled through Coastal Plain sediments in southern Georgia and northern Florida; well cores show that these rocks are shales and sandstone that are essentially unmetamorphosed (Applin, 1951). This suggests that these rocks lie east of the axis of greatest deformation and metamorphism and that here, at least, is evidence of a former two-sided mountain system, with the degree of metamorphism and deformation decreasing both eastward and westward from the sillimanite zone in the Piedmont. Whether such a relationship exists farther north in the Piedmont cannot be said at this time.

*Age of Plutonic Rocks.* The granitic type of rocks found in many parts of the Piedmont were formerly thought to be Precambrian in age, but radiometric determinations indicate ages much younger than Precambrian for many of them. It appears that the intrusive rocks fall mainly into three major age groups (Brown, 1953): (1) early Precambrian, (2) late Precambrian and early Paleozoic, and (3) late Paleozoic. Thus much of the regional metamorphism that took place in the Piedmont may have occurred during Paleozoic time.

*Areas of Triassic Rocks.* From New Jersey to South Carolina rocks of the Newark series of late Triassic age form long strips in the Piedmont area of crystalline rocks (see Fig. 5.1). They are mainly continental red sandstones, shales, and conglomerates that seem to have accumulated in downfaulted troughs whose dimensions were little greater than their present outcrop areas. Similar rocks have been encountered in wells as far south as Florida (Applin, 1952). The Triassic rocks have been little metamorphosed or folded, but they have been broken and tilted by normal faulting. In places, notable igneous activity accompanied Triassic sedimentation, and the rocks of the Newark series are interbedded with basaltic flows or intruded by diabase dikes and sills. Triassic dikes are also fairly common in the metamorphic rock belt of the Piedmont. The Triassic rocks provide a terminal date beyond which rock deformation has not taken place. The Piedmont has been differentially uplifted since Triassic time, perhaps, but it has not undergone tectonic deformation. The areas of sedimentary Triassic rocks stand out conspicuously because of their striking red soils and because they usually are lowland tracts as a result of their greater erosibility compared with that of the surrounding crystalline rocks. Triassic igneous rocks com-

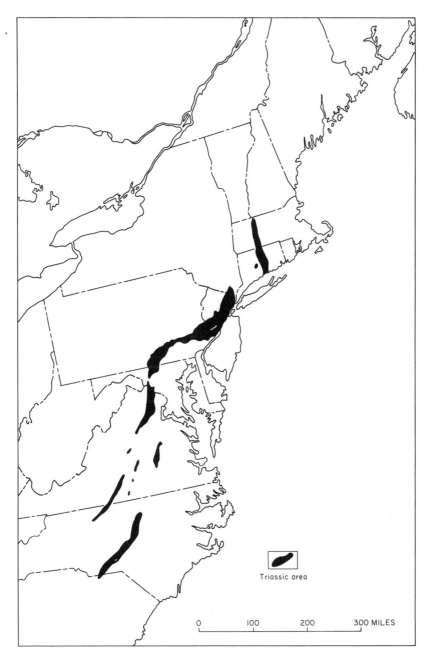

Triassic area

0        100        200        300 MILES

FIG. 5.2   Triassic areas of eastern United States.   (*After Plate 1, U. S. Geol. Survey, Prof. Paper 248, and Plate 5, Va. Geol. Surv. Bull. 29.*)

monly form ridges or scarps which locally are very prominent.

## BOUNDARIES OF PIEDMONT PROVINCE

The inner boundary of the Piedmont Plateau lies at the foot of the Blue Ridge Mountains along most of its course, but between the Schuylkill and Susquehanna Rivers the Blue Ridge is lacking and the Piedmont Lowland section and the Ridge and Valley province border each other. Here little difference in topography exists between the two provinces, but a marked contrast between the limestone soils of the Great Valley and the red soils on the Triassic sandstones and shales of the Piedmont lowland is observable. The Piedmont Plateau also borders on the Ridge and Valley province at the extreme south, for here the Blue Ridge does not extend so far south as does the Piedmont Plateau, but in this area there are no Triassic rocks at the inner margin of the Piedmont. From Virginia southward to Georgia the boundary between the Piedmont and the Blue Ridge is a conspicuous topographic rise known as the Blue Ridge Escarpment.

*The Fall Line.* The boundary on the east between the Piedmont Plateau and the Coastal Plain is the well known Fall Line, or what may more appropriately be called the Fall Zone. Here the resistant rocks of the Piedmont stand out in contrast to the weaker Cretaceous and Tertiary rocks of the Coastal Plain; as a result, numerous streams descend from the Piedmont Plateau onto the Coastal Plain over a series of rapids or small waterfalls usually distributed over a distance of several miles. At a few places these falls and rapids are at the contact of the two provinces; more commonly they lie a few miles within the Piedmont Plateau. The Susquehanna River reaches tidewater 3 miles within the eastern edge of the Piedmont Plateau; the Potomac River falls 40 feet in a distance of 3 miles (see Fig. 5.3) beginning at a point 10 miles upstream from the Fall Line; the James River descends to tidewater at Richmond,

Virginia, with a fall of 84 feet that is distributed over 3 miles.

The Fall Line as a topographic feature varies greatly in its distinctiveness. For most of its extent, south of the Potomac River, the eastern edge of the Piedmont Plateau is not notably apparent. The boundary between the Coastal Plain and the Piedmont Plateau is particularly obscure topographically in North Carolina south of the Neuse River, because a belt of Triassic lowland about 10 miles wide at the outer edge of the Piedmont Plateau does not stand out from the topography of the Coastal Plain. The exact position of the Fall Line in the Carolinas is further obscured by the fact that many of the streams that descend from the Piedmont Plateau onto the Coastal Plain have cut through the inner coastal plain sediments into the underlying crystalline rocks. As a consequence rapids may exist along the streams for as much as 20 miles into the Coastal Plain. Examples of such rapids are found along the Roanoke, Tar, Neuse, Cape Fear, and Peedee rivers.

It is mainly between the Potomac and Delaware rivers that the Fall Line is a conspicuous topographic feature. Here there is a rise of 100 to 300 feet, which was attributed by a few early geologists to faulting rather than varying rock resistance.

The Fall Line with its associated waterfalls and rapids necessitated a break in transportation in colonial days, when much traffic was by boat, and as a consequence numerous cities developed at or near the contact of the Coastal Plain and the Piedmont Plateau, but usually on the Coastal Plain. Examples of such Fall Line cities are New York, Philadelphia, Baltimore, Richmond, Raleigh, Columbia, and Macon. Large cities are notably lacking in the Piedmont, the only one of importance being Atlanta, Georgia.

ORIGIN OF FALL LINE. For many years the common explanation for the scarp, where one exists, between the Coastal Plain and the Piedmont was that it was a consequence of the varying resistance to erosion displayed by the rocks of the two provinces. Renner (1927), however, proposed a different interpretation of this topographic break. He believed that the Fall

FIG. 5.3   Falls of the Potomac.   *(Photo by Flournoy, courtesy Virginia Chamber of Commerce.)*

Line represents a morvan relationship (two intersecting erosion surfaces) between the Jurassic Fall Zone peneplain and the late Tertiary Harrisburg peneplain. The Fall Zone peneplain beneath the coastal plain sediments is supposed to be undergoing exhumation in the Fall Zone area. The Fall Line, according to Renner's view, represents the line of intersection of the Fall Zone peneplain with the eastern edge of the Harrisburg peneplain in the Piedmont.

There are grounds for viewing this interpretation of the Fall Zone with skepticism. In the first place, the reality of the Fall Zone peneplain is in question. As we have previously seen (see p. 31), well logs and seismic refraction data indicate a degree of relief on the surface of the basement complex beneath the Coastal Plain that makes it questionable whether this surface

is properly considered a peneplain. Furthermore, the topography along the Fall Line is so variable that it is difficult to view it as a line of intersection between two erosional plains. Perhaps it is more realistic, after all, to interpret the Fall Zone as a topographic break between two regions of different lithology which varies in conspicuousness to the degree to which the adjacent rocks differ in their erosibility.

## SUBDIVISIONS OF PIEDMONT PLATEAU

The Piedmont Plateau province has been divided into the Piedmont Upland and Piedmont Lowland sections. Although treated as one section, the Piedmont Lowland is divided into two parts by a narrow strip of Piedmont Upland topography which parallels the Schuylkill River on the southwest.

## Piedmont Upland

The Piedmont Upland section includes the greater part of the Piedmont Plateau province and has the type of geology and topography that is most commonly associated with this province. Much of its terrain is gently rolling (see Fig. 5.4) and probably comes as near as any area in eastern United States to looking like a former peneplain surface. Most geomorphologists who have worked in the area consider its surface representative of the Harrisburg peneplain, as defined by Campbell (see p. 77). Erosional modification of this erosion surface has been on the whole rather moderate, but is most severe in North Carolina. Dissection is least at the western margin and increases along streams toward the Fall Zone. Numerous monadnocks are present along the western margin, particularly from Virginia southward; examples are Big Cobbler Mountain in Virginia, Kings Mountain, South Mountain, and Brushy Mountain in North Carolina, and Findley Ridge in Georgia. The greater abundance of monadnocks toward the western margin of the Piedmont Upland probably means that the Harrisburg cycle had not progressed as far here as at the east. Monadnocks are particularly abundant in Georgia in what is known as the Dahlonega Plateau. Any subdivision of the Piedmont Upland section into lower magnitude geomorphic units would probably recognize this southern monadnock area as a separate subdivision.

FIG. 5.4   Piedmont topography with monadnock, about 15 miles west of Charlotte, North Carolina.   (*Photo by John S. Shelton.*)

FIG. 5.5  Portion of Parkesburg, Pennsylvania, quadrangle showing part of Chester Valley.

*Chester Valley.* Chester Valley is a remarkable limestone valley that lies along the north edge of the Piedmont Upland in southeastern Pennsylvania and extends from Quarryville northward for 55 miles to the Schuylkill River north of Philadelphia. The valley is coextensive with the outcrop area of the Ordovician Conestoga limestone. It is from 1 to 3 miles wide, is unusually straight, and lies several hundred feet below the uplands to either side (see Fig. 5.5). The south side of the valley is formed by the Wissahickon schist member of the Glenarm series, and the north wall of the valley by the Lower Cambrian Chickies quartzite. There is no evidence to suggest that a stream ever followed the valley; in fact, all streams that enter the valley cross it rather than flow along it. Explanation of this unusual valley is linked with whatever interpretation is given to the so-called "Marctic Overthrust."

*Marctic Overthrust Problem.* In 1929, Knopf and Jonas described what they considered a thrust that was supposed to have carried the Wissahickon schist of presumed Precambrian age northwestward for a distance of 20 miles onto the Conestoga limestone of Ordovician age. Thus the south wall of the Chester Valley was considered by them the eroded front of the low-angle Marctic overthrust sheet.

Some geologists deny the existence of the Marctic overthrust. Those who do contend that the Wissahickon schist of the Glenarm series rests upon a Cambro-Ordovician sequence in normal stratigraphic succession (Mackin, 1935; Cloos and Hietanen, 1941). They further contend that the Glenarm series, of which the Wissahickon schist is a member, is Paleozoic and not Precambrian in age. The oldest rock in the area is the Baltimore gneiss, whose Precambrian age seems established (Tilton et al., 1958). Resting upon this gneiss are the Chickies quartzite, Conestoga limestone, and Wissahickon schist. Those who doubt the existence of the Marctic thrust contend that the gross stratigraphy here is similar to Glenarm stratigraphy found elsewhere, namely, quartzite over gneiss, carbonate over quartzite, and shale over carbonate.

They also claim that the degree of metamorphism in the Wissahickon schist is comparable to that found in the Conestoga limestone. Work done by Tilton and associates (1958) on the time of metamorphism of the Glenarm series placed this at 300 to 350 million years ago. This shows that the metamorphism took place later than Precambrian time but it does not preclude the possibility that the sediments accumulated in Precambrian time.

Explanation of the unusual topographic characteristics of Chester Valley presents a problem as puzzling as the stratigraphic relationships along it. Knopf and Jonas would interpret it as a window in the Marctic thrust. Mackin (1935) contended, however, that the walls of the valley are too straight for a low-angle thrust contact, which is usually irregular or sinuous in plan. He believed that the topography along the south side of Chester Valley suggested more a high-angle fault contact. Bricker and associates (1960) concluded that the valley might be explained as the result of more rapid weathering of a calcareous unit in the stratigraphic sequence. It would be unusual indeed to find a valley with the dimensions and striking linear form of Chester Valley that developed this way. Innumerable limestone valleys exist in the Appalachians whose axes follow the strike of the beds responsible for them but they either have streams flowing along them or display evidence that streams at one time did flow through them. Lack of evidence of a former longitudinal stream in Chester Valley makes it seem more likely that it is a product of faulting, whether this be overthrust faulting as postulated by Knopf and Jonas or normal faulting as suggested by Mackin.

*Piedmont Lowlands*

Two lowland tracts on weak Triassic rocks near the northern end of the Piedmont Plateau province have sufficient size to merit recognition as a separate section of distinctly different geology and topography from that of the Piedmont Upland (see Fig. 5.6). The northernmost of the Triassic lowlands extends from the Hudson River southward to the Schuylkill River where a

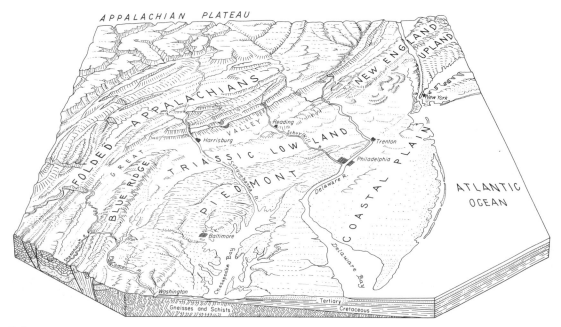

FIG. 5.6  Diagram showing relation of Triassic Lowland to adjacent geomorphic regions.  (*After Johnson, Bascom, and Sharp, 16th Int. Geol. Congr. Guidebook 7, Plate 2.*)

narrow strip of Piedmont Upland, which forms the divide between the Schuylkill and Susquehanna rivers, separates it from the more southerly area. This latter area of Triassic lowland extends from the Schuylkill-Susquehanna divide southwestward about 180 miles across Pennsylvania and Maryland into Virginia as far as the Rappahannock River in the latitude of Fredericksburg, Virginia.

*Northern Triassic Lowland.* The northern Triassic lowland area begins at the Palisades of the Hudson and extends southward to the Schuylkill River. This area of Triassic rock is partially enclosed by three tapering tracts of crystalline rocks, often called prongs. The lowland is bounded on the northwest by the Reading prong, on the northeast by the Manhattan prong, and on the south by the Trenton prong. The fourth of these so-called prongs, the Carlisle prong, does not reach as far north as the northern lowland belt, but it does bound the southern area of the Triassic lowland on the northwest. In New Jersey the Triassic lowland makes contact with the Coastal Plain, but in Pennsylvania it is

separated from the Coastal Plain by a narrow tongue of crystalline rocks which parallels the Delaware River and the northward-extending Trenton prong. Where the Triassic lowland abuts against the Coastal Plain there is no marked topographic break; the Fall Line is missing here. However, the two areas are readily recognizable because of the contrast that the red soils of the Triassic lowland make with the soils of the Coastal Plain.

Triassic igneous rocks are prominent at the northern end of the Triassic lowland. An intrusive diabase sheet, which is as much as 1000 feet thick, forms the Palisades of the Hudson (see Fig. 5.7). Farther west in New Jersey three extrusive basalt flows, which from top to bottom are 650, 850, and 350 feet thick respectively, are responsible for the Watchung Mountains and such lesser ridges as Long and Hook Mountains. The southeast-facing scarps of the Watchung Mountains stand as high as 400 feet above their surroundings. The terrain on the sedimentary Triassic rocks is by no means lacking in relief, for the lithology of the Triassic beds varies enough that moderate relief exists.

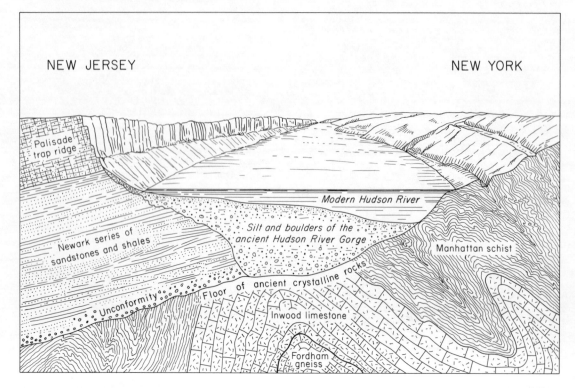

NEW JERSEY

NEW YORK

Palisade trap ridge

Modern Hudson River

Newark series of sandstones and shales

Silt and boulders of the ancient Hudson River Gorge

Manhattan schist

Floor of ancient crystalline rocks

Unconformity

Inwood limestone

Fordham gneiss

FIG. 5.7    Geology and structure under the Hudson River, at the Palisades.    (*After Fig. 7, Guidebook, 61st meeting, Geol. Soc. Am.*)

Located in the New Jersey part of the Triassic lowland is the type area of the so-called Somerville "peneplain" of Davis and Wood (see p. 77). As indicated above (see p. 78), this erosion surface is better described as a strath than as a peneplain, and it may even more correctly be interpreted as the result of more rapid lowering of the Harrisburg erosion surface in a belt of weak rocks.

*Effects of Glaciation.*    The northern edge of the Triassic lowland was glaciated during Wisconsin time. Glacial deposits are not thick enough to modify the topography materially, but some drainage changes were effected, and for a time a lake known as Lake Passaic existed in the area. Lake Passaic (Salisbury and Kummel, 1895) was formed when the Wisconsin ice spread into the lowland back of the Watchung Ridges and closed both the Paterson and Millburn gaps through which streams drained to the southeast. The level of Lake Passaic rose until it overflowed to

the southwest through Moggy Hollow, north of Somerville. Millburn Gap became so clogged with glacial debris that it was never reopened after withdrawal of the ice, but Paterson Gap came into use again and the drainage of the Lake Passaic area now flows through this gap via the Passaic River.

*Southern Triassic Lowland.*    Mine Ridge, Welsh Mountain, and South Mountain, hills of crystalline rocks, separate the northern and southern Piedmont Lowland tracts. The southern lowland is somewhat more diverse in nature than the northern lowland and includes some land that is not underlain by Triassic rocks. The wide expanse of the lowland just east of the Susquehanna River is explained by the fact that included here is a strip of lowland on Ordovician limestone known as the Lancaster Valley or Lowland in Pennsylvania and as the Frederick Lowland in Virginia. South Mountain at the north (not to be confused with the northern end of the Blue

Ridge, which terminates southwest of Harrisburg in what is also called South Mountain) separates the Lancaster Valley of the Piedmont province from the Lebanon Valley on its west in the Ridge and Valley province. The topography of the southern Triassic lowland does not all have low relief. Hills are present, particularly where Triassic diabase rocks crop out. Knobs of trap rocks are particularly conspicuous in the region around Gettysburg, Pennsylvania, where a sill 1800 feet thick is present. One of these hills, Cemetery Ridge, played a historic role in the Battle of Gettysburg. Not all of the areas of Triassic rock are included in the Triassic lowland section. In Virginia, six Triassic basins which range in size from about 30 square miles to nearly 800 square miles are included in the Piedmont Upland. They are too far removed from the main Triassic lowland area to be included in it. They are thus outliers of Triassic lowland topography in the Piedmont upland.

## GEOMORPHIC HISTORY

The Piedmont Plateau has shared in the geomorphic history of the Appalachian Highlands, which was discussed in Chapter 4. If the concept of peneplanation has any application in the Appalachian Highlands, it seems most likely to apply in the Piedmont Plateau. Its topography strongly suggests peneplanation at least once during Tertiary time. Remnants of the Schooley erosion surface seem to be lacking in the Piedmont, and the major and perhaps only erosion surface that merits recognition as a peneplain is the Harrisburg. However, this surface is excellently and extensively preserved.

## REFERENCES CITED

Applin, P. L. (1951). Preliminary report on buried pre-Mesozoic rocks in Florida and adjacent states, *U. S. Geol. Survey Circular* 91, 28 pp.

——— (1952). Volume of Mesozoic sediments in Florida and Georgia, *Geol. Soc. Am. Bull.*, 63, 1159–1164.

Bricker, O. P., C. A. Hopson, M. E. Kauffman, D. M. Lapham, D. B. McLaughlin, and D. U. Wise (1960). Some tectonic and structural problems along the Susquehanna River, *Guidebook 25th Ann. Field Conf.*, *Pennsylvania Geologists*, 99 pp.

Brown, W. R. (1953). Structural framework and mineral resources of the Virginia Piedmont, *Ky. Geol. Surv. Spec. Publ.* 1, pp. 88–99.

Cloos, Ernst, and Anna Hietanen (1941). Geology of the "Marctic overthrust" and the Glenarm series in Pennsylvania and Maryland, *Geol. Soc. Am. Spec. Paper* 35, 207 pp.

Crickmay, G. F. (1935). Granite pedestal rocks in the southern Appalachian Piedmont, *Jour. Geol.*, 43, 745–758.

Davis, W. M., and J. W. Wood, Jr. (1890). The geographic development of northern New Jersey, Boston Soc. Nat. Hist., *Proc.*, 24, 365–423.

King, P. B. (1959). *The Evolution of North America*, Princeton Univ. Press, Princeton, 189 pp.

Knopf, E. B. and A. I. Jonas (1929). Geology of the McFalls Ferry-Quarryville district, Pennsylvania, *U. S. Geol. Survey Bull.* 799, 156 pp.

Mackin, J. H. (1935). The problem of the Marctic overthrust and the age of the Glenarm series in southeastern Pennsylvania, *Jour. Geol.*, 43, 356–380.

Renner, G. T. (1927). The physiographic interpretation of the Fall Line, *Geog. Rev.*, 17, 276–286.

Salisbury, R. D. and H. B. Kummel (1895). Lake Passaic: an extinct glacial lake, *Jour. Geol.*, 3, 533–560.

White, W. A. (1945). Origin of granite domes in the southeastern Piedmont, *Jour. Geol.*, 53, 276–282.

ADDITIONAL REFERENCES

Bascom, Florence (1921). Cycles of erosion in the Piedmont province of Pennsylvania, *Jour. Geol.*, 29, 540–559.

Campbell, M. R. (1933). Chambersburg (Harrisburg) peneplain in the Piedmont of Maryland and Pennsylvania, *Geol. Soc. Am. Bull.*, 44, 553–573.

Fenneman, N. M. (1938). *Physiography of Eastern United States*, McGraw-Hill Book Company, New York, 714 pp.

Harrington, J. W. (1951). Structural analysis of the west border of the Durham Triassic basin, *Geol. Soc. Am. Bull.*, 62, 149–158.

Kulp, J. L., L. E. Long, and F. D. Eckelmann (1957). Age of the Piedmont and southern Appalachians, *Geol. Soc. Am. Bull.*, 68, 1758–1759 (abs.).

Lester, J. G., and A. T. Allen (1950). Diabase of the Georgia Piedmont, *Geol. Soc. Am. Bull.*, 61, 1217–1224.

Nelson, W. A. (1956). Structure and geology of the Virginia Piedmont, *Geol. Soc. Am. Bull.*, 67, 1755–1756 (abs.).

Stose, G. W. (1949). The fault at the west edge of the Triassic in southern Pennsylvania, *Am. Jour. Sci.*, 247, 531–536.

Wasserburg, G. J., F. J. Pettijohn, and J. Lipson (1957). $A^{40}/K^{40}$ ages of micas and feldspars from the Glenarm series near Baltimore, *Science*, 126, 355–357.

# 6

# Blue Ridge Province

## GENERAL DESCRIPTION

The Blue Ridge province extends from southern Pennsylvania to northeastern Georgia, a distance of some 550 miles. The Roanoke River, the southernmost stream to flow eastward through the Blue Ridge, divides the Blue Ridge province into two distinctly different parts. North of the Roanoke River the term "ridge" is an appropriately descriptive term, for at numerous places there is a central ridge with subordinate ridges grouped about it. At the extreme north, in Pennsylvania, the province actually narrows to a single ridge, which terminates near Carlisle, Pennsylvania, in what is called the Carlisle prong or South Mountain. Three major rivers, the Potomac, James, and Roanoke, rise west of the Blue Ridge and flow eastward through it, and numerous wind gaps attest to streams that formerly did.

South of the Pennsylvania-Maryland boundary, the Blue Ridge divides into two ridges developed on the two limbs of the 25-mile wide Catoctin-Blue Ridge anticlinorium. On the east are Catoctin and Bull Run Mountains, and on the west are South Mountain, Short Hill, and Blue Ridge.

South of Roanoke, Virginia, the Blue Ridge province broadens, and in the latitude of Asheville, North Carolina, it attains a width of 80 miles. Here, it is a mountainous upland not pierced by a single through-flowing stream. Most of the drainage of the southern Blue Ridge is to the west, as the divide between Atlantic and Gulf of Mexico drainage lies near the eastern edge of the mountains. From Roanoke, Vir-

ginia, to near Gainesville, Georgia, the front of the Blue Ridge province is a prominent scarp called the Blue Ridge Front or Scarp. The crest of this frontal scarp has an altitude of about 2500 feet near Roanoke; its elevation increases southward until in the vicinity of Blowing Rock, North Carolina, it is 4000 feet; from Blowing Rock southward the scarp's altitude decreases until near Gainesville, Georgia, it is only 1000 feet.

## GEOLOGY AND STRUCTURE

The Blue Ridge province is underlain by Lower Cambrian and Upper Precambrian sedimentary rocks and Precambrian basement complex gneissic and plutonic rocks. The sedimentary rocks are those of the Precambrian Ocoee and the Lower Cambrian Chilhowee series. These rocks are mainly clastics that have undergone varying degrees of metamorphism and are now conglomerates, quartzose sandstones, graywackes, and slates (King, 1955). They are older than the rocks of the Ridge and Valley province on the west and, in contrast to the rocks in the Piedmont Plateau, can be grouped into a reasonably good stratigraphic sequence. Metasedimentary rocks are found largely at the western side of the Blue Ridge province. East of them are basement rocks displaying an injection complex similar to that found in the Piedmont, but the early and late Paleozoic igneous plutons of the Piedmont are lacking in the Blue Ridge.

Many geologists have thought that the Blue Ridge province is separated from the Ridge and

Valley province on the west by a more or less continuous low-angle thrust fault which has been called the "Blue Ridge overthrust." King (1950), however, although recognizing the existence of low-angle thrusts, did not believe that they were present along the entire western boundary. There seems to be better evidence for overthrusting in the Tennessee area than elsewhere. Here, along two great thrusts, the Holston Mountain and the Great Smoky, rocks of the Blue Ridge have been thrust northwestward over carbonate rocks of the Ridge and Valley province. Keith (1927), who first described the Great Smoky overthrust, thought that it could be mapped in Tennessee for a distance of at least 300 miles. Numerous windows (Oriel, 1951) through the thrust sheets expose the carbonate rocks of Ridge and Valley type and suggest westward thrusting in places of as much as 35 miles. The thrusts along the west edge of the Blue Ridge differ from those found

in the Ridge and Valley province in that they extend to greater depth and involve rocks of the basement complex and not just the veneer of sediments, as seems to be true in the Ridge and Valley province.

## NORTHERN BLUE RIDGE

The Blue Ridge from Roanoke, Virginia, to its northern extremity in the Carlisle prong in Pennsylvania is a complex ridge of variable width and elevation. It nowhere exceeds 14 miles in width, and in its narrower parts, as at Afton, Virginia, it is a single ridge that stands about 1200 feet above the Great Valley of the Ridge and Valley province on the west (see Fig. 6.1) and 2000 feet above the Piedmont on the east (Wright, 1927). Elsewhere it is wider and more irregular and has numerous sprawling spurs extending from it. Some peaks in the northern section exceed 4000 feet in altitude.

FIG. 6.1 View westward from Blue Ridge showing spurs extending toward Shenandoah Valley in middle background. Massanutten Mountain is visible in distant background. (*Photo courtesy Virginia Department of Highways.*)

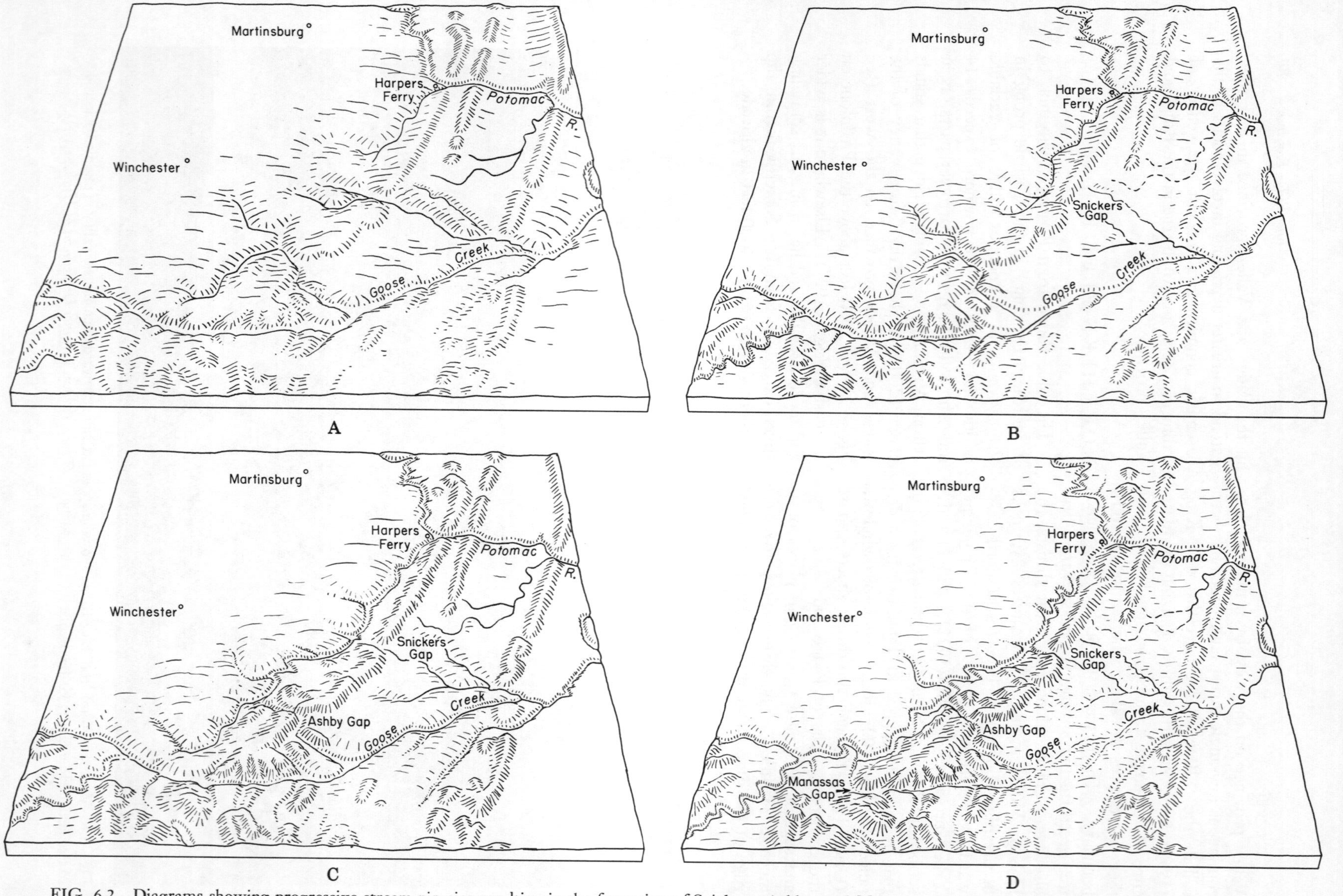

FIG. 6.2 Diagrams showing progressive stream piracies resulting in the formation of Snickers, Ashby, and Manassas wind gaps. (*Drawing by William J. Wayne.*)

## Stream Piracies

The northern Blue Ridge is broken into several segments by water gaps of the James and Potomac rivers and by such wind gaps as Manassas, Ashby, and Snickers. These three wind gaps bear witness to an interesting example of progressive stream piracy. The streams that formerly flowed through these gaps were pirated by a tributary of the Potomac River, the Shenandoah River, which extended itself southward along a weak rock belt west of the Blue Ridge and successively captured the headwaters of the streams that once flowed through the wind gaps (see Fig. 6.2). The altitudes of Snickers, Ashby, and Manassas gaps are approximately 1100, 1000, and 900 feet respectively. Thus there was a lowering of Ashby Gap of about 100 feet between the time of the capture of the stream through Snickers Gap and the time of the one through Ashby Gap, and another 100 feet of lowering of Manassas Gap between the capture of the stream in it and the conversion of Ashby Gap into a wind gap.

Altitudes along the northern Blue Ridge show a regional decrease from south to north, but this is not continuous and progressive, for there is a beveling of the ridges towards the streams which cross the Blue Ridge. This is particularly noticeable to either side of the Potomac River.

## SOUTHERN BLUE RIDGE

### Distinguishing Characteristics

The Southern Blue Ridge section differs from the northern section in five major respects: (1) it is higher; (2) it is much broader and in general does not display lineation of topography; (3) it displays a pronounced frontal scarp on the east side; (4) many outliers of the Blue Ridge lie east of it, in the Piedmont Plateau; and (5) drainage of this part of the Blue Ridge province is mainly to the northwest and ultimately to the Gulf of Mexico. The massive mountains and high peaks in the Tennessee-North Carolina region contrast strongly with the northern Blue Ridge. Mount Mitchell, the highest peak in the

eastern United States, has an altitude of 6684 feet, and Grandfather Mountain, almost at the edge of the Blue Ridge Escarpment, has an altitude of 5964 feet above sea level. It is claimed that 46 peaks in the Blue Ridge south of the Roanoke River exceed 6000 feet in altitude (Fenneman, 1938). Mt. Le Conte, located on a spur that projects westward from the main mountain mass, stands a mile above the town of Gatlinburg, Tennessee, 6 miles to the west of it.

### Mountain Terminology in the Southern Blue Ridge

Not all of the sprawling mountain mass of western North Carolina and eastern Tennessee is encompassed under the name Blue Ridge. In this area, the name Blue Ridge is largely restricted to the frontal scarp and the mountains along the drainage divide back of this scarp. The mountain group west of the Blue Ridge is commonly called the Unakas, but the connotation of this name varies considerably. The easternmost of these ranges is a mountain chain athwart the North Carolina-Tennessee boundary known as the Great Smoky Mountains. Other ranges included in the Unaka group, and west of the Great Smoky Mountains, are such ranges as the Chocolocco, Holston, Iron, Stone, and Rebecca ranges. These names are largely used locally and in more general terminology the ranges are included in the more comprehensive name of Unakas.

### Topographic Features

Despite their great height, for the eastern United States, the mountains of the southern Blue Ridge display subdued forms as compared with many mountain ranges in the western United States. Angularity of topography is notably lacking even along major valleys. Lineation of topography is also largely absent, except at the west, where the Cambrian Chilhowee rock series crops out.

*Origin of Coves.* Features known as coves are particularly common along the northwest side of the Great Smoky Mountains. They are rather smooth-floored, somewhat oval-shaped "valleys"

FIG. 6.3   The Blue Ridge in western North Carolina.   (*After W. A. White, Geol. Soc. Am. Bull.*, **61.**)

that rarely exceed 10 square miles in area. Cades, Wear, and Tuckaleechee coves are among the better known examples. Each of these coves is underlain by Ordovician limestone and shale, correlative with formations in the Tennessee Valley to the northwest, and is rimmed by rocks belonging to the Precambrian Ocoee series. It is thus apparent that the coves are windows in the Great Smoky thrust sheet and as such are inliers of Great Valley topography.

*Origin of Balds.* The term "bald" is applied locally to domal-like mountain tops that have grassy summits rather than tree covers. The absence of trees has never been satisfactorily explained. Certainly it is not a result of altitude too high for tree growth, nor is there any obvious pedologic explanation. As stated above (see p. 77), Willis (1889) suggested that the balds are remnants of a former erosion surface older than the floor of the Asheville Basin, but this interpretation is based on very meager evidence. Grassy, mountainous tracts in the midst of otherwise forested areas are not restricted to the Great Smoky-Unaka Mountains. The lawns of the White Mountains in New England (see p. 172) are examples of the same thing, and similar grassy tracts are found in the western United States on the subsummit erosion surface in the Bighorn and Beartooth Mountains (see p. 381). Possibly some ecological explanation

exists which relates to soil or drainage conditions existant during a prior geomorphic regime, but if such is true, the specific causes have not been recognized.

### Blue Ridge Escarpment

One of the most striking topographic features of the southern Blue Ridge is the frontal scarp which bounds it on the east (see Fig. 6.3). This scarp is 1500 feet high near Hillsville, Virginia, just north of the Virginia-North Carolina state line, and increases in height southwestward to 2500 feet near Blowing Rock, North Carolina, some 65 miles farther southwest.

*Theories As to Origin.* The cause of this sharp topographic break between the Piedmont Plateau and the Blue Ridge provinces has been sought by numerous geologists. Hayes and Campbell (1894) described it as an eroded monoclinal flexure in which the Piedmont was depressed and the Blue Ridge elevated. They considered the erosion surfaces below and above the scarp to be of the same age. Campbell, however, later changed his mind on this matter and in a letter to Fenneman attributed the escarpment to faulting.

Davis (1903) suggested that the scarp is not a result of warping or faulting or a reflection of differences in rocks' resistance in the Piedmont and Blue Ridge. He considered it the normal and expectable development of a stream divide between two peneplains whose rivers flowed greatly different distances to the sea. According to this interpretation the erosion surface developed by the streams flowing to the Atlantic Ocean "breaks joint" at the Blue Ridge Escarpment with the one developed by streams flowing to the Gulf of Mexico. It is obvious that if the gradients of graded river systems in the two opposed drainage basins were projected inland to their headwater areas in the Blue Ridge, the headwater levels of the Atlantic streams would lie far below those of the Gulf of Mexico streams. This explanation of the Blue Ridge scarp has been applied in two different ways. Davis thought that the two peneplains were of the same age and represented the Harrisburg cycle of erosion in each drainage basin, whereas Wright believed that they were of different ages.

Wright (1928, 1931), who probably devoted as much attention to the geomorphic history of the southern Appalachians as any other American geomorphologist, thought that Davis' theory might offer a partial explanation of the Blue Ridge Escarpment, but he correlated the erosion surface in the Blue Ridge with the Schooley peneplain and that in the Piedmont with the Harrisburg peneplain. Wright concluded, however, that the greater resistance to erosion of the rocks in the Blue Ridge Mountains also needed to be taken into account in any explanation of the Blue Ridge Escarpment. According to his views, the Blue Ridge Escarpment came into existence when two Schooley erosion surfaces developed at different levels in the Blue Ridge and Piedmont. This scarp was then further accentuated by much more extensive development of the Harrisburg surface in headwaters areas in the Piedmont than in the Blue Ridge.

White (1950) has revived the theory that the Blue Ridge front is a fault scarp. He attributed the scarp to reactivation during late Tertiary time of a normal fault, called by him the Blue Ridge border fault, which was supposed to have formed the western boundary of a Triassic basin that lay east of the Blue Ridge. Straightness

of the Blue Ridge front was considered strong evidence for faulting. White doubted the importance of differences in rock resistance in the two provinces as a factor in scarp development, and it must be admitted that significant variations between the basement complex rocks of the two provinces are not readily apparent.

Stose and Stose (1961) have questioned the validity of White's explanation of the Blue Ridge scarp. They pointed out that in the area where the presumed Triassic basin was supposed to have been the rocks are gneisses and schists and contain no Triassic sediments, diabase dikes, or flows, as found in nearly all Triassic areas of the Appalachians. They preferred Davis' theory of two levels of the Schooley peneplain in the Blue Ridge and Piedmont as an explanation of the escarpment.

The straightness of the Blue Ridge scarp is in places impressive, particularly between the Roanoke and Catawba rivers, but even along this stretch outliers of the Blue Ridge in the Piedmont do exist, and farther south they are numerous. These outliers suggest that the front of the scarp may have been considerably farther east in Tertiary time. Thus, even if the scarp was initiated by faulting, it would seem doubtful that the base of the scarp lies near the fault.

### Drainage Relationships

The Roanoke River is the southernmost stream to flow eastward through the Blue Ridge; south of it most of the drainage is to the northwest and ultimately to the Gulf of Mexico. Thus the drainage divide at the south is very close to the eastern edge of the Blue Ridge, and streams that descend to the Piedmont are short and steep compared with those which flow westward.

*Piracies along Blue Ridge Escarpment.* Conditions are even more favorable for stream piracy along the southern Blue Ridge front than at the north, because of the pronounced differences in stream gradients on the two sides of the divide. The Roanoke River now drains a small area west of the Blue Ridge that is about 200 square miles in extent. Most of this area was formerly part of the drainage basin of New River; it was captured by the Roanoke River at the close of the Harrisburg erosion cycle. It appears likely that the Roanoke River during the Harrisburg cycle headed a short distance west of the Blue Ridge in the Ridge and Valley province. Thus two Harrisburg levels existed in the Great Valley, a high one for New River drainage and a lower one for the Roanoke drainage. A steep escarpment about 600 feet high marks the junction of the two base levels of erosion. Inequality of stream gradients on the two sides of this escarpment has permitted the headwaters of the Roanoke to be extended westward into the former drainage basin of New River.

A more spectacular example of stream piracy was that which led to the development of the Linville Gorge in western North Carolina. Linville River heads on Grandfather Mountain and flows southwestward in a broad valley back of the Blue Ridge front. The altitude of this part of its valley is in harmony with the valleys of the Toe, Watauga, and other streams which flow westward from the Blue Ridge Escarpment. Turning eastward from its southwesterly course, the Linville River abandons its old perched valley and descends over falls and rapids in a steep-sided gorge for a distance of 15 miles to enter the Piedmont. The Linville Gorge, just west of the Blue Ridge-Piedmont boundary, is 1700 feet deep. Unquestionably the Linville River has been diverted from a former westerly course to an easterly one by a stream that headed at the Blue Ridge divide and flowed eastward into the Piedmont.

*History of New River.* Two streams, the New and the Tennessee, carry most of the drainage of the southern Blue Ridge. New River is unique in that it is the only Appalachian stream that flows directly westward across the Ridge and Valley and Appalachian Plateau provinces. The Tennessee River follows the Ridge and Valley province southwestward for a long distance before it finally turns westward across the southern end of the Appalachian Plateau toward the Ohio River. New River is badly misnamed, for it ought to be called "Old River"; it is proba-

bly one of the oldest rivers in the eastern United States. It certainly dates far back into Tertiary time and possibly beyond that. It was a part of the Teays River system (see p. 139) and likely comes as near as any existing drainage line in the eastern United States to being in essentially the same position that it had in Tertiary time.

New River heads near the crest of the Blue Ridge, near Blowing Rock, North Carolina, 8 miles west of Grandfather Mountain, at an altitude near 3800 feet. Within 10 miles from its source New River has descended 750 feet and is flowing in a broad open valley slightly below the level of the Harrisburg erosion surface. For the remaining distance to the Ridge and Valley province New River flows in an entrenched meandering course with an average gradient of 8.5 feet per mile. The river then flows 115 miles across the Ridge and Valley province to cover a straight-line distance of 40 miles. It then enters the Appalachian Plateau, across which it has developed one of the deepest gorges of eastern North America (see Fig. 8.7). Near Gauley Bridge, West Virginia, it is joined by the Gauley River to form the Kanawha River, which flows on to the Ohio River near Pt. Pleasant, West Virginia. The only part of the New-Kanawha river system that is "new" is that from Nitro, West Virginia, where the Kanawha leaves the route of the ancient Teays and flows northwestward to Pt. Pleasant on the Ohio River. This part of the New River course apparently was established as a result of diversion of the Teays River from its course by an early Pleistocene ice sheet.

The divide in the Blue Ridge between westward-flowing New River and the southeastward-flowing Yadkin is at an altitude of 3775 feet (Fridley, 1950). As a result of the unequal stream gradients on its two sides this divide is being pushed westward. How far east it may have been originally is uncertain, but Fridley considered it possible that at one time it was near the Fall Line, and that westward migration of the divide caused reduction of part of the ancestral Blue Ridge to form the Piedmont Plateau. This is an extreme view as to where the eastern edge of Blue Ridge was originally, but good grounds exist for believing that the divide between Atlantic and Gulf of Mexico drainage has shifted significantly westward.

## EROSION SURFACES

### Pre-Harrisburg Surfaces

In the northern Blue Ridge suggestions of former erosion surfaces are found in accordant summit levels, but these are not extensive enough to be conclusive evidence of former peneplanation. In the southern Blue Ridge section, however, more extensive remnants of former erosion surfaces are preserved. The suggestion made by Willis (see p. 77) that the numerous peaks whose summits fall close to 6000 feet may be remnants of an ancient erosion surface that possibly correlated with the so-called Fall Zone peneplain has to be viewed with extreme skepticism. Divide areas at altitudes ranging from 3000 to 4000 feet have been called the Cretaceous, Kittatinny, Subsummit, and Upland peneplain and correlated by many workers in the area with the Schooley surface in the northern Appalachians.

### Harrisburg Erosion Surface

*Local Straths.* Evidence of the Harrisburg cycle, which is so extensively developed in the Piedmont, is mainly restricted to several high-lying mountain-rimmed basins in the southern Blue Ridge province which represent straths that are mainly developed along westward-flowing streams and are notably higher than corresponding erosion surfaces in the Great Valley and Piedmont. This difference in altitude might be attributed to one or more of three possible causes: (1) greater remoteness from the sea, (2) the effect of a hard rock barrier between them and the Great Valley, and (3) differential uplift. Wright (1931) explained the higher altitudes of the mountain basins as due partly to greater remoteness from the sea but more particularly to the effect of a hard rock barrier between them and the Great Valley.

The largest and best developed of the local high-level straths is found along the French Broad River and its tributaries in the Asheville Basin (see Fig. 6.4). Willis (1889), who first described this basin, considered it an older erosion surface than the floor of the Great Valley, but Wright (1931) has presented rather convincing arguments to the effect that the two surfaces are correlative. The floor of the Asheville Basin is characteristically between 2300 and 2400 feet in altitude, and the French Broad River leaves it at an altitude of 2100 feet and flows northwestward through a gorge to enter the Great Valley at an altitude of 1200 feet. Wright thought that not only did the hard rock barrier account for the difference in altitude of the Harrisburg erosion surface in the two areas, but it also explained why the Harrisburg surface had been so well preserved in the Asheville Basin since uplift.

About 20 miles southeast of Asheville around Hendersonville, North Carolina, is another strath developed at altitudes around 2400 feet. Other examples of similar high-level mountain-rimmed basins whose floors seem to correlate with the Harrisburg erosion surface are the Hiwasse, Pigeon, and Ocoee basins. A few of the Harrisburg straths lie east of the present drainage divide as a result of the stream piracies that have taken place along the eastern margin of the Blue Ridge. The Linnville Basin is an example of such.

### Lack of Post-Harrisburg Surfaces

It is doubtful if any post-Harrisburg subcycles of erosion, other than the present one, can be identified in the Blue Ridge. Wright, after many years of study in the southern Appalachians, concluded that even in the Valley and Ridge province the so-called Coosa cycle is highly questionable. He attributed the lower topography in the Coosa Basin to more rapid lowering of the land by solution on limestone terrain. Concerning the southern Appalachians he stated (1942): "No bench or terrace was found in any of the valleys of the southern Appalachians which is persistent enough to indicate more than one uplift since the close of the Harrisburg cycle."

FIG. 6.4   The Asheville Basin.   (*Photo courtesy Asheville Chamber of Commerce.*)

This statement may apply to the Blue Ridge province, but as we shall see later, it is questionably applicable to the Ridge and Valley and Appalachian Plateaus provinces.

## REFERENCES CITED

Davis, W. M. (1903). The stream contest along the Blue Ridge, *Geog. Soc. Philadelphia Bull.*, **3**, 213–244.

Fenneman, N. M. (1938). *Physiography of Eastern United States*, McGraw-Hill Book Company, New York, 714 pp.

Fridley, H. M. (1950). The geomorphic history of the New-Kanawha river system, *W. Va. Geol. Surv. Rept. Invest.* 7, 12 pp.

Hayes, C. W., and M. R. Campbell (1894). Geomorphology of the southern Appalachians, *Nat. Geog. Mag.*, **6**, 63–126.

Keith, Arthur (1927). The Great Smoky overthrust, *Geol. Soc. Am. Bull.*, **38**, 154–55 (abs.).

King, P. B. (1950). Tectonic framework of southeastern United States, *Am. Assoc. Petroleum Geologists Bull.*, **34**, 635–671.

—— (1955). A geologic section across the southern Appalachians: An outline of the geology in the segment in Tennessee, North Carolina, and South Carolina, in *Guides to Southeastern Geology*, Geol. Soc. Am., 332–373.

Oriel, S. S. (1951). Structure of the Hot Springs window, North Carolina, *Am. Jour. Sci.*, **249**, 1–30.

Stose, G. W., and A. J. Stose (1951). Blue Ridge front—A fault scarp, *Geol. Soc. Am. Bull.*, **62**, 1371–1374.

White, W. A. (1950). Blue Ridge front—a fault scarp, *Geol. Soc. Am. Bull.*, **61**, 1309–1346.

Willis, Bailey (1889). Round about Asheville, *Nat. Geog. Mag.*, **1**, 291–300.

Wright, F. J. (1927). The Blue Ridge of southern Virginia and western North Carolina, *Denison Univ. Bull., Jour. Sci. Labs.*, **22**, 116–132.

—— (1928). The erosional history of the Blue Ridge, *Denison Univ. Bull., Jour. Sci. Labs.*, **23**, 321–344.

—— (1931). The older Appalachians of the South, *Denison Univ. Bull., Jour. Sci. Labs.*, **26**, 143–250.

—— (1942). Erosional history of the southern Appalachians, *Jour. Geomorph.*, **5**, 151–161.

### ADDITIONAL REFERENCES

Bloomer, R. O., and H. J. Werner (1955). Geology of the Blue Ridge region in central Virginia, *Geol. Soc. Am. Bull.*, **66**, 579–606.

Neuman, R. B. (1951). The Great Smoky fault, *Am. Jour. Sci.*, **249**, 740–754.

Nickelsen, R. P. (1956). Geology of the Blue Ridge near Harpers Ferry, West Virginia, *Geol. Soc. Am. Bull.*, **67**, 239–270.

Smith, H. T. U. and A. P. Smith (1945). Periglacial rock streams in the Blue Ridge area, *Geol. Soc. Am. Bull.*, **56**, 1198 (abs.).

Whitaker, J. C. (1955). Geology of Catoctin Mountain, Maryland and Virginia, *Geol. Soc. Am. Bull.*, **66**, 435–462.

Woodward, H. P. (1932). Geology and mineral resources of the Roanoke Area, Virginia, *Va. Geol. Surv. Bull.*, **34**, 7–24.

# 7

# Ridge and Valley Province

## GENERAL DESCRIPTION

The Ridge and Valley province extends for a distance of 1200 miles, from the St. Lawrence Lowland to Alabama. Its width varies from about 14 miles at the New York-New Jersey state line to 80 miles along a line between Harrisburg and Williamsport, Pennsylvania. The province has sometimes been called the "Folded Appalachians," but this designation is not entirely appropriate because folding extends beyond the province to both the east and the west, and in some parts thrust faulting is as diagnostic as folding. Involved in the folds and faults of the Ridge and Valley province are 30,000 to 40,000 feet of Paleozoic sediments of predominately early Paleozoic age, although at the north, in Pennsylvania, rocks as young as Pennsylvanian are involved extensively in the folds (see Fig. 7.1).

The Ridge and Valley province displays many striking geomorphic features, of which some of the most outstanding are: (1) marked parallelism of ridges and valleys, commonly in a northeast-southwest direction; (2) conspicuous influence of alternating strong and weak strata upon topographic forms; (3) a few major transverse streams with notable development of subsequent streams, giving to many areas a trellis drainage pattern; (4) many ridges which display enough accordance of summit level to suggest that their crests may represent former erosion surfaces; and (5) hundreds of water gaps through hard rock ridges (see Fig. 7.2) and equal numbers of wind gaps which testify to innumerable past cases of stream diversion.

The Ridge and Valley province may be though of as an assemblage of valleys or valley low lands surmounted by narrow, linear, often even-topped ridges; the proportion of valleys and ridges varies notably. Most of the province may be divided longitudinally into an eastern part, which is dominantly valley and is not crossed by a single transverse ridge along its entire length from the St. Lawrence River to Alabama, and a western part, which is characterized by linear sandstone ridges separated by limestone and shale valleys. In the Hudson-Champlain section at the north the separation into valley and ridge areas breaks down, for here there are no ridges. In Virginia, the eastern valley part is split longitudinally by 50-mile-long Massanutten Mountain.

The valley portion of the province on the east is commonly thought of as a continuous 1200-mile lowland extending from the St. Lawrence Lowland to Alabama, but it is actually an assemblage of valleys whose floors vary in altitude from 400 feet to 2400 feet. In following this lowland longitudinally a person would cross numerous major stream divides. The eastern lowland part is called the Appalachian or Great Valley. Different parts of the Appalachian Valley have their local names, and from south to north the following individual valleys are recognized; the Coosa, Valley of Eastern Tennessee, Shenandoah, Hagerstown, Cumberland, Lebanon, Walkill, Hudson, and Champlain. The width of the valley portion of the province varies from 2 miles near Buchanan, just north of Roanoke, Virginia, to 50 miles at the extreme south.

The western half of the province has in it a

FIG. 7.1   Rock structure displayed by mining of coal along strike of beds, near Tremont, Pennsylvania.   (*Photo by John S. Shelton.*)

variable number of ridges. Between the Delaware and Hudson rivers there is only one ridge, Kittatinny Mountain, as it is called in New Jersey, or Shawangunk Mountain, in New York. Elsewhere, as in the Staunton-Monterey area in Virginia, there may be as many as 8 or 10 linear ridges. The Appalachian ridges do not extend quite so far south as does the Appalachian Valley.

## GEOLOGIC STRUCTURE

The term "Appalachian type of structure" has sometimes been applied to the structures of the Ridge and Valley province. This is hardly appropriate, for the Ridge and Valley structures represent only one phase of Appalachian structure. Furthermore, the type of structure in the Ridge and Valley province varies considerably. At the north, closed folding with minor amounts of faulting is characteristic, but southward faults become more common. Near the latitude of Roanoke, Virginia, the folds become compressed, overturned, and broken by thrust faulting to the northwest (Rodgers, 1953). Some thrust faults are present in Pennsylvania, but they are an exception rather than the rule. Some geologists believe that thrusts are just as common at the north as at the south but are at depth, whereas at the south they have reached the surface. Greater compression at the south than north is indicated by the fact that south of the James River the folded belt is reduced to about half the width that it has in Pennsylvania without significant decrease in the number of fold ridges.

Faults are particularly numerous in Tennessee. Most of the faults here appear to be shallow and do not involve rocks of the basement complex. Rocks as old as middle Cambrian are brought to the surface along the faults, but no early Cambrian or Precambrian rocks are so affected. It thus appears that faulting was confined to those sediments above the basement complex that could be sheared off and piled one on another in shingle-like fashion (Rich, 1934).

Typical of the many faults in the Virginia-Tennessee area is the Pulaski fault (Cooper, 1946). The name "Pulaski fault" has been applied to what appears to be a fault zone which is over 200 miles long and in which there has been horizontal displacement of at least 11 miles and perhaps 20 miles. The sole of the thrust is mainly the Rome or Elbrook formations of Cambrian age. A thick zone of tectonite is associated with the fault. Initially the Pulaski thrust was a rather flat surface, but it was later folded, and erosion of the folded thrust sheet has produced numerous windows and klippen.

Many of the early diagrams showing "Appalachian type of structure" depicted the structures as a series of alternating open anticlines and synclines. Such structures may be encountered locally, but they are by no means characteristic. Many of the folds are closed; many are overturned; many have been thrust-faulted,

FIG. 7.2    View of Delaware Watergap, looking upstream.    (*Photo by John S. Shelton.*)

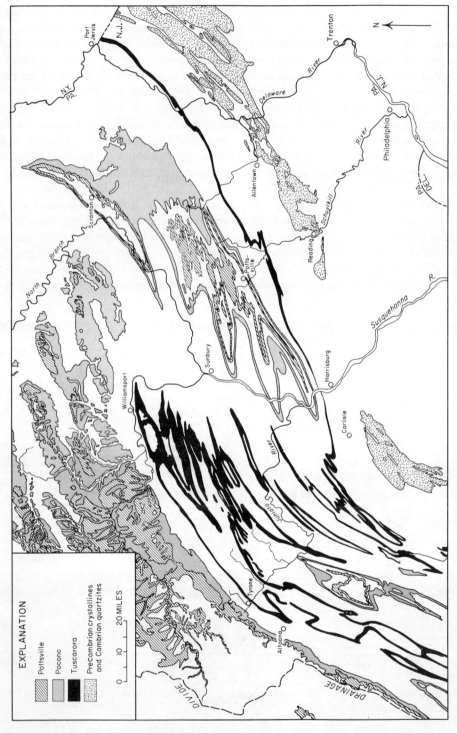

FIG. 7.3    Pattern made by major ridge-making formations in Pennsylvania and a portion of New Jersey.    *(After H. D. Thompson, Anns. N. Y. Acad. Sci., 52.)*

with accompanying development of secondary folds in the overthrust sheets; and most of the folds are plunging folds.

### Ridge-Forming Beds

Involved in the folds are alternating weak and strong beds.   Certain geologically strong formations repeat themselves and are widespread ridge makers (see Fig. 7.3).   At the north, ridges develop on the Pottsville sandstone of Pennsylvanian age, the Pocono sandstone of Mississippian age, the Oriskany and Chemung sandstones of Devonian age, and the Tuscarora, Oswego, and Oneida sandstones of Silurian age.   At the south, common ridge makers are the Pennsylvanian Pottsville formation, the Mississippian Ft. Payne chert, and the Silurian Clinch and Rockwood formations.   Locally the Cambro-Ordovician Knox dolomite and other resistant formations give rise to ridges.

### Topographic Expression of Folds

Present Ridge and Valley topography is a result of truncation of folds during several erosion cycles.   Differential erosion of the weak and strong beds has brought out the structure in striking fashion.   Six possible topographic expressions of the geologic structure are commonly encountered; anticlinal valleys, anticlinal ridges, synclinal valleys, synclinal ridges, homoclinal valleys, and homoclinal ridges.   The topography on a particular fold depends on whether the erosion surface which cuts across the fold passes above, through, or below resistant beds in the crest of the fold.

## DIVISION OF PROVINCE INTO SECTIONS

The Ridge and Valley province has been divided into Northern, Middle, and Southern sections (Fenneman, 1928).   The Northern section, also known as the Hudson-Champlain section, stretches from the Delaware River to the St. Lawrence Lowland; the Middle section

reaches from the Delaware River southward to a little beyond New River, and the Southern section extends southward from near New River to where the Ridge and Valley province ends against the East Gulf Coastal Plain.

### Hudson-Champlain Section

*Major Characteristics.*   The Hudson-Champlain section differs from the other sections in four significant respects: (1) it is much narrower, (2) longitudinal ridges are notably fewer and are entirely lacking in the northern two-thirds of the section, (3) major drainage lines are longitudinal rather than transverse, and (4) it has been glaciated.

Kittatinny-Shawangunk Mountain, a ridge of Lower Silurian sandstone, lies near the west side of the section and is separated from the Appalachian Plateaus by the narrow Port Jervis Trough developed on Devonian limestone; Schunemunk Mountain, a short ridge of Devonian sandstone, lies near the east side of the section.   These two mountains are the most conspicuous ridges found between the Delaware and Hudson Rivers.   Although most of the drainage of the Hudson-Champlain section is longitudinal, the Hudson River where it leaves the province crosses the narrow extension of New England geology known as the Reading prong and in its course through the Highlands (see Fig. 9.10) is a transverse stream.

The Hudson-Champlain section is bordered along most of its extent by conspicuously higher topography on both the east and the west.   The only exception to this is where it is in contact with the Mohawk Valley.   On the west the Pocono, Catskill, and Adirondack Mountains stand well above the lowland, and on the east the Highlands of the Hudson, Taconic Mountains, and Green Mountains also overlook the Hudson-Champlain Lowland.

*Geology of Section.*   Much of the Hudson-Champlain Lowland between the Delaware and Hudson Rivers is developed on the Ordovician Hudson River shale.   Beginning near where the northward-flowing Walkill River enters the

FIG. 7.4   Helderberg Escarpment, looking southwest near Indian Ladder, New York.   (*Photo by N. H. Darton, U. S. Geol. Survey.*)

Hudson River near Kingston, New York, a distinct difference in the geology on the east and west sides of the Hudson Lowland becomes apparent.   On the west side of the valley are the Hudson River shales and Devonian limestones.   The Devonian limestones are responsible for a prominent escarpment known as the Helderberg Escarpment (see Fig. 7.4).   East of the Hudson River the rocks are mainly slates of the so-called Slate Belt (Dale, 1899).   The boundary between the two types of rocks has long been known as Logan's Line.   According to some geologists it is a boundary between unmetamorphosed and metamorphosed rocks and marks the western edge of the alleged Taconic Thrust (see p. 159), the reality of which, like that of the Marctic Thrust, has long been a subject of dispute among American geologists.

Regardless of whether or not a fault boundary separates the east and west sides of this part of the Hudson Valley, a difference in the landscape on the two sides of the valley is evident. West of the Hudson River, marked lineation in the topography reflects folds similar to those farther south, in Pennsylvania and Virginia, but here developed on a miniature scale.   Ridge heights are measured here in tens of feet rather than hundreds, and ridge lengths in miles rather than tens of miles.

Three diverse structural provinces come together in the Lake Champlain region.   On the west is the Adirondack Mountains, a dome of Precambrian rocks; on the east are the folds and thrust sheets of the Green Mountains; between these two regions are the lower Paleozoic rocks of the Champlain Lowland, broken by numerous north-south normal faults whose downthrown sides are on the east.   These faults do not have particular topographic expression in the Champlain Lowland, but they extend westward into the Adirondack Mountains and there are reflected in the topography.

*Effects of Glaciation.* To what extent glaciation has affected the topography of the Hudson Valley is difficult to say. Glacial erosion may have reduced the relief somewhat, and it seems probable that the pronounced lineation of topography reflects the effects of differential glacial erosion upon weak and strong beds in the folded structures. The Slate Belt east of the Hudson River either lacks lineation or shows it to a lesser degree; the texture of the topography here is coarser than at the west, and the hills, instead of being streamlined, are rounded knolls resembling a type of glaciated terrain sometimes described as mammilated topography. It has been suggested (Fenneman, 1938) that lack of lineation on the east reflects a more uniform lithology there.

North of where the Hudson River crosses the Highlands glacial deposits are evident along its valley. These materials consist of ground moraine, outwash sand and gravel, lacustrine silts and clays, and kame terrace deposits. The silts and clays were deposited in a body of water that has been called Lake Albany (Woodworth, 1905). Woodworth believed that Lake Albany began as an ice marginal lake along the retreating ice front and that as soon as the ice front had retreated to a position north of Albany drainage from Lake Iroquois (see p. 235) came into the lake to form Lake Albany proper. Later, with the melting of the ice within the Champlain Lowland, Lake Albany became confluent with a body of water here. The former shore line of Lake Albany is indicated by the altitude of deltas of the larger streams which flowed into the Lake. Whether Lake Albany was a freshwater lake or an embayment of the sea is uncertain. Fairchild (1919) held that when the ice withdrew from the Hudson Valley the land was low enough that marine waters extended up the valley first as an estuary and later as a strait that connected with the St. Lawrence Valley. It is perhaps more commonly believed that marine waters did not extend north of the Highlands and that Lake Albany formed as a freshwater lake in the area where the Mohawk River joins the Hudson River.

The site of Lake Albany is marked by clays known as the "Albany brick clays." Glacial meltwaters from the Mohawk Valley built a large delta known as the Mohawk delta eastward into the Hudson Valley. The site of this delta is now marked by a sandy plain whose surface is dotted with numerous low dunes built of reworked outwash.

### Lake Champlain History

Lake Champlain, which lies between the Adirondack Mountains and the Green Mountains, drains to the north to the St. Lawrence River via the Richelieu River. On either side of the lake is terraced lake plain that marks former levels of Lake Champlain.

When in the late stages of Wisconsin deglaciation the ice had withdrawn into the Champlain Lowland, there came into existence a lake called Lake Vermont (Chapman, 1937) which was the predecessor of present Lake Champlain. Four stages of lake history have been recognized (see Fig. 7.5): (1) the Coveville stage, with an outlet to the south at Coveville; (2) a lower level Fort Ann stage, with an outlet at Fort Ann; (3) an upper marine stage, marked by an invasion of marine waters from the St. Lawrence Lowland; and (4) a subsiding marine stage, consisting of five phases known as the Beekmantown, Port Kent, Burlington, Plattsburg, and Port Henry phases. This complex final stage corresponds to what has been called the Champlain Sea. It was terminated when continuing rise of the land at the north established the Richelieu threshold at the north end of the Champlain Lowland and brought into existence the present Lake Champlain.

### Middle Section

*Extent and Boundaries.* The Middle section of the Ridge and Valley province extends from the Delaware River at the north to the divide between the New and Tennessee rivers in southwestern Virginia. Throughout its length the Middle section is bounded on the west by the prominent escarpment that forms the eastern edge of the Appalachian Plateaus. This escarpment, here known as the Allegheny Front, attains a height

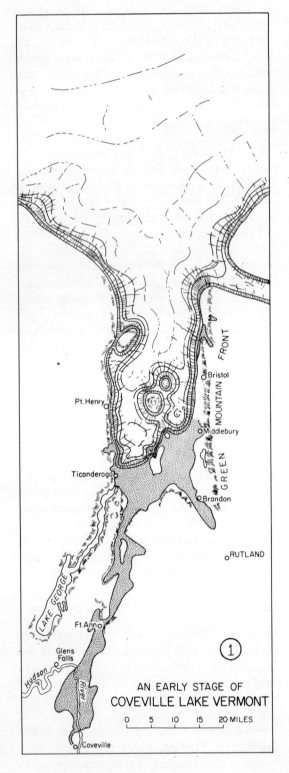
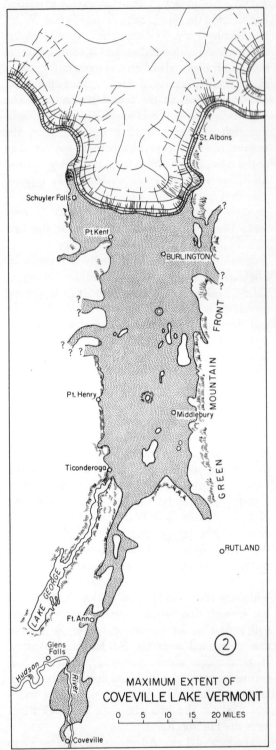

FIG. 7.5   Stages preceding development of present Lake

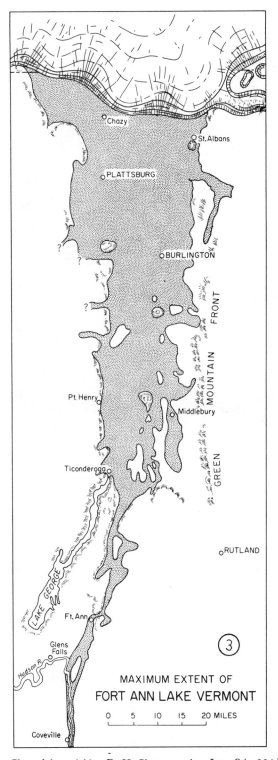

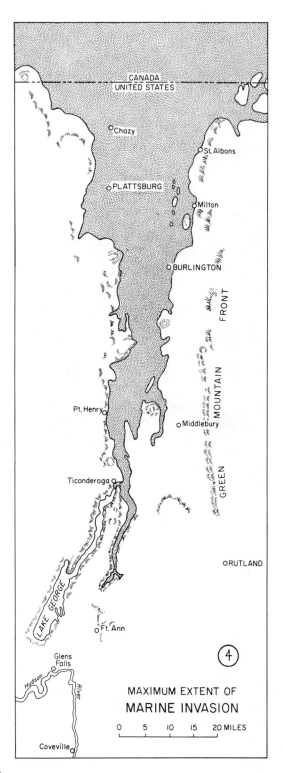

Champlain. (*After D. H. Chapman, Am. Jour. Sci.,* **234.**)

FIG. 7.6  A sigmoidal or "Z" fold south of Hollidaysburg, Pennsylvania, looking southeast.  (*Photo by John S. Shelton.*)

of 1800 feet near Altoona, Pennsylvania, where the Pennsylvania Railroad climbs it in a striking series of horseshoe bends.   This height is maintained essentially as far south as the Maryland state boundary.  The Allegheny Front in this area is capped with the Mississippian Pocono sandstone.   The Blue Ridge to the east is not so continuous as the Allegheny Front, for between the Susquehanna and Schuylkill rivers it practically disappears, and the Ridge and Valley province here abuts against the Piedmont Plateau.

*The Zig Zag Mountains.*   A strongly folded belt, which in central Pennsylvania is as much as 80 miles wide, terminates at the north in eastern Pennsylvania in what in the early days were called the Zig Zag Mountains (see Fig. 7.6) from

the pattern produced by the strongly compressed plunging folds.  Here deep synclines have lowered the rocks sufficiently below former baselevels of erosion that the Pennsylvanian Pottsville and Mississippian Pocono formations are the common ridge makers, rather than the older Paleozoic sandstones encountered farther south.   Ridges on the Pottsville and Pocono formations often parallel each other with a valley on the Mississippian Mauch Chunk shale between them.   The Mauch Chunk valleys are usually conspicuous because of their red soils.

An unusual structural feature in eastern Pennsylvania is the synclinal Wyoming Valley, a 40-mile-long valley like a finger pointed into the Allegheny Plateau.   In it are located the two largest of the cities associated with the anthracite coal fields of eastern Pennsylvania, Scranton and Wilkes-Barre.

*Area between Susquehanna and James Rivers.* If any part of the Ridge and Valley province can be said to illustrate best the structure and topography commonly associated with this province, it is the stretch between the Susquehanna and James Rivers. Here is found the nearest approach to regular repetition of similar folds; the mountain ridges are most numerous and most nearly parallel (see Fig. 7.7), and the mountains are the most nearly even-crested and continuous. Present also is a broad valley lowland on the east which is as much as 40 miles wide. Of course, no part of the Ridge and Valley province is more "typical" than any other, and it is the

great variety of topography found here that makes the province so attractive to a geomorphologist.

*Nittany Valley and Environs.* Extending northeastward from Altoona, Pennsylvania, for 100 miles is the Nittany Valley, one of the outstanding anticlinal valleys of the province. Nittany Valley is 30 miles wide and is enclosed by homoclinal ridges of Silurian Tuscarora sandstone. The Nittany Arch, along which this valley is developed, is the westernmost fold in this part of the Ridge and Valley province and is one of the largest in the entire province. It is overturned to the northwest (Fox, 1950), so that some of the beds on its northwest flank approximate the direction of dip of the beds on the southeast flank. Nittany Valley is floored mainly on

FIG. 7.7  Alternating ridges and valleys, looking toward Harrisburg, Pennsylvania, from over Port Royal.  Juniata River in the foreground.  (*Photo by John S. Shelton.*)

Ordovician limestone. The Juniata River cuts across the southern end of the fold, but most of the drainage in the valley is longitudinal. Bald Eagle Mountain flanks Nittany Valley on the northwest, and this homoclinal ridge of Tuscarora sandstone is continuous from near Altoona to Williamsport, Pennsylvania, a distance of 140 miles. Between Bald Eagle Mountain and the Allegheny Front is a narrow valley on the Devonian Helderberg limestone, which is followed by northeastward-flowing Bald Eagle Creek for some 60 miles.

Southeast of Nittany Valley and parallel to it is another anticlinal valley, Kishacoquillas Valley. Except for being smaller it is essentially a repetition of Nittany Valley as to stratigraphy, structure, and topography. Between the two anticlinal valleys is the Broadtop syncline with its plateau-like topography. Eastward from here as far as the Great Valley is a succession of ridges and valleys in which ridges rather than valleys dominate the landscape. Most of the higher ridges are on the Tuscarora sandstone, but the Devonian Oriskany sandstone is responsible for some secondary ones. So many of the higher ridges have altitudes near 1900 to 2000 feet that there is a suggestion that their crests may be remnants of a former extensive erosion surface.

*The Great Valley.* The northernmost portion of the Great Valley in the Middle section is known as the Cumberland Valley; this valley grades southwestward into the Hagerstown Valley, which in turn connects with the Shenandoah Valley, in Virginia. As far south as the marked constriction of the Great Valley near Buchanan, Virginia, no striking difference exists in the Great Valley between Pennsylvania and Virginia. One minor difference exists in Virginia: near the middle of the valley is synclinal Massanutten Mountain, which divides the Shenandoah Valley longitudinally into eastern and western parts which are drained by the south and north forks of the Shenandoah River respectively.

*Burkes Garden.* Near the southwest end of the Middle section of the Ridge and Valley province is Burkes Garden. This striking topographic feature (Cooper, 1934) is an elliptical basin that is almost completely rimmed by Garden Mountain (see Fig. 7.8), a high ridge of the Silurian Clinch sandstone. The Ordovician limestones beneath the floor of Burkes Garden have influenced the development of a drainage pattern that might be described as centripetal-karst. The streams form a centripetal pattern which converges on an outlet through a watergap at the north side of Garden Mountain, but many of the streams before reaching the central part of the basin become sinking creeks. The structure on which Burkes Garden has developed is an elliptical dome or doubly pitching anticline, not essentially different from the many other anticlinal structures in the province except that it is somewhat shorter and more oval in form.

*Development of Karst.* The Appalachian Valley and most of the lesser limestone valleys exhibit some degree of karst development. The Great Valley is one of the major karst regions of the United States. Such well known commercial caverns as Luray, Endless, Shenandoah, and Massanutten are found in the Shenandoah Valley portion in Virginia. Sinkholes, swallow holes and sinking creeks are present in great numbers. Lapiés is probably better displayed here than in any karst region of the United States, because the steeply dipping limestone beds on the flanks of the valleys often have so little soil cover that the solutionally corrugated surface of the limestone is well exposed. Valley and Ridge karst is of particular interest to one concerned with the evolution of caves, because of their development here in steeply dipping rocks, in contrast to the nearly horizontal bedding in the karst regions of Indiana, Kentucky, and Florida. Davies (1959) has shown that cavern floors in the Appalachian Valley are developed across the steeply dipping limestone beds at levels marking former positions of the water table related to terrace benches present along major valleys. The vertical intervals between cavern levels correspond closely with the intervals between the stream terraces.

*Natural Bridge.* Two karst features in this region that have attracted more than local attention are Natural Bridge and Natural Tunnel, in

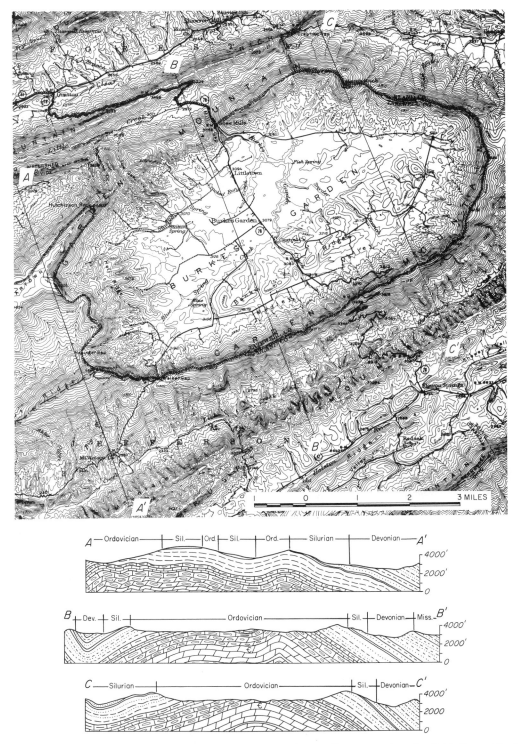

FIG. 7.8   Topographic map of Burkes Garden with structure sections.   (*Structure sections after B. N. Cooper, Va. Geol. Surv. Bull.* 60.)

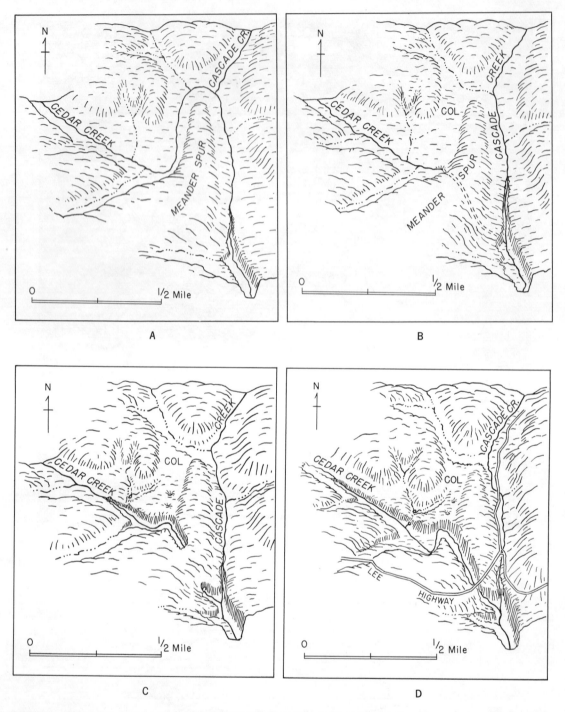

FIG. 7.9   Postulated stages in the development of Natural Bridge, Virginia, as a roof pendant of a subterranean cutoff. (*After C. A. Malott and R. R. Shrock, Am. Jour. Sci.*, **219**.)

FIG. 7.10 Natural Tunnel, Virginia.

Virginia. Natural Bridge is located 14 miles southwest of Lexington, Virginia; it is a rock span 90 feet long, 50 to 150 feet wide, and about 50 feet thick that stands about 200 feet above the narrow gorge of Cedar Creek. Thomas Jefferson, who owned Natural Bridge for a time, attributed it, in keeping with the geologic thinking of his time, to some great "convulsion of nature." Gilmer, in 1818, suggested that the bridge was a product of solution of limestone but was not specific as to how solution created the bridge. It is now recognized that the rock span is the remnant of the roof of a subterranean passageway that has nearly been deroofed. The main argument in recent years has been as to whether the subterranean passageway developed through subterranean stream piracy or as a subterranean cutoff.

Malott and Shrock (1930) advanced the theory that Cedar Creek, as a result of a subterranean cutoff beneath a meander spur, developed a karst tunnel which was gradually deroofed except for the part left as Natural Bridge (see Fig. 7.9). Woodward (1936) thought, however, that Natural Bridge could be more logically explained by subterranean stream piracy. According to his interpretation the upper part of Cedar Creek originally flowed eastward as a part of Poague Run drainage and the lower part of present Cedar Creek was a short stream that was the predecessor of the present Cascade Creek. Both streams were tributaries to the James River, but it was only 3 miles to the James via Cascade Creek, whereas it was 15 miles via Poague Run. As a consequence there was as much as a 200-foot difference in the levels of the two streams in the Natural Bridge area. This difference in elevation made possible diversion of the head-waters of Poague Creek via an underground route to Cascade Creek. Wright (1936) found the evidence presented by Malott and Shrock for development of a subterranean cutoff unconvincing and favored Woodward's view that Natural Bridge was a result of subterranean stream piracy.

*Natural Tunnel.* Natural Tunnel is located in Scott County, Virginia, about 3 miles north of Clinchport. It is located well toward the western tip of Virginia and actually is in the southern section of the Ridge and Valley Province, but because of its similarity to Natural Bridge it seems appropriate to discuss it here. Just as Natural Bridge is unique in being used as a highway bridge, Natural Tunnel is used as a railway tunnel by a branch of the Southern Railway (see Fig. 7.10). Its 900-foot length is about ten times that of Natural Bridge; it averages 75 feet in height and 130 feet in width. Stock Creek, a tributary of the Clinch River, flows through the tunnel. As with Natural Bridge there is disagreement as to the specific method by which the underground passage of Natural Tunnel was formed.

### Southern Section

*Distinguishing Characteristics.* The Southern section of the Ridge and Valley province is not so strikingly different from the Middle section as is the Hudson-Champlain section, but it displays enough differences, even if only of degree, to justify its recognition as a separate section. In at least four respects the topography of this section differs from that of the Middle section. (1) Thrust faults are more numerous (see Fig. 7.11), and as a result the regional structure is prevailingly homoclinal with a preponderance of southeast dips; consequently, homoclinal

rather than anticlinal and synclinal ridges are characteristic. (2) Ridges are not so numerous as in the Middle section, and in the latitude of Knoxville, Tennessee, typical Appalachian ridges are practically lacking, so that the entire 40 miles between the Great Smoky Mountains and the Cumberland Escarpment is largely the Appalachian Valley type of topography. (3) As a consequence of the sparsity of ridges no division into an eastern valley belt and a western ridge belt is apparent here, as it is in Virginia and Pennsylvania. (4) Longitudinal drainage is more prevalent than in Virginia, Maryland, and Pennsylvania.

As mentioned in Chapter 5, the Blue Ridge province does not extend so far south as the Ridge and Valley province, unless such low mountains as the Rebecca, Talladega, and Choccolocco of Alabama be considered an extension of the Blue Ridge. The result is that the Ridge and Valley province at the extreme south abuts against the Piedmont, and there is not the marked contrast between adjacent types of topography that there is where the province borders the Blue Ridge.

*Tennessee River Drainage.* The prevalence of longitudinal drainage in the Southern section is well illustrated by the headwater drainage of the Tennessee River. Four streams, the Powell, Clinch, Holston, and Nolichucky-French Broad, form the headwaters of the Tennessee, flowing for many miles in parallel valleys before joining to form the Tennessee River proper. The Tennessee continues in a southwestward longitudinal course until it reaches Chattanooga, Tennessee, where it abruptly turns westward through Walden Ridge (see Fig. 8.14) into the Sequatchie Valley; it again flows southwestward in this longitudinal valley for 75 miles before finally turning northwestward to join ultimately the Ohio River at Paducah, Kentucky. Both longitudinal segments of the Tennessee River are in anticlinal valleys, whereas the transverse gorge through Walden Ridge is across a syncline.

The abrupt change in direction of the Tennessee River southwest of Chattanooga, Tennessee, from a southwest to a northwest course,

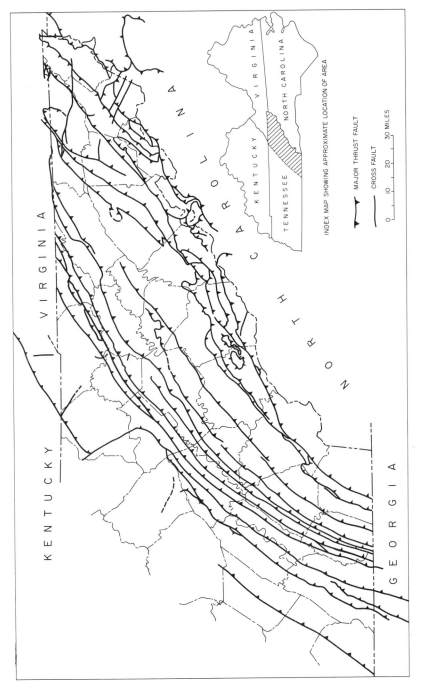

FIG. 7.11  Major thrust faults in eastern Tennessee. *(After J. D. Rogers, Bull. 58, Tennessee Div. Geol.)*

along with its gorge through Walden Ridge, has long puzzled geologists. Hayes and Campbell (1894) suggested that throughout the Tertiary erosion cycle the Tennessee River flowed southwestward east of Walden Ridge to the Gulf of Mexico via the routes of the present Coosa and Alabama rivers or by a more northerly route such as that now followed by the Black Warrior River. At the close of the Tertiary erosion cycle capture of the Tennessee River was supposed to have taken place near Chattanooga by a westward-flowing stream that occupied the valley west of Walden Ridge. Hayes, in 1899, more fully presented this interpretation and called the southward-flowing ancestral stream the Appalachian River. Simpson, in 1900, pointed out that the freshwater mussels in the Coosa and Tennessee rivers are so closely related as to support the viewpoint that these two rivers were once part of the same drainage system. Those who believe that the Tennessee has been diverted by piracy from a formerly southwesterly course to its present one cite in support of this viewpoint such arguments as the following: (1) the present divide between the Tennessee and Coosa drainage is low enough to suggest that a stream once flowed through it; (2) *Pleurobema*, a genus of *Unio*, a freshwater clam, is found in both the Tennessee and Coosa-Alabama drainage basins; (3) comparison of the volume of sediments presently being deposited by the Coosa and Alabama rivers with the volume of material that has been removed from the Appalachian Valley suggests that the present Coosa-Alabama rivers are inadequate in size to account for the volume of sediment that has been removed.

Johnson (1905) maintained that the Tennessee River has had essentially its present course since the Schooley (Cumberland) erosion cycle. He thought that the river acquired its course across Walden Ridge sometime before the close of the Schooley period of baseleveling, when the surface of Walden Ridge was continuous with the rest of the Schooley peneplain, and that the gorge through Walden Ridge was cut after uplift of this peneplain.

Those opposed to the idea of diversion of the Tennessee River from a former southerly route discount the biological evidence that has been offered in support of this idea by arguing that the larvae of the clams could have been carried from the Coosa basin into the Tennessee basin by either birds or insects. Some rather strong geological arguments can be offered against the theory of stream capture: (1) the meandering course of the gorge through Walden Ridge is not what would be expected of a stream that was vigorously cutting headward, for pirating streams usually have rather straight courses; (2) meanders would be expectable along a route inherited from an old age erosion surface; (3) there is not enough difference in altitude between the valleys on either side of Walden Ridge to permit stream piracy. Furthermore, as Wright (1936) has pointed out, the Harrisburg erosion surface slopes northward toward Chattanooga from the divide between the Coosa and Tennessee rivers, which must mean that stream drainage during the Harrisburg cycle (the cycle during which the piracy is presumed to have taken place) must have been northward from this divide.

Even if we conclude that the course of the upper Tennessee River was not changed by piracy in late Tertiary time, the route of the Tennessee River still appears anomalous and difficult to explain. The nearness of its westerly course across Alabama and its northerly route across Tennessee and Kentucky to the inner margin of coastal plain sediments suggests that possibly this may be more than an accidental relationship. Adams (1928) thought it likely that the Tennessee River established its northwestward course along the margin of the emerging Coastal Plain as it was elevated and given a westward tilt. This conclusion is based, however, solely on the nearness of the Tennessee River to the contact between Cretaceous and Paleozoic rocks. This may seem an attractive theory, but it should be pointed out that the Tennessee River by no means follows this contact and there is nothing resembling an inner lowland along the course of the river.

### Erosion Surface and Cycles

Conventional interpretation of the geomorphic history of the Ridge and Valley province has long been in terms of two major erosion cycles now most commonly called the Schooley and Harrisburg cycles. Numerous accordant ridge crests are believed to be remnants of the Schooley peneplain, whereas the Harrisburg erosion surface did not attain so advanced a stage of development as did the Schooley. Remnants of the Harrisburg erosion surface are largely confined to valleys and are better considered weak rock straths than peneplain surfaces. The Harrisburg surface is well represented in various segments of the Great Valley, such as the Shenandoah, which explains why at one time it was called the Valley peneplain (Wright, 1925).

King (1949, 1950) has taken issue with the interpretation of the floor of the Shenandoah Valley as the preserved surface of the Harrisburg peneplain. From studies in the Elkton, Virginia, area he came to the conclusion that the levelness of this valley floor has been exaggerated and that it appears level only in contrast with the mountains to either side. The relief in the valley appeared to him to represent a complex of rockcut surfaces, residuum, and gravel benches standing at various heights above the present floodplain. Although he did not deny the development of the Harrisburg peneplain, he concluded that the Cenozoic history of the area was much more complex than is usually assumed. The sequence of materials described by King is given in Table 7.1.

King believed that presence in the Shenandoah Valley of these various types of deposits served to destroy the earlier simple concept that the floor of the valley represents the surface of the Harrisburg peneplain. Actually, the greater part of the valley floor, according to King, is a depositional surface formed at a time much more recent than the time of development of the Valley peneplain. The noted entrenched meanders of the Shenandoah River (see Fig. 7.12), commonly interpreted as having been inherited from the surface of the Harrisburg peneplain, were believed by King to have developed during the closing stage of deposition of the intermediate gravels.

On the basis of fossils found in Alabama and Georgia in materials believed by King to correlate with the ancient gravels, he postulated an early rather than late Tertiary age for the Har-

TABLE 7.1 Types of Materials in Shenandoah Valley According to King

| Age | Type of Material | Place of Occurrence |
|---|---|---|
| Recent | Alluvium | Floodplains |
| Quaternary | Younger gravel | Terraces 50–75 feet above rivers |
| | Intermediate gravel | Broad plains and benches on intermediate slopes |
| | Older gravel | Narrow benches 700 feet above rivers |
| Tertiary | Ancient gravel | Very limited areas |
| | Residiuum | Mainly on the Cambrian Tomston and Wayneboro formations |

risburg peneplain. He considered the older, intermediate, and younger gravels related in their mode of origin and associated them with cycles of erosion and deposition related to climatic fluctuations during the Pleistocene.

An interpretation differing as radically as does King's from conventional ideas can hardly be accepted on the basis of a single local study, but it does point up the need for critical evaluation of the conventional interpretation through more detailed field studies. The possibility exists that what has been considered a simple topographic surface is much more complex in nature than previously believed.

We must, of course, always keep in mind the possibility that the topography of the Ridge and Valley province can be interpreted reasonably without resort to erosion cycles and peneplains. To some it would seem both more simple and logical to say that the topography which we see today is the product of an extremely long period of gradation in a region of complex structure and variable lithology. According to this view the differences in relief reflect differences in the rate of lowering of the landscape as related to differences in erosibility, and the areas of subaccordant altitudes, which have been considered by numerous geologists as remnants of former

FIG. 7.12   Shenandoah Valley and the meanders of the Shenandoah River, viewed from overlook about 6 miles southeast of Bentonville, Virginia.   (*Photo courtesy of Norfolk and Western Railway.*)

peneplains, merely reflect uniform lowering of surfaces on rocks of equal resistance to degradation.

## REFERENCES CITED

Adams, G. L. (1928).  The course of the Tennessee River and the physiography of the southern Appalachian region. *Jour. Geol.*, **36**, 481–493.

Chapman, D. H. (1937).  Late-glacial and postglacial history of the Champlain Valley, *Am. Jour. Sci.*, **234**, 89–124.

Cooper, B. N. (1944).  Geology and mineral resources of the Burkes Garden quadrangle, Virginia, *Va. Geol. Surv. Bull.* 60, 299 pp.

———  (1946).  Metamorphism along the "Pulaski" fault in the Appalachian Valley of Virginia, *Am. Jour. Sci.*, **244**, 95–104.

Dale, T. N. (1899).  The Slate Belt of eastern New York and western Vermont, *U. S. Geol. Survey 19th Ann. Rept.*, Pt. 3, 153–300.

Davies, W. E. (1959).  Origin of caves in folded limestone, *Geol. Soc. Am. Bull.*, **70**, 1802 (abs.).

Fairchild, H. L. (1919).  Pleistocene marine submergence of the Hudson, Champlain, and St. Lawrence valleys, *New York State Museum Bull.* 209–210, 76 pp.

Fenneman, N. M. (1938).  *Physiography of Eastern United States*, McGraw-Hill Book Company, New York, 714 pp.

Fox, H. D. (1950).  Structure and origin of the windows exposed on the Nittany arch at Birmingham, Pennsylvania, *Am. Jour. Sci.*, **248**, 153–170.

Gilmer, F. W. (1818).  On the geological formation of the Natural Birdge of Virginia, *Amer. Philos. Soc. Trans.*, **1**, 187–192.

Hayes, C. W. (1899).  Physiography of the Chattanooga district, *U. S. Geol. Survey 19th Ann. Rept.*, Pt. 2, pp. 1–58.

———  and M. R. Campbell (1894).  Geomorphology of the southern Appalachians, *Nat. Geog. Mag.*, **6**, 63–126.

Johnson, D. W. (1905).  The Tertiary history of the Tennessee River, *Jour. Geol.*, **13**, 194–231.

King, P. B. (1949).  The floor of the Shenandoah Valley, *Am. Jour. Sci.*, **247**, 73–93.

———  (1950).  Geology of the Elkton area, Virginia, *U. S. Geol. Survey Profess. Paper* 230, 82 pp.

Malott, C. A., and R. R. Shrock (1930).  Origin and development of Natural Bridge, Virginia, *Am. Jour. Sci.*, **219**, 257–273.

Rich, J. L. (1934). Mechanics of low-angle overthrust faulting as illustrated by Cumberland thrust block, Virginia, Kentucky, and Tennessee, *Am. Assoc. Petroleum Geologists Bull.*, **18**, 1584–1596.

Rodgers, John (1953). The folds and faults of the Appalachian Valley and Ridge province, *Ky. Geol. Surv. Spec. Pub.* 1, 150–166.

Simpson, C. T. (1900). The evidence of the *Unionidae* regarding the former courses of the Tennessee and other southern rivers, *Science, N.S.*, **12**, 133–136.

Woodward, H. P. (1936). Natural Bridge and Natural Tunnel, Virginia, *Jour. Geol.*, **44**, 604–616.

Woodworth, J. B. (1905). Ancient water levels in the Champlain and Hudson valleys, *New York State Museum Bull.* 84, 265 pp.

Wright, F. J. (1925). The physiography of the upper James River basin in Virginia, *Va. Geol. Surv. Bull.* 11, 67 pp.

—— (1936). The Natural Bridge of Virginia, *Va. Geol. Surv. Bull.* 46-G, 53–78.

ADDITIONAL REFERENCES

Bates, R. L. (1939). Geology of Powell Valley in northeastern Lee County, Virginia, *Va. Geol. Surv. Bull.* 51-B, 31–94.

Davies, W. E. (1950). The caves of Maryland, *Md. Dept. Geol., Mines and Water Resources Bull.*, 7, 70 pp.

Quinn, A. W. (1933). Normal faults of the Lake Champlain region, *Jour. Geol.*, **41**, 113–143.

Ver Steeg, Karl (1930). Wind gaps and water gaps of the northern Appalachians, their characteristics and significance, New York Acad. Sci., *Annals*, **32**, 87–220.

Woodward, H. P. (1932). Geology and mineral resources of the Roanoke area, Virginia, *Va. Geol. Surv. Bull.* 34, 7–24.

Wright, F. J. (1934). The newer Appalachians of the South, Part I, *Denison Univ. Jour. Sci. Labs.*, **29**, 1–105.

—— (1936). The newer Appalachians of the South, Part II, *Denison Univ. Jour. Sci. Labs.*, **31**, 93–142.

# 8

# Appalachian Plateaus Province

The Appalachian Plateaus province extends from near Watertown, in northwestern New York, to the Coastal Plain in northwestern Alabama. In the Ohio-Pennsylvania-West Virginia area it attains a maximum width in excess of 200 miles, but it begins to narrow in eastern Kentucky, and in Tennessee its width has diminished to hardly 30 miles.

## DISTINCTIVE CHARACTERISTICS

The Appalachian Plateaus province differs from the other provinces in the Appalachian Highlands in at least six ways. (1) Altitudes nearly everywhere are higher than those in adjacent provinces. The only exception to this is along the southern margin of the Adirondack province. No altitudes in the Appalachian Plateaus are as high as those found in the southern end of the Blue Ridge province, but in the Catskill Plateau altitudes exceed 4000 feet. (2) Rocks of the Appalachian Plateaus are largely younger than those of other Appalachian provinces, except for the Triassic rocks in the Piedmont. Strata of the Appalachian Plateau are mainly Mississippian and Pennsylvanian in age; at the north some beds of Devonian age crop out, and a small area including parts of Pennsylvania, Ohio, and West Virginia is underlain by the Dunkard series of Permian age. (3) Rocks of the Appalachian Plateaus are dominantly clastic in nature; conglomerates, sandstones, and shales with some interbedded coals predominate. In contrast to the adjacent Ridge and Valley, Interior Low Plateaus, and Central Lowland prov-

inces, limestones are uncommon. (4) The Appalachian Plateaus have not been subjected to the intense deformation that affected the other Appalachian provinces. A few mild folds exist, particularly adjacent to the Ridge and Valley province, but they are broad open folds and not strongly compressed or faulted like those in the Ridge and Valley province. A few thrust faults also are present, near the eastern edge of the province, particularly at the south in Virginia and Tennessee. This indicates that what Price (1931) called the Appalachian structural front is somewhat within the Appalachian Plateaus. (5) The Appalachian Plateaus are bounded on all sides by outfacing escarpments, which reflect the regional synclinal structure of the plateau. (6) Most of the province has undergone considerable dissection. This is so great near the eastern margin that the topography here commonly is designated as mountains. Extensive upland tracts viewed from a distance suggest a gently rolling plateau surface, but it is not possible to travel far across the uplands without coming to a deeply incised stream valley which may be a few hundred feet deep if a minor valley, or 1000 to 2000 feet deep if a major one.

## BOUNDARIES

Along most of its boundary the Appalachian Plateaus province is set off from its neighbors by a conspicuous outfacing scarp or dissected mountain front. The scarps along the eastern margin of the province are in general higher and more clearly defined than those on the west. Only in two areas is the province boundary not readily evident. From a point east of Columbus, Ohio, to near Cleveland, no west-facing escarpment exists, but the contact between the till plain topography of the Central Lowlands on the west and the hilly terrain of the plateau on the east is readily recognizable. In central West Virginia the mountains of the Ridge and Valley province have about the same altitude as the dissected plateau to the west of them. However, the boundary between the two provinces can be drawn fairly accurately from differences in the topographic patterns. The mountains of the Ridge and Valley province show a lineation associated with the parallel folds of that province, whereas the topography of the plateau lacks lineation, and the valley systems here display a well-developed dendritic pattern.

## SUBDIVISIONS OF PROVINCE

### Major Characteristics

The Appalachian Plateaus province has been divided into seven sections.

1. The Mohawk section includes that part of the province north of the escarpment which overlooks the Mohawk valley from the south. Except for the Tug Hill cuesta north of the Mohawk Valley it is essentially a strike lowland at the base of the Helderberg-Onondaga escarpment. Most of the section bears a strong imprint of glaciation.

2. The Glaciated Allegheny Plateau is maturely dissected plateau which was modified notably by Pleistocene glaciation, particularly the late Wisconsin glaciations.

3. The Catskill section is a small area at the northeast corner of the province which rises with mountainous relief above its surroundings. Although the region was glaciated, the effects of glaciation are hardly so conspicuous as in the Glaciated Allegheny Plateau.

4. The Allegheny Mountains section is at the northeastern margin of the Appalachian Plateaus. Here dissection is so advanced that the topography has lost its plateau characteristics. Several open folds are expressed in

the topography as linear ridges. The topography was unmodified by glaciation.

5. The unglaciated Allegheny Plateau section is the maturely dissected middle portion of the Appalachian Plateau.

6. The Cumberland Mountains section represents the southern counterpart of the Allegheny Mountains section.

7. The Cumberland Plateau section is in a sense the southern counterpart of the Unglaciated Allegheny Plateau, but stream dissection on the whole is hardly so far advanced as at the north.

### Mohawk Section

*Mohawk Lowland.* The Mohawk section lies between the Adirondack Mountains on the north and the Glaciated Allegheny Plateau on the south and consists essentially of the Mohawk Lowland and the Tug Hill Cuesta to the north of it. The Mohwak Valley is a strike valley developed primarily on rocks of Ordovician age. It forms a low-level connection between the Hudson Valley and the Ontario Plain of the Central Lowlands, which was the basis for its use as the route of the Erie Canal. Not all of the Mohawk Lowland is valley flat, for numerous benches along it stand several hundred feet above the valley floor. At the eastern end of the lowland several of these benches are developed on upfaulted blocks (Fenneman, 1938), some of which attain altitudes in excess of 1000 feet. The highest altitudes attained in the valley are near Little Falls, New York, where benches at altitudes between 1200 and 1400 feet seem to represent the preglacial divide between drainage to the Hudson River and that to the stream that then flowed westward into what is now the Ontario Basin.

*Tug Hill Cuesta.* North of the Mohawk Lowland in the longitude of Utica and Rome, New York, lies the Tug Hill Cuesta, whose northeast-facing scarp is capped by the Ordovician Oswego sandstone. The dip slope of the cuesta descends to the Ontario plain on the west. Paralleling the cuesta scarp on the northeast is the northwest-flowing Black River. The Tug Hill scarp stands as much as 1200 feet above the Black River Valley at its base. The valley of Black River is developed mainly upon the Ordovician Trenton limestone but locally it comes in contact with the Precambrian rocks of the Adirondack province. Black River parallels the front of the Tug Hill Cuesta as far as its northwest end and then flows westward into Lake Ontario.

*Origin of Mohawk Valley.* Much of the topography of the Mohawk section is related to the roles which the Mohawk and Black rivers played during later Pleistocene time. The Mohawk Valley may antedate the Pleistocene glaciations, but this is uncertain. It has been argued that there was no Mohawk Valley at the time of the Schooley erosion cycle. Fairchild (1925) believed that tributaries of the Susquehanna River headed on the southwest slope of the Adirondack Mountains and flowed southward across what is now the Mohawk Valley. Close correlation between the course of the Mohawk Valley and the strike of the rocks led Chamberlin (1882) to suggest that initiation of this valley came about through headward erosion by two opposed streams, one of which flowed to the Hudson and the other to the Ontario Basin. The preglacial divide between these two streams was presumed to have been in the neighborhood of Little Falls, New York. Integration of the two valleys into a single eastward route presumably came late in Pleistocene time as overflow waters from certain portions of the evolving Great Lakes discharged eastward (see Fig. 12.16).

*Effects of Glaciation.* During at least the Wisconsin glaciation a lobe of ice known as the Mohawk lobe extended up the Mohawk Valley from the main mass of ice in the Hudson Valley. This lobe apparently moved up the valley about as far as Little Falls; from the ice sheet in the St. Lawrence Valley a lobe extended southward up the Black River Valley until it finally merged with the Mohawk Valley lobe. As deglaciation began, a series of ice-marginal lakes developed in the Black River Valley whose levels are marked by lacustrine and deltaic deposits. After the ice had withdrawn from the Mohawk Valley,

the glacial meltwaters that flowed down this valley into the Hudson Valley built the previously described Mohawk delta near Albany, New York (see p. 115).

## Glaciated Allegheny Plateau Section

*General Description.* Only the fact that it has been glaciated justifies setting this section apart from the Unglaciated Allegheny Plateau section; despite this, the topographies of the two sections have much in common. The southern boundary of the section is drawn at the outer limits of Wisconsin glaciation, because the effects of the more extensive Illinoian and Kansan glaciations are poorly expressed in the topography. The northern boundary is the escarpment along the south side of the Mohawk Valley and its continuation westward through New York and Pennsylvania into northeastern Ohio. This escarpment is developed on various rock formations of Devonian age. Strata have a regional dip to the south, and altitudes increase in this direction; the result is that Devonian rocks are encountered higher and higher in the section as one moves southward. At the extreme southeast, the Wyoming Valley of the Ridge and Valley province separates a belt of Pennsylvanian rocks at the west from Mississippian strata in the Pocono Mountains on the east.

## Glacial History

*Age and Subages of Glaciation.* The Allegheny Plateau was glaciated during at least three of the glacial ages. Remnants of an early glaciation are found beyond the margins of the Glaciated Allegheny Plateau section. This drift, which long was called the "Fringe drift" or Jerseyan, is now commonly considered Kansan in age. Its topographic effects are hardly discernible. Two Illinoian tills have been described in northwestern Pennsylvania (Shepps et al., 1959). However, only the Wisconsin drifts have marked topographic expression. Two or possibly three Wisconsin substages are represented in the Allegheny Plateau. The Olean, Binghamton, and Valley Heads drifts were first described by

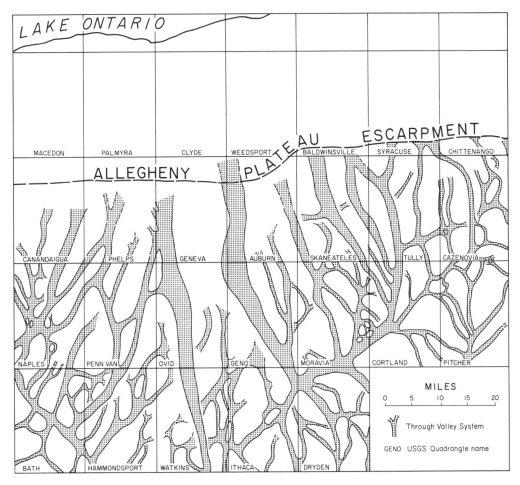

FIG. 8.1   Portion of through-valley network of west central New York.   (*After Chauncey Holmes, Geol. Soc. Am. Bull.,* **63.**)

MacClintock and Apfel (1944). The oldest and outermost of these drifts is the Olean, and the innermost and youngest is the Valley Heads. End moraine is largely restricted to the area of the Valley Heads drift, whose outer moraine is the Valley Heads moraine, a morainic belt described and named by Fairchild (1932), which blocks several of the Finger Lake valleys on the south.

The reality of the Binghamton drift as a separate till sheet has been questioned by Moss and Ritter (1962). They contend that what has been called Binghamton drift is in reality a facies of the Olean drift that is rich in limestone pebbles.

The Olean drift is considered to be Tazewell and the Valley Heads Cary in age.

*Major Effects of Glaciation.* Four topographic effects of glaciation in the Allegheny Plateau region were (1) deposition of ground moraine and patchy end moraine, (2) formation of a system of "through valleys" leading southward from the drift sheets, (3) creation of the Finger Lakes, and (4) development of certain features that reflect the existence of severe climatic conditions marginal to the ice front.

South of the Finger Lakes, the effects of glaciation are not pronounced; they consist mainly of a certain amount of rounding off of hilltops and deposition of patches of till, particularly in the valleys. The Valley Heads moraine is patchy and indistinct along much of its length, but north of it ground moraine is extensive and the topography takes on a distinctly glacial aspect. The effects of glaciation can be seen as far southeast as the Pocono Plateau, where numerous lakes of glacial origin exist.

THROUGH VALLEYS. The "through valleys" of west central New York form a remarkable network (see Fig. 8.1) in which there are many valley junctions at discordant altitudes. This valley system is the result of erosion by both ice and glacial meltwaters. It is difficult to say which agent contributed more to develop-

ment of the valleys, but probably glacial meltwaters were of greater importance. However, the nearness of the through valleys to the Finger Lakes, where glacial erosion has been considerable, suggests the possibility that glacial erosion may have contributed significantly to the shaping of the through valleys. Their trend parallels the major direction of ice movement, which would have facilitated glacial scouring of their bottoms. Drainage of the through valley system discharged to the south into the headwaters of the Susquehanna River. It is evident that the valleys are not products of existing streams, for some streams cross rather than follow them. Furthermore, there is poor correlation between the size of the valleys and the streams now in them.

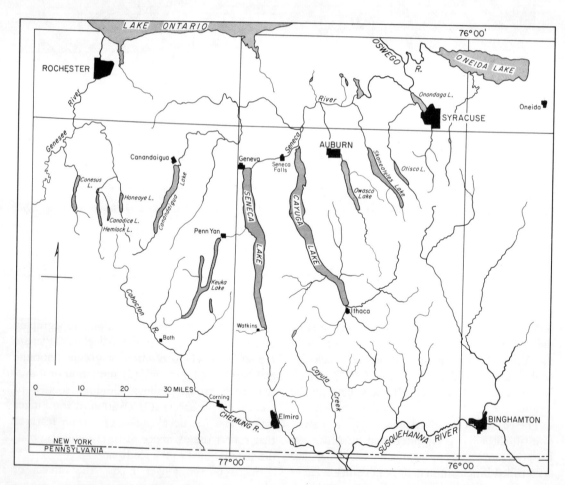

FIG. 8.2  Map of the Finger Lakes.  (*After H. L. Fairchild, Geol. Soc. Am. Bull.,* **45.**)

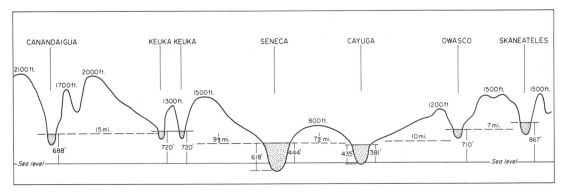

FIG. 8.3   Comparison of the altitudes of the surfaces and floors of the Finger Lakes.   (*After H. L. Fairchild, Geol. Soc. Am. Bull.*, **45**.)

FINGER LAKES. The Finger Lakes system consists of eleven lakes in west central New York, which can be divided into a western group of four lakes that drain to the Genesee River and an eastern group of seven lakes that drain to the Seneca River (see Fig. 8.2). The lakes have certain features in common; a nearly parallel arrangement, steep-walled sides which rise precipitously above the lake levels, and linear forms. Floors of two of the lakes, Seneca and Cayuga, extend below sea level (see Fig. 8.3). The lake basins are mainly in the Hamilton shales of Devonian age but at their northern ends are cut in the Devonian Onondaga limestone and at their southern ends in rocks of the Devonian Portage group.

The lakes occupy preglacial stream valleys that have been overdeepened and oversteepened by glacial erosion. The following table gives several pertinent facts regarding the individual lakes (Von Engeln, 1961).

How much the bedrock floors of the deeper lakes extend below sea level is uncertain. According to Von Engeln (1961), a well drilled at the level of the Lake Cayuga plain near Ithaca, New York, went to a depth of over 600 feet below sea level without reaching bedrock. In many respects the Finger Lakes resemble fiords.

T A B L E  8.1   Data on Finger Lakes

| | | Name of Lake | Altitude of Surface | Greatest Depth | Altitude of Bottom Above or Below Sea Level |
|---|---|---|---|---|---|
| E A S T | G R O U P | Seneca | 444 | 618 | −174 |
| | | Cayuga | 384 | 420 | −34 |
| | | Owasco | 710 | 177 | +533 |
| | | Skaneateles | 867 | 287 | +580 |
| | | Otisco | 784 | 66 | +718 |
| W E S T | G R O U P | Keuka | 709 | 186 | +523 |
| | | Canandaigua | 989 | 274 | +715 |
| | | Honeoye | 818 | ? | ? |
| | | Canadice | 1099 | 91 | +1008 |
| | | Hemlock | 905 | 96 | +799 |
| | | Conesus | 818 | 59 | +759 |

Certainly they are outstanding examples of effective localized glacial erosion in weak rocks along preglacial valleys paralleling the direction of ice movement.

All the lakes at present drain to the north, but difference of opinion exists as to direction of drainage in the preglacial valleys. Von Engeln concluded from the northward convergence of the lakes of the east group (see Fig. 8.2) that the valleys which they occupy drained to the north in preglacial time; convergence southward of the six lakes of the west group suggested to him that their valleys drained to the south in preglacial time. Until more information on the elevations of the bedrock topography is available, this question cannot be settled. Farther west, in northwestern Pennsylvania and northeastern Ohio, there seems to be good evidence that the drainage of what is now the Allegheny-Monongahela portion of the Ohio River went to the north in preglacial time.

PERMAFROST FEATURES. Most of the evidence available points to the conclusion that there was no continuous zone of frozen ground adjacent to the southern margin of the ice sheet which covered much of North America. However, there are grounds for believing that in part of the plateau region of New York and Pennsylvania there was an increased intensity and frequency of freeze and thaw and possibly sporadic or discontinuous permafrost. Evidence for this is found in such features as the Hickory Run boulder field in the Pocono Plateau (Smith, 1953) and a mile-long rock stream of Olean conglomerate in Allegheny County, New York (Chadwick, 1935). Denny (1956) has described excessive rock rubble, patterned ground, and churned earth in Potter County, Pennsylvania, which he attributed to frost action under periglacial conditions. Presence of these features in the Allegheny Plateau is probably attributable to the fact that the high altitudes here caused temperatures to be low enough to produce severe frost conditions.

*Catskill Mountains Section*

*Topography.* The Catskill Mountains section in southeastern New York includes the highest topography in the Appalachian Plateaus province; altitudes exceeding 4000 feet are reached here. The Catskill Mountains are mountains only in an erosional sense, as are the Pocono, Allegheny, and Cumberland "mountains" to the south of them. Structurally these areas are all plateaus and topographically dissected plateaus, but they have been called "mountains" too long to expect that they will ever be known otherwise to the general public.

The Devonian rocks of the Catskill Mountains form a broad syncline. Variations in resistance of the individual formations are responsible for a series of cuestas whose fronts are marked by scarps of varying magnitudes. The boldest of the cuesta scarps is that which forms the eastern margin of the Catskill Mountains and overlooks the Hudson Valley to the east. This escarpment at the south stands as much as 3000 feet above the Hudson Valley. At the north it is not as high, for here it rises above the surface of the Glaciated Allegheny Plateau, which is itself about 2000 feet high.

EFFECTS OF GLACIATION. The Catskill Mountains were covered by an early Wisconsin ice sheet and partially glaciated during late Wisconsin time, but the effects of glaciation are not so strongly impressed on the topography as in the Allegheny Plateau. Local valley glaciers existed in the Catskill Mountains, but whether these formed before or after the continental ice sheet invaded the area is a matter on which there has been disagreement.

DRAINAGE RELATIONSHIPS. The Catskill Mountains are drained mainly by three streams, the Delaware, Susquehanna, and Schoharie Creek. Delaware and Susquehanna drainage is to the south, whereas Schoharie Creek drains northward to the Mohawk River. A number of short streams flow down the east scarp of the Catskills directly to the Hudson River but the area drained by them is not large.

Some rather unusual drainage relationships exist in the Catskills that are resulting in readjustments in the drainage of the plateau. Particularly unbalanced is the drainage divide near the eastern margin of the plateau, where short eastward-flowing streams have very steep gradients compared with those of the headwater tribu-

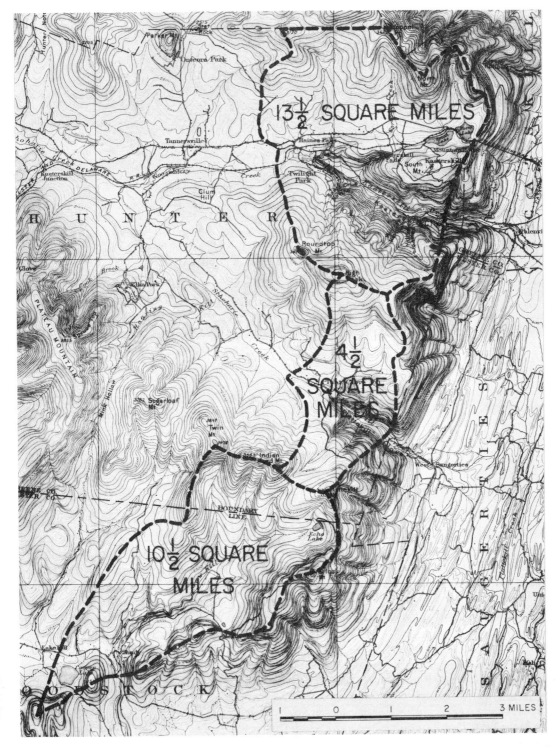

FIG. 8.4 Portion of Kaaterskill, New York, topographic sheet showing extent of stream piracies along front of Catskill Escarpment.

FIG. 8.5    Upland topography in unglaciated Allegheny Plateau.    (*Photo by John C. Frye.*)

taries of the Susquehanna and Delaware rivers. This has resulted in several stream piracies wherein eastward-flowing streams have pirated the headwaters of southwestward-flowing streams (see Fig. 8.4).

The route which the waters of Schoharie Creek take to the sea is unusual. This stream heads within two miles of the eastern escarpment of the Catskills and flows northward to the Mohawk; the Mohawk empties into the Hudson and the Hudson River eventually brings the Schoharie Creek waters to within 10 miles of their point of origin, after flowing for 175 miles along the four sides of a quadrilateral course.

Whether the Susquehanna River headed in the Adirondack Mountains during the Schooley erosion cycle, as believed by Brigham (1898), Fairchild (1925), and Ruedemann (1932), cannot be stated with certainty. If it did, Schoharie Creek is an obsequent stream that developed after the Mohawk Valley came into existence following uplift of the Schooley peneplain and later captured a considerable part of former Susquehanna

drainage; it bids fair in time to capture some of the upper Delaware drainage.

### Allegheny Mountains Section

*Topography.* Two topographic characteristics justify recognition of this area as a separate geomorphic unit. First, the altitudes and degree of dissection are greater here than in the unglaciated plateau to the west. Secondly, the rocks of this section are mildly folded and erosion on anticlines and synclines has produced a number of structurally controlled ridges and valleys that give to the topography a lineation not found in the adjacent Unglaciated Allegheny Plateau section.

The Allegheny Front along the eastern margin of this section is an imposing escarpment on Pocono and Pottsville sandstones which rises 1000 feet or more above the valley floors of the adjacent Ridge and Valley province. Back of the escarpment are a number of folds which are similar in alignment to those of the Ridge and

Valley province but are open rather than closed folds. The synclinal troughs are so wide and shallow that they form broad plateau-like tracts, and the anticlinal valleys have given rise to expansive lowlands rather than the narrow valleys common in the Ridge and Valley province. Chestnut Ridge and Laurel Ridge, near the western margin of the section, are two of the better known of the homoclinal ridges. Others in the area are Dans, Meadow, Negro, Big Savage, and Backbone Mountains. These ridges are developed on either the Pottsville or Pocono formations. Erosion on the anticlines has exposed locally rocks of Devonian age.

### Unglaciated Allegheny Plateau

*Geology and Topography.* Parts of eastern Ohio and Kentucky, most of West Virginia, a fair-sized area in southwestern Pennsylvania, and a very small strip in New York are included in this section. Its stratigraphy is broadly similar to that of the Allegheny Mountains section, but the Appalachian Plateau syncline deepens to the north, and as a result rocks of the upper Coal Measures and even the Permian Dunkard series are present. As a consequence, shales are more abundant than farther east in the Appalachian Plateau. These differences in lithology are reflected in a minor way in slopes that are somewhat smoother than those found where sandstones are more common (see Fig. 8.5).

Altitudes are lowest on the western side of the section in Ohio and Kentucky, where they average 1200 to 1400 feet. From here, they increase eastward and northward and along the Pennsylvania-New York state boundary reach 2000 feet or more. The highest part of the section, however, is at its eastern margin in West Virginia, where altitudes may exceed 4000 feet. It is in this area that New River has cut its deep gorge (see Fig. 8.6). River level in this gorge lies 2000 feet below the level of the plateau surface, making it the most spectacular gorge in the eastern United States.

*Abandoned High-Level Valleys.* Present in the western part of the Allegheny Plateau, in western Pennsylvania, southeastern Ohio, and northwestern West Virginia, are numerous abandoned high-level valleys that lie 200 feet or more above present valley floors. These are dismembered remnants of preglacial drainage lines. They can be traced without much difficulty to the glacial boundary, but within it they soon disappear beneath the cover of glacial drift.

TEAYS VALLEY SYSTEM. Best known and probably best preserved of these valleys is the Teays Valley of West Virginia (see Fig. 8.7). Tight (1903) applied the name Teays to a Tertiary river system of which this abandoned valley was a part. It was the major river of east central United States in Tertiary time. New River (see p. 106) is probably a direct lineal descendant

FIG. 8.6 New River gorge viewed from Hawks Nest State Park overlook. (*Photo courtesy West Virginia Industrial and Publicity Commission.*)

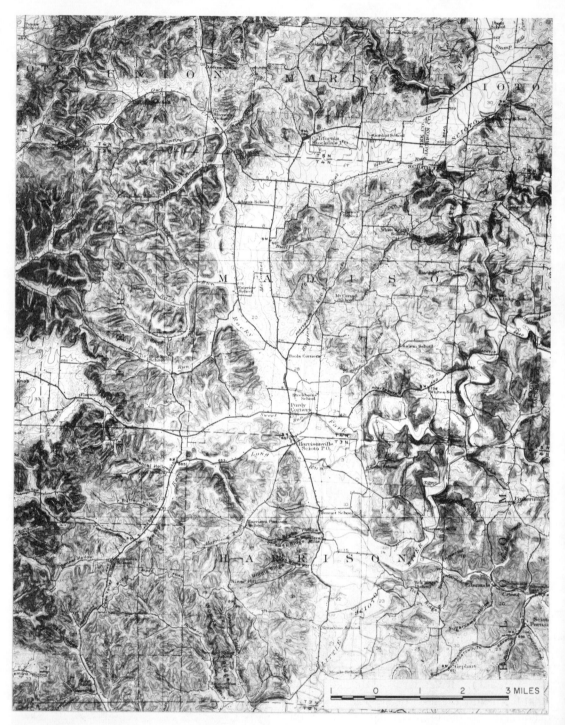

FIG. 8.7  Portion of Sciotoville, Ohio-Kentucky, topographic sheet showing part of the abandoned Teays Valley system.

of this Tertiary river system. The Kanawha River, the downstream continuation of New River drainage, diverges from the route of the Teays at St. Albans, West Virginia, on to its junction with the Ohio River at Pt. Pleasant, West Virginia. The Teays River followed a more westerly course to Huntington, West Virginia, thence essentially along the present route of the Ohio River to Wheelersburg, Ohio, thence northward to Waverly, Ohio, along what is approximately the course of the present Scioto River, and thence to Chillicothe, Ohio, where its route becomes buried beneath glacial drift. However, its westward continuation beneath the glacial drift has been mapped to its junction with the Mississippi River in central Illinois (see Fig. 12.2).

The bedrock floor of the abandoned Teays Valley west of Charleston, West Virginia, is Morgantown sandstone of late Pennsylvanian age. Resting upon this sandstone are stream-rounded quartzitic gravels which apparently came from somewhere in the crystalline Appalachians. Above the gravels are slack-water silts known as the Mimford silts (Stout and Schaaf, 1931). Lamination of the silts indicates that they were deposited in ponded waters. The ponding was undoubtedly produced by the advance of an ice sheet across the westward-flowing Teays River. It is not certain which ice sheet did the ponding, but present knowledge seems to indicate that it was the Kansan glacier that dammed the Teays Valley and diverted its drainage southwestward to the preglacial Ohio.

Stout and Schaaf, because of the presence in the Minford silts of such minerals as sericite and muscovite, concluded that the Teays River headed as far east as what is now the Piedmont. Manos (1961), from a sample of the Mimford silts obtained in West Virginia, found that the silt lacked a typical metamorphic suite of minerals such as kyanite, staurolite, and sillimanite but instead was characterized by such minerals as tourmaline, zircon, muscovite, and epidote. On this ground she concluded that the Tertiary source of the Teays River was more likely in the folded Appalachians than in the Piedmont.

Perhaps one sample is not enough to serve as the basis for a firm conclusion regarding the source area of the Teays River. If New River is a descendant of the Teays, and it seems most likely that it is, we may reasonably conclude that the Teays headed farther east than the present New River. This conclusion is based on the known fact that the divide in the Blue Ridge is at present receding westward (see p. 106).

The derangement of the Teays and other rivers in the Allegheny Plateau region took place during the Parker strath subcycle (see p. 81). The 200-foot difference in altitude between the level of the Teays Valley and the present floodplain of the Kanawha River presumably represents the amount of valley deepening that has taken place along the Kanawha Valley since Kansan time.

Although the diversion of the Teays River from its valley west of Charleston and ponding of this valley are attributed by most geologists to the advance across the drainage of a Pleistocene ice sheet (presumably Kansan), Rhodehamel and Carlston (1963) concluded that the diversion was not related to Pleistocene glaciation but took place in Tertiary time as a result of stream piracy. The deposits in the valley generally called the Mimford silts were considered by them partly ancient Tertiary alluvium and partly Quaternary lacustrine deposits and gravels. A northward-flowing tributary of the Teays system is supposed to have worked southward and captured the main stream near Scary, West Virginia. The case made for diversion of the Teays by self-capture does not seem very convincing or as logical as diversion by glaciation.

## Cumberland Mountains Section

*Basis for Recognition as a Section.* The Cumberland Mountains section of the Appalachian Plateaus is the southern counterpart of the Allegheny Mountains section. To a considerable degree separation of the two is arbitrary, but there is some justification for recognizing the two sections if for no other reason than that the geographical names for the eastern mountainous portions of the Appalachian Plateau are different in the north and south. Other grounds for this separation exist, however, particularly the presence near the eastern margin of the southern section of the large Cumberland thrust block. It is also true that the Cumberland Mountains section as a whole is somewhat less highly dissected than the Allegheny Mountains section, but along the headwater portions of such streams as the Cumberland and Kentucky rivers this is certainly not true, for here is found some of the roughest country in the eastern United States. The basis for separating the Cumberland Mountains from the Cumberland Plateau is essentially the same as that for separating the Allegheny Mountains from the Allegheny Plateau, namely, the difference in the degree of dissection. In addition, the topography is notably higher in the Cumberland Mountains than in the Cumberland Plateau.

Rocks of the Cumberland Mountains section are primarily of Pennsylvanian age. Shales and coals are present, but they lie beneath capping sandstones and exert little influence on the topography. Mississippian strata crop out along the lower slopes.

*Cumberland Thrust Block.* The Cumberland thrust block is 125 miles long and 25 miles wide and lies about equally in the states of Virginia, Kentucky, and Tennessee. Its structural relationships were first recognized by Wentworth (1921) and it was first described in detail by Rich (1933). The thrust block is bounded by four faults (see Fig. 8.8), the Pine Mountain fault on the northwest, the Hunter Valley-Wallen Valley fault on the southeast, the Russell Fork fault on the northeast, and the Jacksboro fault on the southwest. The faults on the northwest and southeast sides are thrust faults, whereas those of the northeast and southwest are tear faults. The fault plane seems to start in the incompetent Rome and Conasauga shales of early and middle Cambrian age, but it cuts through overlying competent beds into the next higher incompetent formation, the Devonian-Mississippian Chattanooga black shale.

The Cumberland thrust block is divided lengthwise into the Middlesboro syncline on the north-

west and the Powell Valley anticline on the southeast. These two parts of the structure lie in different geomorphic provinces, as the Middlesboro syncline is in the Appalachian Plateaus and the Powell Valley anticline in the Ridge and Valley province.

Wentworth (1921) estimated that movement of about 2 miles toward the northwest had taken place at the northeast corner of the thrust block and 10 miles at the southwest corner (see Fig. 8.9). Northwest-facing Pine Mountain, a homoclinal mountain, forms the northwest side of the Middlesboro syncline; a similar homoclinal ridge, Cumberland Mountain, forms the southeast face of the syncline (Rich, 1934). Both ridges are developed on the Pennsylvanian Lee formation and are very prominent features. Cumberland Mountain rises 1500 feet above adjacent Powell Valley to the east, and Pine Mountain is such a formidable barrier that for a distance of nearly 90 miles no stream flows through it. Cumberland Mountain, however, is breached by the North Fork of Powell River at Pennington Gap, Virginia. The synclinal area between the two ridges is maturely dissected plateau of the type that is responsible for the terrain's being called "mountains" rather than "plateau."

A somewhat anomalous topographic feature within the synclinal plateau country is the Middlesboro topographic basin. This basin has been explained as the result of the presence of readily erosible crushed sandstone and shale, but Rich thought that it could be explained just as logically as the result of convergence of several streams on Cumberland Gap with resulting removal of the capping resistant sandstones and development of a basin on the underlying weaker coals and shales.

Our present concern is primarily with that part of the Cumberland thrust block in the Cumberland Mountains, but discussion of the Powell Valley anticline seems appropriate here even though it is topographically a part of the Ridge and Valley Province. The Powell Valley anticline is bounded by the Wallen Valley fault on the southeast and by southeast-facing, homoclinal Cumberland Mountain on the northwest. Anticlinal Powell Valley is about 100 miles long

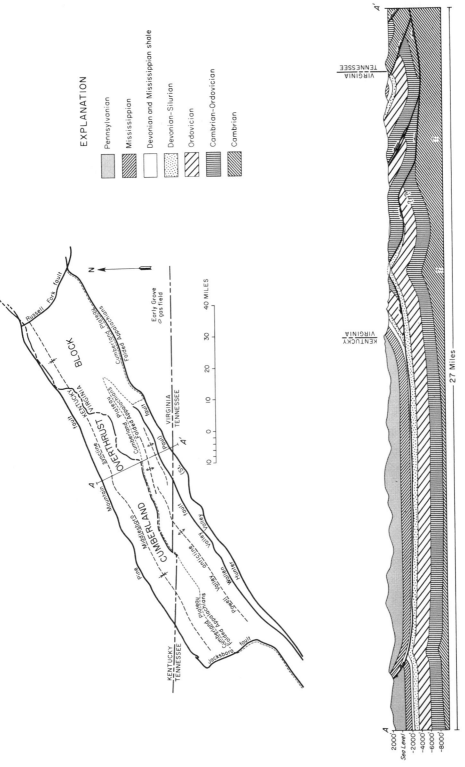

FIG. 8.8  Geology and structure of the Cumberland overthrust block.  (*After R. L. Miller and W. P. Brosgé, U. S. Geol. Survey Bull.* 990.)

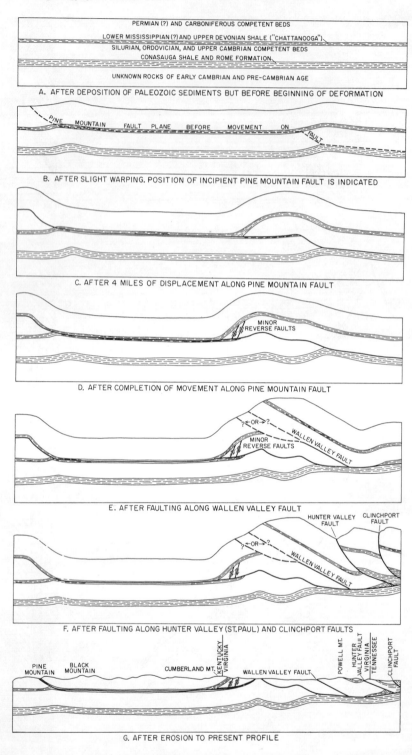

FIG. 8.9    Theoretical stages in the development of the Cumberland overthrust block.    (*After R. L. Miller and W. P. Brosgé, U. S. Geol. Survey Bull.* 990.)

and 15 miles wide. The Powell Valley anticline appears to have been formed by folding, mainly subsequent to the overthrusting (Miller and Fuller, 1954). Several fensters in the anticline (Butts, 1927) expose rocks of Silurian and Devonian age completely enclosed by late Cambrian and Ordovician limestones and dolomites. The Powell River, which flows southwestward along the axis of the anticline, is one of the four parallel tributaries of the Tennessee River that lie in the Ridge and Valley province above where the Tennessee leaves this province through its gorge near Chattanooga, Tennessee.

*Origin of Cumberland Gap.* Cumberland Gap (see Fig. 8.10), at the meeting point of Virginia, Tennessee, and Kentucky, is well known for the historical role that it played during the time that early settlers poured through it along the Wilderness Trail on their way to the interior of the United States. It is interesting geomorphically

as a scenic feature but more particularly for the problem it presents as to its origin. Cumberland Gap is a wind gap 600 feet deep in even-crested Cumberland Mountain (Rich, 1933). A common interpretation of its origin is that it was once occupied by a northwestward-flowing stream at the time of the development of the oldest peneplain of the region (the Schooley or Upland peneplain). The former stream through Cumberland Gap is supposed to have been beheaded by the Powell River as it extended itself headward along the Powell Valley anticline after uplift of the Schooley peneplain.

Rich, however, favored the view that the original drainage through Cumberland Gap was southward from the Middlesboro Basin. He believed that this stream was captured and diverted from its southward course to a northwest route to the Cumberland River. Capture apparently was effected by Yellow Creek, a tributary of the Cumberland River. Rich offered the

FIG. 8.10 Cumberland Gap, looking toward Middlesboro Basin. (*Photo courtesy Louisville Courier-Journal.*)

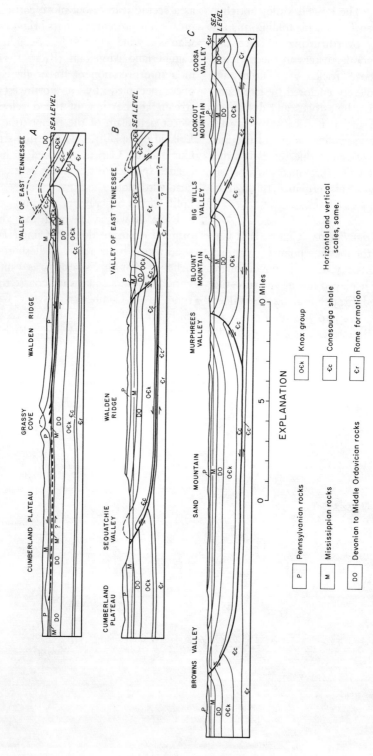

FIG. 8.11   Sections across Sequatchie anticline and related structures.   (*After John Rodgers, Am. Assoc. Petroleum Geologists Bull., 34.*)

FIG. 8.12    Grassy Cove and another small solution valley just north of Sequatchie Valley.    (*Photo by John S. Shelton.*)

following arguments in support of this theory: (1) drainage lines in the Middlesboro Basin north of Cumberland Gap converge toward the south; (2) Powell River, the commonly presumed captor, flows in an extremely meandering and entrenched course, which is hardly compatible with the idea that it was the pirating stream; (3) some drainage from the Middlesboro Basin still goes to the south through gaps in Cumberland Mountain; (4) the Powell River is at too low an altitude ever to have flowed through Cumberland Gap. These arguments lend strong support to the probability that when Cumberland Gap was a watergap, drainage through it was to the south.

### Cumberland Plateau Section

The topography of the Cumberland Plateau section resembles very much that of the Unglaciated Allegheny Plateau to the north.

Differences between the two may be enough to justify their recognition as separate units, but the boundary between the two must be drawn rather arbitrarily. The two main differences between the two sections, and these are not everywhere apparent, are that the percentage of resistant rocks is somewhat higher and dissection has proceeded somewhat farther at the south than at the north. A viewer looking across the Cumberland Plateau does not get so strong an impression that he is viewing the remnants of an ancient erosion surface of low relief as he does in the Allegheny Plateau. Still, it may be argued very well that differentiation of the Allegheny and Cumberland Plateaus is largely for convenience of discussion.

*Sequatchie Anticlinal Valley.* What is probably the most striking topographic feature in the Cumberland Plateau is anticlinal Sequatchie Valley. This valley is in some respects topo-

FIG. 8.13    Gorge of Tennessee River through Walden Ridge.    (*Photo courtesy Tennessee Valley Authority.*)

graphically similar to the synclinal Wyoming Valley in the Ridge and Valley province in eastern Pennsylvania (see p. 118). Wyoming Valley represents an extension of Ridge and Valley topography into the Appalachian Plateau and is separated in part from the Ridge and Valley province, to which it belongs, by the Pocono Mountains. Sequatchie Valley represents a bit of Ridge and Valley structure and topography, but it is considered a part of the Cumberland Plateau because it is separated from the Ridge and Valley province by Walden Ridge and Sand Mountain.

The Sequatchie anticline is some 200 miles long and extends from Cumberland County in east-central Tennessee to central Alabama (Stearns, 1954). It is an asymmetrical fold overturned to the west and broken by a thrust fault along much of its length (see Fig. 8.11). The structure starts at the north in the Crab

Orchard Mountains as a nearly symmetrical fold involving Pennsylvanian sandstones and conglomerates (Rogers, 1950). A short distance south of the Crab Orchard Mountains the fold is breached and the underlying Mississippian limestones are exposed in a karst basin called Grassy Cove (see Fig. 8.12). A short way south of Grassy Cove the anticlinal structure has risen high enough that Ordovician rocks are exposed in the valley and the fold becomes notably asymmetrical; still farther south the fold's northwest flank is broken by a thrust fault which continues southwestward for approximately 130 miles. South from Guntersville, Alabama, the structural pattern changes in a reverse order to that just described, ending finally in the Black Warrior coalfield as a symmetrical anticline similar to that present in the Crab Orchard Mountains.

Rich (1934) suggested that the Sequatchie

anticline may have been created by movement similar to that which produced the Cumberland thrust block. Stearns (1954) suggested that the system of faults which extends southwestward from the Emory River fault at the northeast end of the anticline may represent a system of faults bounding a low-angle thrust sheet similar to that of the Cumberland thrust sheet. It perhaps is not mere chance that the Sequatchie anticline is in almost exact line with the Pine Mountain fault on the northwest side of the Cumberland thrust block, although separated from this fault by 30 miles of apparently undisturbed rocks.

Grassy Cove throws light on one process by which the Sequatchie Valley has been extended lengthwise. Grassy Cove is a solution or karst valley now detached from the Sequatchie Valley proper. Undoubtedly subsurface solution contributed to the deroofing of this basin; eventually the clastic rocks separating it from the Sequatchie Valley to the southwest will be removed, and Grassy Cove will become a part of the Sequatchie Valley. If Figure 8.12 is examined, in the immediate foreground will be noted the beginning of another solution basin northeast of Grassy Cove. This basin will enlarge and in time attain a size comparable with Grassy Cove; still later, it will become an extension of the Sequatchie Valley.

*Tennessee River Gorge.* The gorge of the Tennessee River through synclinal Walden Ridge (see Fig. 8.13) is a striking feature, the significance of which has been discussed in Chapter 7. After flowing through Walden Ridge the Tennessee River enters the Sequatchie Valley and follows it for about 75 miles before turning northwest again into the Cumberland Plateau.

### Erosional History of Appalachian Plateaus

West of the mountainous eastern portion of the Appalachian Plateaus the upland topography, except adjacent to major valleys, is so commonly rolling in nature that it is not surprising that many geologists have been inclined to interpret the plateau surface as a former erosion surface or peneplain. Some geologists have thought they saw evidence of other erosion surfaces below the upland level. There has been marked disagreement as to how many erosion surfaces are preserved in the plateau topography; the number ranges from one (Ashley, 1935) to four (Cole, 1941, and Shaffer, 1947). Table 8.2 represents the views held by some workers in this area. At the north, the names Kittatinny, Schooley, and Upland have been variously applied to the oldest and highest erosion surface; in the south, Cumberland, as proposed by Hayes (1899), is more commonly used to designate a presumably equivalent erosion surface.

One of the major points of difference concerns the reality and position of the alleged Allegheny peneplain (see p. 80). At least three interpretations have been given to it: (1) it is the same as the Schooley or Kittatinny, (2) it is younger than the Schooley-Kittatinny but older than the Harrisburg, and (3) it is the same surface that has been called the Harrisburg. Fridley and Nölting (1931), who introduced the term Allegheny, thought that the Allegheny peneplain occupied an intermediate position between the uppermost erosion surface, called by them Kittatinny, and the lower Harrisburg surface of Campbell (1903). Ver Steeg (1940) considered the Allegheny surface equivalent to the Harrisburg. It may well be that Ashley's views are pertinent to the "Allegheny peneplain" problem and that this surface is a part of the differentially lowered older Schooley-Kittatinny surface.

Good evidence exists in the western part of the Appalachian Plateaus province for the Parker strath subcycle in the form of benches along major valleys not only in the Allegheny and Cumberland plateaus but also westward in the Interior Low Plateaus province. This subcycle may have extended into early Pleistocene time, but it was mainly preglacial; it seems to have been ended by the oncoming of the glaciers. Whether it was the Nebraskan or Kansan ice advance that terminated this subcycle can not be stated definitely, but present evidence seems to favor the Kansan ice advance. The Parker strath has been correlated by several geologists with the Somerville surface in the east. Two objections might be made to this: first, the areas

TABLE 8.2   Correlations of Erosion Surfaces in Appalachian Plateaus

| Hayes (1899) | Fridley-Nölting (1931) | Ver Steeg (1940) | Cole (1941) | Shaffer (1947) |
|---|---|---|---|---|
|  |  |  | Upland | Upland |
| Cumberland | Kittatinny | Kittatinny-Schooley |  |  |
|  | Allegheny-Weverton |  |  |  |
| Highland Rim | Harrisburg | Harrisburg-Worthington-Lexington | Harrisburg | Lexington |
| Coosa |  | Parker Strath-Somerville | Somerville | Parker Strath |

are too far apart to justify such a correlation; second, there is reason to doubt the cyclical significance of the Somerville lowland, whereas the Parker strath is regional in extent and is developed across rocks of varying lithology and therefore has much better grounds for being considered cyclically significant.

## REFERENCES CITED

Ashley, G. H. (1935).   Studies in Appalachian mountain structure, *Geol. Soc. Am. Bull.*, **46**, 1395–1436.

Brigham, A. P. (1898).   Topography and glacial deposits of Mohawk Valley, *Geol. Soc. Am. Bull.*, **9**, 183–210.

Butts, Charles (1927).   Fensters in the Cumberland overthrust block, *Va. Geol. Surv. Bull.* 28, 1–12.

Campbell, M. R. (1903).   Geographic development of northern Pennsylvania and southern New York, *Geol. Soc. Am. Bull.*, **14**, 277–296.

Chadwick, G. H. (1935).   Rock streams in New York, *Geol. Soc. Am. Proc. for 1934*, 70 (abs.).

Chamberlin, T. C. (1882).   Preliminary paper on the terminal moraine of the second glacial epoch, *U. S. Geol. Survey 3rd Ann. Rept.*, 295–402.

Cole, W. S. (1941).   Nomenclature and correlation of Appalachian erosion surfaces, *Jour. Geol.*, **49**, 129–148.

Denny, C. S. (1956).   Surfiacil geology and gemor-

phology of Potter County, Pennsylvania, *U. S. Geol. Survey Profess. Paper* 288, 72 pp.

Fairchild, H. L. (1925).   The Susquehanna River in New York and evolution of western New York drainage, *New York State Museum Bull.* 256, 99 pp.

——— (1932).   New York moraines, *Geol. Soc. Am. Bull.*, **43**, 627–662.

Fenneman, N. M. (1938) *Physiography of Eastern United States*, McGraw-Hill Book Company, New York, 712 pp.

Fridley, H. M., and J. P. Nölting (1931).   Peneplains of the Appalachian Plateau, *Jour. Geol.*, **39**, 749–755.

Hayes, C. W. (1899).   Physiography of the Chattanooga district, *U. S. Geol. Survey 19th Ann. Rept.*, Pt. 2, 1–58.

MacClintock, Paul, and E. T. Apfel (1944).   Correlation of the drifts of the Salamanaca reentrant, New York, *Geol. Soc. Am. Bull.*, **55**, 1143–1164.

Manos, Constantine (1961).   Petrography of the Teays-Mahomet Valley deposits, *Jour. Sed. Petrology*, **31**, 456–465.

Miller, R. L. and J. O. Fuller (1954).   Geology and oil resources of the Rose Hill district–the fenster area of the Cumberland overthrust block, Lee County, Virginia, *Va. Geol. Surv. Bull.* 71, 383 pp.

Moss, J. H., and D. F. Ritter (1962).   New evidence regarding the Binghamton substage in the region between the Finger Lakes and the Catskills, *Am. Jour. Sci.*, **260**, 81–106.

Price, P. H. (1931). The Appalachian structural front, *Jour. Geol.*, **39**, 24–44.

Rhodehamel, E. C., and C. W. Carlston (1963). Geologic history of the Teays Valley in West Virginia, *Geol. Soc. Am. Bull.*, **74**, 251–274.

Rich, J. L. (1933). Physiography and structure at Cumberland Gap, *Geol. Soc. Am. Bull.*, **44**, 1219–1236.

—— (1934). Mechanics of low-angle overthrust faulting as illustrated by Cumberland thrust block, Virginia, Kentucky, and Tennessee, *Am. Assoc. Petroleum Geologists Bull.*, **18**, 1584–1596.

Rodgers, John (1950). Mechanics of Appalachian folding as illustrated by Sequatchie anticline, Tennessee and Alabama, *Am. Assoc. Petroleum Geologists Bull.*, **34**, 672–681.

Ruedemann, Rudolph (1932). Development of drainage of Catskills, *Am. Jour. Sci.*, **223**, 337–349.

Shaffer, Paul (1947). Correlation of erosion surfaces of the southern Appalachians, *Jour. Geol.*, **55**, 343–352.

Shepps, V. C., G. W. White, J. B. Droste, and R. F. Sitler (1959). Glacial geology of northwestern Pennsylvania, *Pa. Geol. Surv. Bull.*, *4th Series*, G-32, 59 pp.

Smith, H. T. U. (1953). The Hickory Run boulder field, Carbon County, Pennsylvania, *Am. Jour. Sci.*, **251**, 625–642.

Stearns, R. G. (1954). The Cumberland Plateau overthrust and geology of the Crab Orchard Mountains area, Tennessee, *Tenn. Div. Geol. Bull.* 60, 47 pp.

Stout, Wilber, and Downs Schaaf (1931). The Mimford silts of southern Ohio, *Geol. Soc. Am. Bull.*, **42**, 663–672.

Tight, W. G. (1903). Drainage modifications in southeastern Ohio and adjacent parts of West Virginia and Kentucky, *U. S. Geol. Survey Profess. Paper* 13, 111 pp.

Ver Steeg, Karl (1940). Correlation of Appalachian peneplains, *Pan-American Geologist*, **73**, 203–210.

Von Engeln, O. D. (1961). *The Finger Lakes Region; Its Origin and Nature*, Cornell Univ. Press, Ithaca, 156 pp.

Wentworth, C. K. (1921). Russell Fork fault of southwest Virginia, *Jour. Geol.*, **29**, 351–369.

ADDITIONAL REFERENCES

Cole, W. S. (1934). Identification of erosion surfaces in eastern and southern Ohio, *Jour. Geol.*, **42**, 285–294.

—— (1938). Erosion surfaces of western and central New York, *Jour. Geol.*, **46**, 191–206.

Denny, C. S. (1956). Wisconsin drifts in the Elmira region, New York, and their possible equivalents in New England, *Am. Jour. Sci.*, **254**, 82–95.

Fairchild, H. L. (1934). Cayuga Valley lake history, *Geol. Soc. Am. Bull.*, **45**, 233–280.

Fridley, H. M. (1929). Identification of erosion surfaces in south central New York, *Jour. Geol.*, **37**, 113–134.

—— (1950). The geomorphic history of the New-Kanawha river system. *W. Va. Geol. Surv. Rept. Invest.* 7, 12 pp.

Happ, Stafford (1934). Drainage history of southeastern Ohio and adjacent West Virginia, *Jour. Geol.*, **42**, 264–284.

Holmes, C. D. (1952). Drift dispersion in west central New York, *Geol. Soc. Am. Bull.*, **63**, 993–1010.

Miller, R. L., and W. P. Brosgé (1954). Geology and oil resources of the Jonesville district, Lee County, Virginia, *U. S. Geol. Survey Bull.* 990, 240 pp.

Monette, V. E. (1924). The Finger Lakes of central New York, *Am. Jour. Sci.*, **208**, 33–53.

Shaw, E. W. (1911). High terraces and abandoned valleys in western Pennsylvania, *Jour. Geol.*, **19**, 140–156.

Stearns, R. G. (1955). Low-angle overthrusting in the central Cumberland Plateau, *Geol. Soc. Am. Bull.*, **66**, 615–628.

Stout, Wilber, and G. F. Lamb (1938). Physiographic features of southeastern Ohio, *Ohio Jour. Sci.*, **38**, 49–83.

White, G. W. (1934) Drainage history of north central Ohio, *Ohio Jour. Sci.*, **34**, 365–382.

Wilson, C. W., Jr., and R. G. Stearns (1958). Structure of the Cumberland Plateau, Tennessee, *Geol. Soc. Am. Bull.*, **69**, 1283–1296.

Young, D. M. (1957). Deep drilling through Cumberland overthrust block in southwestern Virginia, *Am. Assoc. Petroleum Geologists Bull.*, **41**, 2567–2573.

# New England Province

## RELATION TO OTHER PROVINCES

Fundamentally New England is a northward extension of Appalachian geology and topography. The Piedmont, Blue Ridge, and Ridge and Valley provinces to some degree have their counterparts in New England, but not the Appalachian Plateaus. Recognition of New England as a separate province is to a certain extent a matter of convenience. New England sends two arms or prongs southwestward that help to connect it geologically with the Appalachian provinces. The Manhattan prong terminates at the tip of Manhattan Island, but the more northerly Reading prong extends beyond the Hudson River to Reading, Pennsylvania. The Reading prong is about 140 miles long and attains a maximum width of 25 miles in the Highlands, where the Hudson River has cut a gorge through it. The major difference between New England and the other Appalachian provinces is the fact that all of New England bears an imprint of glaciation, whereas only the northern end of the Appalachian Highlands was glaciated.

The Reading and Manhattan prongs are counterparts of the Blue Ridge, and this same type of geology continues northward through the Hoosac Mountains and Berkshire Hills into the Green Mountains. Southeast of this geological belt is the New England Upland, the counterpart of the Piedmont Plateau. West of the Hoosac Mountains and Berkshire Hills are the Taconic Mountains, which, although considerably different topographically, might be considered the geological equivalent of the Ridge and Valley province. The White Mountains, which are large enough and distinctive enough to merit recognition as a separate section, have no counterpart at the south, unless the extensive belt of monadnocks in the western Piedmont area from Virginia to Georgia is considered such.

## GEOLOGY AND STRUCTURE

New England has an affinity with the southern Appalachian Highlands in that its rocks have been subjected to folding, faulting, and intrusion by igneous bodies, after which they were deeply denuded first by fluvial agents and later, in New England, by glaciers. Extensive areas of gneiss, schist, slate, marble, and quartzite are evidence of the widespread metamorphism that has taken place. Similarly, large bodies of granite, diorite, granodiorite, and other granitoid rocks are the surface manifestation of many intrusive rock masses that are present in the area (see Fig. 9.1).

As in the Piedmont area, most of the igneous-metamorphic rock complex in New England was once thought to be Precambrian in age, but it is now known that many of the metamorphic rocks are metamorphosed Paleozoic sedimentaries or volcanics and that numerous igneous intrusive bodies are Paleozoic in age. Rocks of the Manhattan prong, known as the Fordham gneiss, Lowerre quartzite, Inwood marble, and Manhattan schist and gneiss, present a lithologic sequence very similar to that found north of the Highlands (Reading prong) where Precambrian gneisses are overlain by a Cambro-Ordovician sedimentary sequence known as the Poughquag quartzite, Wappinger dolomite, and Hudson

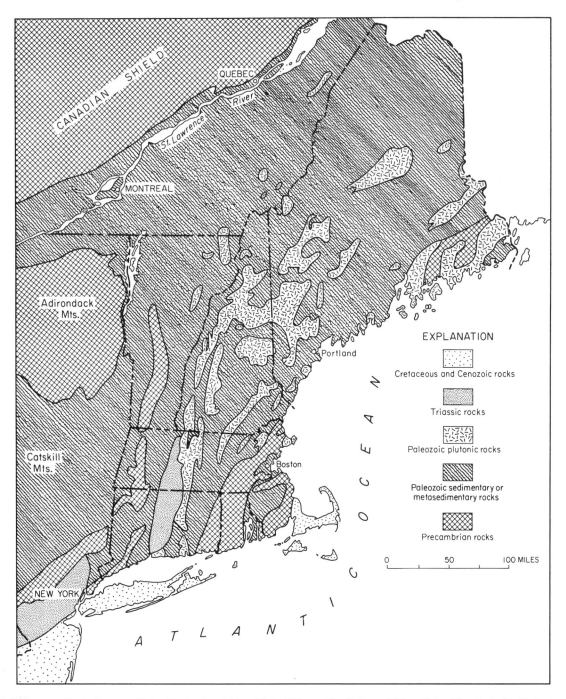

FIG. 9.1   Geologic map of New England.   *(After M. P. Billings, The Geology of New Hampshire, Pt. 2, N. H. State Planning and Development Commission.)*

River shale. Potassium-argon age determinations (Long and Kulp, 1958) indicate that metamorphism of the rocks of the Manhattan prong took place about 365 million years ago. This does not date the rocks, but it does make it reasonable to consider the rocks of the Manhattan prong metamorphosed Cambro-Ordovician sediments, similar in age to the essentially unmetamorphosed sediments north of the Reading prong.

Billings (1933) has estimated that in New Hampshire probably 90 per cent of the igneous rocks are younger than early Devonian. These rocks intrude metasedimentary and metavolcanic rocks ranging in age from Cambrian to Carboniferous. Four magma series have been recognized here, the Highlandcraft (late Ordovician ?), the Oliverian (middle Devonian), the New Hampshire series (middle or late Devonian), and the White Mountain series (probably Mississippian) (Billings, 1945). These igneous bodies or plutons take the forms of stocks, sheets, lenses, batholiths, and the less common ring dikes. Ring dikes are particularly common in New Hampshire, and as many as 36 have been described. Some of the more striking ones are those in the Percy Mountains (Chapman, 1935), the Ossippee Mountains (Kingsley, 1931), the Belknap Mountains (Modell, 1936), and the Pliny region (Chapman, 1942).

## EFFECTS OF GLACIATION

### Uncertain Glacial History

Details of the glacial history of New England are still poorly known. A combination of circumstances has made it more difficult to unravel the glacial history of New England than that of Midwestern United States, where the glacial stratigraphy is fairly well understood. More rugged topography, a preponderance of crystalline rocks, and a scarcity of calcareous rocks have resulted in thinner, patchier, and generally noncalcareous tills in New England. New England tills are notably stony, and many of the fields are littered with glacial boulders. Stone fences consisting of boulders cleared from the fields are common sights in New England. Absence of large glacial sluiceways such as the Mississippi, Illinois, Ohio, and Wabash accounts for the lack of intertill loesses that are so useful stratigraphically in the Midwest. The general noncalcareous nature of the till means that comparative depths of leaching can not be used as a means of getting relative ages of tills. Furthermore, end moraines are scarce in New England and can be little used in the mapping and correlation of stages and substages of glaciation. The fact that the outer border of the glaciated area from Cape Cod northward is now submerged has further complicated interpretation of New England's glacial history. At present, the glacial history of New England can be sketched only in rather general terms. It can not be said with certainty that any tills or glacial deposits older than Wisconsin are present. Tills at several places have been described which have been considered pre-Wisconsin, but their age is uncertain. How many times New England was glaciated we do not know.

### Topographic Effects

The difficulties encountered in working out the glacial history of New England by no means imply that the effects of glaciation are inconspicuous topographically. For much of New England the effects of glacial erosion are more conspicuous than are those of deposition, but this may be true partly because the outer margins of the glaciated area, where the effects of glacial deposition are most noticeable, is now submerged. Apparently none of New England escaped glaciation. Mountain peaks in the Presidential Range, Mount Katahdin, and the Green Mountains all give evidence of having been overtopped by the ice sheets that invaded New England.

Possibly the most widespread effect of glaciation was a general smoothing off of the bedrock topography, resulting in the development in many areas of rounded rock bosses that are drumlinoid in form. Lineation of topography in many areas reflects the effects of differential erosion along the foliation in belts of metamorphic rocks, and

FIG. 9.2  Portion of drowned New England coast at Boothbay Harbor, Maine.  (*Photo by Fairchild Aerial Surveys, Inc.*)

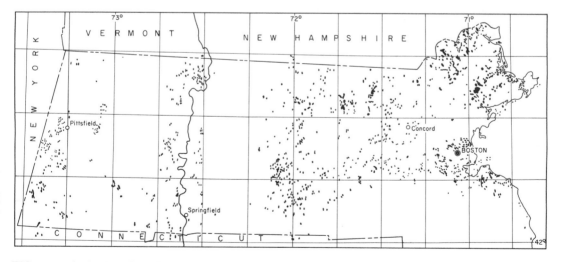

FIG. 9.3  Distribution of drumlinoid features in Massachusetts.  (*After W. C. Alden, U. S. Geol. Survey Bull.* 760-B.)

FIG. 9.4   Distribution of Pleistocene ice contact and marine deposits in New England.   (*After Glacial Map of United States East of the Rocky Mountains, Geol. Soc. Am.*)

many valleys parallel the strike of the rock belts. This shows up strikingly along the northern Maine coast, where submergence has resulted in parallel embayments extending up valleys on the belts of weak rock (see Fig. 9.2).

Depositional features are not lacking, despite the general patchiness of the glacial deposits. One of the major drumlin belts of the United States is in Massachusetts and southeastern New Hampshire. About 3000 drumlinoid features mark this belt, but many of them are erosional "rock drumlins" rather than true drumlins (see Fig. 9.3). Scarcity of end moraines is in part compensated for by a great abundance of ice-contact features. Maine is noted for its fine esker systems and other ice-contact forms such as kames and kame terraces (see Fig. 9.4).

*Method of Final Ice Wastage*

There is much evidence to suggest that during the final phases of deglaciation downwasting of stagnant ice was relatively more important in New England than in other parts of the United States. Scarcity of end moraines, abundance of ice contact features (kames, kame terraces, eskers, and crevasse fillings), and scarcity of glacial outwash all support this view. Different ideas have been expressed as to the nature of the final dissipation of the ice. Three methods of ice wastage have been suggested: (1) "normal retreat," with a moving ice mass whose front receded because melting in the terminal zone exceeded alimentation; (2) active ice with a narrow marginal zone in which large blocks of ice became stagnant and wasted in place (this zone of stagnant ice was supposed to have shifted northward with the retreating ice front ice); (3) regional stagnation of most of the ice south of a line extending from the Adirondacks to the mountains of northern Maine.

Flint (1929, 1930) at first advocated the third method and pictured a large body of stagnant ice detached from the main mass of ice to the north. He later (1932) abandoned this theory in favor of the idea of a marginal zone of stagnant ice adjacent to an actively retreating ice front. This seems to be the viewpoint that is most favored at present. It is still believed that the many ice-contact features were associated with masses of stagnant ice, but stagnation is now pictured as being local rather than regional in extent, as first thought.

As pictured by Goldthwait (1938), downwasting resulted in uncovering first the higher peaks and mountainous areas, leading to the development of a very ragged ice border which continued to shrink in disorderly fashion, leading eventually to many stagnant narrow ice tongues in valleys around which the kame terraces, crevasse fillings, and other ice contact deposits accumulated.

## DIVISION OF NEW ENGLAND INTO SECTIONS

Much of New England may be described as a plateau-like upland that rises gradually inland from the sea and is surmounted at numerous places by mountain ranges or individual peaks. The principal mountain ranges are the Green, Taconic, and White. Lesser areas that rise above the general level of the New England upland are the Hoosac Mountains and Berkshire Hills in western Massachusetts and such isolated peaks as Mount Monadnock, in New Hampshire, and Mount Katahdin, in Maine.

Sufficient variety in topography and geology exists to justify recognition of five, if not six, geomorphic sections. The Fenneman classification recognizes the Taconic, Green Mountain, New England Upland, White Mountain, and Seaboard sections. It might be argued that the Connecticut Valley could be given sectional rank rather than considered a part of the New England Upland.

The Taconic section consists mainly of somewhat disorderly mountains developed on metamorphosed sedimentary rocks. The mountains are bordered on the east by a linear valley and on the west by a plateau-like tract. Most of the area lies below an altitude of 2000 feet.

The Green Mountains are the topographic expression of a great anticlinorium with a core of crystalline Precambrian rocks mantled by a variety of metamorphosed Paleozoic rocks.

They merit the name "mountains" more than do the Taconics, as maximum altitudes in the Green Mountains exceed 4000 feet.

The New England Upland is an area of complex geology and structure that was maturely dissected by fluvial processes and later subjected to severe glaciation. Its general altitude varies from a little over 500 feet at its seaward margin to around 1200 feet inland.

The White Mountain section includes a somewhat irregular group of residual mountains that rise well above the level of the New England Upland and are extensive enough to merit recognition as a separate geomorphic unit.

The Seaboard Lowland is a strip of land along the coast that rises little more than 500 feet above sea level and whose topography and geomorphic history seem to be sufficiently different from that of the adjacent New England Upland to justify recognition as a separate section.

### Taconic Section

*Topographic Setting.* The Taconic Mountains at the south lie west of the Hoosac Mountains and Berkshire Hills, southern extensions of the Green Mountains, and at the north are separated from the Green Mountains by a narrow steep-walled valley known as the Valley of Vermont. On the west the Taconic Mountains are bounded by the Hudson-Champlain Lowland. The Taconic Mountains merge with the Highlands of the Hudson in the vicinity of Poughquag, New York. Any farther south than here a distinction between the Taconic Mountains and the Hoosac Mountains and Berkshire Hills is difficult to make, as the two highland tracts merge into the southwestward extensions of New England geology known as the Reading and Manhattan prongs.

The Valley of Vermont (see Fig. 9.5) is about 85 miles long in Vermont, but along the Vermont-Massachusetts boundary it is interrupted for a short distance by an east-west ridge. The valley reappears, however, just north of Williamstown, Massachusetts, and the Stockbridge, Canaan, and Pawling valleys are southern continuations of this valley. There is, however, no through-going stream in the valley. The Lower Cambrian Rutland dolomite underlies much of the valley floor.

*Topographic Characteristics.* The Taconic Mountains are composed predominantly of slates, schists, and phyllites, but there are belts of carbonate rocks which generally form valleys, none of which is as large or continuous as the Valley of Vermont on the east. Summit altitudes commonly are around 1800 to 2000 feet, but a few are as high as 2500 feet. In general, altitudes decrease southward.

Two nonmountainous areas are included in the Taconic section. One is the previously mentioned limestone valley on the east and the other is the Rensselaer Plateau on the west. This plateau is about 20 miles long and less than 10 miles wide. It is underlain by Cambrian quartzites and is boulder covered as a result of glaciation. Its surface is rolling topography, in contrast to the sharp ridges and narrow valleys which characterize the Taconic Mountains proper.

If analogies were to be drawn between geologic and topographic belts in New England and the southern Appalachians, the Taconic Mountains might be considered the counterpart of the Ridge and Valley province. Certain similarities exist between the two areas, but there are also marked differences. They are alike in that rocks of essentially equivalent ages are found in both regions; there is lineation of the topography in both areas related to the axes of folds; and a prominent limestone valley lies at the east side of each area, the Great Valley in the Ridge and Valley province and the Valley of Vermont in the Taconic section.

However, the topography of the two areas is so different that it may seem to be stretching a point to consider the two areas comparable. The Taconic Mountains do not display the straightness, parallelism, continuity, regularity of width, or subaccordance of summit levels that are found in the ridges of the Ridge and Valley province. Valleys are proportionately less important in the Taconic section, and even where present they lack the width and length of the Appalachian valleys. Many of the valleys in the Ridge and

FIG. 9.5 Valley of Vermont with Taconic Mountains in background, near Bennington, Vermont. (*Photo by Fairchild Aerial Surveys, Inc.*)

Valley section are expansive enough to be considered lowlands, but this is not true of Taconic valleys.

Yet despite these differences there is a rough resemblance of Taconic geomorphology to that of the Ridge and Valley province in that the ridges are elongate and they are separated to a certain degree by longitudinal valleys, which may be either anticlinal or synclinal in nature. At least five streams in the area are transverse to the regional structure. Accordance of ridge summits is too poorly evident to suggest the existence of an upland erosion surface.

*Taconic Klippe Problem.* The age and structural relationships of the rocks comprising the Taconic Ranges have long been in dispute. Perhaps the most prevalent viewpoint is that the Taconic Mountains are the remnants of a great thrust sheet commonly called the Taconic Overthrust. The idea of a Taconic klippe was originally proposed to account for the presence of an argillaceous rock sequence in the Taconics adjacent to carbonate sequences in the Hudson, Champlain, and Vermont valleys. The Taconic problem is a very old problem in American geology and as it originally evolved was largely a stratigraphic problem involving age determination of a large-scale stratigraphic sequence dated by few fossils. It will be apparent that the problem of the "Taconic Thrust" is essentially the same problem encountered in the "Marctic thrust," and there is about as much difference of opinion regarding its reality as there is for the Marctic thrust.

Apparently Ruedemann (1909) was the first

to suggest that the rocks of the Taconic Range had been thrust westward along a low-angle thrust plane over carbonate rocks such as can be seen to the west, north, and east of the Taconic Range. According to this interpretation, the limestone tracts within the Taconic valleys are fensters. The sole of the Taconic thrust has nowhere been seen, and the amount of probable movement is rather uncertain. Kay (1937) drew the boundaries of the "Taconic klippe" on a palinspastic map and showed the thrust as having originated in the vicinity of Boston. The "Taconic klippe" was shown on the Tectonic Map of the United States (1944) as being about 100 miles long north-south and as much as 40 miles wide.

Numerous geologists in recent years have denied the existence of the "Taconic klippe." Bucher (1957) considered the evidence in the southern half of the region as incompatible with this interpretation. Weaver (1953) concluded that the geology in the Copake area, New York, did not support the klippe concept. He considered the structure to be imbricate in nature, consisting of several reverse fault blocks involving both carbonate and argillaceous rocks. Craddock (1957) from his work in the Kinderhook, New York, quadrangle concluded that the biggest argument against the "Taconic klippe" is that it is next to impossible to define its boundaries accurately. MacFadyen (1956), from a study of the Bennington, Vermont, area, decided that there is no klippe and that the phyllites of the Taconic Range are in normal stratigraphic sequence and simply represent a change of facies. Herz (1955) found that his mapping in western Massachusetts failed to reveal the sole of the thrust between marble and schist, and he interpreted the contact between the two as a major unconformity and considered the rocks otherwise in normal sequence.

On the other hand, Hawkes (1941), Kaiser (1945), Cady (1945), and Fowler (1950) concluded that the Taconic thrust sheet or klippe does exist. We thus seem to be no nearer reaching a firm conclusion regarding the "Taconic klippe" than we were when the argument began over 50 years ago. Certainly the rocks of the Taconic Mountains are different from those to the east, west, and north. Whether this is so because they have been thrust a long distance from the east, because of a change in facies, or because of the presence of an unconformity cannot be stated, but the change in lithology is responsible for a marked difference in the landscape of the Taconic Mountains from that on the limestone terrains to the east and west.

### Green Mountain Section

The Green Mountains are the dominant topographic feature of Vermont; their southern extension into Massachusetts is known as the Hoosac Mountains and their northern extension into Canada as the Notre Dame Mountains. The Green Mountains are about 20 miles wide at the Canadian border and 35 miles wide at the Massachusetts boundary. Their average altitude is not much over 2000 feet, but Mount Mansfield, their highest peak, exceeds 4000 feet in altitude.

*Rocks and Structure.* According to Brace (1953), the Green Mountains structurally consist of a central anticlinorium, a western synclinorium marked by numerous thrust sheets, and an eastern homoclinal structure. Rocks forming the core of the mountains are Precambrian schists, gneisses, quartzites, and other metamorphic rocks which have been intruded by granite and basic rocks (Jacobs, 1950). Degree of metamorphism increases from west to east. A view held by several geologists is that the Green Mountains are a great allocthone which has been thrust westward into the Champlain Lowland along what is called the Border fault. The Green Mountains are the geological counterpart of the Blue Ridge, even to the extent that both are believed to be bounded on the west side by faults. Along the entire mountain length Precambrian rocks of the central core separate Cambrian and Ordovician limestones, dolomites, and quartzites on the west from argillaceous and volcanic rocks of uncertain age on the east (Brace, 1958).

*Erosion Surfaces.* The Green Mountains are mature mountains that retain suggestions of former periods of local baseleveling at least in

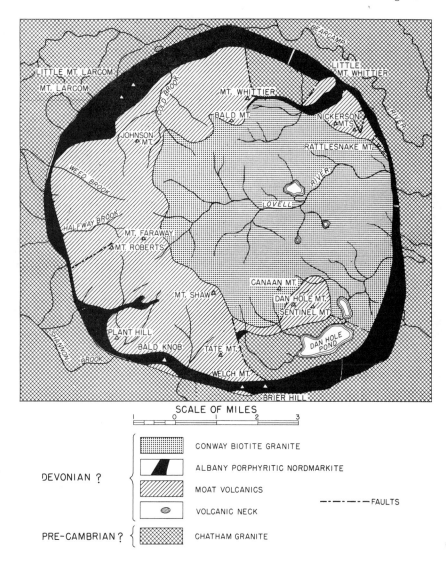

DEVONIAN ?
- CONWAY BIOTITE GRANITE
- ALBANY PORPHYRITIC NORDMARKITE
- MOAT VOLCANICS
- VOLCANIC NECK

------- FAULTS

PRE-CAMBRIAN ?
- CHATHAM GRANITE

SCALE OF MILES

FIG. 9.6 Geologic map of Ossipee Mountains, New Hampshire, showing nordmarkite ring dike. (*After Louise Kingsley, Am. Jour. Sci.*, **222**.)

the persistence of certain topographic levels. Meyerhoff and Hubbell (1928), from a study of topographic profiles of the Green Mountains, concluded that there is a strong suggestion of a series of fluvial terraces that can best be interpreted as the result of intermittent vertical uplift (see p. 164).

*New England Upland Section*

*Rocks and Structure.* The rocks of the New England Upland are folded, faulted, and meta-morphosed sediments and volcanics that have been intruded by numerous plutonic masses. In addition to the granite plutons, numerous ring dikes varying in diameter from 1.6 miles to 18.4 miles are present. Ring dikes encompassing 360 degrees are rare, but one such (see Fig. 9.6) is found in the Ossipee Mountains (Kingsley, 1931).

*Topographic Characteristics.* The surface of the New England Upland slopes southeastward from maximum inland altitudes around 2200 feet to

FIG. 9.7    Mount Monadnock and New England Upland, looking northwest.    (*Photo by John S. Shelton.*)

about 400 to 500 feet at its seaward edge. Some question may exist as to whether this section should be continued to the sea, but a narrow belt along the coast has been set aside as the Seaboard section—not because its geology is particularly different from that of the New England Upland, but because its geomorphic history has been somewhat different. The topography of the New England Upland is that of a maturely dissected plateau which has been appreciably modified by glaciation. Numerous hills and mountains rise above the general level of the upland (see Fig. 9.7), and at the north these mountainous areas become numerous and extensive enough to justify their inclusion in the separate White Mountain section.

*Glacial Modifications.* Both the erosional and depositional effects of glaciation are widespread and conspicuous in the New England Upland. Probably the most important erosional effect has been a rounding off of the bedrock topography

with resultant production of many drumlinoid rock bosses. Lakes are numerous; most of them are in rock basins, for morainal dams are not common in New England.

The glacial drift on the New England Upland on the whole is thin, patchy, and stony, largely because the resistant rocks of New England were not readily eroded and ground to the silt- and clay-size particles that characterize many of the tills of Midwestern United States. As already noted, end moraines are notably lacking, but ice-contact features such as kames, kame terraces, and eskers are abundant (see Fig. 9.4).

*Interpretations of New England Upland*

THEORY OF PENEPLANATION. The erosional history of the New England Upland has been the subject of considerable debate. Davis (1896) interpreted the upland of southern New England as a single-cycle erosional surface of fluviatile origin, developed presumably in late Cretaceous time, which in terms of present terminology would mean that it was the northern continuation of the Schooley or Kittatinny peneplain. Later, conventional Appalachian geomorphic interpretation was given to the region by Atwood (1940). He correlated the upland surface with the Schooley peneplain, considered such mountains as the Green, White, and Katahdin as monadnocks rising above this erosion surface, and found evidence of the Harrisburg cycle in benches several hundred feet above present valley floors. The present cycle was supposed to be represented by the entrenched valleys below the level of the Harrisburg benches.

THEORY OF MARINE TERRACING. Barrell (1913, 1920) challenged peneplanation as an explanation of the New England Upland landscape and suggested that the topography, instead of rising regularly inland, as a peneplain surface should, represents a flight of marine terraces. This conclusion was reached from a study of a large number of projected profiles (see Fig. 9.8). Barrell thought he saw evidence of eleven terraces in the New England Upland (see Fig. 9.9). The marine terraces were believed to extend southward as far as the Piedmont province and were correlated by Barrell with geological formations underlying the Atlantic Coastal Plain ranging in age from Upper Cretaceous to Pleistocene.

The terrace sequence, characteristic altitude, and age of each terrace as suggested by Barrell were as follows:

| Terrace Name | Characteristic Altitude | Suggested Age |
|---|---|---|
| Becket terrace | 2440–2450 | Cretaceous |
| Canaan terrace | 2000 | Cretaceous |
| Cornwall | 1720 | Oligocene |
| Goshen | 1380 | Pliocene |
| Litchfield | 1140 | Pliocene |
| Prospect | 940 | Pliocene |
| Towantic | 730–740 | Pliocene |
| Appomattox (Lafayette) | 500–540 | Pliocene |
| New Canaan | 340–400 | Pleistocene |
| Sunderland | 200–240 | Pleistocene |
| Wicomico | 80–120 | Pleistocene |

Barrell (1913) saw in the terrace sequence implication of the following chronological events:

1. Advance of the sea over a Cretaceous peneplain, with ensuing cutting of the Becket terrace at its inward margin.
2. A slight emergence followed by stability during which the Canaan terrace was cut.
3. A marked emergence in Eocene time during which there was a long period of subaerial erosion.
4. Readvance of sea with cutting of Cornwall terrace.
5. Emergence of several hundred feet accompanied by fluvial dissection of the emergent surface.
6. Readvance of sea with cutting of Goshen terrace.
7–9. Successive emergences marked by standstills of sea level long enough for cutting of the Litchfield, Prospect, and Towantic terraces.
10–13. Eustatic changes of sea level resulting in the cutting of the Appomattox (Lafayette), New Canaan, Sunderland, and Wicomico terraces.

Adams (1945) agreed that Barrell's projected profiles did demonstrate that the new England Upland surface is by no means a smoothly seaward-sloping plain, but he was not convinced that the features described by Barrell as marine terraces are even significant features of the landscape; he was inclined to regard them as some of the many facets of a topography which has various slopes that may be attributed to fluvial erosion.

Sharp (1929) and Johnson (1931) also took issue with Barrell's interpretation of the New England Upland surface. They believed that the New England Upland surface consists of two distinct erosional surfaces, an older ressurected peneplain (the Fall Zone peneplain) adjacent to the coast and a younger peneplain surface inland that was never covered by marine sediments. They rejected the theory of marine terracing for the following reasons:

a. The faint inclinations of the supposed sea cliffs are unlike those of known marine cliffs.
b. The alleged sea cliffs are in numerous areas more faintly inclined than hill slopes con-

sidered by Barrell to be parts of terrace surfaces.

c. Slopes similar to the supposed sea cliffs can be seen facing away from the sea.

d. No sea cliffs are discernible on Mt. Desert Island, Maine, where conditions are excellent for their preservation.

THEORY OF FLUVIAL TERRACING.   Meyerhoff and Hubbell (1928) agreed that the topographic evidence supports the conclusion that the New England Upland is terraced.   They thought that they recognized evidence of fourteen terraces, three more than Barrell saw, but they considered the terraces to be fluvial rather than marine and the result of intermittent uplift of New England without warping.   Although they did not agree with Barrell as to the origin of the terraces, they did agree with him that (1) erosional terraces do exist, (2) the terrace intervals are essentially those recognized by Barrell, (3) the terraces are independent of lithologic or structural control, and (4) the terraces are genetically related to changing levels of land and sea.

The nature of the surface of the New England Upland remains in doubt.   On only one point is there agreement, and that is that it is not a smoothly sloping erosional plain.   Regardless of whether it is a product of fluvial or marine erosion, the surface that we see today is to a considerable degree a product of glacial modification, and thus only in its broader aspects does it retain the character of the pre-Pleistocene topography.

ORIGIN OF HUDSON RIVER GORGE.   In the southwestern extension of New England geology known as the Reading prong one particularly interesting geomorphic problem is the transverse course of the Hudson River across this strong rock belt.   Through what is known as the High-

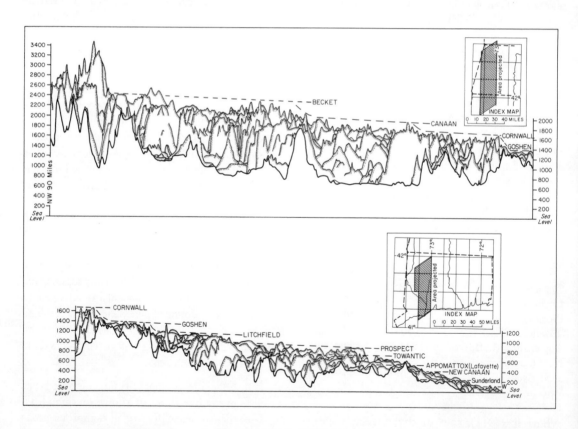

FIG. 9.8   Projected profiles across New England Upland.   (*After Joseph Barrell, Am. Jour. Sci.,* **199**.)

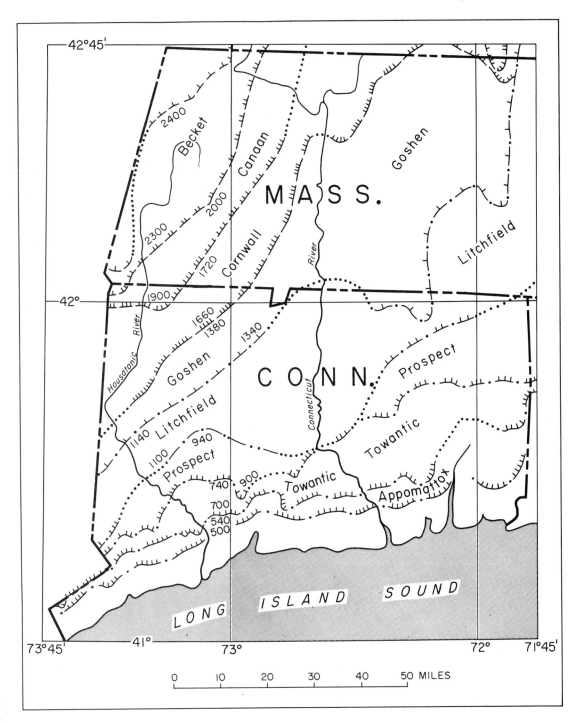

FIG. 9.9   Locations and elevations of postulated marine terraces in Connecticut and western Massachusetts.   (*After Joseph Barrell, Am. Jour. Sci.,* **199.**)

FIG. 9.10    Hudson gorge through the Highlands at Bear Mountain bridge.    (*Photo by Fairchild Aerial Surveys, Inc.*)

lands the Hudson River has cut a gorge (see Fig. 9.10), when it seems it might well have avoided this strong rock barrier by following a southwesterly course down the Valley and Ridge province to where the Schuylkill River flows southeastward at the southern end of the Reading prong.    Various geologists have attempted to explain the seemingly anomalous route of the Hudson River through the Highlands as the result of either stream piracy or superposition. Davis (1891) suggested that the Hudson River assumed its present course on the surface of the Schooley peneplain prior to or at the time of uplift of this erosion surface, and once it was entrenched it was able to maintain its route. Tarr (1902), while admitting the feasability of Davis' theory, suggested as an alternative explanation that a pre-Triassic lowland existed along the general course of the Hudson Valley and that in Triassic or Cretaceous time an arm of the sea extended up this lowland; following withdrawal of the sea the Hudson River was superposed upon the estuarine deposits in this former arm of the sea.    Johnson (1931), as part of his general theory of regional superposition of southeast drainage from a Cretaceous cover mass, included the Hudson gorge as one of the stream courses thus superposed.

Ruedemann (1932) believed that the Susquehanna River originally headed in the Adirondacks and explained the present course of the Hudson River as the result of capture of a southwest-flowing tributary of the ancestral Susquehanna River by a stream that flowed by a shorter route to the Atlantic ocean.    Thompson (1936) supported Ruedemann's general thesis and thought that the present course of the Hudson River was a result of progressive drainage adjustments involving competition of several short Atlantic slope streams for the southwest-draining Susquehanna.    The Hudson was more successful in this competition because its route lay along a weak rock belt between the Palisades and the crystalline belt to the east.    He thought that the capture of the upper drainage of the present Hudson took place during the Harrisburg erosion cycle.    Adams (1958) thought it likely that the course of the Hudson through the Highlands was produced by headward erosion along a weak rock belt, but his view was that the present course represents a modification of one superposed from a Cretaceous cover mass.

*Connecticut Lowland.* The Connecticut River rises in Canada in the province of Quebec and flows southward for some 400 miles into Long Island Sound. In its upper course the river flows in a narrow valley, but a short distance south of the Vermont-New Hampshire-Massachusetts boundary the valley expands into what

is known as the Connecticut Valley Lowland. The Connecticut River follows this lowland to within about 20 miles of Long Island Sound, where, at Middleton, Connecticut, it leaves the lowland and pursues an anomalous southeasterly course across a crystalline rock belt.

The Connecticut Lowland stands out both geologically and topographically from its surroundings, and if it were not for its limited geographic extent it might well be recognized as a separate section of the New England province rather than a subdivision of the New England Upland. The lowland is bordered on the west

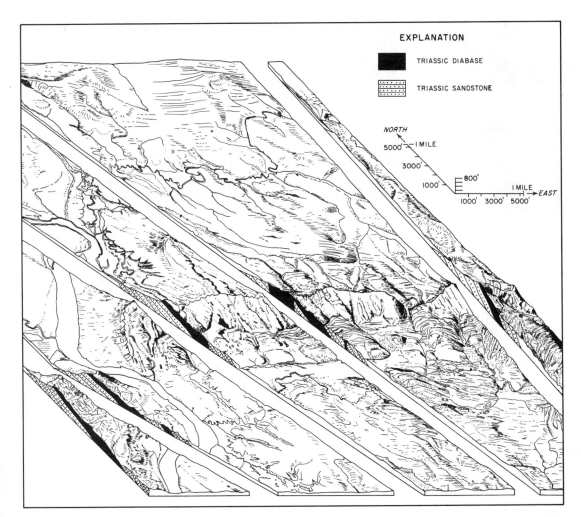

FIG. 9.11 Diagram showing geologic relationships of the Mount Holyoke extrusive sheet. (*After Robert Balk, Geol. Soc. Am. Bull.,* **68.**)

FIG. 9.12    Connecticut River separating two trap ridges, Mt. Tom Range at left and Holyoke Range at right.    (*Photo by John S. Shelton.*)

by the Berkshire Hills and on the east by what is called the Central Upland or Worcester County Plateau, both areas of metamorphic and igneous rocks.

ROCKS AND STRUCTURE. The Connecticut Lowland is underlain largely by Triassic arkosic sandstones, conglomerates, and shales, along with basic igneous rocks of both intrusive and extrusive origin (see Fig. 9.11). The area is one of several basins of Triassic rocks that extend from South Carolina to Bay of Fundy (see Fig. 5.2). Although much of the Triassic rock area is lowland, from its floor rise numerous ridges. Some, such as Mt. Holyoke, Mt. Tom, and the Deerfield Range, are developed on the so-called trap rock (mainly basalt and diabase) associated

with the Triassic sediments (see Fig. 9.12); the two Sugarloafs, however, are ridges of resistant arkosic sandstones and conglomerates. In addition, there are a few hills in the Connecticut Valley that consist of pre-Triassic rocks and represent detached masses of the same rocks that underlie the uplands to either side of the lowland.

Faulting is common in the Connecticut Valley, and many of the trap ridges are offset by faults. Structurally the area may be described as a homocline that is thought to be bounded on the east and west by faults. The Triassic rocks of the Connecticut Valley dip to the east, whereas those in New Jersey dip westward. This has led to speculation as to whether or not the two Triassic areas were at one time connected across the intervening crystalline rock area. This idea is supported by the presence of two small detached areas of Triassic rocks west of the Connecticut Valley. One of these is in the Pomperaug Valley (Hobbs, 1901), and the second is in the Cherry Brook Valley (Platt, 1957). The Pomperaug area lies some 12 miles west of the main Triassic area, whereas the Cherry Brook area is only 1½ miles west of the western edge of the Connecticut Valley Triassic area. In both of these areas the Triassic rocks dip to the east.

GLACIAL HISTORY OF THE CONNECTICUT LOWLAND. As the Wisconsin ice front receded northward, there developed in the Connecticut Lowland, north of Middleton, Connecticut, a body of water which Jahns and Willard (1942) called the Connecticut Valley Lake. This body of water was originally described as a chain of three lakes (Emerson, 1898) named, from south to north, Lake Springfield, Lake Hadley, and Lake Montague. It now seems that Flint's view (1933) that a single body of ponded water lay back of a drift dam at Rocky Hill, Connecticut, with a spillway bottomed on bedrock near New Britain, Connecticut, fits in best with the field evidence. This lake expanded to the north as the ice front receded and was free from contact with the ice except at the north. The drift dam and bedrock spillway at the south probably allowed the lake to maintain a fairly constant level during most of its existence, except toward the end, when the drift dam was breached. At the time of its maximum extent the surface of Connecticut Valley Lake had an altitude of 300 feet, at which time such eminences as Mt. Toby, the Deerfield Range, and Mt. Tom were islands in the lake. Antevs (1922), from varve counts, estimated the life of the lake at about 4000 years.

TYPES OF GLACIAL DEPOSITS. A variety of glacially derived deposits is to be seen in the Connecticut Valley. Flint (1933) grouped the various types of deposits into three categories:

a. Terraces composed of ice-contact deposits of dominantly fluvial origin but containing subordinate amounts of lacustrine materials.
b. Deposits of laminated or varved clay, silt, and minor amounts of sand that were laid down in an open lake and are now terraced as a result of post-lake fluvial erosion.
c. Post-lake deposits, including fluvial deposits of gravel, sand, and silt, and eolian deposits of sand and loess.

Jahns and Willard (1942) divided the glacially derived deposits of the Connecticut Valley into five classes (see Fig. 9.13):

a. Local and irregular deposits of till with associated masses of gravel, sand, and silt.
b. Ice-contact deposits consisting of gravel, sand, and silt made by through-going meltwater drainage lines that were held above the level of the Connecticut Valley lake by temporary spillways; in this category are such forms as kames, kame terraces, eskers, and crevasse fillings.
c. Local irregular accumulations of sand and gravel and subordinate amounts of silt derived from wasting ice but not associated genetically with any through-going meltwater drainage lines.
d. Deposits of gravel, sand, silt, and clay laid down on the bottom or along the margin of Connecticut Valley Lake; in part these are ice contact in nature and are terraced but lie at lower levels than the deposits in classes b and c.
e. Recent fluvial sediments and sand dunes laid down on the surfaces of post-lake terraces after the draining of Connecticut Valley Lake.

Flint (1933) divided the lacustrine clays into four groups called the New Haven, Middleton and Berlin, Clayton, and Hartford clays. He recognized that they were alike in that they are primarily varved clays but he thought that the evidence indicated that they were not all part of a single continuous body that was deposited in the same lake. He considered the Hartford clays to be by far the most extensive of the lacustrine deposits. Jahns and Willard (1942) thought it likely, however, that the Hartford clays and the other associated clays were one continuous body of lacustrine sediment, although not equally thick everywhere. They thought

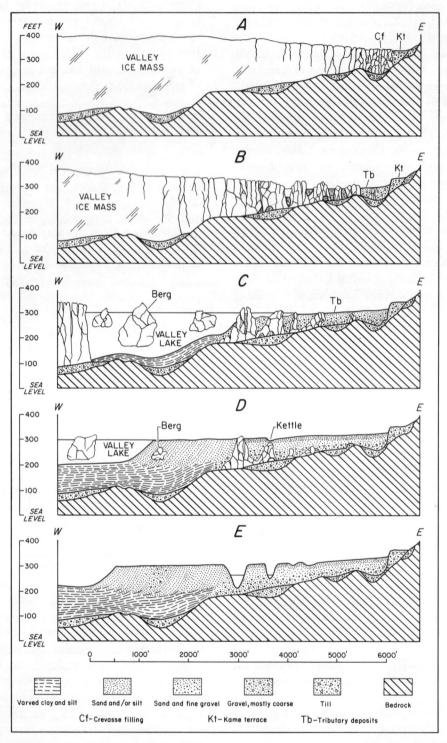

FIG. 9.13    Generalized cross-sections suggesting sequence of deposition of outwash in Connecticut Valley.    (*After R. H. Jahns and M. E. Willard, Am. Jour. Sci., 240.*)

that the varved clays are open-lake or deep-water deposits that accumulated at the same time as the marginal deposits of gravel and sand.

Jahns and Willard (1942) described high terraces around the margins of Connecticut Lake that were interpreted as deltaic outwash plains built over and around stagnant ice blocks into the open waters of Connecticut Valley Lake (see Fig. 9.13). The deposits beneath the terraces exhibit fluvial bedding in the portions which have kettles in them and deltaic bedding where kettles are lacking. These high-terrace deposits were considered by Emerson (1898) to be ordinary deltaic deposits built in open water, whereas Fairchild (1914) interpreted them as estuarine deposits laid down during a marine submergence of the Connecticut Valley.

Below the so-called high terraces there is, according to Jahns and Willard (1942), a set of four terraces at average heights of 80, 49, 37, and 30 feet above the present floodplain. They are underlain primarily by lacustrine clay and silts but have on them a thin veneer of alluvial material left by the Connecticut River as it swung back and forth across the valley during the development of the terraces.

LOWER CONNECTICUT RIVER COURSE. Why at Middleton, Connecticut, the Connecticut River abruptly turns southeastward from the belt of Triassic rocks and flows in a narrow valley across the crystalline rocks to the east has been the cause for much speculation. Davis (1898) at first thought that the anomalous course could be attributed to the effects of post-Triassic folding and faulting, but he later viewed with more favor the theory that coastal plain sediments may at one time have extended inland as far as Middleton and that the Connecticut River was superposed on these sediments across the belt of crystalline rocks.

Johnson (1931) accepted the theory of superposition as an explanation for the course of the Connecticut River, but he believed that the coastal plain sediments had extended much farther inland than suggested by Davis. He believed that the lower Connecticut River is a remnant of the initial southeastward-flowing consequent stream which developed as the Coastal Plain was

uplifted. The middle part of the Connecticut River was considered a subsequent stream which evolved when a tributary of the original consequent Connecticut River worked northward into the belt of infaulted Triassic rocks and ultimately took over all the drainage of the middle Connecticut River.

Meyerhoff (1938) and Olmsted and Little (1946) have suggested that the anomalous course of the lower Connecticut River may be explained as a result of superposition from a Miocene cover mass rather than a Cretaceous one. They believed that there is both topographic and stratigraphic evidence of a Miocene overlap as far inland as the Fall Line along the Middle Atlantic coast and in New England as far inland as the position of the 600 foot contour.

Aside from the question of whether Cretaceous or Miocene sediments ever extended over part of the New England Upland so as to permit superposition of the course of the lower Connecticut River, the theory of superposition encounters difficulty in accounting for the remarkable coincidence of the middle part of the Connecticut River with the belt of Triassic rocks. To explain this it seems necessary to assume that this part of the Connecticut River is a subsequent stream. Johnson's theory that a tributary of the Connecticut River worked headward along this weak rock belt is not unreasonable, but it is very unusual for a tributary of a stream to capture the main stream. This could have happened only if the tributary in the Connecticut Lowland was significantly lower than the main stream to the east of it.

*White Mountains Section*

*Extent.* The White Mountains section is a somewhat irregular and not too sharply defined area which includes a number of mountains that stand conspicuously above the New England Upland and are extensive enough that they are better treated as a separate section than as monadnocks on an erosion surface. In addition to the White Mountains, the Katahdin, Caledonia, Franconia, and Boundary Mountains are included in this section. Their bases lie above an altitude of

FIG. 9.14   View of so-called "lawns" on Mount Washington.   (*Photo by Fairchild Aerial Survey, Inc.*)

1500 feet.   Maximum altitudes in the White Mountains are over 6000 feet and in the Katahdin Mountains over 5000 feet.   The other ranges are not so high as this.

*Possible Erosion Surfaces.*   The White Mountains are developed on a large granite pluton.   The part of the White Mountain uplift which contains the highest peaks is known as the Presidential Range.   It has been suggested that subdued higher slopes in the Presidential and Katahdin ranges are remnants of an erosion surface older than that of the New England Upland (Goldthwait, 1914; Goldthwait, 1940).   This interpretation has been given (Lane, 1921) to the so-called "lawns" (see Fig. 9.14), features found at heights of 1000 to 1200 feet above the level of the adjacent New England Upland erosion surface.   A possible Cretaceous age has been suggested for this older erosion surface.   It may be that the lawns can be as logically explained

as the product of altiplanation processes.   Stone stripes are present on the lawns in the Presidential Range (Goldthwait et al., 1951) which attest to the existence of severe frost action on the lawns, but the stripes may have developed long after the bedrock surfaces were developed.

*Age of Glacial Cirques.*   The effects of mountain glaciation are conspicuous in both the Katahdin and White ranges, but especially in the Presidential Range.   The features known locally as "gulfs" are glacial cirques.   The Great Gulf in the White Mountains is a cirque which has a headwall 1500 feet high.

Difference of opinion exists, however, as to whether the cirques were cut before or after the continental ice cap covered the ranges.   Goldthwait (1914) favored the view that cutting of the cirques preceded regional glaciation because of the presence of boulder clay (till) in the cirques instead of the morainic ridges that he thought should be present if local mountains glaciers established themselves after continental glaciation. Johnson (1917), largely on the grounds that evidence in the Catskills and Adirondacks seemed to him to indicate that the mountain glaciers there formed after the continental ice had disappeared, felt that the White Mountain area needed further study, since it seemed to him that conditions here should have been similar to those in the Adirondacks and Catskills.

Thompson (1960, 1961), from detailed study of the Presidential Range and Mount Katahdin, concluded that the glacial cirques in this area were occupied by glaciers following uncovering of the mountains by wastage of the continental ice sheet. He attributed the apparent lack of moraines in the cirques to dispersal of the morainic material by the mass-wasting processes of rock glacier movement and felsenmeer creep. He concluded that the processes associated with severe frost action are still very important in the alpine and subalpine zones of the Presidential Range, as well as on Mount Katahdin.

## Seaboard Lowland Section

*Bases for Recognition.* Casual observation of the coastal margin of New England would lead to the conclusion that it is merely the lower seaward-sloping margin of the New England Upland. More careful observations reveal, however, that the coastal strip not only differs topographically from the typical New England Upland but also has had a somewhat different geomorphic history.

Not only is the coastal strip slightly lower than might be expected if considered the seaward edge of the New England Upland, but it is also smoother. The lower altitudes of some parts can be explained in terms of weak rock belts. This is true particularly of the Boston and Narragansett basins, which are underlain by Carboniferous sedimentary rocks, but altitudes are also lower on belts of strong rocks. The change in topography takes place in most areas between the 400- and 500-foot contours (Fenneman, 1938). The width of the Seaboard Lowland varies appreciably but in general is narrowest at the south. Its width varies from as little as 6 miles, in Connecticut, to as much as 60 miles near the Maine-New Brunswick boundary.

*Origin of Seaboard Section.* Two explanations of the Seaboard Lowland have been offered. It has been suggested that the lowland is an exhumed part of the Fall Zone peneplain (Sharp, 1929; Johnson, 1931). Renner (1927), in his interpretation of the Fall Line, considered this possibility but was not convinced that this was a correct explanation. Increasing skepticism in recent years as to the reality of the Fall Zone peneplain makes this explanation for the Seaboard Lowland less attractive than it once was.

Olmsted and Little (1946) thought they saw evidence of a noticeable topographic break inland at an elevation of about 600 feet, and they believed that this contour represents roughly a Miocene marine shoreline. The topography seaward from this shoreline was interpreted as a series of marine benches which bevel the rocks of the Seaboard Lowland. The irregularity in the trend of the supposed shoreline suggested to them that the marine cycle was interrupted while still in a youthful stage.

Evidence for a Miocene marine transgression in New England is not so convincing as that for a late Pleistocene submergence. The extent of this submergence (see Fig. 9.15) can be fairly accurately mapped from the distribution of a sheet of gray, silty clay called the Presumpscot formation (Bloom, 1960). This formation contains a marine fauna and attains a maximum thickness of 100 feet, but is commonly less than 20 feet thick. Its physical characteristics suggest that it is composed primarily of glacial flour.

Radiocarbon dating indicates that the marine submergence was in progress 11,800 years B.P. This suggests that the submergence was a consequence of a rise of sea level during the Two Creeks interglacial interval. In places the sediments of the Presumpscot formation are overlain by glacial drift at depths as much as 60 feet below the present sea level. This glacial drift apparently was deposited during the final advance of the ice, known as the Kennebunk advance, when it entered the sea and deformed the marine beds of the Presumpscot formation.

*New England Coastline.* The numerous embayments along the Maine coastline reflect the effect of the rise of sea level that accompanied deglaciation. A marked difference in the degree of irregularity of the coastline can be noted which is related to whether the strike of the rocks is parallel to the coast or at right angles to it. South of Casco Bay the coastline is fairly regular, because here the strike of the rocks parallels the coast, but northward from Casco Bay the coast has many deep bays and inlets resulting from drowning of the belts of weak rock. Super-

ficially the embayments north of Casco Bay resemble fiords and were so interpreted by early geologists, but, as Johnson (1925) has pointed out, the similarity is superficial. With the exception of the Mount Desert Island area, the embayments along the Maine coast lack the steep walls and depth that characterize glacial troughs. Glacial erosion was undoubtedly greater on the weak than on strong rock belts, resulting in an accentuation of lineation of topography, but the valleys were not deepened enough to be considered fiords. Except for their linear forms they resemble more the estuaries of the Middle Atlantic coast.

On Mount Desert Island, an east-west-extending mass of resistant granite, are a number of

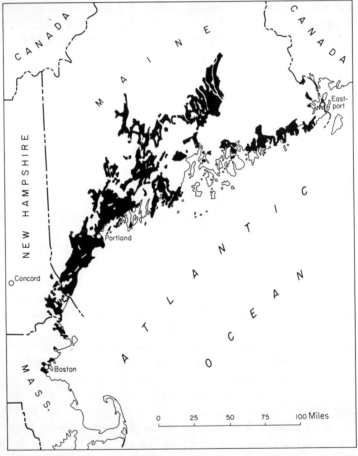

FIG. 9.15   Extent of Pleistocene Presumpscot formation.   (*After Glacial Map of United States East of Rocky Mountains, Geol. Soc. Am.*)

FIG. 9.16  Somnes Sound on Mount Desert Island, looking south.  (*Photo by John S. Shelton.*)

deep north-south notches that display the high, steep walls associated with fiords. Most of them have trough lakes in them, but in one, Somes Sound, there is an arm of the sea (see Fig. 9.16) which has the essential characteristics of a fiord. Its eastern wall at one place rises over 1000 feet above the bottom of the sound. These notches and troughs in Mount Desert Island were probably cut by tongues of ice that extended through them when the ice had banked up against the north side of Mount Desert Island.

## REFERENCES CITED

Adams, G. F. (1945). Upland terraces in southern New England, *Jour. Geol.*, **53**, 289–312.

—— (1958). The geology of the Triassic lowland of southeastern New York and northern New Jersey, *New York State Geol. Assoc. Guidebook for 30th Annual Meeting*, 27–31.

Antevs, Ernst (1922). The recession of the last ice sheet in New England, *Am. Geog. Soc. Research Series*, 11, 120 pp.

Atwood, W. W. (1940). *The Physiographic Provinces of North America*, Ginn and Co., New York, 536 pp.

Barrell, Joseph (1913). Piedmont terraces of the northern Appalachians and their mode of origin, *Geol. Soc. Am. Bull.*, **24**, 688–690.

—— (1920). The piedmont terraces of the northern Appalachians, *Am. Jour. Sci.*, **199**, 227–258, 327–361, and 407–428.

Billings, M. P. (1933). Paleozoic age of the rocks of central New England, *Science*, **79**, 55–56.

—— (1945). Mechanics of igneous intrusions in New Hampshire, *Am. Jour. Sci.*, **243–A**, 40–68.

Bloom, A. L. (1960). Late Pleistocene changes of sea level in southwestern Maine, Dept. Economic Development, *Maine Geol. Surv.*, 143 pp.

Brace, W. F. (1953). The geology of the Rutland area, Vermont, *Vt. Geol. Surv. Bull.* 6, 124 pp.

—— (1958). Interaction of basement and mantle during folding near Rutland, Vermont, *Am. Jour. Sci.*, **256**, 241–256.

Bucher, W. H. (1957). Taconic klippe: a stratigraphic-structural problem, *Geol. Soc. Am. Bull.*, **68**, 657–674.

Cady, W. M. (1945). Stratigraphy and structure of west central Vermont, *Geol. Soc. Am. Bull.*, **56**, 515–587.

Chapman, R. W. (1935). Percy ring-dike complex, *Am. Jour. Sci.*, **230**, 401–431.

—— (1942). Ring structures of the Pliny region, *Geol. Soc. Am. Bull.*, **53**, 1533–1568.

Craddock, J. C. (1957). Stratigraphy and structure of the Kinderhook quadrangle, New York, and the "Taconic klippe," *Geol. Soc. Am. Bull.*, **68**, 675–724.

Davis, W. M. (1891). Dates of origin of certain topographic forms on the Atlantic slope, *Geol. Soc. Am. Bull.*, **2**, 570–571.

—— (1896). The physical geography of southern New England, in *The Physiography of the United States*, Nat. Geog. Soc., 269–304.

—— (1898). The Triassic formation of Connecticut, *U. S. Geol. Survey 18th Ann. Rept.*, Part 2, 1–192.

Emerson, B. K. (1898). Geology of Old Hampshire County, Massachusetts, *U. S. Geol. Survey Mon.* 29, 508–748.

Fairchild, H. L. (1914). Pleistocene marine submergence of the Connecticut and Hudson valleys, *Geol. Soc. Am. Bull.*, **25**, 219–242.

Flint, R. F. (1929). The stagnation and dissipation of the last ice sheet, *Geog. Rev.*, **19**, 256–289.

—— (1930). Glacial geology of Connecticut, *Conn. State Geol. and Nat. Hist. Surv. Bull.* 47, 294 pp.

—— (1932). Deglaciation of the Connecticut Valley, *Am. Jour. Sci.*, **224**, 152–156.

—— (1933). Late Pleistocene sequence in the Connecticut Valley, *Geol. Soc. Am. Bull.*, **44**, 965–988.

Fowler, Phillip (1950). Stratigraphy and structure of the Castleton area, Vermont, *Vt. Geol. Surv. Bull.* 2, 83 pp.

Goldthwait, J. W. (1914). Remnants of an old graded surface on the Presidential Range of the White Mountains, *Am. Jour. Sci.*, **187**, 451–463.

—— (1938). The uncovering of New Hampshire by the last ice sheet, *Am. Jour. Sci.*, **236**, 345–372.

——, R. P. Goldthwait, and Lawrence Goldthwait (1951). *The geology of New Hampshire, Part 1, Surficial Geology*, N. H. State Planning and Development Comm., Concord, 83 pp.

Goldthwait, R. P. (1940). Geology of the Presidential Range, *N. H. Acad. Sci. Bull.* 1, 1–43.

Hawkes, H. E., Jr. (1941). Roots of the Taconic fault in west central Vermont, *Geol. Soc. Am. Bull.*, **52**, 649–666.

Herz, Norman (1955). Alternative to the "Taconic overthrust" hypothesis in western Massachusetts, *Geol. Soc. Am. Bull.*, **66**, 1714 (abs.).

Hobbs, W. H. (1901). The Newark system of the Pomeraug Valley, Connecticut, *U. S. Geol. Survey 21st Ann. Rept.*, Part 3, 7–160.

Jacobs, E. C. (1950). *The Physical Features of Vermont*, Vermont State Development Commission, Montpelier, 169 pp.

Jahns, R. H., and M. E. Willard (1942). Late Pleistocene and Recent deposits in the Connecticut Valley, Massachusetts, *Am. Jour. Sci.*, **240**, 161–191, 265–287.

Johnson, D. W. (1917). Date of local glaciation in the White, Adirondack, and Catskill Mountains, *Geol. Soc. Am. Bull.*, **28**, 543–552.

—— (1925). *The New England-Acadian Shoreline*, John Wiley and Sons, Inc., New York, 591 pp.

—— (1931). *Stream Sculpture on the Atlantic Slope*, Columbia Univ. Press, New York, 142 pp.

Kaiser, E. P. (1945). Northern end of the Taconic thrust sheet in western Vermont, *Geol. Soc. Am. Bull.*, **56**, 1079–1098.

Kay, Marshall (1937). Stratigraphy of the Trenton group, *Geol. Soc. Am. Bull.*, **48**, 233–302.

Kingsley, Louise (1931). Caldron-subsidence of the Ossipee Mountains, *Am. Jour. Sci.*, **222**, 139–168.

Lane, A. C. (1921). White Mountain physiography, *Am. Jour. Sci.*, **201**, 349–354.

Long, L. E., and J. L. Kulp (1958). Age of the metamorphism of the rocks of the Manhattan prong, *Geol. Soc. Am. Bull.*, **69**, 603–606.

MacFadyen, J. A. (1956). The geology of the Bennington area, Vermont, *Vt. Geol. Surv. Bull.* 7, 72 pp.

Meyerhoff, H. A. (1938). Tertiary marine planation in the Piedmont and southern New England, *Geol. Soc. Am. Bull.*, **49**, 1954–1955 (abs.).

—— and Marion Hubbell (1928). The erosional landforms of eastern and central Vermont, *Rept. Vt. State Geologist*, **16**, 315–381.

Modell, David (1936). Ring-dike complex of the Belknap Mountains, New Hampshire, *Geol. Soc. Am. Bull.*, **47**, 1885–1932.

Olmsted, E. W., and L. S. Little (1946). Marine planation in southern New England, *Geol. Soc. Am. Bull.*, **57**, 1271 (abs.).

Platt, J. N., Jr. (1957). Sedimentary rocks of the Newark group in the Cherry Brook Valley, Canton Center, Connecticut, *Am. Jour. Sci.*, **255**, 517–522.

Renner, G. T. (1927). The physiographic interpretation of the Fall Line, *Geog. Rev.*, **17**, 276–286.

Ruedemann, Rudolph (1909). Types of inliers observed in New York, *New York State Museum Bull.* 133, 164–193.

—— (1932). Development of drainage of Catskills, *Am. Jour. Sci.*, **223**, 337–349.

Sharp, H. S. (1929). The physical history of the Connecticut shoreline, *Conn. State Geol. Nat. Hist. Surv. Bull.* 46, 97 pp.

Tarr, R. S. (1902). *The Physical Geography of New York State*, The MacMillan Company, London, 297 pp.

Thompson, H. D. (1929). Hudson gorge in the Highlands, *Geol. Soc. Am. Bull.*, **47**, 1831–1848.

Thompson, W. F. (1960). The shape of New England mountains, Part I, *Appalachia*, **33**, 145–159.

—— (1961). The shape of New England mountains, Part II, *Appalachia*, **33**, 316–335; Part III, *Appalachia*, **33**, 458–478.

Weaver, J. D. (1953). "Taconic allochthone" in the Copake area, New York, *Geol. Soc. Am. Bull.*, **64**, 1489 (abs.).

ADDITIONAL REFERENCES

Alden, W. C. (1925). The physical features of central Massachusetts, *U. S. Geol. Survey Bull.* 760-B, 13–105.

Bain, G. W. (1932). The northern area of Connecticut Valley Triassic, *Am. Jour. Sci.*, **223**, 57–77.

—— (1941). The Holyoke Range and Connecticut Valley structure, *Am. Jour. Sci.*, **239**, 261–275.

Billings, M. P. (1956). *The Geology of New Hampshire*, Part II, Bedrock geology, N. H. Planning and Development Comm., Concord, 203 pp.

Brown, T. C. (1933). The waning of the last ice sheet in central Massachusetts, *Jour. Geol.*, **41**, 144–158.

Fowler-Billings, Katherine (1949). Geology of the Monadnock region of New Hampshire, *Geol. Soc. Am. Bull.*, **60**, 1249–1285.

Hatch, Laura (1917). Marine terraces in southeastern Connecticut, *Am. Jour. Sci.*, **194**, 319–330.

Laforge, Laurence (1932). Geology of the Boston area, Massachusetts, *U. S. Geol. Survey Bull.* 839, 105 pp.

Lobeck, A. K. (1917). The position of the New England peneplain in the White Mountain region, *Geog. Rev.*, **3**, 53–60.

Meyerhoff, H. A. (1946). Upland terraces in southern New England: a discussion, *Jour. Geol.*, **54**, 126–129.

Osberg, P. H. (1952). The Green Mountain anticlinorium in the vicinity of Rochester and East Middlebury, Vermont, *Vt. Geol. Surv. Bull.* 5, 128 pp.

Perkins, E. H. (1927). Contributions to the geology of Maine, *Am. Jour. Sci.*, **214**, 352–364.

Pond, A. M. (1928). Preliminary report on the peneplanes of the Taconic Mountains of Vermont, *Vt. State Geol. Surv. 16th Ann. Rept.*, 292–314.

Toppan, F. W. (1935). The physiography of Maine, *Jour. Geol.*, **43**, 76–87.

White, W. H., and R. H. Jahns (1950). Structure of central and east-central Vermont, *Jour. Geol.*, **58**, 179–220.

Wolfe, C. W., and W. V. Swarzenski (1960). The tectonic significance of the erosion surfaces in northwestern Maine, *Zeitschrift für Geomorph.*, **4**, Heft I, 53–68.

# 10

# *The Adirondack Province*

## GENERAL DESCRIPTION

The Adirondack province is one of two extensions of Canadian Shield geology into the United States, the other being the Superior Upland province west of the Great Lakes. A wedge of Precambrian rocks, which crosses the St. Lawrence River in the Thousand Islands area, connects the Adirondacks with the Precambrian rocks of the Canadian Shield. The Adirondack province is a roughly circular area lying between the St. Lawrence Lowland on the north, Lake Champlain on the east, the Mohawk Valley on the south, and Black River and the Tug Hill Cuesta on the west. The province is not all mountainous, for on the northwest the topography is more plateau-like. The rise from the west to the mountainous eastern portion is gradual, but the ascent on the east from the Lake Champlain Lowland is steep and rugged. The western plateau portion averages around 1000 feet in altitude, whereas in the mountainous eastern half 16 peaks exceed 4000 feet in altitude (Kemp and Ruedemann, 1910). Mt. Marcy, the highest peak, has an altitude of 5344 feet (see Fig. 10.1) and Mt. McIntyre, the next highest, has an altitude of 5112.

### Geologic Conditions

*Rocks.* Except on the northwest flank the rocks of the Adirondack province are mainly Precambrian in age and include two principal groups, the metamorphosed Grenville series and igneous rocks representing at least two distinct periods of intrusion. The Grenville rocks are very old

Precambrian rocks that are complexly deformed and metamorphosed; quartzites, schists, gneisses, marble, and other metamorphic types total 20,000 feet or more in maximum thickness (Engel and Engel, 1953). The main area of Grenville rocks lies at the northwestern side of the Adirondacks, but a lesser one lies south of the igneous core of the mountainous portion of the province. Lineation in a northeast-southwest direction is very noticeable in Grenville rocks.

Igneous rocks predominate, however, in the Adirondacks. The mountainous core is roughly 100 miles in diameter, and here igneous rocks make up three-fourths of the bedrock (Buddington, 1948), and two-thirds of these belong to the granite family. Of particular interest, however, is the presence in the east central part of a large mass of anorthosite 40 to 50 miles across and covering about 1200 square miles (Balk, 1933). This is in the part of the Adirondacks where Mt. Marcy and the other high peaks are located. The intrusive body is commonly called the Adirondack batholith.

Cambrian and Ordovician sedimentary rocks are present around the margins of the Adirondack province, particularly on the northwest and east. On the north and northwest extensive areas of the Cambrian Potsdam sandstone form a veneer over the Precambrian granite. Ordovician limestones and shales are also present in the marginal belts around the crystalline core.

*Structure.* The general structure of the Adirondacks is anticlinal or anticlinorial, as suggested by the two belts of Grenville rocks on the north and south flanks of the uplift. Bud-

FIG. 10.1   Mount Marcy (left foreground) and other Adirondack peaks.   (*Photo by Fairchild Aerial Surveys Inc.*)

dington (1939) described the large-scale structure of the Adirondacks in terms of four major petrologic belts:

1. The Frontenac belt along the St. Lawrence River in which the rocks are predominantly granite with subordinate bands of Grenville rocks.
2. A northwest belt of Grenville rocks consisting largely of metamorphosed sediments intruded by granites.
3. The central core of the Adirondacks composed of 75–85% of intrusive quartz syenite, granite, anorthosite, and gabbro.
4. A southern Grenville belt with its associated intrusives.

Each of the above belts is oriented in a general northeast-southwest direction.

Faults, particularly high-angle normal faults, are common, especially on the eastern and southern peripheries (Quinn, 1933; Rogers, 1937). The Adirondacks lie to the west of the Green Mountains and Champlain Lowland, where great thrust sheets are present (see p. 160); these thrusts seem to die out in the Champlain Lowland and give way to normal faults at the eastern margin of the Adirondacks.

## TOPOGRAPHY OF THE ADIRONDACKS

### Preglacial Topography

*Precambrian Erosion Surface.* It is rather commonly believed that the surface upon which the Cambrian Potsdam sandstone rests in the northwestern part of the Adirondacks is a pre-Paleozoic peneplain surface (Buddington and Leonard, 1962). This erosion surface has been partially stripped of its cover of Cambrian sediments and has undergone modification since its exhumation. To what degree has it been modified, however? One view is that the topography we see today in the western Adirondacks is essentially the Precambrian erosion surface modified somewhat by glaciation. Another view is that the Precambrian peneplain has been largely destroyed, and a younger topography of Tertiary age has been developed on the Precambrian rocks.

As no middle or late Paleozoic rocks or Mesozoic rocks are present in the Adirondacks, it seems probable that during all this time the area was above sea level and subject to degradation. If this is a correct assumption, it seems unlikely that the view of Buddington and Leonard (1962) that the present topography in the Adirondacks is essentially the exhumed pre-Paleozoic peneplain surface stripped of its former cover and modified to some degree by erosion during Tertiary time is correct. Reasoning by analogy with the history of adjacent regions, Buddington and Leonard concluded that the Adirondacks were uplifted in late Mesozoic or early Tertiary time to form an asymmetrical dome whose crest was in the Mt. Marcy region. They considered the large-scale features of the topography as mainly consequent on the warping and faulting of the pre-Paleozoic peneplain surface, whereas only the small-scale relief features were attributed to erosion of the deformed surface during Tertiary time.

It seems very probable that lower Paleozoic rocks once did extend across the Adirondack dome and that as these rocks were removed from the crest of the uplift encircling cuestas with infacing escarpments formed around the Adirondacks. The Tug Hill Cuesta on the west and the escarpment along the south side of the Mohawk Valley are good existing examples of such cuestas. The probability exists that a similar escarpment is present on the north but is obscured by glacial drift.

*Possible Tertiary Erosion Surfaces.* Crowl (1950) interpreted the erosional history of the Adirondacks in terms of conventional Appalachian geomorphic history. He thought that erosion surfaces beveling the Precambrian peneplain could be recognized in both the eastern and western piedmont areas. He described what he believed to be remnants of two peneplains, the Big Moose and Childwold, and two strath terraces, the Mohawk and Albany. These erosion surfaces were correlated with the Upland, Schooley, Harrisburg, and Somerville erosion surfaces respectively.

*Relation of Topography to Rock Types.* A fairly close correlation exists between rocks types and topography in the Adirondacks. The topography on igenous rocks is generally higher than that found on the metasedimentary Grenville series. Isolated small masses of intrusive granite or similar rock types within the Grenville areas commonly give rise to hills or groups of hills. The most readily erosible rocks are the Grenville marbles, crystalline limestones, and dolomites. Lowlands or valleys on these calcareous rocks are commonly elongate in a direction paralleling the regional foliation. Buddington and Leonard (1962) believed that the basins now occupied by Placid, Tupper, Raquette, and Long Lakes were all formed by erosion of the less resistant rocks of the Grenville series.

*Reflection of Faults in Topography.* As stated above, faulting is particularly conspicuous along the eastern part of the Adirondacks. Presence of faults here is indicated by such phenomena as: straight boundary lines between formations, crushed zones, fault or fault-line scarps, and outliers of Paleozoic rocks in the area of Precambrian rocks (Quinn, 1933). Fault control of drainage patterns is evident in such areas as the Elizabethtown quadrangle (see Fig. 10.2). Some major lake basins, such as that of Lake George, may be outlined by faults. The Saranac basin is likely a graben (Buddington and Leonard, 1962). Displacement of the Potsdam sandstone here varies from a few feet to as much as 4000 feet.

*Topographic Belts in Northwestern Adirondacks.* Few detailed studies of Adirondack topography have been made or published. As part of an economic study, Buddington and Leonard (1962) have given a reasonably detailed description of

FIG. 10.2   Rectangular drainage in part of Elizabethtown, New York, quadrangle area.

the topography in the piedmont area of the northwestern Adirondacks extending from the St. Lawrence Lowland southeastward into the mountainous area.   The St. Lawrence Lowland on the north has altitudes of only 200 to 400 feet and is underlain by flat-lying lower Paleozoic formations.   Southeast from the St. Lawrence Lowland, the Adirondack Piedmont includes

three belts, the Grenville Lowland, the Fall Zone, and the Childwold terrace.

Altitudes in the Grenville Lowland range from 300 to 1000 feet.   The rocks here are the Precambrian metasedimentary rocks of the Grenville series plus a few intrusive igneous rocks.   However, glacial drift obscures much of the bedrock in this area.   In contrast to the St. Lawrence

Lowland, the topography in this belt consists of a series of elongate ridges and valleys or depressions whose axes parallel the regional geologic structure.

Southeast of the Grenville Lowland is the Fall Zone belt. This 8–10-mile-wide belt stands out from the Grenville Lowland because of its distinctly higher altitudes and its increase in altitude toward the southeast. Waterfalls are common along streams in this belt. Granitic rocks predominate here rather than the metasedimentary rocks of the Grenville series.

Southeast of the Fall Zone belt is a structural terrace known as the Childwold terrace, which is 15 to 20 miles wide and ranges in altitude from 1000 to 2000 feet. Relief is usually less than 400 feet. The rocks here are the same as in the Fall Zone belt, and it appears that the Childwold terrace is probably a result of upwarping, as a known fault zone belt lies to the northwest of it and the Saranac graben to the southeast of it.

The mountainous belt of the Adirondacks lies mainly above the 2000-foot contour and exceeds 5000 feet in altitude in Mt. Marcy and Mt. McIntyre. Over 3000 feet of relief exists between Mt. Marcy and South Meadow and Ausable Lake. Topographic features in the mountainous belt show a general northeast-southwest trend. This is apparent in Ellenberg Mountain Range and the Santa Clara and Saranac troughs. What is known as the "lake belt" extends in a southwest direction from Loon Lake and stands out distinctly from the high peaks to the south of it. The long straight valleys in which such lakes as Lower Ausable, Long, and others lie seem to be controlled by faults.

## Glacial Topography

*Lakes.* Lakes are abundant in the Adirondacks; it is estimated that there are around 2000 lakes and ponds here, mostly of glacial origin. Their basins are of different sorts; some lie in fault-controlled valleys, most of the smaller ones are in rock basins produced by glacial scouring, and many lie back of morainal dams.

During the waning of the last ice sheet a number of proglacial lakes formed around the margins of the Adirondacks. In this group were such lakes as Lake Vermont in the Champlain Lowland, Lakes Herkimer, Schoharie, and Albany in the Mohawk Valley, and a series of lakes in the Black River Valley (Fairchild, 1912). Lacustrine terraces and deltas mark the sites of these former lakes.

Waterlaid deposits are abundant in the Adirondacks, but end moraines are poorly developed. A rather unusual line of eskers (Chadwick, 1928) crosses the Adirondacks (see Fig. 10.3) in a northeast to southwest direction and follows fairly closely the Saranac trough. The esker belt is at least 85 miles long and is unique in that all tributary eskers join the main esker from the north. Two lines of lake basins form esker troughs on either side of the esker. This esker system seems to indicate that the ice stagnated for a time on the northwest flank of the Adirondacks during its final retreat.

*Date of Glacial Cirque Cutting.* Glacial cirques are present on the faces of many of the Adirondack peaks, but in general they are not so strongly developed as those in the White and Catskill Mountains. Ogilvie (1902) described a system of moraines which suggested that they were deposited by glaciers radiating from the center of the Adirondacks after the melting of the ice sheet. The same difference of opinion exists with respect to the date of cirque cutting in the Adirondacks that we previously encountered in the White and Catskill Mountains (see p. 172).

## Drainage of the Adirondacks

The streams which flow out of the Adirondacks form a roughly radial pattern. It is commonly assumed that this drainage pattern has persisted since the updoming of the Adirondacks. The present tangential relationships of the streams on the four sides of the Adirondacks has caused a few geologists to consider them subsequent streams which developed by headward erosion along the strike of marginal weak rock belts and pirated streams which formerly extended much farther back into the Adirondacks. Fairchild (1925) believed that the headwaters

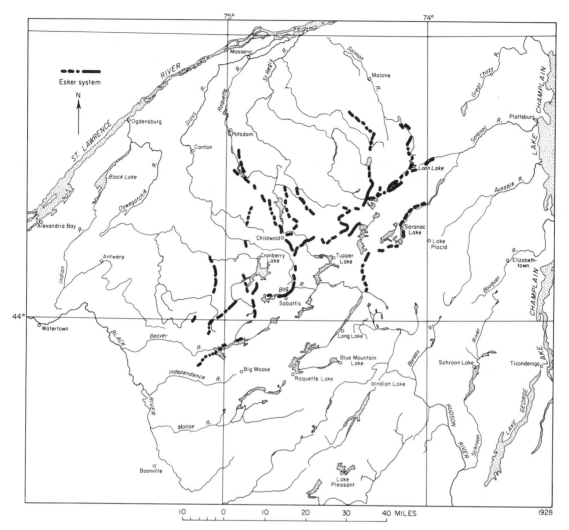

FIG. 10.3   Esker system of northwest Adirondacks.   (*After A. F. Buddington and B. F. Leonard, U. S. Geol. Survey Profess. Paper* 376.)

of the Susquehanna originally were in the Adirondacks.   Ruedemann (1931) thought likewise, and both believed that following uplift of the Adirondack dome a roughly circular series of cuestas developed around the dome along the contact of the Precambrian and sedimentary rocks.   A tributary of the Hudson (the present Mohawk River) was able to extend itself along the strike of the rocks and capture the headwaters of the Susquehanna.   Similarly, the preglacial stream that flowed westward into the basin now occupied by Lake Ontario was

also pirated by headward erosion of the Black River.   This is an interesting theory, but it is so speculative that not too much credence can be put in it.

## REFERENCES CITED

Balk, Robert, (1933).   The Adirondack Mountains, *16th Int. Geol. Cong. Guidebook*, **1**, 21–36.

Buddington, A. F. (1939).   Adirondack igneous rocks and their metamorphism, *Geol. Soc. Am. Memoir* 7. 354 pp.

——— (1948).   Origin of the granite rocks of the northwest Adirondacks, in "Origin of Granite," James Gilluly, Editor, *Geol. Soc. Am. Memoir* 28, 21–43.

—— and B. F. Leonard (1962). Regional geology of the St. Lawrence County magnetite district, northwestern Adirondacks, *U. S. Geol. Survey Profess. Paper* 376, 145 pp.

Chadwick, G. H. (1928). Adirondack eskers, *Geol. Soc. Am. Bull.*, **39,** 923–929.

Crowl, G. H. (1950). Erosion surfaces of the Adirondacks, *Geol. Soc. Am. Bull.*, **61,** 1565 (abs.).

Engel, A. E. J., and C. G. Engel (1953). Grenville series in the northwest Adirondack Mountains, Pt. 1, General features of the Grenville series, *Geol. Soc. Am. Bull.*, **64,** 1013–1048.

Fairchild, H. L. (1912). The glacial waters in the Black and Mohawk valleys, *New York State Museum Bull.* 160, 47 pp.

—— (1925). The Susquehanna River in New York and evolution of western New York drainage, *New York State Museum Bull.* 256, 99 pp.

Kemp, J. F., and Rudolf Ruedemann (1910). Geology of the Elizabethtown and Port Henry quadrangles, *New York State Museum Bull.* 138, 173 pp.

Ogilvie, I. H. (1902). Glacial phenomena in the Adirondacks and Champlain Valley, *Jour. Geol.*, **10,** 397–412.

Quinn, A. W. (1933). Normal faults of the Lake Champlain region, *Jour. Geol.*, **41,** 113–143.

Rodgers, John (1937). Stratigraphy and structure of the upper Champlain Valley, *Geol. Soc. Am. Bull.*, **48,** 1573–1588.

Ruedemann, Rudolf (1931). The tangential master-streams of the Adirondack drainage, *Am. Jour. Sci.*, **222,** 431–440.

# 11

# Interior Low Plateaus Province

## GENERAL DESCRIPTION

The term "plateau" has no specific implication as to height but rather implies a tract of land with considerable summit area set off from adjacent areas by a marginal escarpment. The Interior Low Plateaus province is thus not inappropriately named, for within the province is a series of cuestas the fronts of which are prominent, although not high, escarpments. Very little of the province rises above 1000 feet in altitude, and a considerable part of it is as low as 500 or 600 feet. Hence the term "low plateaus" properly describes much of the province.

*Boundaries.* The Interior Low Plateaus province is bounded on the east in Kentucky and Tennessee by the west-facing escarpment of the Appalachian Plateaus. This escarpment is commonly known as the Pottsville (see Fig. 11.1) and is held up by sandstones of early Pennsylvanian age. Throughout most of its length it forms a readily recognizable boundary, although locally it is so deeply indented by stream erosion that it has more the appearance of a line of ridges than that of a continuous escarpment. The southwest boundary of the province follows closely the Tennessee River. Geologically, this is the boundary between the poorly indurated Cretaceous deposits of the Coastal Plain and well indurated Paleozoic rocks. The northern boundary is in most respects the least satisfactory. From southern Illinois to Louisville, Kentucky, the boundary follows the outer limits of the Illinoian glaciation, but from Louisville northeastward it is arbitrarily placed at the Ohio River, disregarding the fact that glacial ice crossed the Ohio River into Kentucky. This boundary does not everywhere mark a change in topography. In areas where the glacial drift is moderately thick there may be a change from bedrock-controlled to glacial topography, but where the drift is thin the topography of the Interior Low Plateaus continues a short distance into the Central Lowlands province north of the glacial boundary. A boundary could be drawn between glacially controlled and bedrock-controlled topography, but it would be so irregular in plan that it would be difficult to keep in mind.

## REGIONAL STRUCTURE AND GEOLOGY

### Major Structures

The dominant regional structure of the Interior Low Plateaus province is a broad structural high known as the Cincinnati arch, the axis of which runs northeast-southwest through Kentucky and Tennessee. This structure splits in northern Kentucky and send two limbs to either side of the Michigan Basin. Two major domal structures are developed along the axis of the Cincinnati arch, the Jessamine dome of central Kentucky and the Nashville dome in central Tennessee. These are separated from each other by a shallow structural sag called the Cumberland saddle, from Cumberland County, Kentucky (Wilson and Born, 1943). East of the Cincinnati arch rocks dip toward the geosynclinal Appalachian Plateaus, and on the west toward the Illinois Basin. At the extreme western edge of the Interior Low Plateaus the

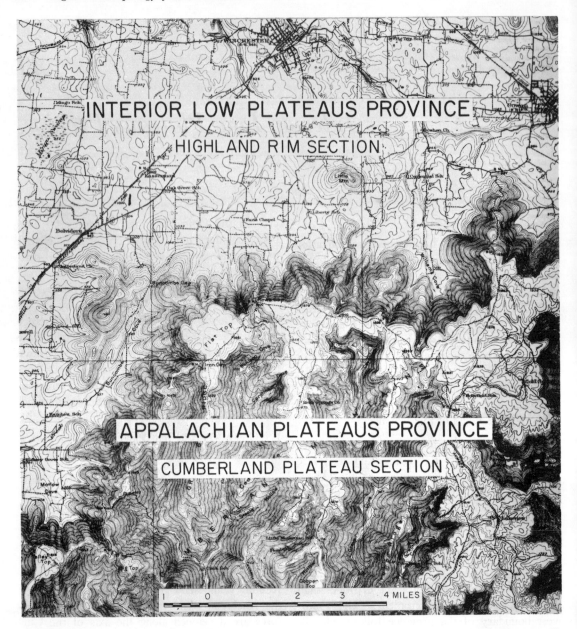

FIG. 11.1   Contact of Appalachian Plateaus and Interior Low Plateaus province in Decherd, Tennessee, topographic map area.

influence of the Ozark dome is apparent, and here rocks dip eastward off this structure into the Illinois Basin.

*Bedrock Geology*

Rocks of the Interior Low Plateaus province range in age from Ordovician to Cretaceous (actually to Tertiary, if the somewhat unconsolidated and discontinuous Tertiary deposits are included).   The oldest exposed beds are at the crests of the Jessamine and Nashville domes. The Camp Nelson formation at the crest of the Jessamine dome and the Murfreesboro formation on the Nashville dome are both Middle Ordovician formations of essentially the same age.   In the narrow strip between the Tennessee and Cumberland rivers the Tuscaloosa, Eutaw, and Ripley formations of Cretaceous age are exposed.

Dips are moderate on both sides of the Cincinnati uplift. Around the Jessamine dome they average 20 to 30 feet per mile to the east and west and about 10 feet per mile to the north and south. Locally faults may result in steeper dips, but for much of the area they are rarely greater than 25 or 30 feet per mile.

### Faults and Lesser Structures

Faults are not common except in western Kentucky, southwestern Indiana, and southern Illinois; here several have magnitudes sufficient to have topographic expression. The faults are mainly high-angle, normal faults, and some have displacements of as much as 2500 feet. A number of basic intrusive dikes and sills (mainly peridotite) are found in association with the faults.

Several so-called cryptovolcanic structures (Bucher, 1936) are known in the Interior Low Plateaus province. The Flynn Creek structure in Jackson County, Tennessee, Wells Creek Basin in Houston and Stewart Counties, Tennessee, Howell structure in Lincoln County, Tennessee, and Jeptha Knob in Shelby County, Kentucky, are all of this type, and Serpent Mound, in Adams and Highland Counties, Ohio, is barely outside the province. These structures are small circular uplifts, at most a few miles in width, which display at their centers complex faulting and brecciation of the involved rocks. A ring-shaped depression around the margin of the structure is rather characteristic.

## DIVISION INTO SECTIONS

Regional geology and structure are expressed in a series of cuestas, escarpments, basins, and plateaus which permit division of the province into four readily recognizable sections. The largest section, the Highland Rim, is underlain mainly by Mississippian limestones and topographically resembles a stripped plain, although the surface of the plateau actually truncates several geological formations. Karst features are dominant over a considerable area and are present to some extent in all parts. This section completely encircles the Nashville dome and extends around the Jessamine dome. Its encirclement of the latter structure would be complete were the glacial cover at the north removed and the preglacial topography exposed.

In the Bluegrass section, limestones also predominate, with the exception of one area known as the Eden shale belt. The limestones range in age from Ordovician to Devonian (McFarlan, 1943). Certain physical characteristics of the limestones have prevented karst features from being so strongly developed as in the Highland Rim section.

The Nashville Basin is the smallest, most compact, and most homogeneous of the sections. Its boundary is an in-facing escarpment known as the Highland Rim Escarpment. Rocks of the Nashville Basin are mainly Ordovician, Silurian, and Devonian limestones. Karst features are more conspicuous here than in the Bluegrass section but less so than in the Highland Rim section.

The Shawnee Hills section is the least homogeneous geologically and topographically of the four sections. It is set off rather sharply on the east and south by an escarpment known in Indiana as the Chester Escarpment and in Kentucky as the Dripping Springs Escarpment. The northern and western boundaries are transitional in nature because of the thinness and patchiness here of the outer glacial drift. Rocks range in age from late Mississippian to Pennsylvanian and present a greater diversity of lithology than is found in any other section. Extensive faulting characterizes the western part of the section.

## GENERAL DESCRIPTION OF TOPOGRAPHY

Except for the areas of intense folding and faulting in the Ridge and Valley province, there is probably no region in the eastern United States where structure and lithology are any better expressed in the topography than in the Interior Low Plateaus. The sections and subsections are largely an expression of regional structural control, and the local variations in topography within sections and subsections mainly reflect differences in lithology.

## Major Escarpments and Cuestas

The dominant topographic pattern consists of a series of cuestas developed on the flanks of the Cincinnati arch. The forward edges of the cuestas are marked by escarpments that face updip from the regional slopes. Three escarpments are extensive regionally (see Fig. 11.2) and provide the basis for dividing the Interior Low Plateaus into natural subdivisions. These are the Highland Rim, the Knobstone or Muldraugh's Hill, and the Dripping Springs escarpments. A fourth escarpment, the Pottsville, is locally present but is usually not continuous for any considerable distance.

*Highland Rim Escarpment.* The name Highland Rim may be applied to any one of three features in the Interior Low Plateaus province, the infacing escarpment around the Nashville Basin, the plateau on the dip slope back of this escarpment, and an erosion surface of Tertiary age. The rather ragged Highland Rim Escarpment around the Nashville Basin is capped by the Mississippian Fort Payne chert. Its crest stands an average height of about 450 feet above the central floor of the Nashville Basin. The escarpment itself is nowhere that high, for the Nashville Basin immediately adjacent to the escarpment is not reduced to an altitude as low as the central part of the basin. Numerous spurs of the escarpment project into the basin, and numerous outliers occur within the basin.

*Knobstone-Muldraugh's Hills Escarpment.* More or less encircling the Bluegrass section on the west, southwest, south, and southeast is an escarpment on rocks of Mississippian age (the Borden or Waverly group). This escarpment is known in Indiana as the Knobstone Escarpment (from Knobstone, an old name for the Borden group); its continuation in Kentucky is called Muldraugh's Hill (see Fig. 11.2). It is most conspicuous immediately north and south of the Ohio River, where it rises as much as 600 feet above the

adjacent Scottsburg Lowland or Outer Bluegrass region immediately east of it. This escarpment continues eastward and northeastward across Kentucky and at its eastern limits is only a short distance west of the Pottsville Escarpment at the western edge of the Appalachian Plateaus.

*The Knobs.* The term "knobs" as a geomorphic term is usually applied to somewhat rounded and more or less isolated hills of various origins. In the Interior Low Plateaus province, however, the term "The Knobs" has come to have a rather specific meaning. It is applied to the belt of outliers and projecting spurs of the Knobstone-Muldraugh's Hill Cuesta. The Knobs first appear in Indiana just south of the Muscatatuck River. North of here glaciation has pretty well obliterated or obscured them. They become conspicuous features some 30–40 miles north of the Ohio River and continue to be so in Kentucky in a roughly circular belt around the southern and eastern margins of the Bluegrass section. The narrow belt of Knobs between the eastern edge of the Bluegrass section and the Appalachian Plateau is the only representation of the Highland Rim section in that part of Kentucky.

*Dripping Springs-Chester Escarpment.* On the southeastern side of the Illinois Basin is an escarpment on rocks of Chester (Upper Mississippian) age that is known in Kentucky as the Dripping Springs and in Indiana as the Chester Escarpment. The most prominent scarp-forming formation is the Cypress sandstone, but various geological formations of Chester age crop out in the escarpment. The Dripping Springs-Chester Escarpment is hardly so conspicuous as the Knobstone Escarpment, for it seldom exceeds 300 feet in height (see Fig. 11.3). It is also more irregular in plan, as it is highly indented with valleys that form large reentrants in its front. Many of these reentrants are solution or karst valleys that mark extensions of the karst topography that is extensively developed updip from the escarpment. The Chester Escarpment disappears in Indiana beneath glacial deposits near the West Fork of White River, and the Dripping Springs Escarpment of Kentucky is terminated

FIG. 11.2  Major escarpments of Indiana and Kentucky.

FIG. 11.3    Contact of Dripping Springs Escarpment and karst plain of the Pennyroyal Plateau, west of Park City, Kentucky.    (*Photo by W. R. Scott, courtesy National Park Concessions, Inc.*)

in the maze of faults in western Kentucky.   The Dripping Springs-Chester Escarpment forms the eastern and southern boundary of the Shawnee Hills section of the Interior Low Plateaus.

*Pottsville Escarpment.*   Downdip from the Dripping Springs Escarpment the Pottsville Escarpment may be present locally.   This is true more in Kentucky than in Indiana.   This Pottsville Escarpment is not to be confused with the one along the west side of the Appalachian Plateau, although both are developed on rocks of comparable age.   Most commonly the outcrop area of the lowest Pennsylvanian rocks is marked by a line of rugged hills rather than by a continuous escarpment.

## EROSIONAL HISTORY

Little is known of the Mesozoic history of the Interior Low Plateaus province except that the region was above sea level and subject to degradational processes.   No evidence of any Mesozoic erosion surface remains, and even evidence of any early Tertiary erosion surfaces is lacking. No erosion cycle that might be considered equivalent to the Schooley cycle of the Appalachians has been recognized.

### Lexington-Highland Rim Peneplain

There is good evidence for one period of regional baseleveling that culminated in the development of an erosion surface known in the northern part of the province as the Lexington (Campbell, 1898) and in the southern part as the Highland Rim peneplain (Hayes, 1899). Remnants of the Lexington peneplain are particularly well preserved in the Bluegrass section in north-central Kentucky at altitudes between 900 and 1000 feet. Here the peneplain is only moderately dissected, and extensive tracts of undulating topography are preserved much as they may have appeared in Tertiary time (see Fig. 11.4). Only near such major streams as the Kentucky and Ohio is there much dissection; the Kentucky River across the Bluegrass section has entrenched itself about 500 feet below the level of the peneplain.

Northward extensions of this erosion surface can be recognized in southeastern Indiana and southwestern Ohio, areas that are somewhat arbitrarily placed in the Central Lowlands province because they were glaciated. Actually most of the upland tracts in southeastern Indiana

and southwestern Ohio owe their low relief more to the fact that they are parts of the up-lifted Lexington peneplain than to the leveling effects of a thin veneer of glacial drift. Extensive tracts of the same Tertiary erosion surface encircling the Nashville Basin are known as the Highland Rim peneplain. Characteristic altitudes of the erosion surface in the Highland Rim plateau are between 1000 and 1100 feet (Wilson, 1935).

The Lexington-Highland Rim peneplain was formerly considered to be of early Tertiary age; some geologists thought that it developed as early as Eocene time, but it is now rather generally believed that it is probably Miocene or early Pliocene in age. It is probably roughly contemporaneous in age with the Harrisburg erosion surface of the Appalachians.

The regional slope of the Lexington-Highland Rim peneplain was to the west-northwest, as is evidenced by a decline in altitude in this direction. From an average altitude of about 1050

FIG. 11.4 Lexington peneplain, looking north from Halls Gap in Muldraugh's Hill, Lincoln County, Kentucky. (*Photo* © *by Caufield and Shook.*)

feet in the Bluegrass region the surface declines to about 900 feet in southwestern Ohio and southeastern Indiana, to 800 feet in Anderson County, and to 560 feet in Henderson County, in western Kentucky.

## Parker Strath

Uplift of the Lexington-Highland Rim peneplain was followed by a partial erosion cycle that lead to development of a wide-valley phase called the Parker strath about 200 feet below the level of the Lexington-Highland Rim peneplain. The system of abandoned high-level valleys in the Appalachian Plateau, such as the Teays (see p. 139), was developed during the Parker subcycle. This means that the Parker strath is certainly pre-Kansan in age; it may well be that the subcycle overlapped late Pliocene and early Pleistocene time.

## Post-Parker Strath History

Cutting of the Parker strath was followed by uplift and valley deepening along major streams. Locally, however, on belts of weak rock expansive lowlands were formed. One such weak rock lowland is the central floor of the Nashville Basin; another, partly in the Interior Low Plateaus and partly in the Central Lowlands, is the Scottsburg Lowland of Indiana and Kentucky (Malott, 1922), a lowland on Devonian shales and limestones. These lowlands probably were developed in early Pleistocene time.

Evidence of still further uplift is found in the presence of buried bedrock valleys below present valley floors. These valleys are filled with 100 to 300 feet of alluvium, glacial outwash, and lacustrine materials and were cut before the advent of glaciation and then later partially filled. These filled bedrock valleys represent what has been called the Deep Stage (Ver Steeg, 1936).

## Lafayette Gravels

Widely distributed throughout the Interior Low Plateaus and other parts of central United States are deposits of cherty gravels that have been variously called Lafayette (McGee, 1893), Irvine (Campbell, 1898), and Grover (Rubey, 1952). Possibly gravels in Wisconsin known as the Windrow formation (Thawites and Twenhofel, 1921) may be similar in age and origin. Although widely distributed throughout the Interior Low Plateaus, the gravels are particularly extensive and thick in western Kentucky. Here they attain thicknesses as great as 50 feet. Although the Lafayette "formation" no longer has stratigraphic standing, having been replaced in part by the Citronelle formation, the name is still commonly applied to the upland cherty gravels in the Interior Low Plateaus. Since the origin of these gravels is intimately linked with the geomorphic history of the region, a discussion of them is pertinent.

*Lithology of Gravels.* The Lafayette gravels are a distinctive deposit consisting primarily of insoluble residue components such as chert, quartz and quartzite pebbles, and cobbles mixed with varying amounts of geodes, geodized fossils, sand, silt, and clay. Iron and manganese oxides commonly stain and cement the gravels.

*Age of Gravels.* Ever since their recognition as a distinct deposit the Lafayette gravels have been the focus of controversy as to both their age and their origin. This argument has been brought into the foreground in recent years as a part of the controversy between upper and lower Mississippi Valley geologists regarding the Pleistocene history of the Mississippi Valley (see p. 60). Most upper Mississippi Valley geologists consider the gravels Pliocene in age; Fisk (1944), however, ascribed a Pleistocene age to them.

A thorough study of the mineralogy and geomorphic relationships of the Lafayette gravels has been made by Potter (1955). He dealt with an area near the head of the Gulf embayment and particularly in western Kentucky. His conclusions were: (1) the gravels here are remnants of coalescing alluvial fans deposited by the ancestral Tennessee, Cumberland, Ohio, and Mississippi rivers; (2) the heavy minerals and feldspars in the gravels indicate a preglacial rather than Pleistocene age, as does their association with certain Tertiary erosion surfaces.

*Topographic Relationships.* The gravels are found on uplands 200 to 400 feet above present streams, although reworked gravels may be found at lower altitudes. In the vicinity of Irvine, Kentucky, the type locality for the Irvine formation, they are present at an altitude around 900 feet, and near Frankfort, Kentucky, they are found at an altitude of 800 feet (Malott, 1922). Lusk (1928) has described two exposures of the gravels on the surface of the Highland Rim peneplain in Tennessee which are 400 feet above present river levels. In general the altitudes at which the gravels are found decrease downstream, and in southern Illinois and western Kentucky they are found at altitudes as low as 500 feet. This suggests that they were deposited by graded streams on an erosion surface at or near baselevel.

An interpretation that seems to fit best the nature and topographic relationships of the Lafayette gravels in the Interior Low Plateaus province and adjacent regions is that they represent a lag concentrate of insoluble siliceous materials that accumulated under mid- to late-Tertiary subtropical climatic conditions on the Lexington-Highland Rim peneplain. Uplift of this erosion surface was followed by cutting of the Parker strath, and during its development large quantities of gravels were swept off the peneplain surface and concentrated on the Parker strath along such rivers as the Ohio, Tennessee, Cumberland, and Kentucky. Farther west, near the mouths of the Tennessee, Cumberland, and Ohio rivers, the gravels filled the valleys and covered the uplands in broad fan-like accumulations.

# DESCRIPTION OF SECTIONS

## Highland Rim Section

*Geology and Topography.* Rocks of the Highland Rim section are mainly early and middle Mississippian in age. The Highland Rim is the lower stratigraphically of the two major cuestas present in the province. It is developed mainly on rocks belonging to the Kinderhookian, Osagian, and Meramecian series. North and west of it lies the second cuesta, on rocks mainly of Chesterian age. Much of the Highland Rim section is plateau-like, although along major streams there is marked dissection. Highest summit elevations are slightly above 1000 feet and apparently represent remnants of the Highland Rim peneplain. Topographically the Highland Rim section displays two distinctive types of topography, karst and nonkarst. The karst topography is developed on the rocks of Meramecian age and the nonkarst topography on the rocks of Osagian and Kinderhookian age. The nonkarst area lies immediately back (downdip) from the Knobstone-Muldraugh Hill's Escarpment, whereas the karst area lies farther downdip and extends to the Dripping Springs-Chester Escarpment.

The term Pennyroyal (Sauer, 1927) is applied in Kentucky to the limestone plain south of the Dripping Springs Escarpment; it is a karst plain pockmarked with tens of thousands of sinkholes (see Fig. 11.5). Dicken (1935) has called this plain a solution cuesta, implying that it is lower in altitude than the plateau back of the Dripping Springs Escarpment largely because of mass solutional lowering. Surface streams of any considerable length are extremely rare. In Kentucky, Green River is the only major stream that crosses the limestone plain, and in the Indiana portion the East Fork of White River is the sole stream to cross the karst plain between the Ohio River and its northern terminus at the glacial boundary. The karst plain portion of the Highland Rim Plateau is in many places very similar to the topography found in the Bluegrass section, although its soils are generally not so fertile. The topography on the Warsaw and Salem formations particularly resembles the Bluegrass karst, for sinkholes here are not nearly so numerous, deep, or steep sided as those on the St. Louis and Ste. Genevieve limestones.

*Lost River, Southern Indiana.* Sinkholes, swallow holes, sinking creeks, and dry beds of abandoned surface streams are the more common features of the karst plain. Surface drainage has largely disintegrated and been diverted to subsurface routes. Lost River in southern Indiana (Malott,

FIG. 11.5    Detail of karst plain about 20 miles northeast of Bowling Green, Kentucky.    (*Photo by John S. Shelton.*)

1952) is an outstanding example of abandoned surface drainage. The Lost River drainage basin encompasses some 350 square miles and can be divided into three rather distinct parts: a lower part in which the stream is a deeply entrenched surface stream, a middle abandoned dry-bed stretch that is used only after heavy rains, and an upper part in which Lost River is an unentrenched surface stream. The middle part of its route crosses the portion of the karst plain upon the St. Louis and Ste. Genevieve limestones. This limestone plain is dotted with thousands of sinkholes and is practically devoid of surface streams. The meandering abandoned dry-bed route of Lost River across this plain (see Fig. 11.6) is 22 miles long, whereas its underground route is only 8 miles long and is directly

down the regional dip. Lost River sinks in a series of swallow holes ranging in altitude from 620 to 560 feet. After extremely heavy rains all its water may not be accommodated by these swallow holes, and the excess goes around the dry-bed channel. Lost River reappears at the end of its underground route as a karst spring at an altitude of 490 feet.

*Cavern Distribution.* Caverns are about equally numerous in the karst plain region of the Highland Rim Plateau and in the Shawnee Hills section north and west of the Dripping Springs-Chester Escarpment (see Fig. 11.7), but large caves are very rare beneath the karst plain. Mammoth Cave, Floyd Collin's Crystal Cave, and Great Onyx Cave in Kentucky, and Wyandotte and

Marengo in Indiana, all commercial caverns, are back of the Dripping Springs-Chester Escarpment. The main reason for the large caves being in the Shawnee Hills section seems to be that here are numerous deeply entrenched valleys which make it possible for surface waters to enter swallow holes on the upland and follow long underground routes before reappearing as karst springs along valley floors.

*Barrens.* The name "barren" is commonly encountered in the Pennyroyal region of Kentucky. This name has much the same connotation as "glade" (see p. 201) in the Nashville Basin region. It was applied by early settlers to more or less treeless tracts, which probably owed their existence to the thin soils or rocky nature of parts of the karst plain. Such tracts are essentially one aspect of lapiés development.

*Stages of Karst Development.* The karst topography of the Highland Rim and adjacent Shawnee Hills sections displays different stages of development. The most youthful karst is found imme-

diately back of the Dripping Springs-Chester Escarpment in what is called the Crawford Upland in Indiana (Malott, 1922) and the Mammoth Cave Plateau (Lobeck, 1928) in Kentucky. Here solution valleys and sinking creeks mark the beginning of karst encroachment upon the Shawnee Hills section. Lateral expansion of a number of adjacent solution valleys eventually leads to their coalescence and transformation of what was an area of surface drainage into a local karst plain with a few remnants of the former upland as outliers in it. By this method the karst topography of the Highland Rim section is constantly expanding downdip at the expense of the marginal areas of the Shawnee Hills section.

The part of the karst plain immediately updip from the Dripping Springs-Chester Escarpment displays a mature stage of karst development. Here sinkholes exist by the tens of thousands, and surface streams are practically lacking. Farther updip on the belt of the Salem and Warsaw limestones sinkholes are less common

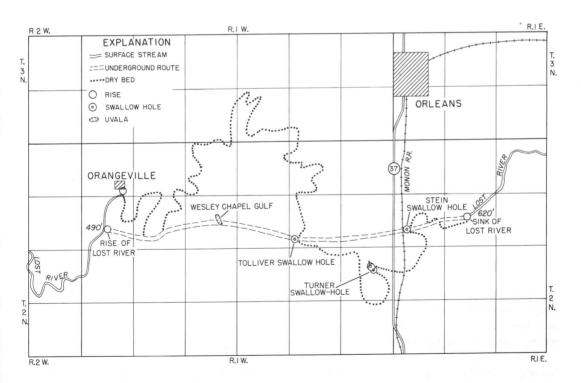

FIG. 11.6  Map of middle portion of Lost River, Orange County, Indiana. (*After C. A. Malott.*)

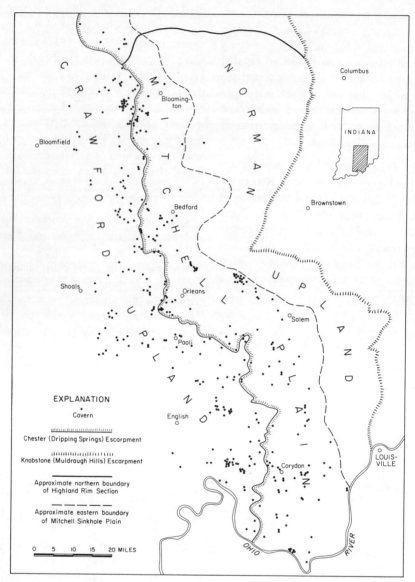

FIG. 11.7   Distribution of caves in southern Indiana with respect to the Chester Escarpment.   (*After R. L. Powell, Ind. Geol. Surv. Circular 8.*)

and more shallow. Two factors seem to be responsible for this difference. The streams which head near the crest of the Dripping Springs-Chester Escarpment are not yet entrenched in their headward portions, so that conditions are not so conducive to the diversion of surfaces waters to underground routes as is true farther downdip. Secondly, the Salem and Warsaw limestones are not so thinly bedded or highly

jointed as are the St. Louis and Ste. Genevieve limestones, and as a consequence openings for entrance of surface waters are more widely spaced.

*Bluegrass Section*

Use of Bluegrass as the name of one of the sections of the Interior Low Plateaus involves extension of this term beyond its local connotation. In common usage, the term Bluegrass is restricted to the innermost part of the section, or what will be referred to as the Inner Bluegrass. In the original Fenneman classification this section was called the Lexington Plain section. Either designation involves extension of the name beyond its local connotation. Differences of lithology with associated differences in topography make possible the recognition of three subdivisions or belts in the Bluegrass section, the Inner Bluegrass, the Eden Shale Belt, and the Outer Bluegrass (see Fig. 11.8).

*Characteristic Topography.* In contrast to the Nashville Basin section, which like the Bluegrass section is developed on a domal structure, the Bluegrass region is not properly thought of as a lowland. It is true the section is partially enclosed by The Knobs on the east and west, but these hills, particularly on the west, are so far downdip from the central Bluegrass region that altitudes on them are no higher than in the Inner Bluegrass, if as high.

The most typical topography of the Bluegrass

section is gently undulating limestone terrain, except near large streams such as the Kentucky and Licking rivers, where deep dissection has taken place. Deep residual soils mantle much of the region and account for its agricultural fame. Much of the topography is what might be called mild karst topography, for the karst features are much more subdued and less numerous than in the adjacent Highland Rim section.

*The Inner Bluegrass.* The Inner Bluegrass belt is at or near the crest of the Jessamine dome and is also topographically the highest part of the Bluegrass section. Here are found some of the best preserved portions of the Lexington peneplain. Dissection, following uplift of this erosion surface, has so little affected the terrain that the topography as we see it today (see Fig. 11.9) is probably not greatly different from what it was at the culmination of the Lexington cycle. Extensive areas at altitudes of 1000 to 1100 feet appear to be remnants of the Lexington peneplain. Such modification of the Tertiary erosion surface as has taken place has been more by mass solutional lowering than by corrasive

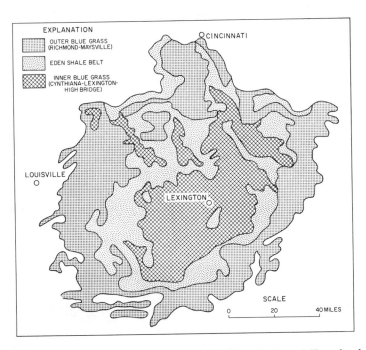

FIG. 11.8 Subdivisions of Bluegrass section. (*After A. C. McFarlan, Geology of Kentucky, by permission of University of Kentucky Press.*)

FIG. 11.9    Inner Bluegrass topography, near Winchester, Kentucky.    (*Photo by John C. Frye.*)

stream erosion.    Only adjacent to large streams is dissection of the landscape significant.

It seems anomalous that in a region where the limestone is hundreds of feet thick karst features should be developed so sparingly.    No large caves exist within the area, and sinkholes, where present, are much more shallow and less conspicuous than those in the Highland Rim section. The explanation of this anomalous condition lies in the nature of the Ordovician limestones; they have in them numerous shale partings which interfere with downward movement of groundwater; furthermore, they are not highly jointed. Modest karst development is evident even adjacent to the deeply entrenched Kentucky River, where it would seem conditions would be excellent for cavern formation.

*Eden Shale Belt.*    The Eden Shale Belt is the one exception to the previously made statement that the typical topography of the Bluegrass section

is gently undulating limestone terrain.    The Ordovician Eden shale crops out in an irregular

FIG. 11.10    Topography of Eden Shale Belt between Cynthiana and Falmouth, Kentucky.    (*Photo by A. C. McFarlan.*)

belt that encircles the Inner Bluegrass. The hilly terrain of the belt contrasts strongly with the lower relief of both the Inner and Outer Bluegrass belts (see Fig. 11.10). The impervious shales make for a maximum of surface runoff and erosion. The Eden Shale Belt varies in width from 5 to 30 miles; it is widest on the north and narrowest on the south. Soils are thin and relatively infertile, particularly as compared with those of the Inner Bluegrass.

*The Outer Bluegrass.* The Outer Bluegrass is the outcrop area of Upper Ordovician, Silurian, and Devonian formations. Use of Outer Bluegrass in this sense is somewhat more inclusive than is true in Kentucky, where the term is likely to imply the area underlain by rocks of Maysville and Richmond age. Limestones are abundant here, and the topography resembles that of the Inner Bluegrass, but the soils are not so deep or fertile as those of the Inner Bluegrass. The westward-sloping surface of the Outer Bluegrass almost coincides with the regional dip and descends into a lowland on Devonian limestones and shales, which in Indiana has been called the Scottsburg Lowland (Malott, 1922). The

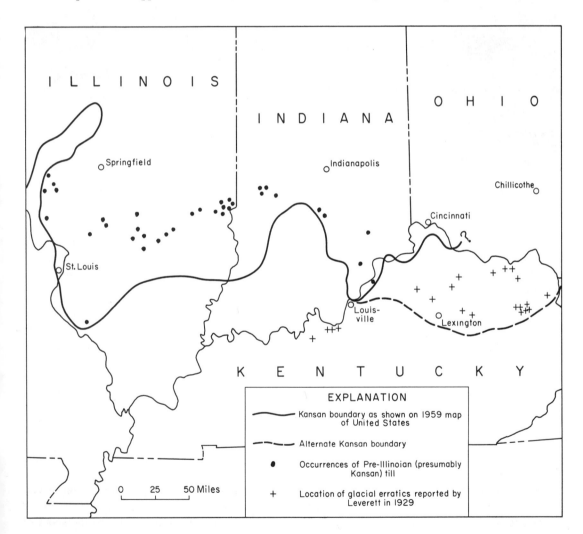

FIG. 11.11 Probable Kansan glacial boundary based on distribution of glacial erratics in Kentucky and exposures of presumed Kansan till as reported by numerous persons.

FIG. 11.12    Falls of the Ohio at Louisville, Kentucky.    (*Photo © by Caufield and Shook.*)

Scottsburg Lowland of Indiana has been glaciated and is included in the Central Lowlands, but its extension into Kentucky, in the Louisville area, appears to have escaped glaciation.

*Relation of Glaciation.* Although the glacial boundary as commonly drawn follows the Ohio River between Louisville and Cincinnati, it is now known that glacial ice actually crossed the Ohio River into Kentucky (Ray, 1957); thus use of the Ohio River as the boundary between the Interior Low Plateaus and the Central Lowlands is largely a matter of convenience. However, the topographic effects of glaciation are obscure south of the Ohio River, whereas they are apparent north of it. Leverett (1929) described numerous glacial erratics in the northern part of the Bluegrass section (see Fig. 11.11) whose age has puzzled geologists for some time. It was generally believed that they were pre-Illinoian, but considerable uncertainty existed as to whether they were Nebraskan or Kansan. In view of our present knowledge of the distribution of Kansan drift it now seems more likely that they are Kansan in age (see p. 220).

*Falls of the Ohio.* The so-called Falls of the Ohio (actually a rapids) at the western margin of the Outer Bluegrass, at Louisville, Kentucky (see Fig. 11.12), are anomalous in that they represent the only place along the Ohio River where bedrock is exposed in the stream channel. This is particularly unusual because the "falls" are in a weak rock stretch of the Ohio Valley which is wide and open and not gorge-like, as is the valley both above and below Louisville. The presence of the "falls" here is related to the glacial history of this part of the Ohio River. The preglacial valley of the Ohio River, in the Louisville area, lies a few miles to the south of its present valley and is filled with as much as 125 feet of glacial outwash (Guyton, 1946).

During the time that Wisconsin outwash was coming down the Ohio Valley, the river was shifting back and forth across the lowland at Louisville. When the Wisconsin ice sheet withdrew far enough to the north that outwash no longer came into the Ohio River Valley, a change in stream regimen took place which turned the Ohio from an aggrading into a degrading stream. It happened that at the time this change took place the river was at the north side of the lowland, and in cutting down it encountered a biostrome in a buried bedrock spur of Devonian limestone beneath the valley train deposits; the resistant nature of this sedimentary structure cause the rapids to develop in the river.

## Nashville Basin Section

*Topography.* The Nashville Basin (Wilson, 1935) is an excellent example of inversion of topography, for the area is structurally high but topographically low. Most of the basin lies between altitudes of 500 and 700 feet, in contrast to altitudes of 1000 to 1100 feet in the Inner Bluegrass. The lowland is rimmed by the infacing Highland Rim Escarpment. The Central Basin of Tennessee, as the lowland is known locally, is about 60 miles wide and 120 miles long and trends in a general direction of north 30 degrees east. It coincides very closely in position with the crest of the Nashville dome.

Average dips on the flanks of the dome are about 15 feet per mile and rarely exceed 25 feet. Numerous minor folds superposed on the major structure cause local variations in dips. The Cumberland River cuts across the northern end of the structure, and it may be that its sharp bend to the northwest is a result of downdip migration of the stream course. A few normal faults are known, but they usually extend for only a few miles, and their displacement is commonly less than 100 feet.

The central floor of the basin is a rolling plain of low relief, but outward toward the Highland Rim Escarpment relief increases, and numerous outliers of the Highland Rim Plateau stand 200 to 400 feet above the basin floor. As the highly irregular Highland Rim Escarpment is approached, the outliers increase in number and height and are ultimately replaced by spurs of the Highland Plateau projecting into the basin.

*Karst Features.* On the limestones in the central part of the Nashville Basin, the topography is that of a moderate karst plain. Local areas in the central basin are known as glades. This term is applied to fairly flat areas of bare or nearly bare rock; they are often marked by a concentration of cedar trees and hence commonly are called cedar glades. According to Galloway (1919), the term glade has gone through at least two changes of meaning before coming to have its present connotation. The word originally meant an open space in a woods; then it came to be applied to the thing that was responsible for the open space, an area of bare rock; now it is used to indicate any rocky area whether surrounded by trees or not. Much of the terrain designated as glades is bare, furrowed limestone surface technically known as lapiés.

*Geomorphic History.* The geomorphic history of the Nashville Basin as outlined by Galloway still holds good except for the dating of events. He recognized the following stages in the development of the topography:

1. Formation of the Highland Rim peneplain at the end of the Eocene.
2. Development of the high gravel terrace by the end of Pliocene time.
3. Formation of the Central Basin by middle Pleistocene time.
4. Uplift during late Pleistocene and Recent time.

We would now consider the Highland Rim peneplain as of Miocene if not early Pliocene age. The so-called high-terrace gravel stage is what is now called the Parker strath; it got its name from terraces along the Cumberland River about 200 feet below the level of the Highland Rim peneplain, and from the presence on these terraces at numerous places of Lafayette gravels.

What Galloway called the Central Basin peneplain is well developed in Rutherford County, Tennessee, at an altitude near 500 feet, or about 100 feet above the present entrenched Cumberland River. Presumably it correlates in age with the Scottsburg Lowland of southeastern Indiana and the Havana strath of southern Illinois (see p. 217). These local straths are either early Pleistocene or middle Pleistocene in age, as suggested by Galloway. The Cumberland River is now entrenched about 100 feet below the level of the Central Basin strath. However, the amount of Pleistocene uplift was actually greater than 100 feet, for the river valley is deeply alluviated above its bedrock floor.

### Shawnee Hills Section

As originally defined (Fenneman, 1917), the Interior Low Plateaus was divided into three parts, the Lexington Plain, Nashville Basin, and Highland Rim sections. The Lexington Plain and Nashville Basin met fairly well the requirement that a geomorphic unit should possess a marked degree of homogeneity as to relief, altitudes, and land forms, but the Highland Rim section as originally constituted included areas markedly diverse in geology and topography. In an attempt to correct this situation Flint (1928) proposed that the Highland Rim section be divided into two sections, that the western section be named the Shawnee Hills section, and that Highland Rim be retained as the name of the more southerly and easterly section. The Dripping Springs-Chester Escarpment was selected as the boundary between the two sections.

*Nature of Topography.* The thus restricted Highland Rim section possesses a considerable degree of geomorphic homogeneity despite the existence in it of karst and nonkarst topography. The newly created Shawnee Hills section, however, possesses great diversity of topography because of the variety of its geology. In this section are over twenty Upper Mississippian (Chester) formations, including limestones, shales, and sandstone, and a nearly equal number of Pennsylvanian formations not quite so variable in lithology. In addition to the variety in lithology, two other things distinguish the Shawnee Hills section: intense faulting at its western end and widespread alluviation or valley-filling along all major valleys and their larger tributaries.

The variable geology in the Shawnee Hills section is expressed by great variety of topographic form. Much of the area is rugged hilly topography, but some extensive lowland tracts exist. Some hilltops may represent remnants of Tertiary erosion surfaces but this is difficult to determine because structural control of the topography is so common. Numerous topographic levels can be observed, but when they are investigated carefully it is usually found that the various hillside benches and upland tracts coincide in extent with some particular sandstone formation. Recognition of erosion surfaces controlled by former baselevels of erosion is therefore extremely difficult.

*Importance of Faults.* Faulting is common in an area including nine counties in western Kentucky, southwestern Indiana, and southern Illinois. The faults are high-angle normal faults with maximum displacements as great as 2500 feet. The faulting was post-Pennsylvanian in age, and Rhoads and Mistler (1941) have presented evidence that indicates that rather than being associated in any way with the Appalachian orogeny it was as recent as Cretaceous or Eocene. What has been called the Rough Creek fault zone (Russell, 1938) is an eastern continuation into Kentucky of the Shawneetown fault zone of southern Illinois. Configuration of the topography in the Shawneetown area is strongly influenced by the faults.

*Alluviation and Causes.* Valley-filling characterizes the Ohio Valley along its whole course between the Interior Low Plateaus and Central Lowlands but becomes particularly conspicuous along tributaries of the Ohio River from the Green River westward. Deeply alluviated valleys are an outstanding feature of the landscape of northwestern Kentucky, southwestern Indiana, and southern Illinois. Maximum depths of the valley fill are as much as 150 to 300 feet. At many places along the valleys may be seen partially buried bedrock hills projecting through the valley fills. These were called "island hills" by Shaw (1915) from the town of Island, Kentucky (see Fig. 11.13), which sits on one, and were referred to as "hills of circumalluvi-

FIG. 11.13  Portion of Central City, Kentucky, topographic sheet, showing several "island hills."

FIG. 11.14   Dicksburg Hills in lower Wabash Valley near Hazelton, Indiana.   Loess-veneered hills of Pennsylvanian sandstone projecting through alluvial fill.   (*Photo by M. M. Fidlar.*)

ation" by Fidlar (1948), who described several of them in the lower Wabash Valley (see Fig. 11.14). Most of the hills have veneers of loess, and in some instances sand, that obscure in varying degrees their bedrock cores.

It has been suggested (Malott, 1922) that the deep alluviation of the valleys may be explained as (1) a direct and indirect effect of filling of the major valleys with glacial outwash, (2) the result of seaward extension of the Mississippi delta, and (3) a consequence of regional depression of the land. It seems likely that glaciation was indirectly responsible for most of the valley-filling, although it cannot be denied that the other two causes may have contributed in some degree, particularly seaward growth of the Mississippi delta.

Malott, although ascribing major importance to glaciation, contended that the other two causes of alluviation must be taken into account. He thought that there was evidence of regional depression and cited in support of this view the difference in the altitudes of the Lafayette gravels east and west of Anderson Creek, Perry County, Indiana. East of Anderson Creek the gravels are found at altitudes of 700 feet or more, whereas

west of here they are found at altitudes as low as 500 feet. These are differences in altitude that seem greater than can be ascribed to the gradients on the Parker strath and therefore suggest that there has been downwarping to the west with accompanying alluviation.

Malott further argued that seaward extension of the Mississippi delta was partially responsible for the valley-filling. The delta of the Mississippi River has grown seaward at least 125 miles since the beginning of the Pleistocene. The mouth of the Mississippi River at the beginning of the Pleistocene was probably near the junction of the Red River with the Mississippi. This point is now 50 feet above sea level as a result of the regrading of the river as its mouth was extended into the Gulf of Mexico. While this readjustment of valley floor was taking place along the lower Mississippi, accompanying regrading must have gone on in the upper part of its valley, resulting in a rise of its valley floor by a corresponding amount. Thus, Malott argued that as much as 50 feet of the valley fills may be attributed reasonably to seaward growth of the Mississippi delta.

Certainly most of the alluviation may be ascribed to the effects, mainly indirect, of glaciation. A lot of the valley fill material along the Ohio and Wabash valleys is glacial outwash, as is evidenced by the presence of pebbles of glacial origin. The Ohio and Wabash rivers acted as glacial sluiceways during the Kansan, Illinoian, and Wisconsin glaciations; hence the fill must be composite in nature.

While Wisconsin outwash was being discharged down the Ohio and Wabash valleys, the rising valley trains ponded their tributaries, giving rise to an extensive system of backwater lakes in them (Shaw, 1915). Deposits in these lakes are mainly heavy, blocky clays or silts. The sites of the former lakes are now marked by lacustrine plains which are terraced in their lower parts but little dissected toward their heads. Conditions comparable to those that produced the Wisconsin system of backwater lakes probably existed during the Kansan and Illinoian glaciations, but in only a few places have pre-Wisconsin lacustrine deposits been identified.

*Course of Tennessee River.* The anomalous course of the Tennessee River has been discussed in a previous chapter (see p. 124). Across the Shawnee Hills section the Tennessee River follows very closely the contact between Paleozoic and post-Paleozoic rocks, and it may be that its course here was determined by the contact between the relatively strong Paleozoic rocks and the weaker Cretaceous and Tertiary rocks. The Tennessee River joins the Ohio River at Paducah, Kentucky; from Paducah, the Ohio River flows westward through the Metropolis Lowland to join the Mississippi near Cairo, Illinois. The pre-Pleistocene courses of these two streams in this area were considerably different from what they are now. The Ohio River crossed southern Illinois via the Cache Lowland. Fisk (1944) believed that the Tennessee River flowed northeastward from Paducah to join the Cumberland River and thence on northwestward to the Ohio a few miles south of Golconda, Illinois (see Fig. 11.15 A). A short tributary of the Ohio in the Metropolis Lowland flowed westward to the Ohio River somewhere south of Cairo. A low

divide in the Metropolis Lowland separated this westward-flowing tributary from an eastward-flowing stream that joined the Tennessee east of Paducah. Floodwaters of the Tennessee poured across the low divide in the Metropolis Lowland and in time all the Tennessee and Cumberland drainage was diverted through the Metropolis Gap. Diversion southward of the Ohio River to the abandoned part of the Cumberland-Tennessee drainage course came later as a result of aggradation of the Cache Valley route of the Ohio with glacial outwash until its floor was high enough that it spilled southward into the lower former Cumberland-Tennessee route.

What may be a more logical interpretation of the drainage changes near the Tennessee-Cumberland-Ohio junction area would assume that originally there was a divide between the Ohio River in the Cache Valley and the Cumberland-Tennessee drainage through the Metropolis Lowland about midway between these two westward drainage lines (see Fig. 11.15 B). At this time the Cumberland flowed southwestward to join the Tennessee at Paducah rather than the Ohio in the Cache Valley. Aggradation of the Cache Lowland route with glacial outwash caused the Ohio River to spill southward across the divide between the Ohio and Cumberland-Tennessee systems and establish a more southerly route through the Metropolis Lowland.

The possibility of another drainage change in this area is very evident. The valleys of the Tennessee and Cumberland rivers are remarkably close together in their terminal portions. In the not distant future lateral planation piracy is likely to effect a junction of the two streams a short distance upstream from the Ohio River. At one point the Cumberland River is only 1.1 miles from the east shore of Kentucky Lake in the Tennessee Valley. Construction of a dam on the Tennessee River to form Kentucky Lake has temporarily suspended the process of lateral planation by the Tennessee River in this area, but not that by the Cumberland River. The life of Kentucky Lake will represent only a short interlude before the inevitable course of events has its way.

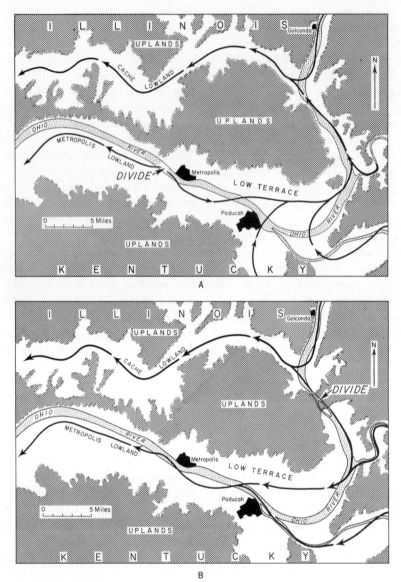

FIG. 11.15    Alternate interpretations of how diversion of Ohio River from Cache Lowland was effected.    (*11.15 A after H. N. Fisk; 11.15 B after author.*)

### Evolution of Present Ohio River

It is somewhat debatable as to where the evolution of the Ohio River would be discussed most appropriately. This stream crosses parts of three geomorphic provinces, the Appalachian Plateaus, the Interior Low Plateaus, and the Coastal Plain and borders part of the Central

Lowlands. However, because a considerable part of the Ohio River is either in or adjacent to the Interior Low Plateaus province, it seems appropriate to discuss its evolution in the present chapter.

The existing Ohio River is a much larger stream than its preglacial progenitor, and its present size is the result of diversion to the preglacial Ohio of several drainage lines by the southward-moving glaciers (see Fig. 11.16). After integration of the diverted drainage with the preglacial Ohio the stream's course was essentially an ice-marginal one. The Ohio River may be divided into three parts: the lower Ohio, which is the preglacial part; the middle Ohio, which represents part of the former Teays drainage; and the upper Ohio, which comprises part of the drainage which in preglacial time flowed northward into an east-flowing stream in the lowland now occupied by Lake Erie.

*Preglacial Divide Location.* Difference of opinion exists as to where the head of the preglacial

Ohio River was. Leverett (1902), Fenneman (1916), and Ver Steeg (1936, 1938) believed that the stream headed above Cincinnati (see Fig. 11.17 A) and differed with Tight's (1903) view that a preglacial stream, called by Tight the Cincinnati River, drained northward along the general route of the present Miami River to join the Teays River (see Fig. 11.18). The conclusion that southwestern Ohio and adjacent parts of Kentucky drained southwestward in preglacial time was based primarily on the belief that the Miami Valley bedrock floor has a southwestward slope and that the slope of the buried preglacial upland of southwestern Ohio was likewise to the southwest.

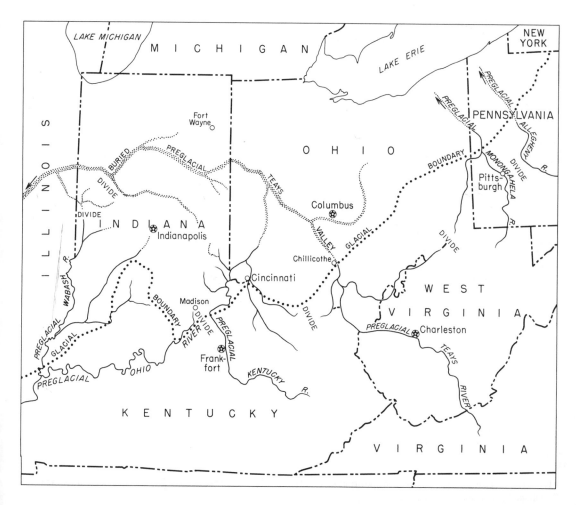

FIG. 11.16 Portions of drainage lines which were integrated to form present Ohio River.

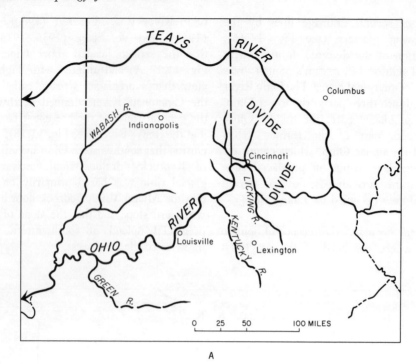

A

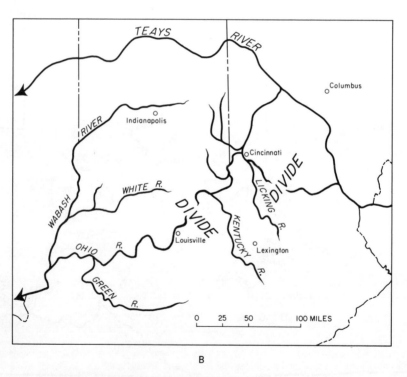

B

FIG. 11.17   Two interpretations as to position of preglacial Ohio River divide: A. Divide southwest of Cincinnati. B. Divide in Madison, Indiana, area.

In more recent years, Malott (1922), Fowke (1925, 1933), and Wayne (1952) have held that the head of the preglacial Ohio drainage was near Madison, Indiana (see Fig. 11.17 B). Several arguments may be advanced in support of this view:

(1) There is a lack of beveling of the upland toward the Ohio Valley in the Madison area, a condition that seems unlikely if a major stream has flowed through the area since Tertiary time. Beveling can be observed along the Kentucky River, which joins the Ohio River above Madison, and along the Ohio Valley downstream from Madison.

(2) Lafayette gravels are present at numerous places along the Kentucky River, to a lesser extent along the Licking River, and along the Ohio Valley below Madison, but none is present in the Madison region. Considering how remarkably well the upland is preserved in the Madison area, it is unusual that none of these gravels can be found if the Kentucky and Licking

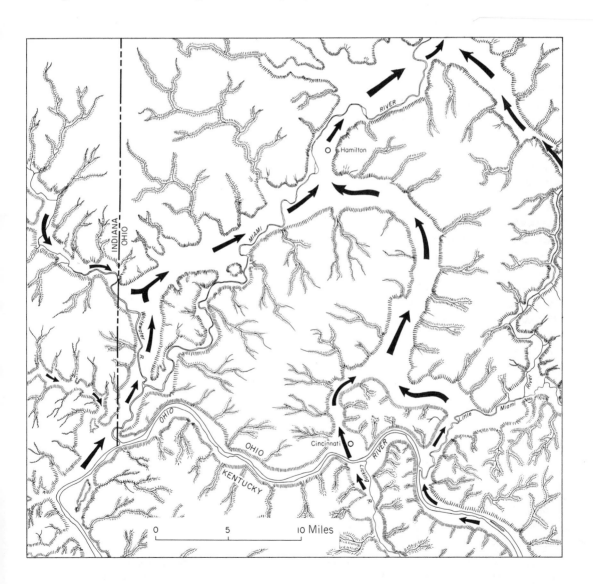

FIG. 11.18 Comparison of present and preglacial drainage in southwestern Ohio. (*After W. G. Tight, U. S. Geol. Survey Profess. Paper* 13.)

Rivers drained into an Ohio River that flowed through the Madison region. If, however, these two streams drained northward to the Teays River, the absence of Lafayette gravel in the Madison area is readily understandable.

(3) Many of the streams that join the Ohio between Madison and Cincinnati form a barbed pattern with the Ohio, but those that join the Ohio below the postulated Madison divide form a normal pattern. When it is taken into account that the streams that enter the Ohio flowing eastward are going against the regional dip, slight though it may be, it seems to suggest that there has been stream diversion and that the present directions of the tributaries are inherited from a previous drainage pattern in which they joined a northeastward-flowing stream.

(4) The presumed southwestward slope of the buried bedrock valley floors in southwestern Ohio is based on somewhat meager data; even if it exists, due consideration has not been given to the possibility of tilting to the south as the result of glacial unloading of the region.

*Date of Diversion.* An early glaciation caused southward diversion of the Monongahela-Allegheny and Teays drainages from their preglacial courses to the preglacial Ohio. It is not certain whether this diversion was effected by the Nebraskan or Kansan ice sheet. In view of recent finding in northern Kentucky of what is believed to be Kansan till (Ray, 1957), it appears more likely that it was the Kansan ice. Certainly this diversion was accomplished before the Illinoian glaciation, for Illinoian outwash is present down the Ohio Valley.

# REFERENCES CITED

Bucher, W. H. (1936). Cryptovolcanic structures in the United States, *Rept. 16th Int. Geol. Cong.*, 1055–1084.

Campbell, M. R. (1898). Description of Richmond quadrangle, *U. S. Geol. Survey Folio 46*, 3.

Dicken, S. N. (1935). A Kentucky solution cuesta, *Jour. Geol.*, **43**, 539–544.

Fenneman, N. M. (1916). Geology of Cincinnati and vicinity, *Ohio Geol. Surv.*, *4th Series, Bull.* 19, 207 pp.

—— (1917). Physiographic divisions of the United States, Assoc. Am. Geographers, *Annals*, **6**, 19–98.

Fidlar, M. M. (1948). Physiography of the lower Wabash Valley, *Ind. Dept. Conserv.*, *Div. Geol., Bull.* 2, 212 pp.

Flint, R. F. (1928). Natural boundaries in the Interior Low Plateaus physiographic province, *Jour. Geol.*, **36**, 451–457.

Fowke, Gerard (1925). The genesis of the Ohio River, *Ind. Acad. Sci., Proc.*, **34**, 81–102.

—— (1933). *The Evolution of the Ohio River*, The Hollenbeck Press, Indianapolis, 273 pp.

Galloway, J. J. (1919). Geology and natural resources of Rutherford County, Tennessee, *Tenn. Div. Geol. Bull.* 22, 81 pp.

Guyton, W. F. (1946). Artificial recharge of glacial sand and gravel with filtered river water at Louisville, Kentucky, *Econ. Geol.*, **41**, 99–109.

Hayes, C. W. (1899). Physiography of the Chattanooga district, *U. S. Geol. Survey 19th Ann. Rept.*, Pt. 2, 1–58.

Leverett, Frank (1902). Glacial formations and drainage features of the Erie and Ohio Basins, *U. S. Geol. Survey Mon.* 41, 85.

—— (1929). Pleistocene of northern Kentucky, *Ky. Geol. Surv. Series 6, Bull.* 31, 1–80.

Lobeck, A. K. (1928). The geology and physiography of the Mammoth Cave National Park, *Ky. Geol. Surv. Series 6, Pamphlet* 21, 69 pp.

Lusk, R. G. (1928). Gravel on the Highland Rim Plateau and terraces in the valley of the Cumberland River, *Jour. Geol.*, **36**, 164–170.

Malott, C. A. (1922). Handbook of Indiana Geology, Pt. 2, *The Physiography of Indiana*, 59–256.

—— (1952). The swallow-holes of Lost River, Orange County, Indiana, Ind. Acad. Sci., *Proc.*, **61**, 187–231.

McFarlan, A. C. (1943). *Geology of Kentucky*, University of Kentucky, Lexington, 531 pp.

McGee, W. J. (1893). The Lafayette formation, *U. S. Geol. Survey 12th Ann. Rep.*, Pt. 1, 347–521.

Potter, P. E. (1955). The petrology and origin of the Lafayette gravel, *Jour. Geol.*, **63**, 1–38, 115–132.

Ray, L. L. (1957). Two significant new exposures of Pleistocene deposits along the Ohio River in Kentucky, *Jour. Geol.*, **65**, 542–545.

Rhoads, R. F., and A. J. Mistler (1941). Post-Appalachian faulting in western Kentucky, *Am. Assoc. Petroleum Geologists Bull.*, **25**, 2046–2056.

Rubey, W. W. (1952). Geology and mineral resources of the Hardin and Brussels quadrangles (in Illinois), *U. S. Geol. Survey Profess. Paper* 218, 179 pp.

Russell, W. L. (1938). Relation of the Rough Creek fault of Kentucky to Ouachita deformation, *Am. Assoc. Petroleum Geologists Bull.*, **22**, 1682–1686.

Sauer, Carl (1927). Geography of the Pennyroyal, *Ky. Geol. Surv. Series* **6**, *Bull.* 25, 5–130.

Shaw, E. W. (1915). Newly discovered beds of extinct lakes in southern and western Illinois and adjacent states, *Ill. Geol. Surv. Bull.* 20, 139–157.

Thwaites, F. T., and Twenhofel W. H. (1921). Windrow formation; an upland gravel formation of the Driftless and adjacent areas of the upper Mississippi Valley, *Geol. Soc. Am. Bull.*, **32**, 293–314.

Tight, W. G. (1903). Drainage modifications in southeastern Ohio and adjacent parts of West Virginia and Kentucky, *U. S. Geol. Survey Profess. Paper* 13, 108 pp.

Ver Steeg, Karl (1936). The buried topography of western Ohio, *Jour. Geol.*, **44**, 918–939.

——— (1938). Thickness of drift in western Ohio, *Jour. Geol.*, **46**, 654–659.

Wayne, W. J. (1952). Pleistocene evolution of the Ohio and Wabash valleys, *Jour. Geol.*, **60**, 575–585.

Wilson, C. W., Jr. (1935). The pre-Chattanooga development of the Nashville dome, *Jour. Geol.*, **43**, 449–481.

——— and K. E. Born (1943). Structure of central Tennessee, *Am. Assoc. Petroleum Geologists Bull.*, **27**, 1039–1059.

ADDITIONAL REFERENCES

Bassler, R. S. (1932). The stratigraphy of the central basin of Tennessee, *Tenn. Geol. Surv. Bull.* 38, 268 pp.

Davis, D. H. (1927). The geography of the Bluegrass region of Kentucky, *Ky. Geol. Surv. Series 6, Bull.* 23, 215 pp.

Dicken, S. N. (1935). Kentucky karst landscapes, *Jour. Geol.*, **43**, 708–728.

Jillson, W. R. (1943). Buried upland channel of the Kentucky River, *Am. Jour. Sci.*, **241**, 761–763.

McFarlan, A. C. (1958). Behind the scenery in Kentucky, *Ky. Geol. Surv. Series 9, Spec. Pub.* 10, 144 pp.

Thornbury, W. D. (1950). Glacial sluiceways and lacustrine plains of southern Indiana, *Ind. Dept. Conserv., Div. Geol., Bull.* 4, 21 pp.

Walker, E. H., Jr. (1957). The deep channel and alluvial deposits of the Ohio Valley in Kentucky, *U. S. Geol. Survey Water Supply Paper* 1411, 25 pp.

# 12

# Central Lowlands Province

## GENERAL DESCRIPTION

Except for the Coastal Plain no geomorphic province is as extended and irregular in form as is the Central Lowlands; even the Coastal Plain does not extend through so many degrees of latitude as does the Central Lowlands. The Central Lowlands extend from western New York to North Dakota and as far south as northern Texas. The province covers over one-half million square miles and includes a great variety of landscapes. The one thing that they have in common is that, except on the south, they are bounded by higher land. Thus in a relative sense the term lowland can be appropriately applied to much of the province. Altitudes at the western edge are as much as 1500 to 1800 feet, in contrast to 300 or 400 feet in southern Illinois and Indiana. One section, the Driftless Area, hardly merits being called lowland, but it is included in the province largely as a matter of convenience. Even though the relief is considerable in the Driftless Area, its geologic structure is similar to that of much of the Central Lowlands. Much of the province is characterized by near flatness of rock strata and widespread topographic effects of glaciation. The results of glaciation can be seen in the Driftless area even though the ice may not have extended into it. In the Osage section, however, the effects of glaciation are very minor indeed and are limited to small amounts of loessial material of possible glacial origin.

### Province Boundaries

From western New York to near Cleveland, Ohio, the province boundary is the prominent

escarpment at the edge of the Appalachian Plateau. This escarpment continues southwestward across Ohio but is not as distinct a feature as in New York and Pennsylvania, partly because glaciation has obscured it and partly because it breaks up in a line of hills lacking a straight and imposing front.

Use of the limits of glaciation as the southern boundary of much the Central Lowlands includes in the Central Lowlands areas where the glacial drift is so thin or scattered as to have little effect on the topography. Such areas may be topographically more like the Interior Low Plateaus or Interior Highlands to the south.

The boundary from southern Ohio to central Missouri follows in general the limits of glaciation, although between Cincinnati and Louisville it is arbitrarily drawn along the Ohio River. From St. Louis westward the Missouri River serves as the boundary. This leaves a small area that was glaciated outside the Central Lowlands.

The boundary between the southernmost extension of the Central Lowlands, the Osage section, and the Interior Highlands is largely transitional in nature. It is drawn where rocks of Pennsylvanian age lap onto the Ozark dome, but it does not mark a sharp change in topography.

Separation of the Central Lowlands from the Great Plains is based on a combination of differences in altitude, topography, and stratigraphy. Along part of this boundary an east-facing escarpment can be identified. In North Dakota this escarpment rises 300 to 400 feet above the Central Lowlands. Southward the escarpment becomes less distinct and across Nebraska is almost completely lacking. Difference of opinion exists as to where the boundary between the Great Plains and Central Lowlands should be drawn in Kansas. Fenneman (1931) drew the boundary along the Smoky Hills and connected them with the Red Hills in southern Kansas and Oklahoma. Frye (1946, 1949), however, has maintained that the Flint Hills, as suggested by Adams (1903), would form a better boundary than the Smoky Hills. The Flint Hills Escarpment is held up by resistant cherty limestones of early Permian age. In Texas the western boundary of the Central Lowlands is at an east-facing escarpment commonly known as the Caprock Escarpment because of its cap of Tertiary deposits (see p. 301).

The northern boundary of the Central Lowlands lies mainly in Canada, where the sedimentary rocks of the Central Lowlands abut against the crystalline rocks of the Laurentian Upland.

## Bedrock Geology and Structure

*Age or Rocks.* Bedrock formations of the Central Lowlands are mainly Paleozoic in age, but included at the western edge are some rocks of Cretaceous age. In a rough way the western boundary of the province follows the contact between the Cretaceous and Tertiary rocks. Most of the Central Lowlands in the Dakotas is underlain by Cretaceous rocks, as is a considerable area in Minnesota and Iowa.

*Major Structures.* A number of domes or their extensions bring Precambrian basement rocks either to or near the surface. Four major uplifts with their associated arms or prongs and three lesser ones control regional dips in the Central Lowlands. The four major uplifts are: (1) the Ozark dome, (2) Cincinnati arch, (3) a domelike extension of the Canadian Shield that is commonly called the Wisconsin arch, and (4) another extension of the Canadian Shield which we may call the Ontario dome. Three lesser uplifts which bring Precambrian rocks to the surface are the Sioux uplift in southeastern South Dakota and adjacent parts of Minnesota and Iowa and the Arbuckle and Wichita uplifts in southern Oklahoma.

The Ozark uplift is an assymmetrical dome in which Precambrian rocks are exposed considerably east of the center of the Ozark Plateau. Encircling the Precambrian core are sedimentary rocks ranging in age from Cambrian to Mississippian.

The oldest rocks exposed around the Cincinnati arch are Ordivician in age. This arch bifurcates along the Indiana-Ohio line and sends a prong, known as the Findlay arch, northeastward toward the western end of Lake Erie and the Ontario dome, and another prong, commonly known as the Kankakee arch, northwestward toward the Wisconsin dome.

The so-called Wisconsin dome is not a dome in the strict sense of the term but is an uplift in which Precambrian rocks of the Canadian Shield extend into the United States in what is called the Superior Upland. Outcropping around the west, south, and east flanks of this uplift are Paleozoic rocks ranging from late Cambrian to Silurian in age. Farther east in Ontario the situation is somewhat similar, where the Paleozoic formations lap onto the crystalline rocks of the Canadian Shield.

The major basins of the Central Lowlands are the Michigan, Illinois, and Forest City basins. The Illinois Basin is separated from the Michigan Basin by the northwestern extension of the Cincinnati arch, and the Forest City Basin is separated from the Illinois Basin by a northern extension of the Ozark uplift known as the Lincoln fold. In the Michigan and Illinois basins the youngest rocks are Pennsylvanian in age, but in the Forest City Basin Cretaceous rocks appear.

Locally lesser structures, including folds and faults, complicate the geologic picture and alter the regional dip. The Anadarko Basin to the north of the Wichita uplift is an important feature of this sort, as is the Nemaha uplift in Kansas. The parallel belts of Pennsylvanian and Permian rocks that dip westward from the Ozark uplift into the trough-like depression between the Nemaha and Ozark uplifts has been called the Prairie Plains homocline (King, 1951). The

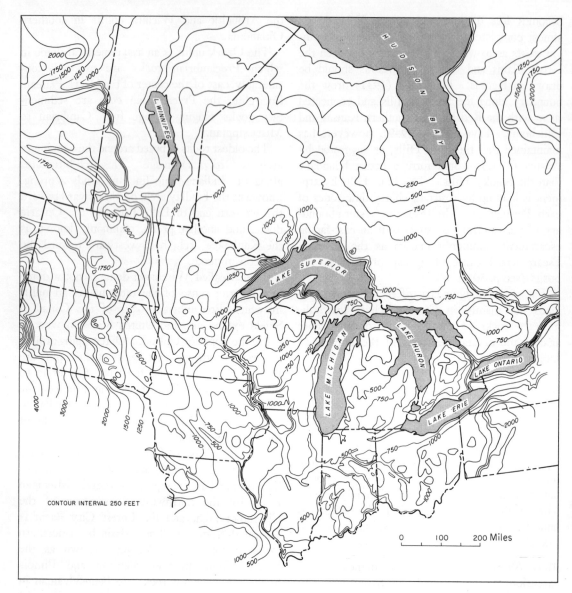

FIG. 12.1    Generalized topographic map of preglacial topography of midwestern United States.    (*After Leland Horberg, Jour. Geol.,* **64.**)

Lasalle anticline at the north edge of the Illinois basin is another example of the lesser structures that locally alter regional dips.

## NATURE OF PREGLACIAL TOPOGRAPHY

The preglacial topography of the Central Lowlands largely reflected the influence of geologic structures and the varying degrees of erosibility of the bedrock.   In broad outline the topography consisted of a series of cuestas encircling the several domal uplifts, similar in a general way to the topography that now exists in the Interior Low Plateaus.   Where thickness-of-drift data are available in sufficient number to permit reconstruction of the buried bedrock topography, as has been done in Illinois in considerable detail

(Horberg, 1950), we find that the topography is essentially similar to that south of the glaciated area. Escarpments developed on the resistant beds and lowland on the weaker beds. Examples of such weak bed lowlands are the basins now occupied by the Great Lakes. Figure 12.1 is a generalized preglacial topographic map of much of the Central Lowlands as drawn by Horberg (1956).

## TERTIARY DRAINAGE OF CENTRAL LOWLANDS

### Major Preglacial Drainage Lines

Many details of Tertiary drainage in Midwestern United States remain to be worked out, but enough information on the paleogeomorphology of the region is available to make major preglacial relationships reasonably clear. As at present, the Central Lowlands area in Tertiary time drained northward to Hudson Bay, eastward to the Gulf of St. Lawrence, and southward to the Gulf of Mexico. The principal results of multiple glaciation were changes in position and extent of major stream courses and location of stream divides.

Figure 12.2 represents the author's interpretation of major Tertiary drainage lines of central United States. It is based on the work of many men. The writer follows Flint (1955) in placing the preglacial divide between Hudson Bay and Gulf of Mexico drainage in central South Dakota, between the present Cheyenne and Bad rivers.

Major rivers of the Central Lowlands that drained to the Gulf of Mexico in preglacial time were the Teays, Ohio, Mississippi, Iowa, and Missouri. Probably least is known about the position and extent of the ancient Iowa River, for not as much work has been done on the buried bedrock topography in its drainage area as elsewhere. It is still uncertain whether south-

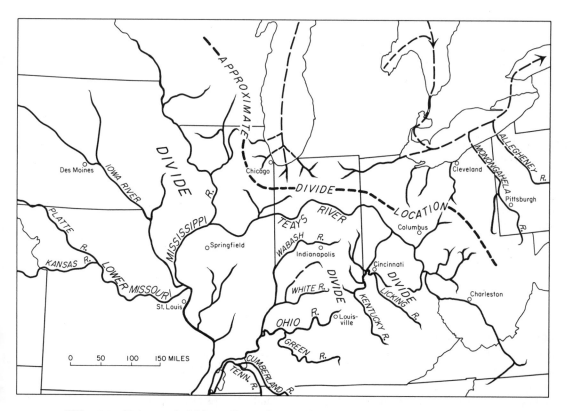

FIG. 12.2 Major preglacial lines of central United States. (*Compiled from numerous sources.*)

ern Minnesota drained southwestward to the ancient Iowa River or southeastward to the preglacial Mississippi River. Trowbridge (1954) favored the Iowa route, whereas Horberg (1950, 1956) thought the area drained to the Mississippi River.

### Drainage Changes Caused by Glaciation

The most notable change in drainage direction resulting from glaciation was reversal of part of the preglacial Hudson Bay drainage. A very considerable area, mainly the present upper Missouri drainage, formerly drained to Hudson Bay rather than to the Gulf of Mexico (see p. 295). Drainage to the Gulf of Mexico was further increased by acquisition of the present Ohio drainage above Wheeling, West Virginia. Except for loss of the Monongahela-Allegheny drainage to the Ohio River, drainage to the Gulf of St. Lawrence is remarkably similar at present to what it was in Tertiary time. Work done in Illinois (Horberg, 1950) and Indiana (Wayne, 1956) indicates that the preglacial divide between Gulf of St. Lawrence and Gulf of Mexico drainage in Illinois and Indiana was not significantly changed as a result of repeated glaciation.

Perhaps even more significant than the changes in drainage distribution were the numerous changes in positions of stream courses that have taken place. Most of the streams in the Central Lowlands are superposed on glacial drift over the Tertiary bedrock topography. Only a few present stream courses coincide with the preglacial ones. Such major streams as the Wabash, Ohio, Mississippi, and Missouri have undergone significant shifts in position.

## PREGLACIAL GEOMORPHIC HISTORY

Little can be said about the geomorphic history of the Central Lowlands region during Mesozoic time. Most of the area has been above sea level since the close of the Paleozoic, but all evidence of Mesozoic erosion surfaces has been obliterated, and even the early Tertiary history is obscure.

Until rather recently the geomorphic history of the glaciated part of the Central Lowlands had to be inferred largely from what is known of the geomorphic history of the Driftless Area and the nearby Interior Low Plateaus and Ozark Plateaus, under the assumption that their histories were basically the same. Since 1930, however, much progress has been made in reconstruction of the bedrock topography of several of the midwestern states, particularly Illinois (Horberg, 1950), Indiana (Wayne, 1952), and Ohio (Ver Steeg, 1934, 1936). The results of these studies seem to confirm the assumption that the Tertiary geomorphic history of these states essentially paralleled that of nearby unglaciated areas.

### Tertiary Erosion Cycles

Opinions as to how many cyclical erosion surfaces (peneplains and straths) can be recognized in the Central Lowlands vary from none (Martin, 1932) to five (Hershey, 1896). Consensus of opinion seems to be that there is good evidence for one major cycle that attained the peneplain or near-peneplain stage and one or two subcycles that resulted in straths.

*Mid-Tertiary Peneplain.* Widespread evidence of a mid-Tertiary erosion surface exists in east-central United States. This erosion surface has been given numerous names; in the Driftless Area it was called the Lancaster peneplain (Trowbridge, 1921); in Tennessee, the Highland Rim peneplain (Hayes, 1899); in Kentucky, the Lexington peneplain (Campbell, 1898); and in the Ozarks, the Ozark peneplain (Hershey, 1902). More recently Rubey (1952) has applied the name Calhoun peneplain to an erosion surface in southern Illinois that presumably is equivalent in age. It is probably not unreasonable to assume that the widespread midwestern erosion surfaces developed during a cycle that was roughly contemporaneous with the Harrisburg cycle in the Appalachians.

*Possible Early Tertiary Cycle.* Meager evidence exists in the Central Lowlands area for a peneplain older than the Lancaster-Lexington-Highland Rim-Ozark erosion surface. Trowbridge (1921), in his classic paper on the Driftless

Area, postulated a pre-Lancaster erosion surface which he called the Dodgeville peneplain. He later (1954) concluded that the Dodgeville peneplain does not exist. There is little suggestion of a pre-Lexington-Highland Rim erosion surface in the Interior Low Plateaus province. However, Horberg (1946, 1950), from his studies of the buried bedrock topography of Illinois, believed he saw evidence in northwestern Illinois of an erosion surface about 150 feet higher than the Lancaster surface and he correlated it with the Dodgeville.

*Parker Strath Cycle.* Following the formation of the mid-Tertiary peneplain a cycle ensued which did not reach the peneplain stage but did lead to the development of a system of wide valleys at a new baselevel of erosion. This subcycle was responsible for development in Illinois of what Horberg (1946) called the Central Illinois peneplain. This subcycle apparently correlates with the one in the Appalachian Plateau during which the Parker strath developed (Butts, 1904) and in recent years it has become common practice to extend the term Parker strath into the Interior Low Plateaus and the adjacent parts of the Central Lowlands. Remnants of the Parker strath now exist as strath terraces along major valleys.

*Havanna Strath Cycle.* Horberg (1946) thought that he recognized evidence in Illinois of still younger baseleved lowlands along the Mississippi, Kaskaskia, Wabash, and buried Teays (Mahomet) valleys which he designated as the Havanna strath. The Scottsburg Lowland in southeastern Indiana is a similar lowland. These lowlands are limited to belts of weak rock and are analogous in origin and possibly age to such straths as the Somerville in New Jersey and the floor of the Central Basin of Tennessee. They apparently developed in very early Pleistocene time.

*Deep Stage.* The Deep Stage (see p. 192) also seems to be represented along some of the buried valleys in the Central Lowlands, but not enough information on the buried bedrock topography is available to say whether it is present along all major buried valleys.

# GLACIATION AND ITS EFFECTS

*Influence of Preglacial Topography*

Except for the Osage and Wisconsin Driftless sections the topography of the Central Lowlands bears the strong imprint of glaciation. In varying degrees bedrock control of topography can be seen in the areas of Kansan and Illinoian glaciations, but within the area of Wisconsin glaciation the Tertiary topography is largely buried. This is not to say that the bedrock influence is entirely lacking in the present topography, for locally it is reflected through the drift and regionally it is exhibited in the control that major preglacial lowlands exerted on the development of lobes and sublobes of the ice and their associated morainic systems as late as the Wisconsin glaciation.

*Causes of Glacial Lobation.* Evidence of glacial lobation is clearly discernible in Figure 12.4, which shows the distribution of the various drift sheets. The main factors that determined the form and extent of the various glacial lobes were (*a*) configuration of the preglacial topography, (*b*) the location of the major lowlands with respect to the centers of outflow of the ice sheet, and (*c*) interference of adjacent lobes with each other's movement. Of these it appears likely that the influence of preglacial topography was by far the most important factor.

*Major Features of Preglacial Topography*

The main features of the preglacial topography that controlled the development of glacial lobes in the Central Lowlands were, according to Horberg (1956), the following:

*Lowlands*
1. The Lake Ontario-Lake Erie Lowland.
2. The complex Lake Huron Basin with a northeast-southwest extension across Michigan.
3. The Lake Michigan Trough.
4. The Lake Superior-St. Croix Lowland.
5. Ancient Minnesota Valley.

6. The ancient Iowa Lowland.
7. A north-south valley that connected the ancient Minnesota Valley with the Iowa Lowland.
8. The James Lowland.
9. The Red River Lowland.

*Uplands*
1. Highlands of southern Ontario.
2. Marshall Upland of southern Michigan.
3. Marshall Upland of northern Michigan.
4. The Niagara Cuesta.
5. Superior Upland.
6. Duluth Upland.
7. Wisconsin Upland.
8. Central Minnesota Upland.
9. Sioux Falls Upland.
10. Great Plains Scarp.
11. Appalachian Plateau Scarp.

Undoubtedly lobation similar to that displayed by the Wisconsin ice sheet occurred during the Nebraskan, Kansan, and Illinoian glaciations, but the end moraines that mark the outer margins of the lobes of these glaciations are largely obscured. Some of the major lobes of the Kansan and Illinoian glaciations can be identified from the drift distribution pattern (see Fig. 12.4), but the lesser lobes and sublobes are not too evident.

*Drift Thickness*

The thickness of the glacial cover in the Central Lowlands varies greatly, depending on how many times an area was glaciated and the amount and configuration of its preglacial relief. On the average, thickness of glacial drift increases in proportion to the number of times an area was glaciated, but within a particular region enormous variations in drift thickness exist related to the configuration of the buried bedrock topography. The drift cover is thickest over buried valleys and thinnest over buried hills and uplands. A drift thickness of several hundred feet is not uncommon in buried valleys in the area of Wisconsin glaciation. Ver Steeg (1934) reported drift thickness as much as 763 feet south of Cleveland in the buried preglacial Cuyahoga Valley. At one place the bedrock

valley floor is 13 feet below sea level and 586 feet below the level of Lake Erie. Drift thicknesses of as much as 1100 feet have been reported in northern Michigan (Melhorn, 1956). Ver Steeg (1933), from a study of an area of some 4500 square miles in central Ohio, found the average thickness of drift to be 96 feet, with an average of 50 feet over buried uplands and 200 feet over buried valleys. In that part of the Central Lowlands extending from central Ohio westward across Indiana and Illinois and into Iowa the drift cover probably averages at least 100 feet and over buried valleys is probably two or three times this amount.

*Glacial Deposition versus Glacial Erosion*

The major effect of glaciation over much of the Central Lowlands has been a leveling of the topography. In some areas of well-developed end moraines considerable relief exists, but even here the relief is generally not so great as it was before glaciation. Present low relief has come about not so much through wearing down of the high places as by filling up of the low places.

This is not to say that the ice sheets did not erode the land over which they moved. The old idea that the continental glaciers acted as giant bulldozers pushing vast quantities of rock debris down from Canada and spreading it over the Central Lowlands has been pretty well disproved. Till petrologies indicate that the bulk of the glacial material was derived from nearby local bedrock. Where ice movement paralleled the direction of major valleys and lowlands there may have been very effective erosion, but the ice moved over much of the land without eroding it deeply.

*Origin of Great Lakes Basins*

For many years there has been difference of opinion as to the extent to which the Great Lakes basins were a product of glacial erosion. At least four factors must be taken into account in any attempted explanation of these basins: (1) the existence of preglacial valleys or lowlands, (2) the effects of crustal warping, (3) the presence

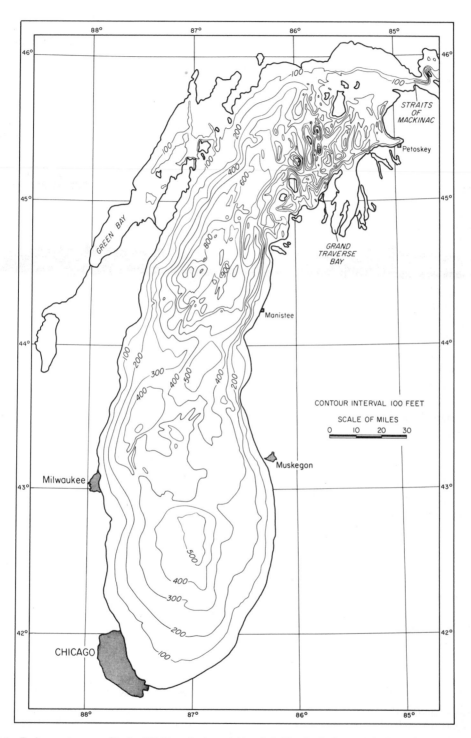

FIG. 12.3 Bathymetric map of Lake Michigan basin. (*After Jack Hough, Geology of the Great Lakes, courtesy Univ. Illinois Press.*)

of dams of glacial drift, and (4) the amount of glacial scouring. The bedrock floors of all the basins except that of Lake Erie now extend below sea level. It is certainly reasonable to assume that their floors were not below sea level in pre-glacial time, if we are correct in our present-day belief that the area now occupied by the Great Lakes was in preglacial time an interconnected lowland draining eastward to the Gulf of St. Lawrence. Whether the bedrock floors of the four lake basins are now below sea level because of depression under weight of the ice or because of deep glacial scouring is impossible to state.

Bathymetric charts of the floors of the lake basins do not suggest unmodified stream-cut topography. The floors are highly irregular, and innumerable closed basins strongly suggest localized glacial scouring. The Lake Michigan basin (see Fig. 12.3) consists of two main parts, North and South basins, separated by a divide area. The divide area consists of two separate ridges on the Traverse and Dundee (Middle Devonian) limestones and what is perhaps in part end moraine (Thwaites, 1947). South Basin is cut in weak upper Devonian-lower Mississippian New Albany or Antrim shale. The regular topography here suggests excavation in homogeneous material. In contrast, the North Basin topography is much more irregular and suggests erosion of nonhomogeneous rock. This section of the lake floor appears to bear the imprint of marked localized glacial scouring.

## Glacial History of Central Lowlands

*Nebraskan Glaciation.* Present knowledge seems to indicate that at no place in the Central Low-lands is the outermost glacial drift Nebraskan in age. Later glaciations reached farther south than did the Nebraskan ice, and thus we see Nebraskan drift only in the subsurface. The Nebraskan glaciation seems to have been pri-marily a western glaciation which extended as far south as northern Missouri. How far east in the Central Lowlands it reached has yet to be determined. Horberg (1953, 1956) has de-scribed what he considered Nebraskan drift in northeastern and central-western Illinois.

Thwaites (1946) postulated a lobe of Nebraskan drift that extended across southeastern Indiana into Kentucky in order to explain scattered glacial erratics described by Leverett (1929) in northeastern Kentucky (see Fig. 11.11), but it now appears more likely that it was a lobe of Kansan ice that left these erratics (Thornbury, 1958).

*Kansan Glaciation.* For the western part of the Central Lowlands, the outermost glacial drift is Kansan in age (see Fig. 12.4). A major lobe of Kansan ice reached as far south as central Mis-souri, northeastern Kansas, and eastern Nebraska. Gradually increasing knowledge of the extent of Kansan glaciation indicates that there were probably two other major lobes of Kansan ice that moved southward into the Central Low-lands. One of these extended into south-central Illinois and southwestern Indiana and the other across southeastern Indiana and southwestern Ohio into northeastern Kentucky.

Kansan till has been known to be present in southern Illinois for some time (MacClintock, 1933), but it was not until the 1950's that its presence in both southwestern and southeastern Indiana was established (Wayne, 1958). Ray (1957) has described Kansan till in Kentucky northeast of Louisville, so there appears to be no question but that a lobe of Kansan ice moved across southeastern Indiana into Kentucky. This same lobe probably extended into south-western Ohio, although as yet no Kansan till has been described in that area.

*Illinoian Glaciation.* The Illinoian ice sheet reached its maximum extent in southern Illinois, where it is the outermost drift, and in south-eastern Indiana and southwestern Ohio (see Fig. 12.4). Details of the relationships between the Illinoian and Kansan drift boundaries in south-western Ohio and southeastern Indiana remain to be clarified. It may be that in some areas the outermost drift is Kansan and in others Illinoian.

In both the areas of Kansan and Illinoian glaciation extensive tracts of loess-veneered till plain are as flat as any Wisconsin till plain, but postdepositional stream dissection is much more advanced on the Kansan and Illinoian till plains

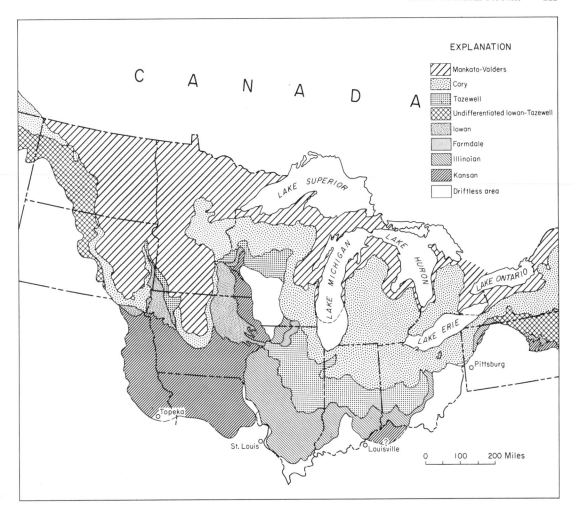

FIG. 12.4   Extent of various glaciations in central United States.   (*Modified after Leland Horberg and R. C. Anderson, Jour. Geol.,* **64.**)

than on the Wisconsin (see Fig. 12.5). Individual land forms such as end moraines, drumlins, kames, and eskers on the Kansan and Illinoian till plains have been notably flattened and obscured by sheetwash and mass-wasting, but locally are still recognizable.

*Wisconsin Glaciation.* The Wisconsin glacial deposits are the only ones which have been extensively subdivided into substages. However, there has been marked division of opinion as to how many substages should be recognized as well as disagreement as to the relative ages of certain

of the substages. The subdivision of the Wisconsin drift shown in Figure 12.4 represents a classification proposed by Leighton (1947) that was in use for several years, but it would not be acceptable at the present time to numerous glacial geologists. Disagreements exist with respect to three aspects of this classification. Some (Frye and Willman, 1960) deny the existence of a Farmdale glacial substage; it is also believed by certain geologists that the Iowan drift is older than Farmdale (Ruhe, Rubin, and Scholtes, 1957); and there is also disagreement as to whether the Mankato and Valders are separate

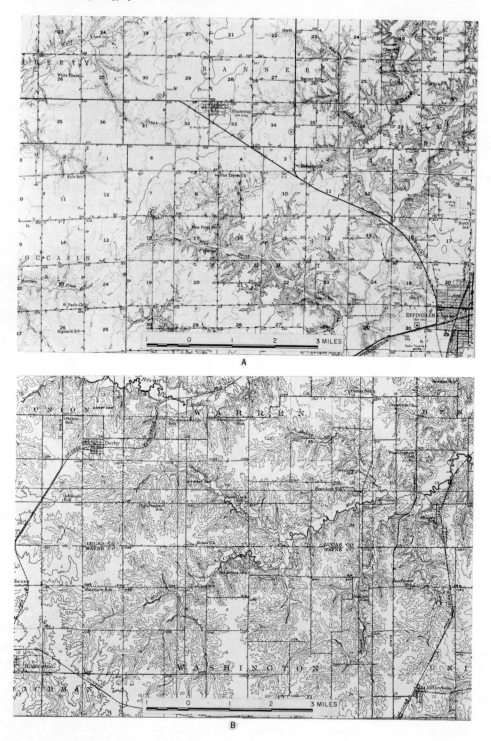

FIG. 12.5   Comparison of degree of dissection of Illinoian (**A**) and Kansan (**B**) till plains as shown on Effingham, Illinois (**A**) and Corydon, Iowa (**B**) topographic sheets.

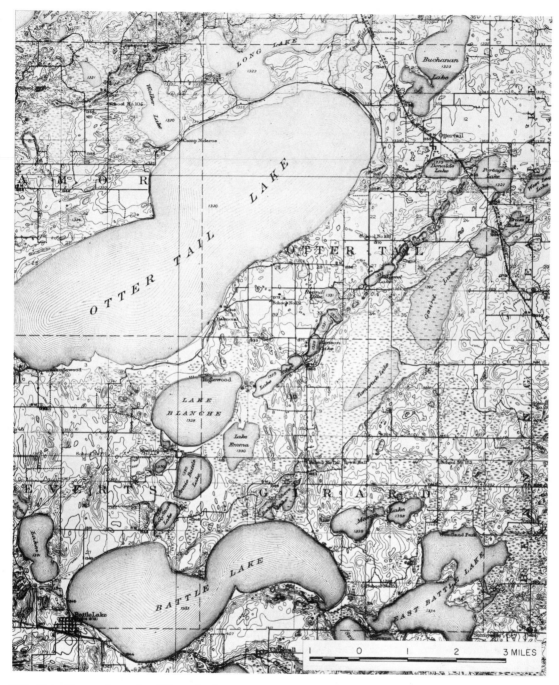

FIG. 12.6 Topography on late Wisconsin glacial materials as shown on part of Battle Lake, Minnesota, topographic sheet.

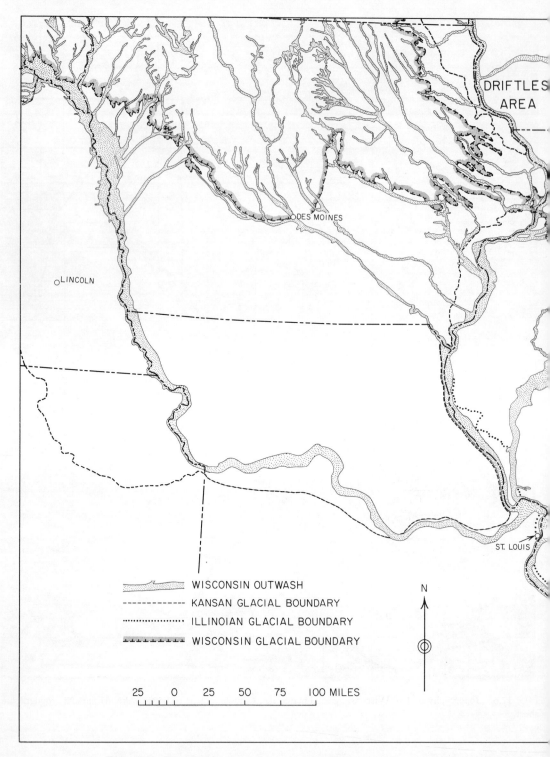

FIG. 12.7   Glacial sluiceways and associated valley trains and outwash plains of Midwestern

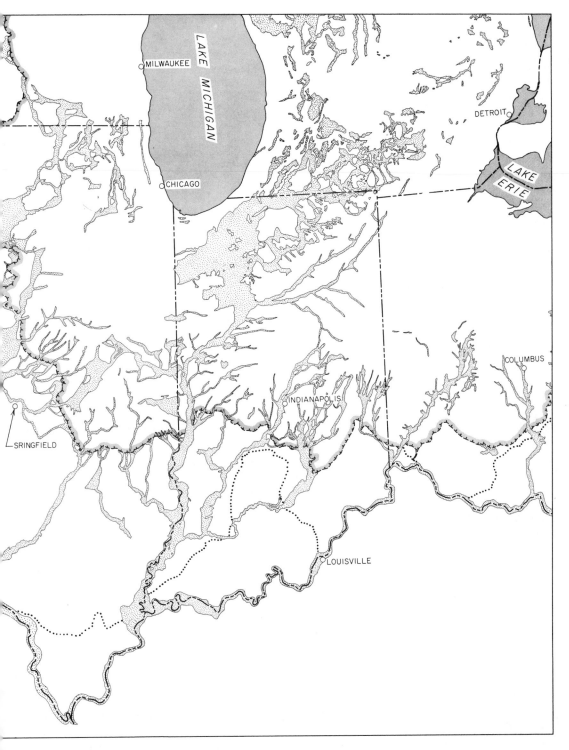

United States. (*After Glacial Map of United States East of Rocky Mountains, Geol. Soc. Am.*)

substages or the same (Wright, 1955; Leighton, 1957). Except for those who would abandon completely the old scheme of substages and substitute for it a time-stratigraphic classification (Frye and Willman, 1960), the Tazewell and Cary substages are still in reasonably good repute; since there are significant differences between the topographic characteristics of the Tazewell and older Wisconsin drifts and the Cary and post-Cary drifts, these terms will be used rather than the once-used terms early and late Wisconsin.

*Three Categories of Glacial Terrain.* The glacial terrain of the Central Lowlands can be divided into three areas of distinctly contrasting topography. These are the areas of pre-Wisconsin glaciation, the areas of early Wisconsin (pre-Cary) glaciation, and the areas of Cary and post-Cary glaciation.

The Kansan and Illinoian glacial terrains have much in common, the only major difference being that the Kansan drift sheet is more dissected than the Illinoian drift. Much good till plain is still found in both areas, but adjacent to major streams dissection is so advanced that the topography has largely lost its glacial aspects. As stated above, the lesser glacial features commonly associated with till plains have been largely obscured by postdepositional erosion and mass-wasting.

*Contrasts within Wisconsin Glacial Terrains.* The boundary between areas of Kansan and Illinoian glacial drift and the early Wisconsin drifts is usually fairly obvious. Glacial topography of Wisconsin age displays a freshness of glacial form that stands in marked contrast to that of the older drifts. Stream dissection, except immediately adjacent to major streams, is notably less advanced than on the Kansan and Illinoian drifts. End moraines, drumlins, kames, and eskers are still readily recognizable in areas of early Wisconsin drift.

The contrast between the topography of the Cary and younger drift areas and pre-Cary Wisconsin drift areas is nearly as great as that between the early Wisconsin and the pre-Wisconsin terrains. Areas of Cary and younger

drift differ from the older Wisconsin glacial topographies in having (1) a greater number of closed basins and lakes (see Fig. 12.6), (2) more conspicuous end moraines, (3) more poorly integrated drainage lines, (4) smaller areas of good till plain, (5) more outwash plains, and (6) a usual lack of a loess cover.

### Major Glacial Sluiceways and Associated Features

During the various glaciations of the Central Lowlands great quantities of glacial outwash were contributed to countless valleys that led away from the ice front (see Fig. 12.7). Many sluiceways carried outwash for brief periods; others repeatedly served as major routes for glacial meltwaters and as a consequence have in them deep fills of glacial outwash. Major sluiceways of the Central Lowlands were the Ohio, Wabash, Illinois, Mississippi, and Missouri valleys. Lesser sluiceways were the valleys of the Scioto, Miami, White (in Indiana), Kankakee, Kaskaskia, Rock, and Des Moines rivers.

*Sluiceway Features.* Valleys that acted as important sluiceways are marked today by gravel terraces, sand dunes on their leeward sides, and loess deposits on the adjacent uplands. The number of terraces along a particular sluiceway varies in relation to the complexity of its glacial history. Along the Illinois Valley five terrace levels have been recognized (Wanless, 1957), all Wisconsin in age.

The amount of meltwater and outwash that went down some of the sluiceways can be realized only when the sizes of the sluiceways and thicknesses of valley fill are taken into account. The Illinois sluiceway, one of the major Wisconsin sluiceways, is locally as much as 20 miles wide and the valley fill in it ranges from a few feet to hundreds of feet in thickness.

*Sources of Loess.* The glacial sluiceways were major sources of loess, as is shown by a decrease in the thickness of the loess with increasing distance from the sluiceways. However, two other possible sources of the loess existed. Areas where till was deposited may have supplied some silt until they were covered with vegetation,

FIG. 12.8   Loess bluff along south wall of Missouri River Valley, St. Louis County, Missouri.   (*Photo by John C. Frye.*)

but this was probably a minor source of silt.   In the western Central Lowlands the poorly indurated Tertiary alluvial cover of the High Plains may have been an important source of loess (Lugn, 1962).   The Sand Hills of north-central Nebraska are lag materials left behind when the finer silts and clays were blown eastward and mixed with silts of glacial origin.   Glacial outwash from the Rocky Mountains down such valleys as the Platte and Arkansas may also have contributed in a small way to loess accumulation in the western Central Lowlands.

Along such major sluiceways as the Mississippi, Illinois, and Wabash as much as 100 feet of loess has been measured immediately adjacent to the sluiceways, but the thickness decreases rapidly away from them.   The following measurements were made by Smith (1942) along a

transverse eastward from the Illinois Valley near Beardstown, Illinois.

TABLE 12.1   Thickness of Loess in Relation to Distance from Sluiceway

| Distance from Bluff (miles) | Thickness of Loess (feet) |
|---|---|
| 0.2 | 92 |
| 0.5 | 68 |
| 1.75 | 32 |
| 2.0 | 26 |
| 4.0 | 18 |
| 5.5 | 17½ |
| 10.0 | 14 |

Where the loess is several tens of feet thick along a valley wall it may be responsible for precipitous bluffs (see Fig. 12.8). It was this tendency to form bluffs that prompted early geologists to refer to the loess as the Bluff formation.

Loess has been identified with each of the glaciations, but the bulk of the surficial loess is of Wisconsin age. However, several Wisconsin loesses have been identified, and in many areas, particularly beyond the limits of Wisconsin glaciation, there is a complex of loesses.

## SECTIONS OF THE CENTRAL LOWLANDS

### Bases for Recognition of Sections

Six sections of the Central Lowland province have been recognized. These sections with their outstanding topographic characteristics are:

1. Great Lakes section. Numerous lakes with associated lacustrine plains, prominent end moraines, poorly integrated drainage, and a still partially exposed cuestaform topography characterize this section.
2. Western Young Drift section. This section is essentially similar to the Great Lakes section, but it is separated from it by the Wisconsin Driftless section and Superior Upland. Only Lake Agassiz, in this section, compares in size and complexity of history with the Great Lakes.
3. Wisconsin Driftless section. The topography consists mainly of a series of maturely dissected cuestas developed on rocks of early Paleozoic age. Glacial outwash extends through the section, and glacio-lacustrine deposits reach into it.
4. Till Plain section. Nearly flat to gently undulating glacial terrain lacking strong end moraines and having few lacustrine plains is typical of this section. Drainage is much better integrated than in the sections to the north, but not nearly so much as in the Dissected Till Plain section to the west.
5. Dissected Till Plain section. This section is marked by well-dissected till plain topography having a thin loess cover and lack-

ing in general the morainic topography that is found in much of the glaciated Central Lowlands.
6. Osage section. This section is underlain by gently dipping rocks, mainly of late Paleozoic age, on which a scarped plain topography has developed. Two structural uplifts in which Precambrian rocks are brought to the surface have hilly to mountainous topography which contrasts strongly with their surroundings.

### Till Plains Section

*Boundaries.* The Till Plains section is a good example of a fairly distinct geomorphic unit which lacks sharp boundaries. The boundaries as drawn by Fenneman (1928) could and should be refined in view of our present more detailed knowledge of the Pleistocene geology of the Central Lowlands. The boundaries as now drawn do not follow consistently any Pleistocene boundary.

*Topographic Characteristics.* In contrast to the regions to the south, the topography of the Till Plains section is not bedrock controlled but is dominantly a depositional topography. Locally preglacial land forms are reflected through the glacial cover, but they are minor rather than major aspects of the terrain. The northern boundary essentially follows the contact of the Cary and Tazewell drift sheets and, as noted above, represents the boundary between two distinctly different aspects of glacial topography.

Probably nowhere in the world is there better till plain than in the area of the Tazewell substage across Ohio, Indiana, and Illinois. Over many thousands of square miles the surface is so flat (local relief of only 10 or 20 feet per square mile) that it is difficult to explain. Certainly it does not reflect a flat preglacial terrain, for sufficient reconstruction of the preglacial topography has been made to establish that the preglacial relief was measureable in hundreds of feet and comparable in magnitude to that south of the glaciated area in the Interior Low Plateaus. Building of the till plain was a cumulative process and the product of at least three,

FIG. 12.9   Wisconsin till plain rising to Bloomington end moraine in background, McLean County, Illinois.   (*Photo by W. D. Faris.*)

if not four, glaciations. Each glaciation helped in some degree to obliterate the preexisting stream-carved topography, and, as indicated above, this was more by filling up of the valleys than by cutting down of the hills.

The low relief of the Till Plains section is partly related to the physical character of the tills of that section. The bedrock of the Central Lowlands is dominantly limestone, dolomite, and shale, with minor amounts of sandstone. These rocks produced pebbly, silty, clay tills. Such tills at the time of their deposition were undoubtedly plastic enough to spread. Mass-wasting subsequent to deposition of the till has undoubtedly reduced the initial relief considerably. The relief of the Tazewell till plain surface was probably never so great as that of the areas of Cary and later glaciations, where the tills are generally more stony because of their nearness to the hard rocks of the Canadian Shield.

Although some of the till plain possesses low enough relief to be considered flat, much more characteristic is the gently undulating topography sometimes described as swell and swale. Eskers are present in the Till Plains section, but they are not nearly so numerous as in areas of younger drift; drumlins are extremely rare; not a single drumlim is known in Indiana. Outwash plains are in general less common than in the area of younger Wisconsin drift, but valley trains are fairly well developed along both major and minor sluiceways. The major relief of the Till Plains section is produced by the systems of end moraines that mainly mark numerous readvances of an oscillating ice front. The end moraines vary from faint topographic swells to ridges that stand as much as 100 to 150 feet above the surrounding till plain (see Fig. 12.9).

Drainage integration has progressed to the point where streams do not flow in, through, or

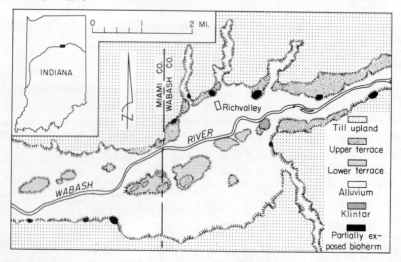

FIG. 12.10　Marked widening of Wabash Valley produced by its intersection with buried Teays Valley.

out of lakes or swamps, as they do in the young drift areas, but except along major streams dissection of the till plains has not proceeded far. Secondary and tertiary drainage lines over much of the till plain area are little more than shallow channels with tiny threads of alluvium along them.

Loess is fairly extensive from Indiana westward, but its topographic effects are not particularly notable, except where it forms bluffs

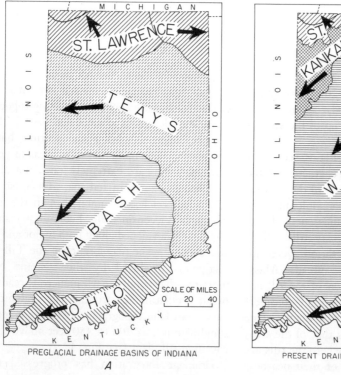

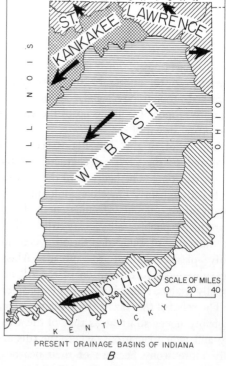

FIG. 12.11　Comparison of preglacial (*A*) and present (*B*) drainage basins in Indiana.

along major streams. Over most of the area the loess forms a thin mantle that conforms to the till plain surface.

*Drainage Modifications.* Extensive modification of preglacial drainage has taken place over the entire Till Plains section. Most of the drainage lines are superposed on glacial drift and in general show lack of coincidence with preglacial valleys. Stream courses may cut across buried uplands, and along some of the larger streams a beginning has been made in exhumation of the buried bedrock topography. This is reflected by the presence of rapids or waterfalls along stream courses or the narrowing down of valleys where they cut through buried bedrock hills or uplands.

Many interesting stream histories have been worked out, but only three will be considered here. The Teays Valley will be used as an example of complete burial and obliteration of a major drainage line; the Wabash Valley as an example of a stream which was greatly enlarged as a result of glaciation; and the Illinois Valley as an example of a valley whose topographic features are related to the fact that it long acted as a major glacial sluiceway.

BURIED TEAYS VALLEY. From Chillicothe, Ohio, where the surficial Teays Valley disappears beneath glacial drift, to where it joins the preglacial Mississippi River in central Illinois (see Fig. 12.2) the Teays Valley is filled with glacial till and outwash. From information obtained from oil, gas, and water well records the course of the buried Teays Valley has been rather accurately mapped across Ohio, Indiana, and Illinois. Over most of this route there is no surficial topographic expression of the buried valley, but in Indiana the superposed Wabash Valley intersects the Teays Valley at two places, and at each place there is a notable widening of the Wabash Valley because the glacial drift in the Teays Valley is much more readily erosible than the bedrock to either side of the buried valley (see Fig. 12.10).

HISTORY OF WABASH RIVER. The area of the Wabash River drainage basin was essentially doubled as a result of changes effected by glaciation (see Fig. 12.11). The acquired drainage was largely part of the preglacial Teays drainage

in Indiana. In preglacial time, the Wabash River was a fairly short stream that headed in central Indiana (see Fig. 12.2); it now heads about 12 miles east of the Indiana-Ohio boundary. The course of the Wabash River across north central Indiana roughly parallels the buried Teays Valley, but, as stated above, the two valleys actually intersect each other at only two places (see Fig. 12.12).

The present route of the Wabash River came into existence accompanying deglaciation during the Tazewell and Cary subages. The major topographic features along the Wabash Valley, such as the gravel terraces, dunes, loess bluffs, areas of miniature scabland, and partially exhumed Silurian bioherms (see Fig. 12.13) owe their development to glacial meltwaters flowing away from the receding ice front or to the overflow waters from Lake Maumee (see p. 237), which for a brief time discharged down the

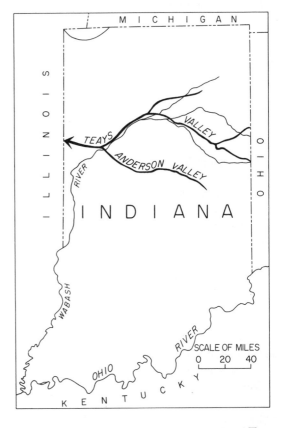

FIG. 12.12 Comparison of courses of Wabash and Teays Valleys across Indiana.

FIG. 12.13   Hanging Rock, near Lagro, Indiana, an exhumed Silurian bioherm (reef).   Half of the bioherm has been cut off by the Wabash River.   (*Photo by C. A. Malott.*)

Wabash Valley. The lower Wabash Valley rivals the Illinois Valley in width, being in places as much as 15 miles wide, but the new part of the valley is much narrower and has along it numerous exposures of bedrock where in its postglacial downcutting the river has encountered buried bedrock ridges and upland tracts.

ILLINOIS VALLEY. Next to the Ohio, the Illinois River is the most important eastern tributary of the Mississippi. The Illinois Valley owes most of its topographic aspects to the fact that it was one of the major glacial sluiceways of the Central Lowlands, as well as the overflow route for Lake Chicago (see p. 236) during most of its existence.

Southward from the Great Bend near Hennepin, Illinois, the Illinois River follows closely the route of the preglacial Mississippi, and this portion of the Illinois Valley is notably wider than the section above the Great Bend, which was established during Wisconsin time. Other features that distinguish the two parts of the valley are: (1) a general absence of rocky bluffs in the lower part of the valley as compared with

an abundance of them in the upper part of the valley; (2) expansive gravel terraces in the lower valley and less extensive ones in the upper valley; and (3) not so great a valley gradient in the lower part as in the upper part of the valley.

A striking feature of the lowermost Illinois Valley is the straightness of its walls (see Fig. 12.14); here projecting spurs are remarkably rare. This has been attributed usually to spur-end trimming by glacial meltwaters, particularly the overflow waters from Lake Chicago, (Barrows, 1910; Cady, 1916), but Rubey (1952) questioned the efficacy of glacial meltwaters to perform so much erosion and attributed the spur-trimming to lateral planation by a stream no larger than the present-day river. It seems likely that he underestimated the erosive power of the enormous volume of meltwater that at times flowed down the Illinois Valley.

*Great Lakes Section*

*Nature of Topography.* Lakes, large and small, are the dominant features of the Great Lakes section.   Here are four of the Great Lakes (Lake Superior lies within the Superior Upland province) and thousands of lesser ones.   The glacial drift of this section belongs to the Cary and Valders substages (Mankato too, if it is considered a substage separate from the Valders) and displays a freshness of glacial topography found elsewhere in the Central Lowlands only in the Western Young Drift section.   Prominent end moraines, outwash plains, closed basins that are sites of lakes or swamps, and locally eskers and drumlins all attest to the recency of glaciation. Till plain topography is relatively rare, but between the end moraines are areas of rolling ground moraine.   The lake basins are of many

origins; some, like the basins occupied by the Great Lakes, are glacially modified preglacial lowlands; others are intermorainal or intramorainal basins resulting from irregular deposition of glacial materials; still others are kettles in pitted outwash plains.

End moraines marking the outlines of the various glacial lobes and sublobes are particularly prominent in this section.   Morainic festoons outline former positions of the Green Bay, Lake Michigan, Saginaw, and Erie ice lobes, as well as some of the lesser lobes.   Some of the more prominent moraines are interlobate moraines formed by joint deposition by two lobes. Such a moraine is the famous Kettle Moraine of

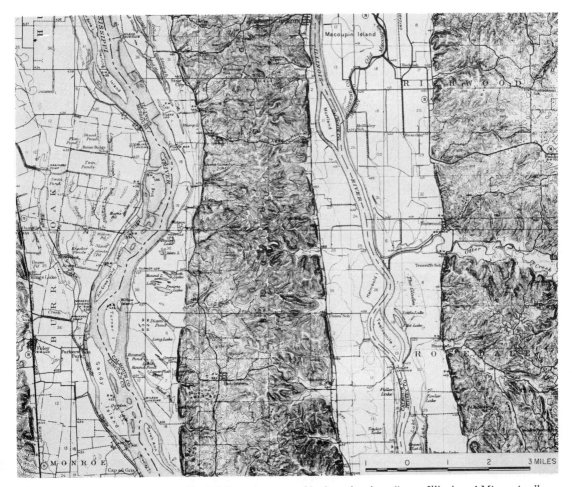

FIG. 12.14   Portion of the Hardin, Illinois-Missouri, topographic sheet showing adjacent Illinois and Missouri valleys.

Wisconsin, which was built by the joint work of the Green Bay and Michigan lobes; another nearly equally prominent interlobate moraine is the Packerton moraine in Indiana, in the interlobate area between the Erie and Saginaw lobes.

## History of the Great Lakes

Despite the many prominent glacial land forms that are found in the Great Lakes section, the four Great Lakes in this section are its dominant features. Even though many details remain to be filled in, the major evolutionary phases of Great Lakes history are now reasonably well known. The basins now occupied by the Great Lakes were weak rock lowlands in preglacial time that drained eastward to the Gulf of St. Lawrence. It is not yet clear how much these lowlands were deepened by glacial scouring, but it appears that locally, at least, it was considerable. This deeping, along with depression of the area under the Wisconsin ice sheet, provided the essential conditions for development in late Wisconsin time of a complex sequence of ice marginal lakes. Unraveling of this lake sequence has provided one of the most interesting problems in glacial geology. It has come about as the result of the work of many individuals, particularly Gilbert, Spencer, Leverett, Taylor, and Goldthwait in the earlier days and Stanley, Bretz, Hough, and others in later days.

Although there were no preglacial Great Lakes, there may well have been similar sequences of lake evolution during the waning phases of the pre-Wisconsin glaciations. So far no evidence for a pre-Wisconsin Great Lakes system has been recognized, but about all that could be expected would be the existence of buried lacustrine deposits of pre-Wisconsin age beneath Wisconsin lacustrine materials.

*Comparison of the Lake Basins.* The lake basins vary notably in size and depth; all except that of Lake Erie extend below sea level. The depth of the Lake Superior basin is so great that it is difficult to account for it as the result of either depression under the ice load or glacial scouring. Lake Erie, with an average depth of something

near 58 feet, has in it only about one-thirtieth the amount of water that is in Lake Superior. The following data on the five lake basins were given by Hough (1958).

TABLE 12.2    Data on Great Lakes

| Name of Lake | Maximum Depth | Lowest Elevation of Floor |
|---|---|---|
| Superior | 1302 | −700 |
| Michigan | 923 | −343 |
| Ontario | 778 | −532 |
| Huron | 750 | −170 |
| Erie | 210 | +362 |

It should be kept in mind that the maximum depths given above represent local deep spots that can probably be accounted for as a result of intense localization of glacial scouring. Such over-deepened areas seem to be common in all except the Erie basin.

*Factors Controlling Evolution.* Evolution of the Great Lakes began soon after retreat of the Cary ice from its maximum advance and continued to as recently as 2500 years ago. The Algoma phase, immediately preceding the present phase of lake evolution, has been dated by radiocarbon (Zumberge and Potzer, 1956) at 2500 years B.P. The lakes started as a series of small ice-marginal water bodies when the receding ice front had attained a position north of the drainage divide between the Gulf of Mexico and the Gulf of St. Lawrence. The complex history of lake evolution in its simplest analysis involved a series of changing outlines and outlets as influenced by five variable factors: an oscillating ice front, irregularities of the topography uncovered by the retreating ice front, variations in the directions and areas of retreat and advance of the ice front, lowering of lake outlets by erosion, and differential uplift of the land adjacent to the ice front during and following deglaciation.

*Evidence of Complex History.* Presentation of the details of the evolution of the Great Lakes would require a book in itself. Figure 12.15 shows in tabular form the major phases of lake

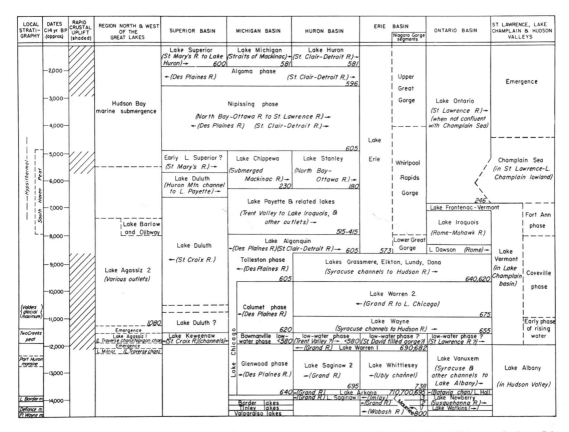

FIG. 12.15   Tabular summary of evolution of Great Lakes.   (*After R. F. Flint, Glacial and Pleistocene Geology, John Wiley and Sons, Inc.*)   According to Dr. Flint, work done since this table was prepared in 1955 has pointed up certain errors in it.   The Champlain Sea and related lake phases apparently were earlier than indicated in the table, and certain other adjustments need to be made in keeping with evidence obtained from C$^{14}$ dating.

evolution as outlined by Flint (1957). For further details the reader is referred to Leverett and Taylor's (1915) "The Pleistocene of Indiana and Michigan and the history of the Great Lakes" and Hough's (1958) *Geology of the Great Lakes.* Hough's book is the most up-to-date treatment of this subject, but the Leverett and Taylor discussion is still valuable despite the fact that some of their ideas have been modified by recent work.

The history of the Great Lakes has been unraveled mainly by tracing topographic and geologic features that indicate the positions of former shorelines and outlets, augmented in recent years by radiocarbon dating of deposits associated with particular lake levels. Wave-cut cliffs and related features, beaches and asso-

ciated bars, lines of dunes back of former shorelines, lacustrine clays and silts, spillways or outlets cut across bedrock or glacial drift and now unused or occupied by underfit streams, have all been utilized in working out the many phases of lake evolution.

Shorelines marking former levels of the lakes vary laterally in their distinctness, depending on how long a particular lake level persisted and the strength of the waves against the shore as determined by its exposure and the fetch of the waves. Some beaches have been partially or wholly effaced because in later phases of lake evolution they were submerged.   Tracing of former shorelines is further complicated by their discontinuity, indistinctness in wooded areas, tilting that accompanied unloading of the land, and the fact that their topographic sequence is not the same as the chronological succession.

Only for the very latest phases of lake evolution do the shorelines extend completely around the lakes. During earlier phases the lakes lay against the ice front at the north. Usually the younger shorelines extend farther north than the older ones. The outlets used during various lake phases were determined by correlating spillway altitudes with those of particular shorelines.

Names have been given to the small ice-marginal lakes that marked the initial phases of lake evolution in each of the lake basins. Lake Maumee was the forerunner of present Lake Erie; Lake Chicago of Lake Michigan; Lake Saginaw of Lake Huron; Lake Duluth of Lake Superior; Lake Iroquois of Lake Ontario; and Lake Nicolet of Green Bay.

*Major Outlets.* As a result of their many changes in outline and altitude, the lakes emptied through numerous outlets. The best known and most used outlets are shown in Figure 12.16, but the possibility exists that in the heavily forested region to the north of the Great Lakes outlets exist that have not been recognized. Major outlets were the Fort Wayne outlet of Lake Maumee to the Wabash Valley (see Fig. 12.17); the Chicago outlet via the Des Plaines River to the Illinois River; the St. Croix River outlet of Lake Duluth to the Mississippi River; the Imlay, Ubly, and Grand River outlets across Michigan; the Trent Valley (Kirkfield) and Ottawa River outlets across Ontario; the Syracuse and Rome outlets to the Mohawk and Hudson; and the Susquehanna outlet to Chesapeake Bay. Probably the most continuously used outlet was the

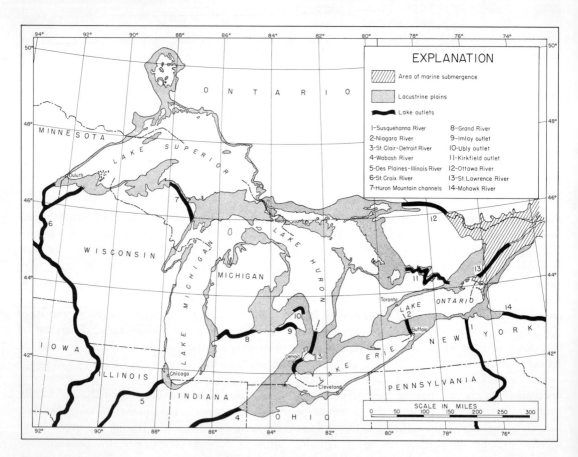

FIG. 12.16   Lacustrine areas around Great Lakes and main outlets used during their evolution.   (*After Frank Leverett and F. B. Taylor, U. S. Geol. Survey Mon. 53.*)

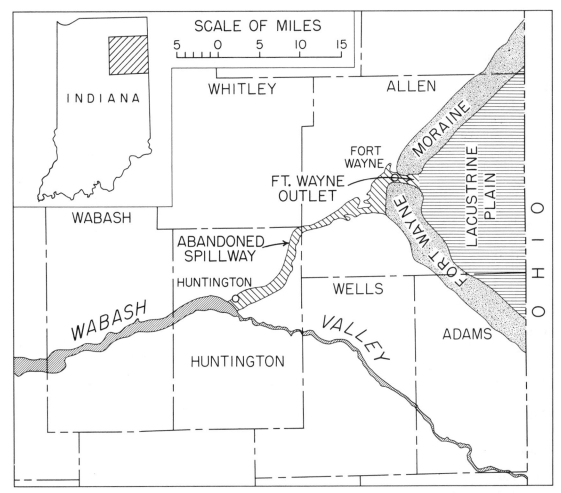

FIG. 12.17   Map showing relations of Lake Maumee and Fort Wayne outlet to Wabash sluiceway.

Chicago outlet; except for two low-water phases of Lake Chicago, this outlet was in use most of the time and as late as the Nipissing phase of lake evolution.

*Low-Water Phases.* Stanley (1938) first pointed out evidence for a low-water phase in the Michigan and Huron basins in the existence of a submerged river valley through the Straits of Mackinac that connects these two basins. This valley varies in width from $\frac{1}{4}$ to $\frac{1}{2}$ mile. Hough (1955) has added further evidence of a low-water stand in the Lake Michigan basin at about 350 feet below the present lake level, which he called Lake Chippewa. He proposed

the name Lake Stanley for its correlative in the Huron basin. The evidence for this low-water phase lies in the presence in the deeper parts of Lake Michigan of a complete sequence of clay deposits, whereas in those parts of the lake basin where water depths are less than 350 feet a part of the deep-water sequence is missing, and in its stead are shallow-water deposits. Hough placed the time of this low-water phase as post-Algonquin and pre-Nipissing (see Fig. 12.15). Flint (1957) correlated it with the warm period variously known as the Hypsithermal, Altithermal, Megathermal, or Climatic Optimum time.

A second low-water phase in the Lake Michigan basin was that which has been called the Bowmanville low-water phase. This lake phase occurred during the Two Creeks interval (see Fig. 12.15) and was probably a result of the withdrawal of the ice beyond the Straits of Mackinac. During this low-water phase the Chicago outlet to the Des Plaines River was abandoned. An equivalent low-water phase in the Superior basin has been called Lake Keeweenaw. This low-water phase has been inferred for the other lake basins, but the evidence for it so far is rather meager.

## Western Young Drift Section

*Basis for Recognition as a Section.* In many respects this section is the western counterpart of the Great Lakes section; except for their separation by the Superior Upland and Wisconsin Driftless Area they would probably be grouped together. Glacial deposits in the two sections are essentially the same age; lakes are present in both areas by the thousands; prominent end moraines, outwash plains, and numerous kames and eskers characterize both sections; and although the Western Young Drift section has in it no lakes as large as the Great Lakes, it does have, in the vast lacustrine plain of Lake Agassiz, the site of a lake that was larger than any of the Great Lakes. The southern boundary of the Western Young Drift section is placed at the Cary boundary of the Des Moines-Dakota lobes. Ruhe (1952) pointed out three features which distinguish the Cary drift area from the adjacent older drifts to the south: (1) conspicuous terminal moraines; (2) a thin, discontinuous, and poorly assorted mantle of loess, as compared with a well sorted and continuous loess cover in the Dissected Till Plains to the south; and (3) much more poorly integrated drainage than is found farther south.

The Des Moines lobe of northern Iowa displays a distinctive swell and swale topography, with relief usually not in excess of 10 or 15 feet. Gwynne (1942) pointed out that this is found on nearly half of the Des Moines lobe and concluded that the swells are systems of annually deposited end moraines built by a receding ice

front. Similar features in the Dakotas have been called washboard moraines (see Fig. 12.19). Those in this area are described (Lemke, 1960) as low, subparallel, arcuate ridges with intervening undrained depressions between them. They were believed to mark halts in the position of the ice front as it retreated northwestward. However, periodicity in their deposition has not been demonstrated.

*Boundaries.* The boundary between the Western Young Drift section and the Superior Upland to the northeast is supposed to be where the bedrock-controlled topography of the Superior Upland (even though thinly veneered with drift) gives way to topography that is largely of glacial origin. The northern boundary of the section is yet to be drawn, as it continues into Canada for an undetermined distance.

The western boundary is a low, east-facing escarpment known as the Missouri Escarpment. This escarpment, which marks the eastern boundary of the Glaciated Missouri Plateau section of the Great Plains province, is some 300 to 600 feet in height. The escarpment actually lies somewhat east of the limits of glaciation, for the ice overrode it and moved a short distance onto the Missouri Plateau.

The deep hairpin-shaped embayment at the south between the Dakota and Des Moines lobes (see Fig. 12.4) was caused by a highland tract in the region between the Minnesota-Red River Lowland and the James River Lowland known as the Coteau des Prairies. This is a flatiron-shaped plateau-like tract pointing northward and probably is a part of the Sioux uplift. The Coteau des Prairies is capped mainly with Cretaceous rocks, but projecting knobs of Precambrian Sioux quartzite show at the south end. Although the ice overrode the Coteau des Prairies (see Fig. 12.18), it was an effective enough barrier to cause the main masses of ice to deploy to the east and west of it and thus give rise to the Des Moines and Dakota glacial lobes.

*History of Upper Mississippi River.* It is not certain where the preglacial Mississippi River headed, but likely it was in the same general region as at present. Certainly the viewpoint

FIG. 12.18  Morainic topography on Coteau des Prairies.  (*Photo by John S. Shelton.*)

that the preglacial divide between drainage to Hudson Bay and that to the Gulf of Mexico was near the southern edge of the Central Lowlands (Fisk, 1944) does not fit with known facts. The source area of the Mississippi River in Minnesota is so deeply mantled with glacial drift that it is not known whether the present course of the river bears any relation to its preglacial course, but from St. Paul southward numerous segments of the Mississippi Valley represent portions of preglacial or interglacial routes used by the Mississippi or its tributaries at one time or another during a complex series of stream derangements not yet fully understood.

Two ideas exist as to the location of the preglacial upper Mississippi valley. One theory (Trowbridge et al., 1941; Trowbridge, 1954) is that the main course of the preglacial upper Mississippi was considerably west of its present position. According to this theory the preglacial valley began in southwestern Minnesota and extended southeastward across Iowa and intercepted the present course of the Mississippi River near the northeast corner of Missouri. The Nebraskan glaciation was believed to have been responsible for the river's displacement eastward to a route that roughly followed the present course of the Mississippi along the eastern border of Iowa. Diversion of the Mississippi eastward into Illinois as far as Hennepin and thence southward along the route now followed by the Illinois River was believed to have been effected during the Kansan glaciation.

Leverett (1942) thought, however, that the

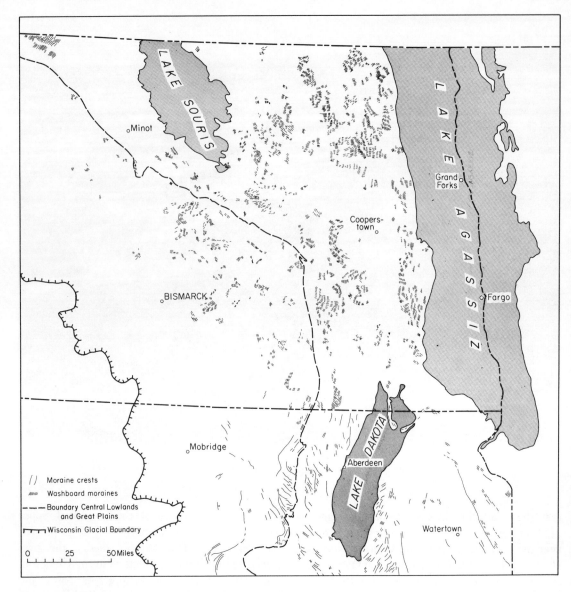

FIG. 12.19  Map of portion of Lake Agassiz and other glacial features.  (*After Glacial Map of United States East of Rocky Mountains, Geol. Soc. Am.*)

headwaters of the preglacial Mississippi River consisted of two distinct streams, a western one that headed in southern Minnesota and flowed southeastward across northeastern Iowa to about Muscatine, Iowa, and from there on along the route of the present river, and an eastern stream that followed a route from above St. Paul, Minnesota, along the present valley to near Le Claire, Iowa, and thence southeastward across Illinois to Hennepin, where it turned south along the route now followed by the Illinois River. These two streams presumably underwent several east and west shifts in position during the various ice advances but ultimately became established in the present route, which follows preglacial or interglacial valleys along some segments and in rock gorges cuts across former upland tracts along other stretches.

Leverett (1942) thought that the diversion westward of the Mississippi River from its route across Illinois was effected during the Illinoian glaciation, but Shaffer (1952) argued that this diversion of the Mississippi took place during the Tazewell subage.

*Lake Agassiz.* The largest of the late Pleistocene ice marginal lakes in North America was Lake Agassiz. This lake during late Wisconsin time occupied the Red River Basin of North Dakota and extensive adjacent areas in Manitoba, Saskatchewan, and Ontario. A lacustrine plain of over 100,000 square miles marks its site, and as many as 50 beach lines can be recognized (Johnston, 1946) (see Fig. 12.19).

During part of its history Lake Agassiz discharged to the southeast through the Minnesota River, or River Warren, as it was called by Upham (1896), to the Mississippi River (see Fig. 12.20), but recent studies of the lake history suggest that eastern outlets were used during part of its history. Although the history of Lake Agassiz was not quite so involved as that of the Great Lakes, as study of it progresses it is becoming apparent that its history was not quite so simple as first envisaged. Following is an outline of the major events in the lake's history as suggested by Elson (1957):

1. Retreat of the ice from the Altamont moraine was accompanied by the formation of Lake Agassiz I, which discharged to the south through the Lake Traverse (River Warren) outlet (see Fig. 12.21).

2. This southern outlet was eroded down to the

FIG. 12.20  Outlet of Lake Agassiz, looking southeast from Browns Valley toward Big Stone Lake. (*Photo by John S. Shelton.*)

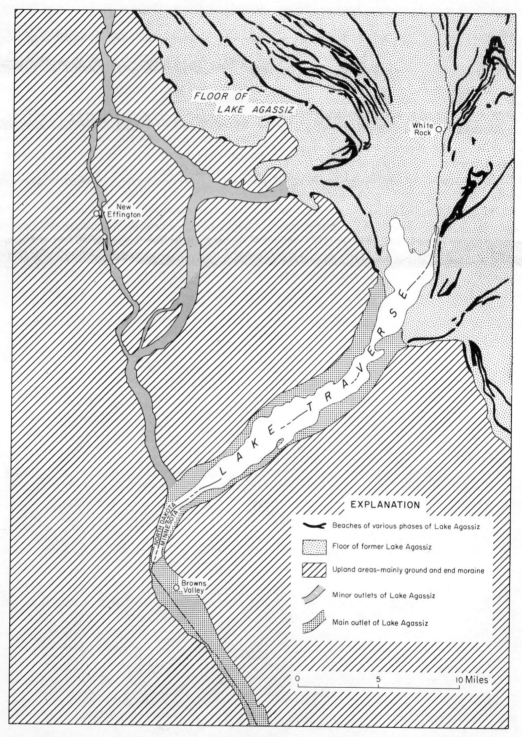

FIG. 12.21   Map of outlet area of Lake Agassiz.   (*After Frank Leverett, U. S. Geol. Survey Profess. Paper* 161.)

level marked by the Tintah or Norcross beach, after which retreat of the ice in the Lake Superior basin opened an eastern outlet.

3. Readvance of the ice closed the eastern outlet and further erosion of the southern outlet to a bedrock sill was followed by formation of the Campbell strandline.
4. Withdrawal of the ice during the Two Creeks interval opened lower outlets and Lake Agassiz I came to an end.
5. Readvance of the Valders ice formed Lake Agassiz II. The lake level temporarily rose to the level of the Tintah or Norcross strandline and later subsided to the level of the second Campbell strandline.
6. Retreat of the Valders ice opened up eastern outlets into Lake Superior. The Campbell strandline was abandoned and others were formed at lower levels.
7. Further retreat of the ice opened up a northern outlet into the incipient Hudson Bay.
8. Melting of residual ice in the Nelson Valley opened an outlet to Hudson Bay. This was prior to 3600 years ago as indicated by dating from Lake Shore projectile points.

Horberg (1951) described certain unusual microrelief features along the axial part of the Agassiz lacustrine plain that he interpreted as frozen ground structures. These features consist of low intersecting ridges, ranging from 3 to 10 feet in height and from 75 to 100 feet in width, separated by shallow depressions. In support of his belief that the features are frozen ground phenomena, Horberg cited the presence of such associated features as deformed lake clays, involutions, fossil ice wedges, and polygonal ground. He suggested that the structures were formed immediately after the draining of Lake Agassiz and prior to the entrenchment of the Red River in its lacustrine plain.

Nikiforoff (1952) doubted that the minor ridges were frozen ground phenomena. He maintained that the climate at the time the lake was drained was no longer glacial and that the ice front must have been at least 150 miles away. He further considered the ridges too large to be interpreted as frozen ground features. He argued that microrelief features of various origins are present in most landscapes and suggested that these may have been produced by wave action on the floor of the lake near its final phase and later modified by wind or running water after draining of the lake and before its bottom was covered with vegetation.

*Lake Souris and Dakota.* Shrinkage of the James Lowland lobe in eastern South Dakota gave rise to Lake Dakota (Todd, 1895; Flint, 1955), which at its maximum was over 100 miles long. The lake lay mainly in South Dakota but extended a short distance into North Dakota (see Fig. 12.19). It represented a temporary flood of meltwater from the glacier held back by a narrow bottleneck in the James River Valley. Glacial Lake Souris in North Dakota and Sasakatchewan (Upham, 1896; Lemke, 1960) was essentially contemporaneous with Lake Dakota. It lay between the receding ice front and a drift-covered bedrock escarpment at the south.

### Wisconsin Driftless Section

*Is it Driftless?* In southwestern Wisconsin and adjacent parts of Illinois, Iowa, and Minnesota is an area of some 20,000 square miles, long known as the Driftless Area (see Fig. 12.4). Whether the adjective "driftless" is appropriate may be questioned, for glacio-fluviatile, glacio-lacustrine, and glacio-eolian deposits are present within it. Furthermore some 5000 of the 20,000 square miles were covered by an early ice sheet, probably either the Nebraskan or Kansan, and within recent years it has been suggested that an early Wisconsin glaciation covered most or all of the area (Black, 1960). The suggestion of a Wisconsin glaciation of the area was based on the presence in the area of scattered foreign rocks such as granite, gabbro, and basalt. As yet it is uncertain whether these may be considered evidence of a late glaciation. Even if this should prove to be true, the ice must have been very thin and of short duration, for any topographic effects of glaciation are practically lacking. We are thus still essentially correct in thinking of this area as one whose topography is essentially nonglacial.

FIG. 12.22    Castle Rock, an outlier of Cambrian sandstone at the edge of the Lake Wisconsin lacustrine plain.    (*Photo by Robert F. Black.*)

*Reasons for Limited Glaciation.*    Three facts help to explain why this area largely escaped being covered by the ice sheets: (1) the Driftless Area lies to the lee of a highland region, the Superior Upland, that retarded the southward movement of ice; (2) the Lake Superior Lowland to the west of the Superior Upland and the basins of Green Bay and Lake Michigan to the east made it easier for the ice to deploy to either side of the Superior Upland than to override it; (3) frequent shiftings of the centers from which the major ice lobes came meant that the region was rarely, if ever, invaded by ice lobes from several directions at the same time.

*Periglacial Features.*    Even though the Driftless Area may have largely escaped glaciation, various phenomena found within the region suggest that it experienced a severe frost climate during at least part of the Pleistocene epoch. Smith (1949) has described block streams, block fields, rubble-choked valleys, and areas of presently stabilized talus which indicate that the area was under the influence of severe periglacial climatic conditions for a time when more active physical weathering and mass-wasting characterized the region than do so at present.

*Bedrock Geology and Topography.*    Except for the Baraboo area of Precambrian rocks, the Driftless section consists of submaturely dissected cuesta-form topography developed on rocks of early Paleozoic age around the west, south, and east sides of the Wisconsin dome. Four cuestas may be recognized in going from northeast to southwest down the dip of the rock toward the flank of the Wisconsin dome. These are: (1) the Cambrian sandstone cuesta, (2) the Magnesian or Prairie du Chien cuesta, (3) the Galena cuesta, and (4) the Niagara cuesta.

The Cambrian cuesta at the north is actually double in nature, the lower part being on the Dresbach sandstone and the upper part on the Franconia formation. Numerous outliers (see

Fig. 12.22) of the Cambrian cuesta stand out prominently above the flat lacustrine plain of Lake Wisconsin (see below), which borders the cuesta on the east. South and southwest of the Cambrian cuesta are the three cuestas commonly called the Dolomite cuestas. The first is on the Ordovician Prairie du Chien dolomite; the next cuesta is capped by the Ordovician Galena dolomite, although three formations, the Platteville limestone, the Decorah shale, and the Galena dolomite, serve as a unit to form its scarp; the southernmost cuesta is on rocks of the Silurian Niagaran group.

*Baraboo-Devils Lake Area.* The one area of Precambrian rock in the Driftless Area is at the east edge of the region in the Baraboo and Devil's Lake region (Trowbridge, 1917; Powers, 1946). Here the Baraboo quartzite, Seeley slate, and Freedom dolomite of Huronian age are found in the remnants of a synclinal trough downfolded into Archeozoic igneous rocks. North and South Ranges, as the two ridges on the two sides of the syncline are called, were presumably monadnocks on a Precambrian erosion surface that were later buried beneath Paleozoic sediments and still later partially exhumed during Tertiary erosion cycles. The surface of the Precambrian rocks on which the Paleozoic sediments rest has commonly been considered a Precambrian peneplain, but Thwaites (1931) has pointed out that well records indicate too much relief on the Precambrian surface for it to be so considered.

Devil's Lake, which occupies a gorge-like trough midway between North and South Ranges, is held in by a morainal dam formed when Cary ice extended into the Baraboo region and blocked the course of the Wisconsin River through the Baraboo Ranges to form Lake Wisconsin (see Figs. 12.22 and 12.23). Lake Wisconsin had an outlet to the northwest, presumably via the Black River, to the Mississippi. When the Cary ice withdrew, the Wisconsin River was prevented by the morainal dam from returning to its preglacial route through the two Baraboo Ranges. Instead, it took a course to the southeast around North Range and thence southwestward to its old route to the Mississippi River.

*Tertiary Geomorphic History.* The erosional history of the Driftless Area has been the subject of considerable discussion since publication in 1921 of Trowbridge's paper entitled "The erosional history of the Driftless Area." At least four interpretations have been given as to the number of peneplains that are recognizable in the uplands of the Driftless Area. Figure 12.24, after Bates (1939), graphically represents the various interpretations. Trowbridge in his 1921 paper postulated two peneplains, an older and higher Dodgeville and a younger and lower Lancaster. More recently (1954) he modified his views and concluded that there is evidence for only one peneplain, the Lancaster. Bates, from a study of numerous projected profiles, came to the conclusion that there is evidence for only one peneplain, which he thought was the Dodgeville. Martin (1932) felt that the topography could be reasonably interpreted as a series of one-cycle cuestas developed during a single period of erosion.

In the face of such diversity of opinion it seems impossible to arrive at any firm conclusion as to the number of erosion cycles that may be recognized in the preglacial history of the Driftless Area. A preponderance of opinion seems to favor the view that there is evidence of peneplanation here, even if there is marked disagreement as to how many periods of peneplanation are represented.

### Dissected Till Plains Section

*Distinguishing Features.* Grounds for recognition of the Dissected Till Plains as a separate section are twofold: a greater degree of dissection here than is found in the other glaciated parts of the Central Lowlands and a general absence of end moraines, lakes, or lake plains such as are found in the areas of younger drift. Probably the original glacial topography of the Dissected Till Plains was similar to that now found elsewhere, but it has been significantly modified by erosion and mass-wasting.

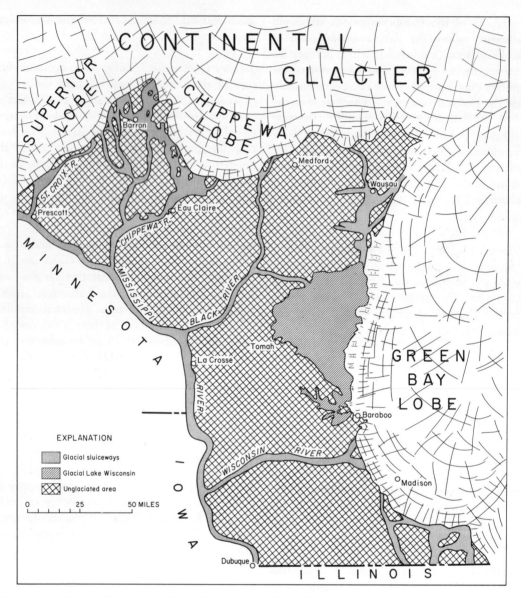

FIG. 12.23   Relation of ice border to Lake Wisconsin and glacial sluiceways.   (*After Lawrence Martin, Wis. Geol Surv. Bull. 36.*)

Loess-mantled Kansan drift covers the surface of most of the Dissected Till Plains section (see Fig. 12.25), but also included in this section are two sizeable strips of Iowan drift on either side of the Des Moines lobe. In age the Iowan till is more closely related to that in the Western Young Drift section than to the Kansan drift, but its topography is more similar to that of the

Kansan drift area. This is true, first, because both drifts are loess veneered and, secondly, because the Iowan drift area is moderately well dissected as a result of its nearness to the Missouri River on the west and the Mississippi River on the east.

Older glacial maps show small areas of Nebraskan drift within the Dissected Till Plains section, but it is now rather generally agreed that Nebraskan till is exposed only in stream bluffs, road cuts, and elsewhere beneath younger drift.

*Iowan Problem.* The age of the Iowan drift has long been in dispute. At first the dispute was whether or not the Iowan glaciation was a dis-

tinct glaciation between the Illinoian and Wisconsin; in more recent years the argument has been as to where it belongs in Wisconsin time. Leverett (1899) for several years maintained that the Iowan drift was deposited during a glaciation between the Illinoian and the Wisconsin. Leighton (1931, 1933) put forth some

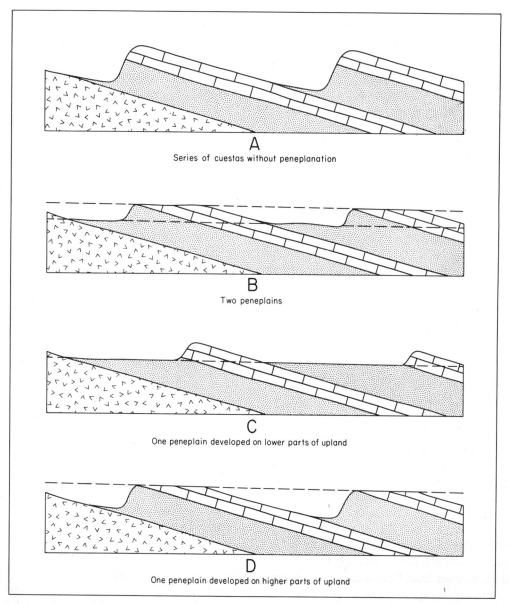

FIG. 12.24 Various interpretations of erosion surfaces in the Driftless Area. (*After R. E. Bates, Geol. Soc. Am. Bull.,* **50.**)

FIG. 12.25    Topography of Kansan drift area, Doniphan County, Kansas. (*Photo courtesy Kansas Geol. Survey.*)

strong arguments in support of the view that the Iowan drift belonged with the Wisconsin stage, and this view was gradually accepted, although Leverett did not completely accept this interpretation until 1942.

For a time the Iowan substage was considered the first of the Wisconsin drift sheets. Later, Leighton (1947) proposed the Farmdale substage of the Wisconsin and suggested that it was older than the Iowan. Now the existence of a Farmdale glaciation is in question (Frye and Willman, 1960), and it has been argued that the Iowan drift is older than the Farmdale deposits (Ruhe, Rubin, and Schlotes, 1957). Thus the only point on which there seem to be agreement is that the Iowan drift is of fairly early Wisconsin age.

*Evolution of the Middle and Lower Missouri River.* The present Missouri River has come into being as the result of the integration of parts of three former drainage basins as represented by the present upper, middle, and lower parts of the river. The upper Missouri River may be defined as that part of the river upstream from where it makes a sharp southward bend at about latitude 48° north in west-central North Dakota; the middle Missouri River extends from the southward bend in North Dakota to Kansas City, Missouri; and the lower Missouri River is that part of the river from Kansas City to its junction with the Mississippi River above St. Louis, Missouri. The history of the upper Missouri River is discussed in Chapter 16 (see p. 295).

The middle Missouri River follows a course essentially marginal to the outer limits of glaciation. G. K. Warren (1868) was perhaps the first geologist to call attention to the probability that the course of the Missouri River through the Dakotas is apparently a result of drainage rearrangement effected by glaciation. Todd (1914) recognized partially filled east-west valleys east of the present river that today contain no through streams. He thought that these suggested that the Heart-Cannonball, Grand-Moreau, Cheyenne-Bad, and White Rivers extended farther east in preglacial time than at present and joined a river in the James Valley Lowland that flowed northward to Hudson Bay. He placed the preglacial divide between Hudson Bay-Gulf of Mexico drainage between the White and Niobrara rivers.

More recently Flint (1949, 1955) and C. R. Warren (1952) have made suggestions as to the possible history of the middle Missouri River. Flint pointed out three anomalous features of Missouri River drainage in South Dakota: (1) the river, instead of flowing eastward down the regional slope, flows to the south at right angles to it; (2) the valley of the Missouri River is trench-like and more youthful than the valleys of several of its tributaries; (3) five major tributaries join the Missouri from the west, but no streams of comparable size join it from the east. Flint came to the conclusion that the preglacial Hudson Bay-Gulf of Mexico divide was in central South Dakota between the Cheyenne and Bad rivers.

Not enough is known of Missouri River history to be sure about how many diversions were involved in the establishment of the present course, nor are the dates of these diversions known (see Fig. 12.26). Warren (1952) has presented evidence that suggested to him that the Missouri River was diverted to its present route across South Dakota by the Illinoian glaciation rather than the Kansan, as suggested earlier by Flint (1949), and Flint in a later paper (1955) tentatively accepted this view.

At Kansas City, the Missouri River leaves the glaciated area and from here on to its junction with the Mississippi its valley widens notably.

This widening begins where the Kansas River enters the Missouri from the west, which suggests that downstream from Kansas City the Missouri River is following the preglacial route of the Kansas River, although it may be, as Greene (1921) suggested, that this valley was really the preglacial route of the Platte River, of which the Kansas River was a tributary.

Thus, it seems likely that the upper Missouri River formerly drained to Hudson Bay, that the middle Missouri flowed to the Mississippi River via a route that probably led eastward across Iowa (the so-called preglacial Iowa River); and that the lower Missouri River flowed to the Mississippi near St. Louis via the Kansas or Platte River.

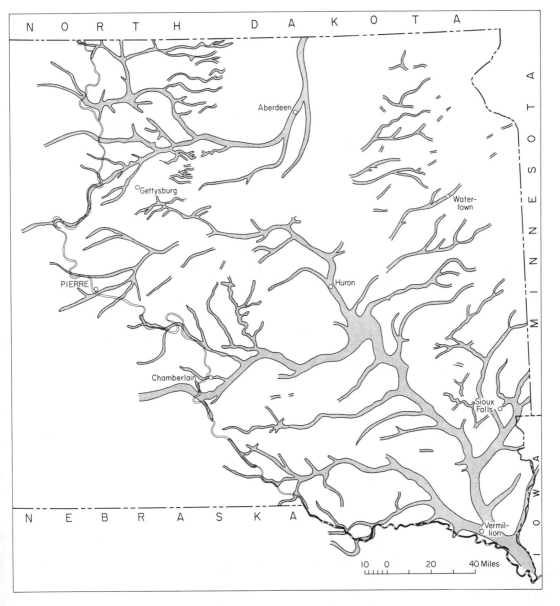

FIG. 12.26  Parts of the inferred prediversion drainage system of eastern South Dakota.  (*After R. F. Flint, U. S. Geol. Survey Profess. Paper* 262.)

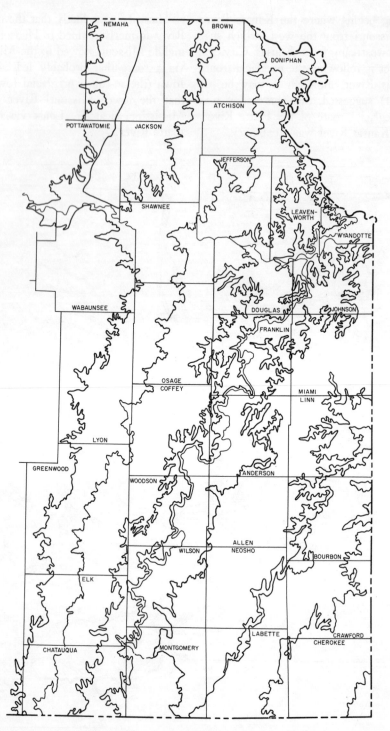

FIG. 12.27    Map showing trends of cuesta scarps in Osage section.    (*After W. H. Schoewe, Trans. Kansas Acad. Sci.,* **24.**)

FIG. 12.28    Flint Hills Escarpment, Cowley County, Kansas.    (*Photo by John C. Frye.*)

## The Osage Section

The Osage section is the only part of the Central Lowlands that can be said to have been essentially unaffected by glaciation. This statement is not entirely true, for the Arkansas River, which crosses this section, heads in the Colorado Rockies and had glacial outwash coming into it. Thus some of the loess deposits of the Osage section may have a glacial increment in them, even though it is not recognizable as such.

*Boundaries.* The eastern boundary of the section is where the westward-dipping Pennsylvanian rocks lap onto the western edge of the Ozark and Ouachita uplifts. The lowest Pennsylvanian formation is the Cherokee shale, and it does not provide a sharp boundary line. On the south, where the Osage section abuts against the Arkansas Valley and Ouachita Mountains, the sectional boundary is readily recognizable, for the north-south grain of the topography of the Osage section (see Fig. 12.27) contrasts with the east-west topographic trends in the Ouachita province. The western boundary is a fairly prominent, ragged, east-facing escarpment known popularly as the "Break of the Plains." This scarp in Texas is capped with the Pliocene (and perhaps Miocene) and Pleistocene mantle that covers much of the Great Plains and is known as the Caprock Escarpment (see Fig. 16.11).

*Geology.* Rocks of the Osage section are mainly Pennsylvanian or Permian in age, but in the southwestern part are some Triassic and Cretaceous rocks as well as Pliocene and Pleistocene outliers of Great Plains geology. Van Siclen (1957) thought that Pliocene detritus from the Rocky Mountains once covered all of the southern part of the Osage section and that it was largely removed by Pleistocene erosion; he further believed that the thin Pleistocene veneer was once much more extensive than at present.

*Nature of Topography.* Much of the Osage section can be most aptly described as scarped plains (see Fig. 12.28). The topography ranges from nearly featureless plain and low escarpments a few hundred feet high to bold escarpments that rise as much as 600 feet above adjacent plains. Lowlands or plains mark the weak rock belts, and hills or escarpments the areas of strong rock.

*Arbuckle Uplift.* Included in the Osage section are two areas that differ markedly in geology and topography from the rest of the section. These are the so-called Arbuckle and Wichita Mountains. The term Arbuckle uplift is more appropriate than Arbuckle Mountains, for none of the topography is mountainous and maximum relief is nowhere as great as 500 feet. Maximum relief is found along the escarpment which bounds the uplift on the north and along the gorge of the Washita River across the uplift. Most of the topography is plateau-like and possesses such slight relief that it has long been interpreted as an uplifted peneplain surface, presumably equivalent in age to an erosion surface in the Athens Piedmont Plateau of the Ouachita province (see p. 284). Melton (1959) named this erosion surface the Pawhuska peneplain and noted that it occurs at altitudes near 1000 feet in the Arbuckle Mountains. He believed that it could be recognized over an area extending from north-central Texas into southern Iowa.

Altitudes within the Arbuckle uplift range from about 1300 feet at the northeast to about 950 feet on the southwest. Topographic detail is largely a reflection of varying erosibility of the rocks. Steeply dipping strata on the southern side have given rise to a number of homoclinal ridges on lower Paleozoic limestones separated from each other by shale valleys. Similar homoclinal ridges and valleys are present on the north side, but they are not so strikingly developed.

Outcropping rocks are primarily Paleozoic sedimentaries ranging in age from Cambrian to Pennsylvanian (Lehman, 1945). The pre-Pennsylvanian section is as much as 10,000 feet thick and is predominantly limestone with minor amounts of sandstone, shale, and chert; Pennsylvanian strata are largely shale. Precambrian granite is exposed over an area covering about 500 square miles in the eastern part of the uplift. The granite is deeply weathered and exhibits low relief in contrast to the granite area in the Wichita Mountains, which stands out as hills. In the west part of the Arbuckle uplift are two small areas of granite known as the East and West Timbered Hills. The granitic rocks of

the Arbuckle Mountains belong to a batholithic complex that is now considered to be older than the Precambrian rocks of the Wichita Mountains (Hamilton, 1956).

Structurally the Arbuckle uplift consists of three northwest-southeast trending anticlines (Dott, 1934) known as the Hunton arch and the Tishomingo and Arbuckle anticlines. The folds have been considerably modified by faulting. The Ordovician Arbuckle limestone makes up the larger part of the flat-lying rocks on the crests of the folds, and the younger and more steeply dipping rocks on the flanks of the folds form cuestas or homoclinal ridges.

The eastern granite area is believed to represent an exhumed pre-Cretaceous erosion surface (Hamilton, 1956). If this interpretation is correct, the surface has not been greatly modified from what it was in Cretaceous time, except perhaps for some mass lowering during Tertiary time.

The Washita River flows across the Arbuckle uplift in an entrenched gorge whose course was apparently superposed onto the folded structure from a Tertiary erosion surface that was contemporaneous with the Hot Springs peneplain of the Athens Piedmont Plateau (Fenneman, 1938). It seems possible that Cretaceous strata once extended across the Arbuckle uplift. If they did, then it may be that the Washita River was superposed from this Cretaceous cover mass or from Ogalalla beds that once extended across the area.

*Wichita Mountains.* Lying some 70 miles west of the Arbuckle Mountains is a group of hills, ridges, and low "mountains" known as the Wichita Mountains. The Wichita Mountains rise 500 to 1400 feet above the surrounding plain. Igneous rocks of Precambrian age make up most of the area. Unlike the area of Precambrian rocks in the Arbuckle uplift, the Precambrian rocks stand out as prominent hills (see Fig. 12.29).

Whereas the igneous rocks in the Arbuckle Mountain are mainly granites, those in the Wichita Mountains exhibit greater variety. In addition to granite there are granophyres, rhyo-

FIG. 12.29   A granite hill in the Wichita Mountains.   (*Photo by J. W. Taylor.*)

lites, anorthosites, and gabbros. Flanking the igneous core are sedimentary rocks beginning with the Cambrian Reagan sandstones and including about 6000 feet of Arbuckle limestone.

The Wichita Mountain system is believed to be a southeastern continuation of a tectonic unit that begins somewhere in northeastern New Mexico or northwestern Texas and is known as the Amarillo uplift. In New Mexico and Texas this uplift has no surface expression, but in the Wichita uplift the igneous rocks were brought close enough to the surface that they were subsequently partially exhumed. North of the Wichita Mountains is a deep structural basin known as the Anadarko Basin. In it is a great thickness of Paleozoic sediments. It is estimated that in this depressed unit of the Amarillo-Wichita system Precambrian rocks are as much as 25,000 feet below sea level (King, 1951).

Topographically the Wichita Mountains differ from the Arbuckle Mountains in that they were not peneplained either before the invasion of the Cretaceous sea from the south or later during the Tertiary erosion cycle that resulted in base-leveling of the Arbuckle uplift. This difference was probably a result of the fact that the Wichita Mountains area is farther inland from the sea and the cycle of erosion did not attain so advanced a stage as in the Arbuckle area. There is, however, a suggestion of summit flattening on the granites at an altitude near 2000 feet.

# REFERENCES CITED

Adams, G. I. (1903). Physiographic divisions of Kansas, *Kans. Acad. Sci. Trans.*, **18**, 109–123.

Barrows, H. H. (1910). Geography of the middle Illinois Valley, *Ill. Geol. Surv. Bull.* 15, 128 pp.

Bates, R. E. (1939). Geomorphic history of the Kickapoo region, Wisconsin, *Geol. Soc. Am. Bull.*, **50**, 819–879.

Black, R. F. (1960). "Driftless Area" of Wisconsin was glaciated, *Geol. Soc. Am. Bull.*, **71**, 1827 (abs.).

Butts, Charles (1904). Description of the Kittanning quadrangle, *U. S. Geol. Survey Folio* 115, 2–3.

Cady, G. H. (1916). Lateral erosion in the upper Illinois Valley by the Chicago outlet, *Ill. Acad. Sci. Trans.*, **9**, 210 (abs.).

Campbell, M. R. (1898). Description of the Richmond quadrangle, *U. S. Geol. Survey Folio* 46, 3.

Dott, R. H. (1934). Overthrusting in the Arbuckle Mountains, Oklahoma, *Am. Assoc. Petroleum Geologists Bull.*, **18**, 567–602.

Elson, J. A. (1957). Lake Agassiz and the Mankato-Valders problem, *Science*, **126**, 999–1002.

Fenneman, N. M. (1928). Physiographic divisions of the United States, Assoc. Am. Geog., *Annals*, **18**, 261–353.

—— (1931). *Physiography of Western United States*, McGraw-Hill Book Company, New York, 534 pp.

Fisk, H. N. (1944). *Geological Investigation of the Alluvial Valley of the Lower Mississippi River*, Mississippi River Commission, Vicksburg, 78 pp.

Flint, R. F. (1949). Pleistocene drainage diversions in South Dakota, *Geograf. Annaler*, **31**, 56–74.

—— (1955). Pleistocene geology of eastern South Dakota, *U. S. Geol. Survey Profess. Paper* 262, 173 pp.

—— (1957). *Glacial and Pleistocene Geology*, John Wiley and Sons, Inc., New York, 553 pp.

Frye, J. C. (1946). The High Plains surface in Kansas, *Kans. Acad. Sci. Trans.*, **49**, 71–86.

—— (1949). The Plains Border physiographic section, *Kans. Acad. Sci. Trans.*, **52**, 71–81.

—— and H. B. Willman (1960). Classification of the Wisconsinan stage in the Lake Michigan glacial lobe, *Ill. Geol. Surv. Circular* 285, 16 pp.

Greene, F. C. (1921). Preliminary sketch of the history of the lower Missouri, *Geol. Soc. Am. Bull.*, **32**, 83–86.

Gwynne, C. S. (1942). Swell and swale patterns of the Mankato lobe of the Wisconsin drift plain in Iowa, *Jour. Geol.*, **50**, 200–208.

Hamilton, W. B. (1956). Precambrian rocks of the Wichita and Arbuckle Mountains, Oklahoma, *Geol. Soc. Am. Bull.*, **67**, 1319–1330.

Hays, C. W. (1899). Physiography of the Chattanooga district, *U. S. Geol. Survey 19th Ann. Rept.*, Pt. 2, 1–58.

Hershey, O. H. (1896). Preglacial erosion cycles in northwestern Illinois, *Am. Geologist*, **18**, 72–100.

—— (1902). Peneplains of the Ozark Highlands, *Am. Geologist*, **27**, 25–41.

Horberg, Leland (1946). Preglacial erosion surfaces in Illinois, *Jour. Geol.*, **54**, 179–192.

—— (1950). Bedrock topography of Illinois, *Ill. Geol. Surv. Bull.* 73, 111 pp.

—— (1951). Intersecting minor ridges and periglacial features in the Lake Agassiz basin, *Jour. Geol.*, **59**, 1–18.

—— (1956). Bedrock topography and Pleistocene glacial lobes in central United States, *Jour. Geol.*, **64**, 101–116.

Hough, J. L. (1955). Lake Chippewa, a low stage of Lake Michigan indicated by bottom sediments, *Geol. Soc. Am. Bull.*, **66**, 957–968.

—— (1958). *Geology of the Great Lakes*, Univ. Illinois Press, Urbana, 313 pp.

Johnston, W. A. (1946). Glacial Lake Agassiz, with special reference to the mode of deformation of the beaches, *Canadian Geol. Surv. Bull.* 7, 20 pp.

King, P. B. (1951). *The Tectonics of Middle North America*, Princeton Univ. Press, 203 pp.

Leighton, M. M. (1931). The Peorian loess and the classification of the glacial drift sheets of the Mississippi Valley, *Jour. Geol.*, **39**, 45–53.

—— (1933). The naming of the subdivisions of the Wisconsin glacial age, *Science*, n.s. **77**, 168.

—— (1947). *State geologists' conference on the loess deposits in Illinois, Iowa, South Dakota, and Nebraska*, 1.

—— (1957). The Cary-Mankato-Valders problem, *Jour. Geol.*, **65**, 108–111.

Lemke, R. W. (1960). Geology of the Souris River area, North Dakota, *U. S. Geol. Survey Profess. Paper* 325, 138 pp.

Leverett, Frank (1899). The Illinois glacial lobe, *U. S. Geol. Survey Mon.* 38, 817 pp.

—— (1929). Pleistocene of northern Kentucky, *Ky. Geol. Surv., Series 6, Bull.* 31, 80 pp.

—— (1942). Note by Frank Leverett, *Jour. Geol.*, **50**, 1001–1002.

—— and F. B. Taylor (1915). The Pleistocene of Indiana and Michigan and the history of the Great Lakes, *U. S. Geol. Survey Mon.* 53, 529 pp.

Lugn, A. L. (1962). The origin and sources of loess, *Univ. Neb. Studies*, n. s. **26**, 105 pp.

MacClintock, Paul (1933). Correlation of the preIllinoian drifts of Illinois, *Jour. Geol.*, **41**, 710–722.

Martin, Lawrence (1916). The physical geography of Wisconsin, *Wis. Geol. Surv. Bull.* 36, 549 pp.

Melhorn, W. N. (1956). Valders drift in the southern peninsula of Michigan, *Guidebook, 7th annual meeting Midwest Friends of the Pleistocene*, 13–19.

Melton, F. A. (1959). Aerial photographs and structural geomorphology, *Jour. Geol.*, **67**, 351–370.

Nikiforoff, C. C. (1952). Origin of the microrelief in the Lake Agassiz basin, *Jour. Geol.*, **60**, 99–103.

Powers, W. E. (1946). The Dells and Devils Lake region, Wisconsin, *The Chicago Naturalist*, **9**, 74–86.

Ray, L. L. (1957). Two significant new exposures of Pleistocene deposits along the Ohio River in Kentucky, *Jour. Geol.*, **65**, 542–545.

Rubey, W. W. (1952). Geology and mineral resources of the Hardin and Brussels quadrangles (in Illinois), *U. S. Geol. Survey Profess. Paper* 218, 179 pp.

Ruhe, R. V. (1952). Topographic discontinuities of the Des Moines lobe, *Am. Jour. Sci.*, **250**, 46–56.

———, Meyer Rubin, and W. H. Scholtes (1957). Late Pleistocene radiocarbon chronology in Iowa, *Am. Jour. Sci.*, **255**, 671–689.

Shaffer, Paul (1952). Tazewell glacial substage of western Illinois and eastern Iowa, *Geol. Soc. Am. Bull.*, **63**, 1296 (abs.).

Smith, G. D. (1942). Illinois loess—variations in its properties and distribution: a pedologic interpretation, *Univ. Ill. Agr. Exper. Sta. Bull.* 490, 184 pp.

Smith, H. T. U. (1949). Periglacial features in the Driftless Area of southern Wisconsin, *Jour. Geol.*, **57**, 196–215.

Stanley, G. M. (1938). The submerged valley through Mackinac Straits, *Jour. Geol.*, **46**, 966–974.

Thornbury, W. D. (1958). The geomorphic history of the upper Wabash Valley, *Am. Jour. Sci.*, **256**, 449–469.

Thwaites, F. T. (1931). Buried pre-Cambrian of Wisconsin, *Geol. Soc. Am. Bull.*, **42**, 719–750.

——— (1946). *Outline of Glacial Geology*, Edwards Brothers, Ann Arbor, 129 pp.

——— (1947). Geomorphology of the basin of Lake Michigan, *Mich. Acad. Sci., Arts and Letters*, **33**, 243–251.

Todd, J. E. (1895). A preliminary report on the geology of South Dakota, *S. D. Geol. Surv. Bull.* 1, 172 pp.

——— (1914). The Pleistocene history of the Missouri River, *Science*, **39**, 263–274.

Trowbridge, A. C. (1917). The history of Devils Lake, Wisconsin, *Jour. Geol.*, **25**, 344–372.

——— (1921). The erosional history of the Driftless Area, *Univ. Iowa Studies Nat. Hist.*, **9**, 127 pp.

——— (1954). Mississippi River and Gulf Coast terraces and sediments as related to Pleistocene history—a problem, *Geol. Soc. Am. Bull.*, **65**, 793–812.

———, A. J. Williams, J. C. Frye, and F. A. Swenson (1941). Pleistocene history of Mississippi River, *Iowa Acad. Sci.*, **48**, 296 (abs.).

Upham, Warren (1896). The glacial Lake Agassiz, *U. S. Geol. Survey Mon.* 25, 658 pp.

Van Siclen, D. C. (1957). Cenozoic strata on the southwestern Osage Plains of Texas, *Jour. Geol.*, **65**, 47–60.

Ver Steeg, Karl (1933). The thickness of the glacial deposits in Ohio, *Science*, **78**, 459.

——— (1934). The buried topography of north-central Ohio and its origin, *Jour. Geol.*, **42**, 602–620.

——— (1936). The buried topography of western Ohio, *Jour. Geol.*, **44**, 918–939.

Wanless, H. R. (1957). Geology and mineral resources of the Beardstown, Glasford, Havana, and Vermont quadrangles, *Ill. Geol. Surv. Bull.* 82, 233 pp.

Warren, C. R. (1952). Probable Illinoian age of the Missouri River, South Dakota, *Geol. Soc. Am. Bull.*, **63**, 1143–1156.

Warren, G. K. (1868). On certain physical features of the upper Mississippi River, *Am. Naturalist*, **2**, 497–502.

Wayne, W. J. (1952). Pleistocene evolution of the Ohio and Wabash valleys, *Jour. Geol.*, **60**, 575–585.

——— (1956). Thickness of drift and bedrock physiography of Indiana north of the Wisconsin glacial boundary, *Ind. Geol. Surv. Rept. Progress* 7, 70 pp.

——— (1958). Early Pleistocene sediments in Indiana, *Jour. Geol.*, **66**, 8–15.

Wright, H. E., Jr. (1955). Valders drift in Minnesota, *Jour. Geol.*, **63**, 403–411.

Zumberge, J. H., and J. E. Potzer (1956). Late Wisconsin chronology of the Lake Michigan basin correlated with pollen studies, *Geol. Soc. Am. Bull.*, **67**, 271–288.

ADDITIONAL REFERENCES

Cooper, W. S. (1935). The history of the upper Mississippi River in late Wisconsin and postglacial time, *Minn. Geol. Surv. Bull.* 26, 116 pp.

Ekblaw, G. A., and L. F. Athy (1935). Glacial Kankakee torrent in northeastern Illinois, *Geol. Soc. Am. Bull.*, **36**, 417–427.

Fidlar, M. M. (1948). Physiography of the lower Wabash Valley, *Ind. Div. Geol. Bull.* 2, 112 pp.

Hoffman, M. G. (1930). Geology and petrology of the Wichita Mountains, *Okla. Geol. Surv. Bull.* 52, 83 pp.

Horberg, Leland (1945). A major buried valley in east-central Illinois and its regional relationships, *Jour. Geol.*, **53**, 349–359.

Kunkle, G. R. (1963). Lake Ypsilanti: A probable late Pleistocene low-lake stage in the Erie basin, *Jour. Geol.*, **71**, 72–75.

Lehman, R. P. (1945). Thrust faulting in the Arbuckle Mountains, *Am. Assoc. Petroleum Geologists Bull.*, **29**, 187–209.

Leighton, M. M., and H. B. Willman (1950). Loess formations of the Mississippi Valley, *Jour. Geol.*, **58**, 599–623.

Leverett, Frank (1895). The preglacial valleys of the Mississippi and its tributaries, *Jour. Geol.*, **3**, 740–763.

——— (1921). Outline of the Pleistocene history of the Mississippi Valley, *Jour. Geol.*, **29**, 615–626.

——— (1942). Shifting of the Mississippi River in relation to glaciation, *Geol. Soc. Am. Bull.*, **53**, 1283–1298.

Nikiforoff, C. C. (1947). The life history of Lake Afassiz: alternative interpretation, *Am. Jour. Sci.*, **245**, 205–239.

Shepard, F. P. (1937). Origin of the Great Lakes basins, *Jour. Geol.*, **45**, 76–88.

Spencer, J. W. (1891). Origin of the basins of the Great Lakes of America, *Am. Geologist*, **7**, 86–97.

Trewartha, G. T., and G. H. Smith (1941). Surface configuration of the driftless cuestaform hill land, *Assoc. Am. Geog., Anns.*, **31**, 25–45.

Trowbridge, A. C. (1934). Upper Mississippi Valley structure, *Geol. Soc. Am. Bull.*, **45**, 519–527.

Zumberge, J. H. (1952). The lakes of Minnesota—their origin and classification, *Minn. Geol. Surv. Bull.* 35, 99 pp.

# 13

# *Superior Upland*

The Superior Upland is one of two extensions of the Laurentian Upland into the United States, the other being the Adirondack Mountains. If the Laurentian Upland is ever divided into geomorphic provinces, what is called the Superior Upland, along with its extension into Canada, would doubtless be one of the provinces.

## BOUNDARIES

So far, the boundaries for this province have only been established in the United States, and even here somewhat tenuously. In theory the province should include only areas of Precambrian rocks, but use of this criterion is complicated by the fact that as a result of glaciation the Precambrian rocks are covered in varying degrees by glacial drift. Areas of Cambrian rock have been included in the Superior Upland where the topography on them is essentially typical of that of the Superior Upland. Particularly on the south, where the Superior Upland is bordered by the Driftless Area, it seems more logical to put areas of Cambrian rock that had been glaciated in the Superior Upland than in the Driftless Area. The arbitrary straight-line boundary at the west reflects the difficulty of determining where it should be drawn here.

## GEOLOGY

### *Rocks*

Rocks of the Superior Upland range in age from Archezoic to Cambrian; most of them are Precambrian. Intrusive and extrusive igneous rocks, meta-igneous rocks, and meta-sedimentary rocks all occur in great variety. The metamorphic rocks display varying degrees of metamorphism, so that actually in some areas metamorphic rocks are the weak rocks. Of particular interest and importance geomorphically are the basic igneous rocks of the Keweenawan intrusive and extrusive series. The intrusive igneous rocks are commonly massive in nature, but many of the sedimentary and metamorphic rocks display bedding or layering which is reflected in a lineation of the geomorphic features developed upon them.

### *Structure*

The structure of the Superior Upland is perhaps as complex as will be found anywhere in the world. Folds and faults are common; they reflect several periods of mountain-building. Probably most of the structures date back to Precambrian time, but it is possible that faulting continued into the Paleozoic era.

Major structural trends in the Lake Superior region, particularly north of Lake Superior, run northeast-southwest and are strikingly reflected in the alignment of homoclinal ridges, escarpments, and valley lowlands. This structural alignment reflects the truncated roots of an ancient mountain system which has been called the Penokean Range.

A major structural feature of the region is the synclinal Lake Superior basin. This structure is asymmetrical with dips of about 15 degrees on the north side and 35 degrees or more on the south side (Schwartz, 1949). An igneous rock

FIG. 13.1   Cross-section across Lake Superior basin.   *(After Jack Hough,* Geology of the Great Lakes, *by permission Univ. Illinois Press.)*

mass known as the Duluth gabbro extends beneath the Lake Superior basin in the form of what has been called a lopolith by Grout (1918), who described the body as "a large lenticular, centrally sunken, generally concordant, intrusive mass, with its thickness approximately one-tenth to one-twentieth of its width or diameter." (See Fig. 13.1.)   The maximum thickness of the Duluth lopolith is estimated at 50,000 feet; at Duluth it is 12,000 feet thick, but it decreases in thickness northeastward.   The outcrop of the gabbro on both sides of Lake Superior is responsible for escarpments which parallel the lake shore.   Above the gabbro in the syncline are sandstones of late Keweenawan age.   These sandstones, in terms of their surrounding rocks, are weak rocks and are responsible for a lowland that extends westward from the head of Lake Superior.

## TOPOGRAPHY

### Preglacial Topography

Numerous geologists have interpreted the surface of the Superior Upland as a peneplain. Whether the peneplain was developed in Precambrian time, as thought by Weidman (1903), or later, as believed by Van Hise (1896), has been in dispute.   If it is a Precambrian peneplain it is most logically considered an exhumed peneplain, for it seems unlikely that an erosion surface formed in Precambrian time could persist so long at the surface.   Thwaites (1931) has shown that the relief on the buried Precambrian topography is as much as 500 feet; it may be stretching the term peneplain too much to apply it to such an erosional topography.   If the surface of the

Superior Upland is to be described as a peneplain surface, it seems far more likely that it acquired its present characteristics rather recently, perhaps during Tertiary time, when central North America appears to have experienced periods of stillstand of long enough duration to permit wide-scale baseleveling.

Numerous hills rise several hundred feet above the general level of the Superior Upland.   Such hills are particularly associated with granites, quartzites, and the trap rock of the Keweenawan flows.   Rib Hill, the highest point in Wisconsin (altitude 1940 feet), is a quartzite ridge that stands 550–600 feet above its surroundings (Martin, 1916).

### Topography around Lake Superior

The region between Lake Superior and the Canadian border can be divided into four topographic belts (Thiel, 1947), the highlands of St. Louis, Cook, and Lake counties at the north, a lowland plain at the west and south, an upland on the Duluth gabbro just north of Lake Superior, and the basin of Lake Superior.

The highland belt represents a part of the presumed Precambrian peneplain and is underlain by a complex of igneous, sedimentary, and metamorphic rocks.   General altitudes range between 1000 and 1700 feet, but certain erosion remnants rise 400 or 500 feet above this level. Strikingly developed near the Canadian border in what is called the Rove slate belt and Gunflint district is a series of east-west monoclinal ridges and valleys with linear lakes in the valleys (see Fig. 13.2).   The ridge scarps face north; along with the long dip slopes to the south, they give to the topography a sawtooth type of profile (Ver Steeg, 1947).

South of this belt of linear topography is the outcrop area of the Duluth gabbro. Developed on it is an upland that is set off from the Rove slate to the north by a prominent escarpment. South of the belt of the Duluth gabbro is the Lake Superior basin, which divides the highland of Precambrian rock in northern Wisconsin and the western part of the Upper Peninsula of Michigan from the main Precambrian area of the Laurentian Highland proper to the north of the lake.

West and north of the Duluth gabbro upland is the St. Louis plain, a poorly drained tract which extends northward to the Mesabi iron range. On the west it is so deeply covered with glacial drift that bedrock hardly shows (Thiel, 1947).

The St. Louis River drains most of the area. This stream flows southwestward for a considerable distance and then abruptly turns southeastward to Lake Superior. This pattern suggests that its drainage may have originally been to the Mississippi River. Martin (1916) attempted to explain its presumed diversion by capture by a short stream that worked backward from Lake Superior; Leverett (1932) concluded, however, that there is no topographic evidence for such a capture.

## GLACIATION AND ITS EFFECTS

The Superior Upland has been repeatedly glaciated, but the present glacial topography is largely a product of the late Wisconsin glaci-

FIG. 13.2   Lake in Rove slate belt, Cook County, Minnesota. *(Photo courtesy Minnesota Department of Business Development.)*

ations, particularly the Cary and Mankato-Valders. Ice entered the Superior Upland from three centers of dispersal. A tongue called the St. Louis sublobe came from the northwest from the Keewatin center. Ice moved southward into the area from the Patrician center north of Lake Superior, and from the Labrador center to the northeast the so-called Superior lobe moved through the Superior basin.

The areas covered by the different lobes are not only recognizable in terms of separate morainic systems, but there is marked color difference between the drift deposited by the St. Louis sublobe from the Keewatin center and that deposited by the Patrician and Labradoran ice. The Keewatin drift is gray in color, related to the gray color of the Cretaceous shales over which the ice moved, whereas the distinctive Valders drift deposited by the Superior lobe is red from the iron oxides obtained from the iron formations over which it moved (Wright, 1955).

As in all areas of late Wisconsin glaciation, lakes are abundant in the Superior Upland. Those at the south and west are mainly in or on glacial or glacio-fluviatile deposits, whereas at the north rock basin lakes are more common.

## ORIGIN OF LAKE SUPERIOR

Lake Superior, the largest freshwater body in the world, is about 360 miles long, 160 miles wide at its maximum, and covers approximately 32,000 square miles. The altitude of the lake surface is 602 feet, and at one point toward the eastern end of the lake, about 13 miles northwest of Caribou Island, there is a known depth of water of 1302 feet. This great depth of the floor of Lake Superior presents a perplexing problem. It appears that only three logical explanations can be offered for the existence of a tract of lake floor 700 feet below sea level: faulting, depression under the ice load, or glacial scouring. Although numerous faults are present around the Lake Superior basin, they date back so far in geologic time that they must be ruled out as a possible cause for the unusual depth of part of the Lake Superior basin. Possibly some of the faults are more recent than Precambrian,

but certainly none is as recent as Pleistocene, as it would have to be to have contributed to the present basin depth.

In the discussion of the history of the other four Great Lakes (see p. 234) it was concluded that there are good grounds for believing that their basins were weak belt lowlands in preglacial time that drained eastward to the Gulf of St. Lawrence. Presumably the drainage from the Lake Superior basin was a part of this major eastward drainage system. Obviously the floor of the basin was not below sea level at this time. Conceivably part of the depth of the Superior basin could be due to lack of complete recovery from depression under the ice load, but it appears very doubtful that isostatic recovery is as incomplete as would be necessary to account for the existing lake depth. We are thus more or less forced to attribute the depth of the lake floor to glacial erosion. Configuration of the lake floor at the east end is very irregular and similar to that at the north end of Lake Michigan (see Fig. 12.3). This irregular topography can perhaps be explained most logically as a product of intense local glacial scouring.

Evolution of the present Lake Superior began in a series of small ice-marginal water bodies around the border of the Lake Superior ice lobe. Lake Upham, in the area of the St. Louis plain, and Lake Nemadjii, at the south, were the initial phases of lake evolution (Leverett, 1929). In time they merged to form Lake Duluth, which had at one time a water line nearly twice as high as the present surface of Lake Superior. The highest untilted shoreline of Lake Duluth has an altitude of 1165 feet and is thus 503 feet above the present lake level. Lake Duluth drained southward down the Brule River in Wisconsin to the St. Croix River and thence to the Mississippi. Heavy red clays underlie the floor of the Lake Duluth lacustrine plain. Later, when the ice had retreated eastward beyond the Huron Mountains, south of the Keweenaw Peninsula, an outlet was established across the Upper Peninsula of Michigan to the Lake Michigan basin. Still later the present St. Mary's River outlet to the Huron basin was established (Hough, 1958).

# REFERENCES CITED

Grout, F. F. (1918). The lopolith: an igneous form exemplified by the Duluth gabbro, *Am. Jour. Sci.*, **196**, 516–522.

Hough, J. L. (1958). *Geology of the Great Lakes*, Univ. Illinois Press, Urbana, 313 pp.

Leverett, Frank (1929). Moraines and shorelines of the Lake Superior basin, *U. S. Geol. Survey Profess. Paper* 154-A, 1–72.

———— (1932). Quaternary geology of Minnesota and parts of adjacent states, *U. S. Geol. Survey Profess. Paper* 161, 149 pp.

Martin, Lawrence (1916). Physical geography of Wisconsin, *Wis. Geol. Surv. Bull.* 36, pp. 347–414.

Schwartz, G. M. (1949). The geology of the Duluth metropolitan area, *Minn. Geol. Surv. Bull.* 33, 136 pp.

Thiel, G. A. (1947). The geology and underground waters of northeastern Minnesota, *Minn. Geol. Surv. Bull.* 32, 247 pp.

Thwaites, F. T. (1931). Buried Pre-Cambrian of Wisconsin, *Geol. Soc. Am. Bull.*, **42**, 719–750.

Van Hise, C. R. (1896). A central Wisconsin baselevel, *Science*, n.s. **4**, 57–59.

Ver Steeg, Karl (1947). The influence of geologic structure on the drainage pattern in northeastern Minnesota, *Jour. Geol.*, **55**, 353–361.

Weidman, Samuel (1903). The pre-Potsdam peneplain of the Pre-Cambrian of north-central Wisconsin, *Jour. Geol.*, **11**, 289–313.

Wright, H. E., Jr. (1955). Valders drift in Minnesota, *Jour. Geol.*, **63**, 403–411.

### ADDITIONAL REFERENCES

Clark, T. H., and C. W. Stearn (1960). *The Geological Evolution of North America*, The Ronald Press, New York, 434 pp.

Leith, C. K., R. J. Lund, and Andrew Leith (1935). Precambrian rocks of the Lake Superior region. *U. S. Geol. Survey Profess. Paper* 184, 34 pp.

Martin, Lawrence (1911). Physical geography of the Lake Superior region, *U. S. Geol. Survey Mon.* 52, 85–117.

Schwartz, G. M., and G. A. Thiel (1954). Minnesota's rocks and waters, *Minn. Geol. Surv. Bull.* 37, 366 pp.

Wilson, A. W. G. (1903). The Laurentian peneplain, *Jour. Geol.*, **11**, 615–667.

# 14

# *Ozark Plateaus Province*

## RELATION OF INTERIOR HIGHLANDS TO APPALACHIAN HIGHLANDS

The Ozark Plateaus and Ouachita provinces together constitute the Interior Highlands division of the United States. Although separated from the Appalachian Highlands by several hundred miles of coastal plain, the geologic and geomorphic affinities of the two areas are so great that it now rather generally is believed that the Appalachian type of geology and structure continues westward beneath the coastal plain sediments to reappear in the Interior Highlands. This supposition has been strengthened in recent years by information obtained from deep wells drilled in the coastal plain areas of Alabama, Mississippi, and Arkansas.

This similarity in rock types, structure, and land forms may be seen readily if the geology and topography along a line running from Atlanta, Georgia, northwestward to Hopkinsville, Kentucky, are compared with those along a line connecting Paris, Texas, with Ste. Genevieve, Illinois. The geologic and topographic belts crossed along each line are similar, except that Paris is located on Cretaceous rocks instead of the igneous-metamorphic complex of the Piedmont province at Atlanta. However, the Cretaceous rocks at Paris rest on basement rocks similar in age and type to those of the Piedmont at Atlanta. The Blue Ridge province does not extend so far south as Atlanta, and consequently the Piedmont province in the Atlanta area abuts against the folded Paleozoic rocks of the Ridge and Valley province, whose rocks correspond

in age and structure to those of the Ouachita Mountains. In the following table the geologic belts are arranged from north to south, top to bottom.

TABLE 14.1 Geologic Belts along Two North-South Lines

| Hopkinsville to Atlanta | Ste. Genevieve to Paris |
|---|---|
| Rocks of Mississippian age of the Interior Low Plateaus | Rocks of Mississippian age of the Salem Plateau |
| Crest of Nashville Dome with rocks of Ordovician age | Crest of Ozark Dome with exhumed Precambrian igneous rocks |
| Rocks mainly of Mississippian age of the Highland Rim Plateau | Rocks of Cambrian to Mississippian age of the Salem Plateau |
| Mississippian and Pennsylvanian rocks of the Cumberland Plateau | Mississippian and Pennsylvanian rocks of Boston Mountains |
| Folded Paleozoic rocks of Ridge and Valley province | Folded Paleozoic rocks of Arkansas Valley and Ouachita Mountains |
| Igneous-metamorphic complex of Piedmont Plateau | Cretaceous rocks resting on an igneous-metamorphic complex |

The two major differences along these two lines of profile are that in the Texas area the crystalline rocks of the Piedmont type are still buried beneath Cretaceous sediments and that the Ozark dome has been more deeply eroded than the Nashville dome and as a consequence has exposed in it the Precambrian igneous rocks of the St. Francois Mountains, whereas the oldest rocks exposed in the Nashville dome are of Ordovician age. The similarities between the Appalachian Highlands and the Interior Highlands are so striking that we can not escape the conclusion that the Interior Highlands are properly thought of as outliers of Appalachian geology, structure, and topography.

## BASIS FOR DIVISION OF INTERIOR HIGHLANDS INTO PROVINCES

Differences in structure, lithology, and topography make possible division of the Interior Highlands into two provinces, the Ouachita and Ozark Plateaus provinces. The Ouachita province is characterized by strongly folded and faulted structures, with resulting parallelism of ridges and valleys similar to those of the Ridge and Valley province, whereas the very mildly folded or faulted structures in the Ozark Plateaus province have produced a cuestaform topography, with receding frontal escarpments and plateau-like uplands on the backslopes of the cuestas. Sandstones and shales predominate in the Ouachita province, whereas, except in the Boston Mountains, carbonate rocks are most prevalent in the Ozark Plateaus.

## OZARK PLATEAUS PROVINCE

The Ozark Plateaus cover an area of some 40,000 square miles lying mainly between the Missouri, Mississippi, and Arkansas rivers and comprising parts of the states of Missouri, Oklahoma, Arkansas, and Illinois. The province lies athwart a structural uplift known as the Ozark dome and is bounded on all sides by topographic lowlands. Much of the area is moderately low plateau, but a few areas exceed 2000 feet in altitude, and in the Boston Mountain section the dissection is so great that the term "mountain" as used here is not entirely inappropriate. The province is divided into four sections, each of

which has its distinctive geology and topography. These are the St. Francois Mountains, Salem Plateau, Springfield Plateau, and Boston Mountains sections (see Fig. 14.1).

### Structure and Stratigraphy

The Ozark uplift or dome is a broad asymmetrical structure with its crest in the St. Francois Mountains only 50 miles or so west of the eastern boundary of the province (King, 1951). Dips to the east toward the Mississippi Valley are of the order of 70 or 80 feet per mile, compared with 10 or 20 feet per mile on the west. Dips on the north and south flanks of the dome are intermediate between the above values. Local faults and folds are superposed on the major structure and make for minor variations in the altitude of the strata, but, except in the Boston Mountains, such structures have only minor topographic expression. The steep dips on the east flank of the Ozark dome are matched or exceeded at the western edge of the Boston Mountains, where there is a steep homoclinal dip of the rocks down to the level of the Arkansas Valley synclinorium. Here dips are locally as great as 25 degrees.

Limestones and dolomites predominate in the Ozark Plateaus. Two notable exceptions to this are in the St. Francois Mountains, where several varieties of igneous rocks occur, and in the Boston Mountains, where sandstones and shales are widespread. It may well be true that the Missouri portion of the Ozarks contains more chert than any other comparable area in the United States. Chert is so abundant in many areas that it mantles the topography, chokes the streams, and all but obscures the soil. Chert is a particularly abundant constituent of the Mississippian formations comprising what was long called the Boone chert formation, but it also is found in many of the limestones and dolomites of Cambrian and Ordovician age.

Sedimentary rocks of the Ozark Plateau range in age from Cambrian to Pennsylvanian (Howe and Koenig, 1961). These are arranged in roughly concentric belts outward from the Precambrian igneous rocks of the St. Francois

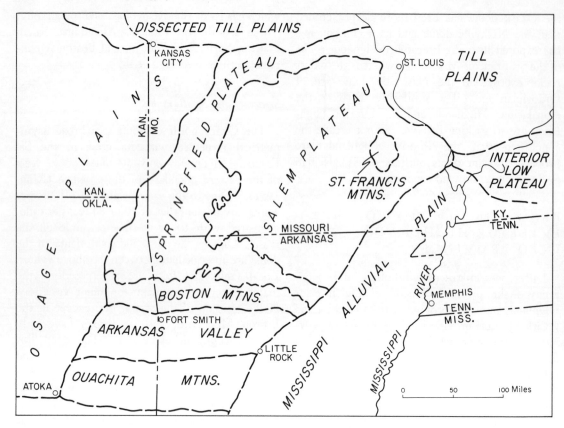

FIG. 14.1    Sections of Ozark Plateaus and Ouachita provinces.    (*After G. G. Huffman, Okla. Geol. Surv. Bull. 77.*)

Mountains area.    The youngest rocks are at the extreme southwest, in the Boston Mountains, where rocks of Pennsylvanian age make up the greater part of the mountains.

*Topographic Characteristics*

The topographic forms of the Ozark region are those expectable in an area of gently dipping rocks of variable hardness which has undergone mature dissection.    Topographic slopes locally are very nearly coincident with rock dips, but regionally there has been truncation of the various geological formations.    Variations in rock hardness are reflected in the development of a series of escarpments on the more resistant formations. The inward-facing escarpments are rather ragged and considerably interrupted but are arranged in

a crude fashion tangential to the dome.    The succession of escarpments is best displayed on the east side of the dome, where three major escarpments can be recognized between the crest of the dome and the Mississippi Valley.    These are, from west to east, the Avon, Crystal, and Burlington escarpments.    The Avon Escarpment is capped by the Cambrian Potosi dolomite; the Crystal Escarpment, by the Ordovician St. Peter and Joachim formations; and the Burlington Escarpment, by the lower Mississippian Burlington and Keokuk limestones.    On the west side of the Ozark dome only two escarpments stand out prominently.    One is the Eureka Springs Escarpment (called Burlington in the older writings), developed on resistant cherts and limestones of Mississippian age, and farther west and south is the Boston Mountain Escarpment, capped by the resistant basal sandstone in the Atoka (Winslow) formation of Pennsylvanian age. Other escarpments can be identified locally, but none is prominent or continuous for any great distance.

Drainage of the Ozark dome is roughly radial in pattern to the Missouri River on the north, the Mississippi on the east and southeast, the Arkansas on the south, and the Neosho River on the west. Long radial interfluves are so broad in many areas that they give an impression of relatively flat terrain. Travelers along some of the main highways may be unaware of the many deep and step-walled valleys that dissect the plateaus. Regional rock dips are in general slightly greater than longitudinal stream gradients, and as a result the broad interfluve tracts, which superficially give the impression of being structurally controlled surfaces, truncate geological formations and cross from older to younger rocks as they descend the dome. The southward-flowing streams have shorter and more direct routes to the Gulf of Mexico than the streams which flow north into the Missouri River. As a result, the streams on the south side of the dome have steeper gradients and have dissected more deeply the terrain which they drain. Consequently, broad upland interfluve areas are fewer in this part of the Ozark province than at the north and west.

A feature of Ozark streams that has attracted considerable attention and caused much speculation as to its cause is their notable meandering. Incised meanders are common and often striking (Tarr, 1924). Whether the conventional explanation that the meanders are inherited from a former erosion surface is correct cannot be stated with certainty.

Locally, departure from the gentle relief of the interstream tracts is provided by erosion remnants of rocks of Mississippian and Pennsylvanian age. These attest to a former greater extent of these rocks and show that much of the dome was denuded of several hundred feet of younger Paleozoic strata as the cuesta scarps migrated down the flanks of the Ozark dome. Probably Paleozoic strata as young as Pennsylvanian once extended across the Ozark dome.

# SECTIONS OF THE OZARK PROVINCE

The St. Francois Mountains section is located near the northern edge of the province upon the crest of the Ozark dome. The Salem Plateau encircles the St. Francois Mountains section but is much more extensive on the west than on the east. The Springfield Plateau extends about two-thirds of the way around the Ozark dome but is largely lacking on the eastern side. The Boston Mountains form a fairly narrow east-west belt at the extreme southern margin of the province (see Fig. 14.1).

## St. Francois Mountains

*Geology.* Located near the eastern edge of the province and on the structural crest of the Ozark dome is an area where the Precambrian topography on which the early Paleozoic formations were deposited is in various stages of exhumation (Dake and Bridge, 1932). The name St. Francois Mountains is applied locally to a small area of less than 100 square miles in which hills of igneous rock comprise most of the terrain (see Fig. 14.2). This area has given its name to the section whose most diagnostic characteristic is the presence of partially exhumed Precambrian hills. The Precambrian rocks are rhyolite porphyries, rhyolite tuffs and agglomerates, granite prophyries, granites, and basic dikes, with rhyolite porphyry being far the most abundant. The oldest Paleozoic rocks in exposed contact with Precambrian rocks are part of the late Cambrian Lamotte formation. Exhumation of the Precambrian topography is by no means completed, as the present relief in the St. Francois Mountains is generally less than 1000 feet, compared with relief of 1500 to 2000 feet on the buried Precambrian surface.

*Topography.* The hills in this section are largely composed of igneous rock, and the valleys or lowlands between them retain remnants of the once more extensive sedimentary rocks. As a result of the varying degrees of exhumation of the Precambrian surface the present topography displays several facets. Most striking are the numerous rounded "granite" peaks, which stand out as a distinctly different type of topography from that of most of the Ozark country (see Fig. 14.3). Tom Sauk Mountain, a granite peak in Iron County, Missouri, with an altitude of 1772 feet, is the highest point in Missouri. Between this peak and the surface of the Precambrian rock beneath the Mississippi alluvial plain in extreme southeastern Missouri there is more than 6000 feet of relief.

Less striking than the granite hills, but equally interesting, are features which locally are called "shut-ins." This term is applied to sections of river valleys with narrow gorge-like characteristics, where in cutting through Paleozoic beds the streams encountered Precambrian rock. The result was a narrowing of valley width along the stretch cut in igneous rocks and wider valley expanses both upstream and downstream from the shut-in on the sedimentary rocks. Some of the shut-ins are short enough to be essentially watergaps; others are long enough that they are better described as gorges.

A third facet of St. Francois Mountain topography is found in the broad valleys or lowlands upstream from some of the shut-ins. Arcadia Valley on the Ironton, Missouri, quadrangle is a good example (see Fig. 14.3). The probability is that most of these lowlands essentially coincide with former valleys of the Precambrian topography that are still floored with Paleozoic sedimentary rocks.

FIG. 14.2    View of St. Francois Mountains looking northeast from near Arcadia, Missouri. (*Photo by John S. Shelton.*)

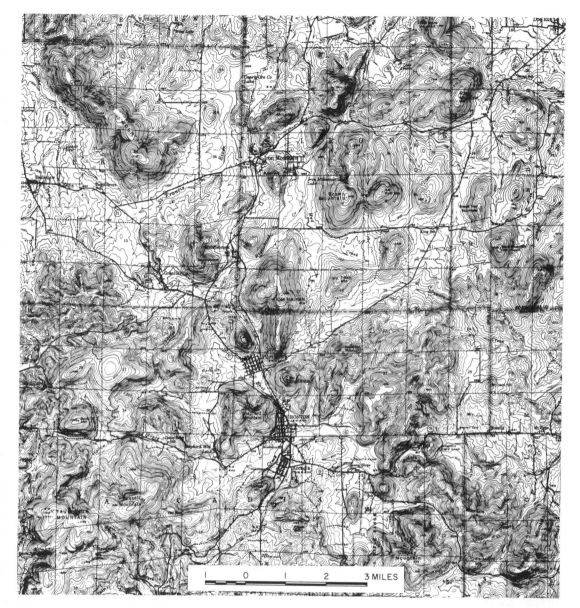

FIG. 14.3   Part of Ironton, Missouri, topographic sheet showing exhumed Precambrian "granite" hills.

*Salem Plateau*

The Salem Plateau section takes its name from what in the early days was called the Salem Platform, from its typical development around Salem, Dent County, Missouri.   As a sectional name the term has been extended to include the area in which the topography is developed mainly on rocks of Ordovician and older age.   However, in the area of the Salem Plateau between the St. Francois Mountains and the Mississippi River, limited areas of rocks of Silurian, Devonian, and Mississippian age occur, and at the west a few outliers of rocks younger than Ordovician can be found.   Limestones and dolomites are the most prevalent rock types.

The Salem Plateau section completely encircles the St. Francois Mountains, but because of the more gentle dips on the west side of the Ozark dome it is more extensive on the northwest, west, and southwest sides of the St. Francois Mountains than on the east.

South of Keysville, Missouri, in southern Crawford County, is the anomalous Crooked Creek structure (Hendricks, 1954). This is one of several structures in midwestern United States which have been designated as crypto-volcanic structures (Bucher, 1936), the exact origin of which is uncertain. This structure is 3 to 4 miles in diameter, and exposed at its center is the Davis formation of late Cambrian age. This formation is about 1000 feet above its normal position. It is bounded by a ring graben 1 to 2 miles in width in which the early Ordovician Roubidoux formation forms a shallow syncline. After considering the various origins which have been suggested for this type of structure Hendricks concluded that it could most likely be the result of deep-seated subterranean explosion or meteoritic impact.

*Topography.* Local relief on the interfluve upland tracts of the Salem Plateau section is rarely as much as 100 feet, but relief adjacent to such major streams as the White and Gasconade may be as great as 500 feet. This deep and rather intricate dissection is one of the features that distinguishes the Salem Plateau from the Springfield Plateau. Deep dissection is more characteristic of the southern side of the Salem Plateau than of other parts.

Despite extensive dissection numerous interstream tracts, known locally as "prairies," justify the section being designated as plateau rather than hills. Near accordance of interstream tract altitudes, along with the fact that their surfaces truncate the dipping strata, has led numerous geologists to consider the upland surface of the Salem Plateau a peneplain surface rather than a stripped structural plain.

In the part of the Salem Plateau section adjacent to the St. Francois Mountains a few shut-ins may be seen where dissection has cut down into the Precambrian rocks.

Widespread distribution of dolomites and limestones among the rocks of the Salem Plateau, along with the deep dissection, is responsible for a marked development of large springs (see Fig. 14.4). Beckman and Hinchey (1944) have noted the concentration of large springs in this area; here 12 of the 69 large springs (average flow of 100 second-feet or more) in the United States are found. Only the Snake River region of Idaho, with 15 large springs (see p. 460), exceeds the Missouri area in the number of large springs; Florida, with 11 such springs, ranks behind Missouri. The flow of some of the large springs is intimately associated with surface runoff, as is indicated by the fact that their flow responds quickly to heavy rains.

Cuestaform topography is developed in varying degrees in the Salem Plateau section. On the east side of the St. Francois Mountains the Avon, Crystal, and Burlington Escarpments are prominent; these same escarpments can be recognized on the west side of the section, but here they are more poorly developed. Locally other escarpments appear and play out as lateral change of facies of rock strata causes the escarpment-producing strata to become less resistant to erosion.

## Springfield Plateau

*Geology.* The Springfield Plateau includes that part of the Ozarks which is underlain mainly by rocks of Mississippian age. This section lies mainly west and south of the Salem Plateau, but a narrow extension may be traced around the northern edge of the Salem Plateau and to the east to a latitude slightly south of St. Louis. On the southwest side, in Missouri and Arkansas, the northeast-facing Eureka Springs Escarpment (known in the early literature as the Burlington Escarpment) forms the boundary between the Salem and Springfield plateaus. This escarpment, which stratigraphically is the retreating edge of the Mississippian strata that once extended across the Ozark dome, is produced by resistant cherty limestones of the so-called Boone chert of the Osagian series. These cherty limestones form a fairly continuous outcrop band

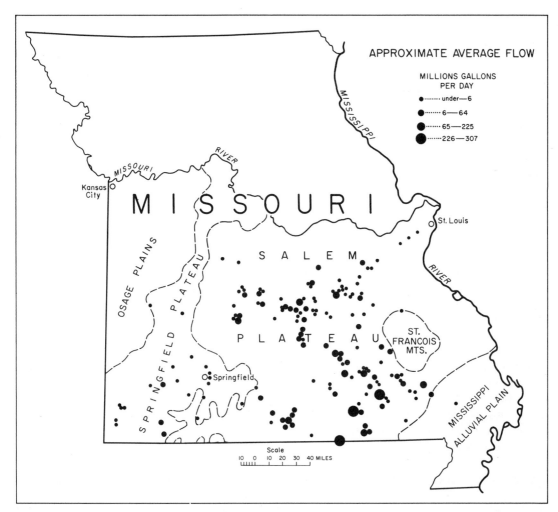

FIG. 14.4   Distribution of large springs in Missouri.   (*After H. C. Beckman and N. S. Hinchey, Mo. Geol. Surv. and Water Res. Bull. 29.*)

around the Ozark dome, but particularly in southwest Missouri and northern Arkansas they are responsible for a conspicuous escarpment. At Eureka Springs, Arkansas, the escarpment is 400 feet high, but it becomes progressively lower and fragmentary northward and disappears near the Osage River Valley.

*Topography.*   Much of the Springfield Plateau consists of the flat interfluve areas called "prairies," which are separated by valleys cut 200 to 300 feet below the upland surface. Locally, outliers of Pennsylvania rock stand a few hundred

feet above the plateau surface, much of which ranges between 1000 and 1500 feet in altitude. Over most of the area is a mantle of chert released by weathering of the Mississippian limestones.

Some geologists have considered the Springfield Plateau a structural plain; the gentle slope of its surface in the direction of the regional dip certainly suggests a strong structural influence. Actually, however, its surface truncates the rock strata, hence it can hardly be called a structural plain. Although rocks in the Springfield Plateau are stratigraphically higher than those in the

Salem Plateau, westward dip of strata results in altitudes here being no greater here than in the Salem Plateau.

## Boston Mountains

The Springfield Plateau is bounded on the south by another prominent escarpment which marks the northern front of the Boston Mountains. This escarpment, known as the Boston Mountains Escarpment, is capped by the basal resistant sandstones of the Pennsylvanian Atoka formation. Viewed from a distance the escarpment appears straight, but actually it is irregular and serrate in outline. It attains a height of as much as 800 feet and thus is the most conspicuous of the several escarpments in the Ozark province. The Boston Mountains, an east-west belt of rugged topography in northern Arkansas and eastern Oklahoma, attain altitudes in excess of 2200 feet. Dissection exceeds that of the Springfield Plateau, as major valleys attain depths of 500 to 1000 feet. Thus the popular designation of the area as the Boston Mountains rather than the Boston Plateau is readily understood. Rocks of the Boston Mountains section are mainly early and middle Pennsylvanian in age and are predominately sandstones and shales, in contrast to the carbonate rocks of the Springfield and Salem Plateaus. Faulting is more conspicuous geomorphically in the Boston Mountains than in any other section of the Ozark Plateaus province. Especially in the Oklahoma portion in Cherokee and Adair counties (Huffman, 1953), faults are very conspicuous. On the southern margin of the Boston Mountains dips steepen rapidly as the rock strata descend into the synclinorium in the Arkansas Valley to the south.

## Erosional History

Except for the locally exhumed Precambrian land forms on the crest of the Ozark dome, the Ozark landscapes can be interpreted in terms of erosion during Tertiary time, although it was once common practice here, as in the Appalachians, for geologists to attribute a Cretaceous age to the oldest facets of the topography. Most geologists who have studied the Ozark landscape have thought that they saw evidence of peneplanation. There has been divergence of opinion, however, as to whether there is evidence of one or several erosion surfaces and what the relationship is between topographic levels in the Boston Mountains and those in the Salem and Springfield Plateaus.

*Number of Erosion Cycles.* Hershey (1895) was apparently the first to recognize the evidence for multiple erosion cycles in the Ozarks. From observations made chiefly in the Springfield Plateau, he thought he saw evidence of an erosion surface that truncated beds of various ages. This erosion surface he designated as a Jura-Cretaceous peneplain. He noted that the valleys in this area have a duplex form "consisting of a small trough excavated in the bottom of a much larger trough or valley." This valley-in-valley cross profile he attributed to two episodes of valley cutting. The upper wide valley portion he attributed to a Tertiary cycle of erosion and the inner gorge-like portion to a Quaternary erosion cycle. Hershey explained the remarkable incised meanders of the Ozark area as being inherited from meandering streams on the Jura-Cretaceous peneplain.

In a paper in 1901 Hershey discussed the evidence for two peneplains, a Cretaceous peneplain represented only by ridge summits in the Ouachita and Boston mountains and the "main Tertiary peneplain" in the Arkansas Valley and the Springfield-Salem Plateaus. He also reaffirmed his belief in the duplex nature of the Ozark valleys.

In a still later paper, Hershey (1902) stated that he considered the presumed peneplain represented by the summits of the Boston Mountains to be older than the more widespread erosion surface (the Ozark peneplain) to the north of it in the Springfield and Salem plateaus. He thought that the summit surface in the Boston Mountains had been warped down in the Arkansas Valley but rose again and was recognizable in the summits of the Ouachita Mountains. He concluded that if the summit peneplain in the

Boston Mountains is not an older erosion surface than the one to the north of it in the Springfield-Salem Plateaus, its higher elevation in the Boston Mountains could only be explained as the result of its uplift by faulting, and he considered the Boston Mountains Escarpment too sinuous in outline to be interpreted as a fault scarp. Therefore, he considered the Boston Mountains a residual area which was not reduced to baselevel during the cycle that produced the Ozark peneplain. Hershey saw little evidence of a Tertiary baselevel of erosion in the Boston Mountains and thus concluded that the Ozark peneplain baselevel had not been extended this far headward. He thought that the uplift which followed the Ozark cycle and led to the development of the broad valley stage (strath terraces) took place in Pliocene time and was contemporaneous with the deposition of the cherty gravels known then as the Lafayette gravels (see p. 192).

Apparently the first description of a presumed peneplain surface in southeastern Missouri was that by Marbut (1896) who described the upland surface in the Salem Plateau as a peneplain no older in age than Cretaceous and no younger than middle or late Tertiary. Marbut saw no evidence in this area of two peneplains such as had been described in the Appalachian region.

Purdue (1901) admitted that the region north of the Boston Mountains displayed evidence of extended denudation but questioned the reality of remnants of a former peneplain in the Boston Mountains; rather, he thought their subaccordance of summit levels could be more logically attributed to the structural control of massive beds of sandstone in the Pennsylvanian strata of the Boston Mountains. Lack of valleys in the Boston Mountains with two cycle cross-profiles was another reason that he doubted the existence of more than one peneplain in the Ozark Plateaus.

Fenneman (1938) favored the interpretation that there are two major erosion surfaces in the Ozarks, one in the Boston Mountains and the other in the Springfield-Salem Plateaus. He thought that the Boston Mountain surface might correlate with the Schooley peneplain of the Appalachians and the Ozark peneplain with the Lancaster peneplain of the Driftless Area. Fol-

lowing uplift of the Ozark peneplain there developed the "broad valley or Lafayette stage," which in turn was succeeded by the "gorge cutting stage."

Bretz[1] has done much recent work on the geomorphic features of the Ozarks, and from this work he arrived at the following conclusions regarding the erosional history of the region:

1. None of the erosional surfaces or interfluve summits owes its existence to pedimentation or to structural control by resistant beds.
2. The topography of the Ozarks is not to be explained in a single dynamic equilibrium cycle as held by Hack (1960).
3. Three successive peneplains, the Boston Mountains, Springfield, and Ozark, are recorded in the Ozarks.
4. All erosion surfaces have been much dissected, and the oldest, the Boston Mountains peneplain, though still retaining a rude accordance of summit level, has lost all its summit flats.
5. All erosion surfaces are warped as a result of the uplifts which inaugurated the successive cycles.
6. Uplift of the Ozark dome after the period of erosion which produced the Ozark peneplain has been interrupted by two pauses which are recorded by two strath terraces. The upper strath terrace is called the Osage strath terrace and the lower one the post-Osage strath terrace.
7. A "deep valley stage" followed the cutting of the post-Osage strath.
8. The Eureka Springs Escarpment, which is a part of the Springfield peneplain surface, has retreated very little since the end of the Ozark cycle.
9. Stream gravels found on the upland surfaces

---

[1] The following summation of Bretz's ideas was obtained from a yet unpublished manuscript which is to appear as a bulletin of the Missouri Division of Geological Survey and Water Resources under the probable title "Geomorphic History of the Ozarks of Missouri." Through the kind graces of Dr. Bretz and Missouri State Geologist Dr. Thomas R. Beveridge, the author had the opportunity of reading the manuscript before publication.

are of different ages and cannot be used alone to correlate erosion surfaces.

10. The Springfield peneplain is correlated with the Dodgeville of Wisconsin and Illinois; the Ozark Peneplain with the Lancaster; the Osage strath with the Central Illinois peneplain; and the post-Osage strath with the Havana strath of Illinois. No attempt at dating the Boston Mountain peneplain was made.

It will be noted that the correlation of the Ozark erosion surfaces essentially follows that made by Horberg (see p. 217) for the erosion surfaces which he believed could be recognized beneath the glacial drift in Illinois. Doubtless several geologists will object to an interpretation of Ozark geomorphic history that postulates so many cycles and subcycles of erosion.

Quinn (1956) has attempted to interpret the step-like surfaceso f the Salem, Springfield, and Boston Mountains plateaus in terms of Walther Penck's concept of piedmont treppen. He would thus consider the Ozark erosion surfaces pediplains that evolved under arid climate. Bretz (1953) has pointed out that according to the concept of piedmont treppen the Ozark dome should have a series of scarps facing outward and retreating parallel to themselves toward the center of the dome with each scarp standing above an erosional surface or benchland in front of it. Actually, the exact opposite is true as to the relationships of the Ozark escarpments, for the scarps are retreating away from the center of the dome rather than toward it. Aside from this, there is no evidence to suggest that the climate of this part of the United States was arid or semi-arid in Tertiary time—not that arid conditions are necessary to the Penckian concept of parallel retreat of slopes.

### Karst Features

Considering the abundance of carbonate rocks in the Ozark Plateaus, particularly in the Springfield and Salem Plateaus, it is somewhat surprising that this area is not one of the major karst regions in the United States. To a certain

degree it is, for caverns and karst springs are present in great number. Bretz stated in 1956 that at that time 437 caverns were known in Missouri alone. This is comparable with the slightly more than 400 known caves in the karst region of Indiana and a probably equal or greater number in Kentucky. As stated above, 12 of the 69 large springs in the United States are in the Ozarks, and they are all karst springs. The anomalous aspect of Ozark karst is that sinkholes and swallow holes, of which there are hundreds of thousands in the Indiana-Kentucky karst region, are so sparingly developed. Sinking creeks that empty into open swallow holes are likewise scarse. It is true that there are areas of reasonably good karst plain where numerous sinkholes can be seen (see Fig. 14.5), but a geologist unfamiliar with the bedrock formations might travel over much of the Springfield and Salem plateaus and from their topographic expression alone not realize that he was traversing areas of abundant carbonate rocks.

*Reasons for Poor Karst.* Certainly most of the conditions essential to maximum development of karst topography are present; a humid climate, soluble rock beneath the surface, deeply entrenched valleys below the limestone or dolomite uplands, and jointed and bedded rocks. It appears that the major reason that some karst features, particularly sinkholes and swallow holes, are so poorly displayed in the Ozarks is the abundance of chert in the limestones and dolomites of the Springfield and Salem plateaus.

Chert mantles much of the topography and literally chokes many of the lesser stream valleys. A weathering residue of chert, clay, and sand can be seen in deep road cuts and other excavations. Water wells drilled on the upland areas frequently go through 100 to 150 feet of detrital material before encountering bedrock (Beckman and Hinchley, 1944). This porous mantle results in reduced concentrated surface runoff; there is mass diversion of surface waters to the subsurface rather than through streams that terminate in swallow holes. Purdue (1901) and Marbut (1896) both described solution valleys in the Ozarks whose floors were littered with

FIG. 14.5 Sinkholes, Boone County, Missouri. (*Photo by A. K. Unklesbay.*)

chert so permeable that little corrosion took place on the valley floors. Some of these solution valleys have abrupt heads similar to the steepheads of the Floridian karst region.

Probably it is not correct to say that sinkholes and swallow holes are largely lacking in the Missouri karst; it is likely more correct to say that to a large degree they are obscured by the chert mantle. If this cover were removed probably the limestone surface would show innumerable basins similar to those found on a typical sinkhole plain.

*Big Springs.* Figure 14.4 shows the distribution in Missouri of the so-called "large springs." It will be noted that they are particularly abundant in the Salem Plateau area. Although a few are in the Springfield Plateau, none of the first-magnitude springs is found here. It is noteworthy that the fifteen largest springs in the state issue from dolomites or dolomitic limestones. The majority of the large springs issue from the Gasconade, Van Buren, and Eminence dolomites of Ordovician age, but some come from the Cotter, Jefferson City, and Roubidoux formations, also of Ordovician age. Springs in the Springfield Plateau are associated with the Burlington-Keokuk and Warsaw limestones or cherty limestone formations of Mississippian age.

Big Spring, Carter County, Missouri, is the largest of the springs. It emerges from the base of a rocky bluff of Eminence dolomite at an elevation of 433 feet above sea level (see Fig. 14.6). Tests over a 20 year period indicate that it has an average daily flow of 390 second-feet or 252,000,000 gallons per day. Its flow thus about equals that of the upper pool of Silver Springs, Florida.

The Missouri springs are fed by rainfall that is absorbed by the permeable chert mantle on the

FIG. 14.6   Big Spring, Carter County, Missouri.   (*Photo courtesy Missouri Resources and Development Commission.*)

uplands, by chert-filled dry valleys, and by some sinkholes. Spring flow is influenced by surface runoff, as is indicated by the fact that, although most of the springs maintain a fairly steady flow during dry periods, their volume fluctuates in quick response to local rains and some even become turbid after heavy rains.

Few springs can be directly associated with specific sinking creeks, because only a small number of the dry valleys lose their waters at observable surface openings. However, part of the water of Big Spring in Carter County, Missouri, is derived from a series of sinks in the valley of Davis Creek near the town of Midco, about 10 miles from Big Spring. This is proven by the fact that when, in 1918, an iron furnace at Midco dumped quantities of chemical waste

into the dry bed of Davis Creek, the water at Big Spring was soon contaminated by this waste. Undoubtedly numerous other springs have similar connections with surface sinkholes and dry valleys.

Bretz (1953) interpreted the big springs of Missouri as the discharges of a large number of cavern systems developed by phreatic water below the water table which are now partly exposed at the surface as the result of stream dissection following uplift of the Ozark peneplain. He thought that movement of the phreatic water was essentially laterally at the level of the water table; he believed that some of the aquifers were still operating under phreatic conditions. The rather steady flow of most of the springs seems to support the belief that they are maintained to a considerable extent by groundwater at or below the water table. Thus their fluctuations in volume reflect changes in the hydrostatic head of the groundwater body produced by periods of rainfall and drought. Probably those springs which become turbid after heavy rains are directly connected with surface sinks and only partially sustained by groundwater at or below the water table.

*Caverns.* The more than 400 known caverns in Missouri are distributed through some 55 counties. The major cave area lies in the southern part of the state and is roughly triangular in shape, with its northern apex being near Boonville, its western corner near the southwest edge of the state, and its southeast corner at the contact of the coastal plain sediments and the Paleozoic rocks of the Ozark dome. Actually this area extends into northern Arkansas, but the caves of this state have not been studied and mapped. Within this triangular area caves are especially numerous south and west of Rolla and southwest of Springfield. According to Bretz's statistics (1956) twelve counties in these two areas contain more than half the known caves. Caves may well be present north of the Missouri River, but the cover of glacial drift, along with the lack of deeply cut valleys, prevents them from being seen here.

Bretz (1956, 1962), from his detailed studies of Missouri caves, concluded that most of them were the result of solution by phreatic waters beneath the mature topography that preceded development of the Ozark peneplain. By the time the topography had been reduced in relief to peneplain conditions, circulation of the phreatic waters through the caverns stagnated to such a degree that most of the caverns became filled with clay derived from the deep red soil on the surface of the Ozark peneplain. Subsequent uplift of the Ozark peneplain resulted in deep dissection of the topography and lowering of the water table. This brought most of the caves into the zone of vadose waters, with consequent partial or complete removal of the clay fills. As stated above, Bretz considered the majority of the big springs of Missouri to be discharges

of groundwater from parts of this earlier cavern system which lay so far below the surficial topography that dissection of the valley floors has only recently brought the caverns into the zone of vadose water. In further support of the phreatic origin of most of the Missouri caves Bretz noted that few cave streams can be traced to sinkhole sources or to engulfment of surface streams in swallow holes.

## REFERENCES CITED

Beckman, H. C., and N. S. Hinchey (1944). The large springs of Missouri, *Mo. Div. Geol. Surv. and Water Resources, Bull.* 29, 2nd ser., 141 pp.

Bretz, J H. (1953). Genetic relations of caves to peneplains and big springs in the Ozarks, *Am. Jour. Sci.,* **251**, 1–24.

——— (1956). Caves of Missouri, *Mo. Div. Geol. Surv. and Water Resources Bull.* 39, 2nd ser., 490 pp.

——— (1962). Dynamic equilibrium and the Ozark land forms, *Am. Jour. Sci.,* **260**, 427–438.

Bucher, W. H. (1936). Cryptovolcanic structures in the United States, *Rept 16th Int. Geol. Cong.,* 1055–1084.

Dake, C. L., and Josiah Bridge (1932). Buried and resurrected hills of central Ozarks, *Am. Assoc. Petroleum Geologists Bull.,* **16**, 629–652.

Fenneman, N. M. (1938). *Physiography of Eastern United States,* McGraw-Hill Book Company, New York, 714 pp.

Hack, J. T. (1960). Interpretation of erosional topography in humid temperature regions, *Am. Jour. Sci.,* 258-A, 80–97.

Hendricks, H. E. (1954). The geology of the Steelville quadrangle, Missouri, *Mo. Div. Geol. Surv. and Water Resources Bull.* 36, 2nd ser., 88 pp.

Hershey, O. H. (1895). River valleys of the Ozark Plateau, *Am. Geologist,* **16**, 338–357.

——— (1901). Peneplains of the Ozark Highlands, *Am. Geologist,* **27**, 25–41.

——— (1902). Boston Mountain physiography, *Jour. Geol.,* **10**, 160–165.

Howe, W. B., and J. W. Koenig (1961). The stratigraphic succession of Missouri, *Mo. Div. Geol. Surv. and Water Resources Bull.* 40, 2nd ser., 185 pp.

Huffman, G. G. (1953). Guidebook for field conference on pre-Atoka rocks, *Okla. Geol. Surv. Guidebook No. 1,* 41 pp.

King, P. B. (1951). *The Tectonics of Middle North America,* Princeton Univ. Press, Princeton, 203 pp.

Marbut, C. F. (1896). Physical features of Missouri, *Mo. Geol. Surv. Bull.* 10, 11–109.

Purdue, A. H. (1901). Physiography of the Boston Mountains, *Jour. Geol.,* **9**, 694–701.

Quinn, J. H. (1956). Origin and age of the plateau

surfaces in northwest Arkansas, *Geol. Soc. Am. Bull.*, **67**, 1726 (abs.).

Tarr, W. A. (1924)   Intrenched and incised meanders of some streams on the northern slope of the Ozark Plateau in Missouri, *Jour. Geol.*, **32**, 583–600.

ADDITIONAL REFERENCES

Bridge, Josiah (1930).   Geology of the Eminence and Cardareva quandrangles, *Mo. Bur. Geol. and Mines Bull.* 24, 2nd ser., 228 pp.

Croneis, Carey (1930).   Geology of the Arkansas Paleozoic area, *Ark. Geol. Surv. Bull.* 3, 457 pp.

Dake, C. L. (1930).   The geology of the Potosi and Edgehill quadrangles, *Mo. Bur. Geol. and Mines Bull.* 23, 2nd ser., 233 pp.

Huffman, G. G. (1958).   Geology of the flanks of the Ozark uplift, *Okla. Geol. Surv. Bull.* 77, 281 pp.

Purdue, A. H. (1901).   Valleys of solution in northern Arkansas, *Jour. Geol.*, **9**, 47–50.

———— and H. D. Miser (1916).   Description of the Eureka Springs and Harrison quadrangles, *U.S. Geol. Survey Folio* 202, 1–4.

Sauer, C. O. (1920).   The geography of the Ozark Highland of Missouri, *Geog. Soc. Chicago Bull.* 7, 245 pp.

# 15

# *Ouachita Province*

The Ouachita province is an east-west extending area roughly 225 miles long and 100 miles wide lying south of and paralleling the Boston Mountains section of the Ozark Plateaus province. Topographically and structurally it is readily divisible into two sections, the Arkansas Valley section on the north and the Ouachita Mountains section on the south. The Arkansas Valley section is dominantly lowland, although numerous mountains rise conspicuously above its general level, whereas mountains dominate the topography of the Ouachita Mountains section. Lineation of topography is noticeable in each section, but particularly in the Ouachita Mountains.

The Ouachita province stands out both structurally and topographically in sharp contrast to the Ozark Plateaus. As stated above, there are strong grounds for believing that the rock structures of Ouachita province are a western continuation of the Appalachian type of structure. Flawn (1959) has maintained that this structural belt continues in a sinuous course from southwestern Alabama for a distance of some 1300 miles into northern Mexico, being exposed at the surface only in the Ouachita Mountains and the Marathon region of southwest Texas. He pointed out the following similarities between the Ouachita-Marathon regions and the Appalachians which lend support to this contention:

1. Both areas represent late Paleozoic belts marginal to the older North American craton.
2. Structures are similar in both areas.
3. There is a similarity in scale and rock sequences in the two areas.
4. They display a similarity in sequence of lithologic and structural belts. In going out from the craton from northwest to southeast in the Appalachians we find the following sequence:
   a. The frontal Ridge and Valley province of unmetamorphosed folded and faulted rocks.
   b. The metamorphosed and overthrust rocks of the Blue Ridge province.
   c. The metamorphosed and widely intruded rocks of the Piedmont province.
   Similarly, in the Ouachitas we find:
   a. The frontal belt of the Ouachita Mountains of essentially unmetamorphosed folded and faulted beds.
   b. The Luling overthrust front, in which occur phylites, slates, and other metamorphic rocks comparable to the rocks in the Blue Ridge front.
   c. The metamorphic-igneous rocks of the basement complex on which the rocks of the Coastal Plain rest.

King (1959) indicated that records of wells drilled in the coastal plain sediments of Mississippi and Alabama strongly support the view that the structures continue beneath the thick prism of coastal plain and Gulf embayment sediments. These records make possible mapping of the two structural belts to within 50 miles of each other, with an indication that if extended they would meet near Meridian, Mississippi.

## GEOLOGY AND STRUCTURE

Except for a few small areas of middle Cretaceous intrusive igneous rocks, such as those in

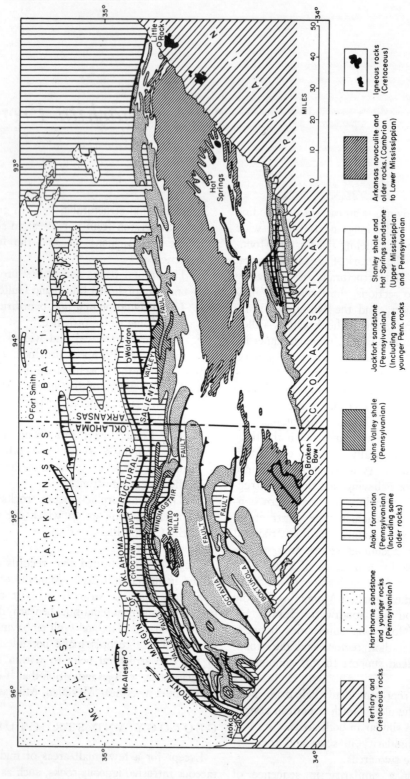

FIG. 15.1   Geologic map of Ouachita Mountains.   (*After H. D. Miser, The Geology of the Ouachita Mountains, A Symposium, Dallas Geol. Soc. and Ardmore Geol. Soc.*)

the Magnet Cove area in Arkansas southeast of Hot Springs, all rocks of the Ouachita province are sedimentary. They range in age from Cambrian or Ordovician (there is dispute as to the age of the lowermost Paleozoic rocks) to Pennsylvanian (see Fig. 15.1). There is a total maximum thickness of around 27,000 feet of Paleozoic rocks with a great abundance of sandstones and shales, particularly in the Mississippian and Pennsylvanian portions of the section. Mississippian and Pennsylvanian rocks have an aggregate thickness of about 22,000 feet, compared with 5000 feet for pre-Carboniferous rocks.

Structurally the province is divisible into two fairly distinct areas, the synclinal Arkansas-McAlester basin at the north and the anticlinorial Ouachita Mountains at the south. Rocks of the Arkansas Valley section are all Pennsylvanian in age and in general are marked by mild folding, whereas the rocks of the Ouachita Mountains section are strongly folded and faulted. The Choctaw fault (see Fig. 15.1) represents the front of the complex structure of the Ouachita Mountains section and separates steeply northward-dipping beds on its north side from steeply southward-dipping beds on its south side. South of the Choctaw fault is a belt of closed folding and thrust faulting, a belt of imbricate structure resembling in many respects the type of structure found in the southern part of the Appalachian Ridge and Valley province (see Fig. 15.2). There is, however, marked difference of opinion as to the number, nature, and extent of the thrust faults in the core region of the Ouachita Mountains section; this difference of opinion constitutes the Ouachita structural dispute, which has at times been rather heatedly debated.

## Ouachita Structural Dispute

The Ouachita structural dispute is essentially a repetition of the "Taconic thrust" and the "Marctic thrust" arguments. The basic question is whether the exposed structures in the Ouachita Mountains can be explained best as an autochthonous folded belt, the view held by such workers as Honess (1923), Misch and Oles

(1957), and Pitt (1955), or as an allochthonous mass of rock of Ouachita facies thrust over rocks of the Arbuckle facies, a view held by Miser (1929), Harlton (1953), and Hendricks (1958, 1959). We can no more hope to solve this problem than we did the Taconic and Marctic thrust problems, for many competent geologists, who have actually worked in the area, strongly differ as to the proper interpretation. We shall merely attempt to present the two views.

The idea of thrust faulting in the Ouachita Mountains probably was expressed first by Taff (1902), but without much development of the idea. Dake (1921) later presented the same idea in a somewhat more extended way. Since then many persons have worked in the area and taken sides in this long-continuing argument. Probably no one would deny the existence of faults in the Ouachita Mountains, not even thrust faults, but the major question relates to the magnitude of horizontal movement that has taken place along the faults. Actually the faults as expressed at the surface are high-angle reverse faults (see Fig. 15.2) rather than low-angle thrusts. Those who question the validity of large-scale thrust faulting interpret the surface faults as local features associated with overturned folds, whereas the believers in large-scale thrust faulting say that these high-angle surficial faults connect with deep low-angle faults along which there has been as much as 50 miles of displacement of rock strata, according to Hendricks (1959), and 60 to 80 miles according to Miser (1929, 1934).

According to the view of wide-scale regional thrust faulting, the rocks of the clastic Ouachita facies have been thrust northwestward many miles over the carbonate rocks of the Arbuckle facies, which in places can be seen in windows in the thrust sheets. The Choctaw fault forms the structural front of this thrust belt, and back of it are numerous other faults such as the Ti Valley, Windingstair, and Octavia, along which the structural blocks moved northwestward. The Choctaw fault is believed to have a length of around 125 miles and the Windingstair a length of 110 miles.

Those who doubt the reality of regional imbricate thrust faulting deny the existence of the

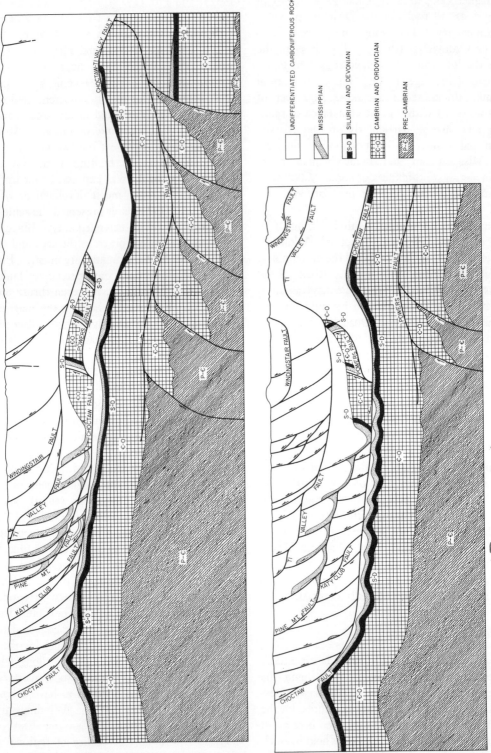

FIG. 15.2   Inferred fault structures in western part of Ouachita Mountains.   (*After T. A. Hendricks, Oil and Gas Investigation Map 66.*)

Potato Hills window, which Miser (1929) and others have cited in support of the idea that a thrust sheet of rocks of Ouachita facies rests on rocks of Arbuckle facies. Instead they maintain that what exists in the Potato Hills is an anticlinorium of steep and partly overturned folds rather than a thrust, and they further maintain that the rocks in the Potato Hills area have a normal stratigraphic sequence.

## SECTIONS OF OUACHITA PROVINCE

### Arkansas Valley Section

The Arkansas Valley section is an east-west strip 25 to 35 miles wide that extends from eastern Oklahoma to the Coastal Plain in Arkansas (Croneis, 1930). Much of it is lowland not more than 300 to 600 feet above sea level, but many ridges rise conspicuously above their surroundings. Magazine Mountain, altitude 2823 feet, has a height of more than 2000 feet.

Rocks in the Arkansas Valley section, with the exception of a few igneous intrusions, are Carboniferous in age and belong mainly to the Atoka, Stanley, and Jackfork groups. The Atoka group of Pennsylvanian age is predominately shales but there are thin sandstones in it. The Stanley and Jackfork groups of rocks are most commonly considered to be Mississippian in age, but there is difference of opinion on this point, and the Pennsylvanian-Mississippian contact may lie within one or the other of these groups of rocks. Sandstones of the Jackfork group are by far the most common ridge makers in the Arkansas Valley. Rocks of the Stanley group, although very thick and widespread, are dominantly shales and therefore are inconspicuous topographically.

The Arkansas Valley is a trough both topographically and structurally. It is transitional between the essentially homoclinal structure of the south flank of the Boston Mountains to the north and the complexly folded and faulted strata of Ouachita Mountains at the south. Intensity of folding increases from the Ozark plateau toward the Ouachita Mountains. In the Salem

and Springfield plateaus the folds are short and most of them are too small to be reflected in the topography; faults are present here, but they usually lack significant topographic expression. In the southern part of the Boston Mountains folding and faulting become more recognizable, and the folds and faults begin to have an east-west trend. Closed folding with an east-west trend characterizes the Arkansas Valley. At the south side of the Arkansas Valley thrust faulting, the most conspicuous structural attribute of the Ouachita Mountains, makes its appearance.

Croneis (1930) described 76 anticlines, 62 synclines, and 19 faults in the Arkansas Valley. In general, the synclines are larger than the anticlines, and some are as much as 50 to 75 miles long, although lengths of less than 20 miles are far more common. The folded structure is most evident topographically in the southern part of the Arkansas Valley, where steep anticlinal ridges and broad, flat-topped synclinal mountains are conspicuously present. The structures and associated ridges commonly overlap one another en echelon. Many of the synclinal ridges are broad and flat-surfaced enough to resemble mesas in appearance. Most of them are capped with sandstones of the Jackfork group.

As in the folded Appalachians, all gradations from anticlinal and synclinal ridges, in areas of fairly steeply dipping rocks, to homoclinal ridges and even cuesta-like topography, in areas of less steeply dipping rocks, may be seen. This latter type of topography resembles the aligned cuestas of the Osage Plains section of the Central Lowlands province (see p. 210), but the alignment is in an east-west direction in contrast to the north-south alignment in the Osage Plains section.

### Ouachita Mountains Section

The Ouachita Mountains section lies between the Coastal Plain and the Arkansas Valley; it averages 50 to 60 miles in width and is better than 200 miles long, extending from near Atoka, Oklahoma, to the Coastal Plain near Little Rock, Arkansas. As a result of its anticlinorial structure rocks of pre-Carboniferous age are exposed

FIG. 15.3    Exposure of Arkansas novaculite in ridge near Atoka, Oklahoma.    (*Photo by B. H. Harlton.*)

in the Ouachita Mountains. Rocks here range in age from Ordovician (possibly Cambrian) to Pennsylvanian; they are predominantly shales and sandstones, but unique to this section is the Arkansas novaculite of Mississippian-Devonian age. This formation consists of novaculite, chert, siliceous shale, clay, and, in Arkansas, some sandstone (see Fig. 15.3). In the central portion of the Ouachita Mountains section it is a common ridge maker, second only to the Jackfork sandstone.

Ridge crest altitudes, although as low as 500 or 600 feet at the east and 700 or 800 feet at the west, attain altitudes as great as 2600 feet near the Oklahoma-Arkansas boundary. The relief between intermontane valleys and basins and ridge tops may be as great as 1500 feet. Many

descriptions of this section emphasize accordance of ridge summits, but this is true only in a very general way. The east-west trend of major topographic features, so evident in the Arkansas Valley, persists in the Ouachita Mountains, although there are numerous local departures from it.

The Ouachita Mountains display a maximum intensity of folding and faulting (Fig. 15.4). Closed folds, overturned folds, and thrust faults constitute the secondary structures of the anticlinorium. Thus structure and topography here duplicate to a considerable degree that found in the Ridge and Valley province of the Appalachians. One notable difference is the scarcity of limestone in the Ouachitas. Thus the limestone valleys of the Ridge and Valley province and their associated karst features have no counterparts in this area, where valleys are largely on shales.

*Subdivisions of Ouachita Mountains Section.* The Ouachita Mountains section has been divided into three districts or subsections (Fenneman, 1938). These are the Fourche-Kiamichi belt at the north, the Novaculite Uplift at the center, and the Athens Piedmont Plateau at the south.

FOURCHE-KIAMICHI BELT. This is a mountainous belt some 25 miles wide extending from eastern Oklahoma to the Coastal Plain near Little Rock. It takes its name from the Fourche Range in Arkansas and the Kiamichi Range in Oklahoma. The rocks here are all Carboniferous in age and belong to the Atoka, Jackfork, and Stanley groups. The Jackfork sandstones are the major ridge makers; all of the higher ridges are developed on these sandstones, but some of the lower ridges are on sandstones in the Atoka and Stanley groups. Most of the ridges display parallel arrangement, but not all.

Maximum ridge altitudes are nearly as great as at Magazine Mountain in the Arkansas Valley, and many of the ridges exceed 2500 feet in altitude. Highest altitudes and greatest relief are found west of the Arkansas-Oklahoma boundary and decrease to both the east and west from here. Where ridges are highest, the local relief may be as great as 1000 to 1100 feet, making this area one of rugged topography.

FIG. 15.4 Sigmoidal fold in Black Knob Ridge, northeast of Atoka, Oklahoma. Right-hand ridge is Ordovician Big Fork chert; left-hand ridge is Devonian-Mississippian Arkansas novaculite. (*Photo courtesy Mobil Oil Company.*)

NOVACULITE UPLIFT. The Novaculite Uplift, so called because of the abundance here of ridges formed on the Arkansas novaculite, consists of a series of mountains and basins extending from a few miles southwest of Little Rock, Arkansas, to near Glover, Oklahoma (Croneis, 1930). Uplift was greatest in this part of the Ouachita province, and as a consequence the exposed rocks are largely pre-Carboniferous in age. Over most of the area the youngest formation exposed is the Arkansas novaculite; the other rocks range upward in age to Ordovician. About the only ridges of importance that are not formed by the Arkansas novaculite are those developed on the Ordovician Crystal Mountain sandstone, of early Ordovician age, and locally in the Hot Springs area by the Hot Springs sandstone, of Mississippian age, which here lies unconformably above the novaculite.

Closed folding leads to repetition of formations and associated ridges. Particularly on the north side of the uplift are the mountains of highly complex structure. Maximum altitudes, which range from 1500 to 2000 feet, are found near the western part of the uplift. Numerous synclines, which are also topographic basins, separate the anticlinal mountain tracts. The main mountain groups are the Caddo, Crystal, Cossatot, Trap, Zigzag and Cross Mountains. Four major basins, the Caddo, Mazarn, Ouachita, and Saline, separate the mountains. The largest of these basins, the Mazarn Basin, is a syncline bounded on the north by the Zigzag and Caddo Mountains and on the south by the Cossatot and Trap Mountains. Its greatest length is about 60 miles and its maximum width is about 10 miles. Its basin floor is by no means smooth, as it has undergone marked dissection, and many low, parallel sandstone ridges and intervening valleys extend in a northeast-southwest direction across the basin. Most of the Mazarn Basin is underlain by the Stanley shale and has altitudes of only 500 or 600 feet.

ATHENS PIEDMONT PLATEAU. Lying between the Novaculite Uplift and the Coastal Plain is a belt 8 to 18 miles wide underlain by rocks of the Stanley and Jackfork groups. Closed folding, overturned folds, and thrust faults similar to those in the Ouachita Uplift characterize this area; the difference is that there are no mountains here. However, the Athens Piedmont Plateau is by no means flat; the area is well dissected, and innumerable east-west-trending ridges a few hundred feet high add to its relief. The complexly folded structure has produced repetition of ridges and valleys and a trellis drainage pattern.

Here of all the Ouachita province accordance of ridge crests most suggests previous baseleveling. In many respects this area resembles the Piedmont Plateau of the Appalachian region. Elevations of the old erosion surface decrease from about 1100 feet at the north to around 400 feet at the southeast.

## GEOMORPHIC HISTORY OF OUACHITA PROVINCE

Very limited study of the erosional history of the Ouachita province has been made, and such interpretations as have been proposed are essentially an Appalachian geomorphic history as interpreted 40 or 50 years ago. Purdue and Miser (1923) in their description of the Hot Springs district stated that field evidence supported a theory of two peneplains, an older Ouachita peneplain and a younger Hot Springs peneplain. Later, Miser and Purdue (1929), in their description of the topography of the De Queen and Caddo Cap quadrangles, restated this idea. They dated the Ouachita peneplain as of early Cretaceous age and thought that summits of the higher ridges in the Ouachita Mountains represented this surface, which slopes at the rate of 80 to over 100 feet per mile southward and passes beneath the early Cretaceous sediments of the Coastal Plain. Cretaceous sediments were presumed to have extended much farther to the north than at present, and the existing drainage presumably represents superposition across the regional structures from the Cretaceous cover mass. The Hot Springs peneplain was believed by Miser and Purdue to have begun its evolution during an erosion cycle inaugurated by uplift near the close of late Cretaceous time. Its age was considered to be early

Tertiary, probably Eocene, because Eocene beds were believed to rest on it locally.

Figure 15.5 shows the presumed relationship of the Ouachita and Hot Springs erosion surfaces, and it will be noted that they exhibit the same morvan relationship that was thought by Renner (1927) to exist between the Fall Zone and Harrisburg peneplains in the Appalachian area. The same arguments were used in support of the existence of this relationship in the Ouachita area that were used by Renner in the Piedmont region (see p. 92). Projection of the surface beneath the coastal plain sediments across the Ouachita Ridges on the basis of a suggested accordance of ridge summits is very questionable and may rightly be viewed with considerable skepticism.

Present-day thinking would cast doubt on the erosion surfaces, if such they are, being as old as thought by Miser and Purdue, and would more likely interpret them both as of Tertiary age. There is naturally an inclination to assume that the Ouachita erosion surface would correlate with that represented by the summits of the Boston Mountains and the Hot Springs surface with the main erosion surface of the Ozarks, the Ozark peneplain. If this is true, the Hot Springs cycle did not reach so advanced a stage of development as did the Ozark cycle to the north. This difference may be attributable to the difference in the geologic structures and rock types in the two areas.

There are grounds for recognition of a later subcycle of erosion than the Hot Springs cycle, as represented by local lowland tracts in the Arkansas Valley and in such basins in the Novaculite Uplift as the Mazarn and Saline.

All in all the grounds for recognition of former peneplains in the Ouachita province, unless it be in the Athens Piedmont Plateau, are hardly so convincing as in the Ozark Plateaus. This may, however, amount to saying that the near horizontality of rocks in the Ozarks has produced a type of topography which suggests former erosion surfaces, whereas in the complexly folded and faulted Ouachita area the geologic structure does not favor the occurrence of extensive areas at nearly accordant levels.

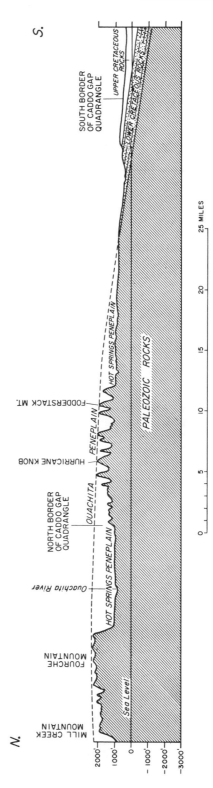

FIG. 15.5  Topographic profile showing inferred relationship of Ouachita and Hot Springs erosion surfaces in Caddo Gap, Arkansas, area.  (*After H. D. Miser and A. H. Purdue, U. S. Geol. Survey Bull. 808.*)

# REFERENCES CITED

Croneis, Carey (1930). Geology of the Arkansas Paleozoic area, *Ark. State Geol. Surv. Bull.* 3, 457 pp.

Dake, C. L. (1921). The problem of the St. Peter sandstone, *Missouri Univ. School Mines and Metallurgy Bull. Tech. Ser.*, **6**, 1–225.

Fenneman, N. M. (1938). *Physiography of Eastern United States*, McGraw-Hill Book Company, 714 pp.

Flawn, P. T. (1959). The Ouachita structural belt, in *The Geology of the Ouachita Mountains, A Symposium*, Dallas Geol. Soc.-Ardmore Geol. Soc., 20–29.

Harlton, B. H. (1953). Ouachita chert facies, southeastern Oklahoma, *Am. Assoc. Petroleum Geologists Bull.*, **37**, 778–796.

Hendricks, T. A. (1958). Interpretation of Ouachita Mountains of Oklahoma as autochthonous folded belt; preliminary report, discussion by T. A. Hendricks, *Am. Assoc. Petroleum Geologists Bull.*, **42**, 2757–2765.

—— (1959). Structure of the frontal belt of the Ouachita Mountains, in *The Geology of the Ouachita Mountains, A Symposium*, Dallas Geol. Soc.-Ardmore Geol. Soc., 44–56.

Honess, C. W. (1923). Geology of the Southern Ouachita Mountains in Oklahoma. *Okla. Geol. Surv. Bull.* 32, 263–278.

King, P. B. (1959). *The Evolution of North America*, Princeton Univ. Press, Princeton, 190 pp.

Misch, Peter, and K. F. Oles (1957). Interpretation of Ouachita Mountains of Oklahoma as autochthonous folded belt: preliminary report, *Am. Assoc. Petroleum Geologists Bull.*, **41**, 1899–1905.

Miser, H. D. (1929). Structure of the Ouachita Mountains of Oklahoma and Arkansas, *Okla. Geol. Surv. Bull.* 50, 30 pp.

—— (1934). Carboniferous rocks of Ouachita Mountains, *Am. Assoc. Petroleum Geologists Bull.*, **18**, 971–1009.

—— and A. H. Purdue (1929). Geology of the Dequeen and Caddo Gap quadrangles, Arkansas, *U. S. Geol. Survey Bull.* 808, 195 pp.

Pitt, W. D. (1955). Geology of the core of the Ouachita Mountains of Oklahoma, *Okla. Geol. Surv. Circular* 34, 34 pp.

Purdue, A. H., and H. D. Miser (1923). Description of the Hot Springs district, *U. S. Geol. Survey Folio* 215, 9.

Renner, G. T. (1927). The physiographic interpretation of the Fall Line, *Geog. Rev.*, **17**, 276–286.

Taff, J. A. (1902). Description of the Atoka quadrangle, *U. S. Geol. Survey Folio* 79, 7.

## ADDITIONAL REFERENCES

Croneis, C. G., and M. P. Billings (1930). Igneous rocks in central Arkansas, *Ark. Geol. Surv. Bull.* 3, 149–162.

Flawn, Peter, August Goldstein, Jr., P. B. King, and C. E. Weaver (1961). The Ouachita system, *Bureau Econ. Geol., Univ. Texas, Pub.* 6120, 401 pp.

Huffman, G. G. (1953). Guidebook for field conference on pre-Atoka rocks, *Okla. Geol. Surv. Guidebook* 1, 41 pp.

Merritt, C. A. (1958). Igneous rocks of the Lake Altus area, Oklahoma, *Okla. Geol. Surv. Bull.* 76, 70 pp.

# 16

# Great Plains Province

## GENERAL DESCRIPTION

The Great Plains extend without interruption from the Pecos and Rio Grande rivers on the south to the latitude of Great Bear Lake in Canada. As a whole the province may be described as plateau-like, although local mountainous uplifts as well as lowland areas are included in it. In the public mind the Great Plains are thought of as a vast monotonous plain that lacks scenic interest but has to be crossed in order to reach the scenic Rocky Mountains to the west. This picture may apply to part of the Great Plains, particularly the High Plains, but it is by no means applicable to all of the province. Within the province is much interesting topography, and even the flat and scenically poor High Plains provide numerous interesting problems relating to their geologic and geomorphic histories.

## BOUNDARIES

The western boundary of the Great Plains province is distinct enough, for the Rocky Mountain front at the west is conspicuous throughout most of its length. Only where the High Plains abut against the Wyoming Basin province is there no sharp western boundary. In the northern Great Plains, however, numerous outliers of Rocky Mountain geology and geomorphology are detached from the mountain mass and must be included in the Great Plains province, even though geologically and topographically they belong more with the Rocky Mountains.

Along a considerable part of the eastern boundary there is a perceptible rise or scarp that marks the eastern edge of the Great Plains. This is particularly true at the north and south, but across Nebraska the eastern boundary must be drawn somewhat arbitrarily. The rise at the north which marks the eastern edge of the Great Plains is known as the Missouri Escarpment. It is the eastern edge of what is called the Coteau du Missouri, the crest of which is the Altamont moraine. At the south, the Balcones Escarpment provides a sharp boundary between the Great Plains and the adjacent Coastal Plain to the east. Through a considerable part of Kansas the eastern margin of the Great Plains is deeply eroded, and some difference of opinion exists as to which of several cuesta scarps would best serve as the boundary for the province.

## GEOLOGY OF PROVINCE

Geologically the Great Plains differ notably from the Central Lowlands to the east of them despite the fact that the topographic boundary cuts across geologic boundaries. The rocks of the Great Plains province are mainly Mesozoic or Cenozoic in age, whereas the rocks of the Central Lowlands are mainly Paleozoic. At the south the boundary between these two provinces is essentially between Paleozoic and younger rocks, but at the north this is not true, for here rocks of Cretaceous age underlie the Central Lowlands, and in the Turtle Mountains along the Canadian boundary there are small outliers of Tertiary rocks in the Central Lowlands.

Rocks of Cretaceous age underlie much of the

Great Plains province, although in many areas they are veneered with Tertiary rocks. In certain places, however, the Tertiary cover has been removed by erosion and Cretaceous beds form the surface geology. In the Pecos Lowland and Plains Border sections, rocks as old as Permian constitute the underlying bedrock. The Tertiary formations range in age from Paleocene to Pliocene. Most common among them are the Ft. Union (Paleocene), Wasatch (Eocene), White River, Chadron, and Brule (Oligocene), Arikaree (Miocene), and Ogallala (Pliocene) formations. Pleistocene deposits are locally important; they include glacial till at the north and local deposits of silt, clay, loess, volcanic ash, dune sand, and fluviatile gravels elsewhere.

## STRUCTURE

Structurally the Great Plains province is a broad geosynclinal area whose axis lies somewhat west of a line running north-south through the middle of the province. The Tectonic Map of the United States shows that actually the structure is that of a number of basins separated by uplifts or arches. Three major basins are the Williston Basin at the north, the Denver Basin in the west-central part, and the Midland Basin at the south. Lesser basins are the Powder River, between the Bighorn Mountains and the Black Hills, and Raton and Delaware basins at the south. Major uplifts, from north to south, are the Bowdoin dome in northern Montana, the Black Hills uplift, the Chadron arch which connects with the Central Kansan uplift, the Amarillo, and the Llano uplifts in Texas. Two of these, the Black Hills and the Llano uplifts, bring Precambrian rocks to the surface.

### Regional Topography

The surface of the Great Plains descends from altitudes of 5000 or 6000 feet at the west to an average altitude of about 1500 feet on the east; the regional slope to the east averages about 10 feet per mile. Although flatness and monotony of topography characterize many thousands of square miles of the Great Plains, areas do exist where the relief is considerable. These

are: (1) deeply dissected tracts adjacent to major entrenched streams, (2) areas along cuesta scarps, particularly at the eastern margin of the Great Plains, (3) badland tracts, (4) structurally high areas such as the Black Hills, the Llano uplift, and the numerous mountain tracts associated with Tertiary intrusives. Moderate to slight relief is to be found in (1) the Sand Hills of Nebraska and other dunal tracts, (2) the glacial moraines in the northern and northeastern part of the province, (3) some of the deeper depressions on the plains surface, and (4) along some stream terraces.

## GEOMORPHIC HISTORY

The Great Plains have been above sea level since the close of the Cretaceous. However, their early Tertiary geomorphic history is somewhat obscure. Most of the landscape features seen today are Pliocene or younger. About the only record left of early Tertiary events is to be found in the Tertiary formations of the region. These are all continental deposits, and presumably they represent the depositional phases of several erosion cycles that may or may not have reached advanced stages. The terrestrial deposits on the plains mainly represent materials that were removed from the Rocky Mountain region to the west. The one event that can be rather accurately established is a period of Pliocene erosion and deposition that resulted in reduction of the Rocky Mountains to a region of moderate relief with local residual mountain masses left standing above the baselevel of erosion. It was during this period of erosion that the great apron of alluvium that became the Ogallala formation was spread over the plains. We still have preserved in the Great Plains and Rocky Mountains much of this compound geomorphic surface, consisting of erosional topography in the mountains and depositional topography on the Great Plains. These two surfaces join in eastern Wyoming through what is called The Gangplank (see Fig. 16.1). Here it is possible to go without interruption from the alluvial deposits of the Great Plains onto the granite of the so-called Sherman peneplain of Wyoming.

FIG. 16.1    The Gangplank between Cheyenne and Laramie, Wyoming.    Tertiary alluvial deposits form the foreground and granite of the Sherman peneplain is exposed in the background.    (*Photo by H. S. Palmer.*)

The topographic surface which developed in the Rocky Mountains during this extended erosion period is variously called the Rocky Mountain, Sherman, Subsummit, South Park, and Green Ridge peneplain.

Uplift followed this period of peneplanation (or pediplanation, as some consider it today) and a number of subcycles followed during which local straths developed along major streams. Intermittent baseleveling and uplift are marked by pediments and alluvial terraces along the stream valleys that extend from the mountains onto the plains.

The oldest known glacial deposits in the Great Plains are believed to be of Kansan age, but the striking glacial elements of Great Plains topography were produced by the Wisconsin glaciation. In the northern part of the Great Plains, near the mountain front in Montana, there was an interaction of mountain and continental glaciers that resulted in a complex relationship between deposits of the two types of glaciers (Horberg, 1954). South of the area covered by ice the effects of glaciation are represented by the lacustrine plains of ice marginal lakes, loess deposits, glacial outwash terraces, dunes derived from glacial outwash, and drainage modifications.

## SECTIONS AND MAJOR CHARACTERISTICS

Local differences in geology, geomorphic history, and resultant land forms make possible subdivision of the Great Plains province into ten sections. These ten sections with their outstanding characteristics are:

1. Glaciated Missouri Plateau section. This is that part of the Great Plains whose topography bears a strong imprint of glaciation. The section contains a few mountains that are outliers of Rocky Mountain geology.
2. Unglaciated Missouri Plateau section. This section is the northernmost part of the unglaciated Great Plains. It consists of plateaus whose Tertiary cover has been largely removed. Badland topography is conspicuous locally. Numerous mountain outliers of Rocky Mountain geology add diversity to the section.
3. Black Hills section. The Black Hills are a maturely dissected domal uplift with an exposed core of Precambrian rocks; encircling hogbacks and enclosed strike valleys rim the section.
4. High Plains section. In this section the

Tertiary and Pleistocene mantle is well preserved and covers the greater part of the land. Most of the land surface is essentially of depositional origin.

5. Edwards Plateau. This section is the southern end of the High Plains and differs from the High Plains section in that the Tertiary alluvial veneer has been removed.

6. Colorado Piedmont section. This section lies adjacent to the Colorado Rockies. Its Tertiary alluvial cover has been removed, causing it to stand lower than the adjacent High Plains section to the east.

7. Raton section. High lava-capped mesas, buttes, and other volcanic features characterize this section.

8. Pecos Valley section. The Pecos Valley section is a lowland lying between the High Plains section to the east and the easternmost of the mountain ranges of the Basin and Range province. Karst features and gravel capped terraces are widespread.

9. Central Texas section. Here a deeply eroded domal uplift exposes Precambrian rocks, and the topographic effects of faulting are conspicuous.

10. Plains Border section. This is a deeply dissected part of the Great Plains whose former alluvial cover has been removed with ensuing development of a series of cuestas.

## Missouri Plateau

*Boundaries.* Although the Missouri Plateau has been divided into glaciated and unglaciated sections, it seems logical to combine them for purpose of discussion. The Missouri Plateau includes, except for the Black Hills, roughly that part of the Great Plains north of the northern boundary of Nebraska. The north-facing Pine Ridge Escarpment separates the Missouri Plateau from the High Plains section to the south. This southward-receding escarpment, which is capped with the Arikaree formation and underlain by the weak Brule shale, is a prominent topographic feature (see Fig. 16.2) which locally attains heights of 1000 feet.

The eastern boundary of the Missouri Plateau is the Missouri Escarpment. This escarpment represents a rise of 500 to 600 feet from the level of the Central Lowlands to the surface of the Missouri Plateau. The origin of this escarpment is uncertain; it apparently is not the product of a particular resistant formation; more likely it marks the boundary between two topographic levels of erosion in the Central Lowlands and the Great Plains.

*Coteau du Missouri.* The area back of the Missouri Escarpment and extending westward to the trench of the Missouri River is generally called the Coteau du Missouri. However, some variation exists in the use of this term. Howard (1960) pointed out that the name "Coteau du Missouri" has been applied not only to the part of the Missouri Plateau between the Missouri River and the Missouri Escarpment but also to the glacial ridges atop this part of the Missouri Plateau. He called attention to the fact that early French settlers in this area spoke of "Les Coteaux du Plateau" or in anglicized form, "the Coteaus of the Missouri Plateau." Since the word *coteau* means "a sharp ridge," it may well be that originally the term was applied to the ridges atop the eastern part of the Missouri Plateau. The word seems to have undergone a change in meaning, however, and is now mainly used to designate the part of the Missouri Plateau where the "coteaux," which are mainly end moraines, characterize the plateau surface.

The Missouri River trench separates the Coteau du Missouri on the east from the main part of the Missouri Plateau and in so doing separates two distinctly different types of topography. The topography east of the trench is glacial in nature, whereas that west of the Missouri River Trench shows little or no effects of glaciation. Deep dissection of the plateau is much more evident west of the trench than east of it. These differences are understood when it is recognized that the Missouri trench represents a relatively new route of the Missouri River established as a result of glacial diversion.

The term "trench" very properly describes that part of the valley of the Missouri River across North Dakota and South Dakota, because

FIG. 16.2   Signal Butte, western Nebraska, a part of the Pine Ridge Escarpment.   (*Photo by John C. Frye.*)

along most of its length it is a deep and narrow cut in the Missouri Plateau. The floor of the trench rarely exceeds a mile in width, except where it coincides with segments of preglacial drainage lines (Flint, 1955).

GLACIAL FEATURES ON COTEAU DU MISSOURI. The relief on the surface of the Coteau du Missouri is mainly of glacial origin. The bedrock is largely the Cretaceous Pierre shale, but Tertiary formations are found locally. Over much of the area, however, the bedrock is veneered with glacial drift. Ground moraine with swell and swale topography is characteristic, but morainal topography, and numerous southwest-sloping abandoned glacial drainage channels also exist. Total relief between the bottoms of the linear swales and the crests of the moraines may amount to several hundred feet.

What are known as the Altamont and Gary end moraines in Iowa and South Dakota here form a morainic belt 6 to 10 miles wide. The outer moraine is the Altamont, for the ice which deposited the Gary moraine barely overtopped the Missouri escarpment. The name Max

moraine has been given to the northern extension of what has long been called the Altamont moraine. Townsend and Jenke (1951) applied this name to the part of the moraine which extends northwest from Bismarck, North Dakota, for some 800 miles. Their reason for not continuing use of the name Altamont is that what was originally called the Altamont moraine ends 200 miles southeast of the southern end of the Max moraine. They recognized that the two moraines may be equivalent in age, but, because they are discontinuous topographically, it seemed appropriate to give them separate names. The crest of the Max moraine rises 200 to 500 feet above its surroundings and is the divide between drainage to Hudson Bay and that to the Gulf of Mexico. It seems likely that at least part of its height is attributable to high bedrock topography beneath it.

*Erosional History.* The preglacial history of the Missouri Plateau was one of long-continued erosion punctuated by occasional uplifts. Willis (1902) first recognized in the Lewis Front Range

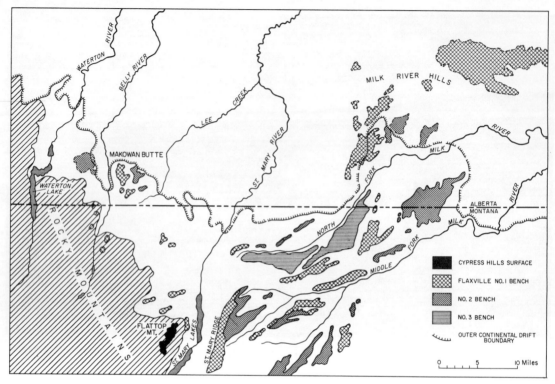

FIG. 16.3    Preserved areas of Tertiary and Quaternary erosion surfaces.    (*After Leland Horberg, Geol. Soc. Am. Bull.*, **65.**)

of the Rocky Mountains and adjacent plains region of Montana the remnants of an erosion surface which he called the Blackfoot peneplain. Later, Alden (1932) gave the name Cypress Plain to an apparently equivalent erosion surface in the Cypress Hills, a short distance across the international boundary line in the province of Alberta. The Cypress Hills are capped with Oligocene gravels which Collier and Thom (1918) considered equivalent in age to the White River beds of the Missouri Plateau. These gravels are mainly yellowish to ash-gray in color, and associated with them are sands, clays, beds of marl, and volcanic ash. The pebbles are largely quartzite and argillite derived from Precambrian rocks in the Rocky Mountain area and are relatively noncemented. The Cypress Plain presumably headed at levels now high in the Rocky Mountains, and probably this peneplain (or pediplain) corresponds in age to such erosional surfaces as the Subsummit surface in the Bear-

tooth and Bighorn Mountains (see page 379). It was considered to be no younger than Miocene.

Intermittent uplift of the Great Plains following development of the Cypress Plain is evidenced by several gravel-capped surfaces or "benches" below the level of the Cypress Plain (see Fig. 16.3). The first bench below the Cypress Plain is a terrace named the Flaxville Plain or Number 1 Bench by Collier and Thom (1918), from the town of Flaxville near the northeastern corner of Montana. The Flaxville surface lies from 300 to 600 feet above the general level of the Missouri Plateau and bevels both Mesozoic and Tertiary strata. Fossils from the Flaxville gravels cannot be dated accurately but a late Miocene to lower Pliocene age seems likely. However, remains of what was interpreted as a Pleistocene camel makes it necessary to entertain the possibility of an early Pleistocene age. Glacial drift lies on the Flaxville Plain at several places (see p. 293) and if its age is Kansan, as thought by Horberg (1956), the Flaxville Plain or Number 1 Bench can be no younger than early Pleistocene. Below the Flaxville Plain or Number 1 Bench are two other terraces, the Number 2 and Number 3 Benches. These terraces are both considered to be Pleistocene in age.

Alden (1932) suggested the following chronology for erosion surfaces in the northern Great Plains:

| | |
|---|---|
| Cypress Hills Plain | Oligocene |
| Flaxville Plain or No. 1 Bench | Pliocene |
| Number 2 Bench | Early Pleistocene (probably pre-Kansan) |
| Number 3 Bench | Late Pleistocene |

It should be emphasized that these "benches" are not wholly erosional features, for each of them is capped with a veneer of gravel, which on the Flaxville Plain or Number 1 Bench is as much as 100 feet thick. Such extensive gravel caps on erosional surfaces that truncate the geological formations make it reasonable to consider them pediments rather than straths.

Howard (1960), from work in northeastern Montana and northwestern North Dakota, arrived at conclusions somewhat similar to those of Alden and of Collier and Thom. He believed that the surface of the Missouri Plateau represents an erosion surface which he called the Missouri Plateau peneplain. He considered the Missouri Plateau peneplain to be of Pleistocene age and correlative with Alden's Number 2 Bench. Howard thought, however, that the Flaxville surface hardly merited being called a peneplain; distribution of the Flaxville gravels suggested to him that they were confined to broad valleys, and thus the Flaxville surface seemed to him better described as a strath. Howard agreed that the Cypress Hills surface is older than the Flaxville Plain.

One perplexing difference between the Missouri Plateau and the High Plains section to the south of it is the absence in the Missouri Plateau of evidence of regional aggradation later than White River (Oligocene) time, whereas in the High Plains aggradation continued into the Pliocene with the laying down of the great sheet of Ogallala sediments. The absence of the Ogallala type of sediments in the Missouri Plateau has usually been attributed to removal by erosion. Howard raised the question as to whether or not they were ever present. It is perhaps more difficult to explain why they were never deposited here than it is to explain why they have been completely removed by erosion at the north but not in the High Plains.

*Effects of Glaciation.* The glacial boundary across the Missouri Plateau in South Dakota and North Dakota is clearly marked by the Altamont moraine and its northern equivalent, the Max moraine. West of where the Max moraine leaves the United States, near the northwest corner of North Dakota, the glacial boundary becomes more complex. East of Glacier National Park mountain glaciers extended onto the Great Plains and came in contact with a westward extension of continental Keewatin ice. The result was an intermixing of mountain and continental drifts (Horberg, 1954). The age of the outermost Wisconsin drift is uncertain, but it probably is either Iowan or Tazewell. Its outer margin follows in a general way the course of the Missouri River. The most conspicuously glacial topography, however, is found in the area of the younger Cary drift.

A pre-Wisconsin glaciation is represented by the Kennedy drift. This drift is exposed in the area immediately east of the Rocky Mountain Front north from Two Medicine Creek into Canada (see Fig. 16.4). This drift was first recognized by Willis (1902), who called it the Kennedy gravels; he interpreted them as fluvial deposits, but Alden (1932) later recognized their true glacial nature. The Kennedy drift is found at numerous places on the Flaxville bench, 600 to 1600 feet above present drainage, and in a few places on the Number 2 Bench, about 500 feet above present drainage (Horberg, 1956). The drift is as much as 250 feet thick and has developed on it a remarkably deep weathering profile. An exposure on Two Medicine Ridge, Glacier Park, Montana, shows a complex B-horizon 19

FIG. 16.4    Exposure of Kennedy drift in Kennedy Ridge, 5 miles east of Chief Mountain, Montana.    (*Photo by Bailey Willis, courtesy U. S. Geol. Survey.*)

feet thick, leaching to a depth of 53 feet, and a calcium carbonate indurated horizon 93 feet thick. Horberg thought that most likely the drift was Kansan in age.

The southwestward advance of the Keewatin ice sheet into northern Montana resulted in the damming of the northeastward-flowing streams and the formation of numerous ice-marginal lakes (see Fig. 16.5). Among the more extensive of these lakes were Cutbank Glacial Lake, formed by the damming of Cutbank Creek and its tributaries, and Great Falls Glacial Lake, formed by the damming of the Sun and Missouri Rivers.

*Badland Topography.* The part of the Missouri Plateau south of the Missouri River and north of the Pine Ridge Escarpment is distinguished from the High Plains section by lack of a cover of late Tertiary alluvium and by deeper dissection. Badland topography is not uncommon in this section, and two areas in particular stand out.

One is the White River tract, east of the Black Hills, between the Cheyenne and White Rivers; the other is along the Little Missouri River in southwestern North Dakota (see Fig. 16.6).

*Rocky Mountain Outliers.* Numerous isolated mountain uplifts rise above the level of the Missouri Plateau, particularly in west-central Montana. The Black Hills of southwestern South Dakota are extensive enough to merit recognition as a separate section but the others are too small to be thus set apart and must be treated as outliers of Rocky Mountain geology in the Great Plains. These mountain uplifts fall into two classes, those that are domal or anticlinal uplifts and are primarily diastrophic in origin, and those that are primarily the results of either extrusive or intrusive igneous activity.

The domal or anticlinal uplifts are products of the Laramide orogeny. In each is exposed a central core of Precambrian igneous or metamorphic rock surrounded by upturned Paleozoic and Mesozoic sediments which have topographic expression as encircling, or partially encircling, hogbacks, homoclinal ridges, and valleys. Most typical of this group is the Black Hills uplift. Others are the Big Belt, Little Belt, Little Rockies, and Big Snowy Mountains.

Mountains of the second group are primarily the products of mid-Tertiary intrusive and extrusive activity. Many were classed formerly as laccolithic mountains, but most of the so-called laccoliths are really small stocks; if laccoliths are present, they are very subordinate features. Intrusive sheets and dikes are present in varying degrees, and extrusive igneous rocks are found in some of the mountains. Included in this group are the Highwood, Judith, Crazy, Bearpaw, and Castle Mountains and the Sweetgrass Hills. The Crazy Mountains are especially noted for a system of radial dikes that rivals those of the Spanish Peaks area in number and extent.

*History of Upper Missouri River.* The evolution of the middle and lower segments of the Missouri River has already been discussed (see p. 248). The upper Missouri River is essentially that part of Missouri River drainage above the junction of the present Missouri and Yellowstone

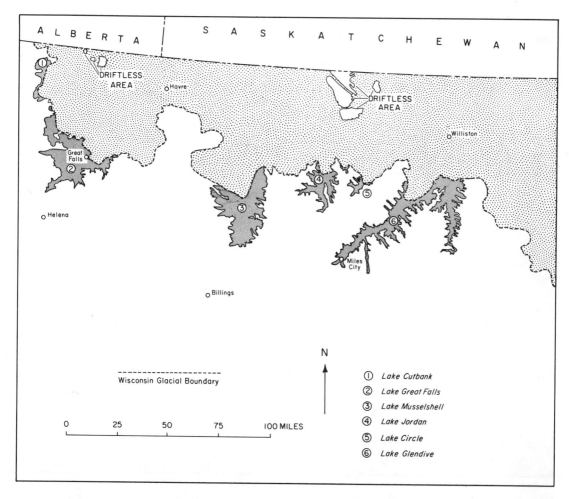

FIG. 16.5 Sites of Wisconsin ice-marginal lakes in eastern Montana and western North Dakota. (*After Glacial Map of United States East of Rocky Mountains, Geol. Soc. Am.*)

rivers. Todd (1914) expressed a belief that the preglacial upper Missouri River drained to Hudson Bay, and this view has been shared by most geologists who have worked on Missouri Valley history, but Leonard (1916) doubted this and thought rather that the river drained southeastward across North Dakota as it does today.

Detailed study of the bedrock topography of a part of southeastern Saskatchewan (Meneley, Christiansen, and Kupsch, 1957) apparently has established the position of the buried Missouri and Yellowstone Valleys in this region. Their work showed (see Fig. 16.7) that the preglacial Missouri River extended northeastward across Montana and entered Canada in Saskatchewan. It was joined by the Yellowstone River about 15 miles north of the international boundary, and from this junction the Missouri River followed a rather circuitous route eastward into Manitoba. A topographic valley cross-profile made about 20 miles below the junction with the Yellowstone River showed that there the buried valley of the Missouri River is 12 miles wide and is cut 250 feet into the bedrock on which the river once flowed.

As with the segment of the Missouri River through the Dakotas, the time of the diversion of the upper Missouri is uncertain. Howard (1960) believed that the Kansan glaciation was responsible for its diversion to the south. He felt that the southerly route had been established by the time of the cycle of erosion which produced the Flaxville Plain. It is likely that the present route of the upper Missouri River is the cumulative effect of several diversions, some of which may have been as late as Wisconsin time.

FIG. 16.6   Badland topography along Little Missouri River.   (*Photo by John S. Shelton.*)

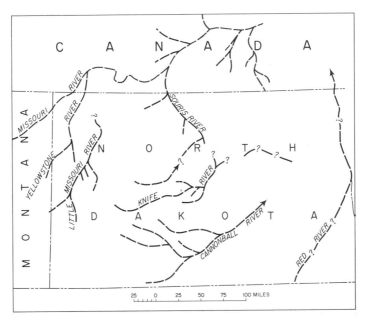

FIG. 16.7   Inferred elements of preglacial drainage courses in North Dakota, Montana, and southern Canada.   (*Compiled by R. B. Colton after Meneley, Christiansen, Kupsch, and others, North Dakota Geol. Survey Miscellaneous Pub. 10.*)

## Black Hills Section

The Black Hills uplift (Darton and Paige, 1925) is elliptical in outline and is approximately 125 miles long and 65 miles wide. The plains surrounding the Black Hills have altitudes of 3000 to 3500 feet, compared with an altitude of 7242 feet for Harney Peak, the highest mountain peak in the Black Hills. Most of the peaks in the central area of the Black Hills have altitudes between 5000 and 6600 feet.

*Geology.* Rocks in the Black Hills range in age from Precambrian to Cretaceous, and around the margins of the uplift are rocks of Tertiary age. The Black Hills lie on an irregularly shaped domal structure that is elongated to the southeast and northwest; dips are steeper on the east than on the west side of the fold. Maximum vertical uplift is of the order of 9000 feet. Faults are not too common, except in areas where igneous intrusions have dislocated beds and elevated them unevenly.

*Topographic Areas.* The Black Hills can be divided into five regions with more or less dis-

tinctive geologic and geomorphic features (see Fig. 16.8). These are, from the center of the uplift outward: (*a*) a central core of granite and metamorphic rocks, (*b*) a limestone plateau that encircles the central core, (*c*) the Red Valley, which nearly encloses the Black Hills but is most strikingly developed on the east side, (*d*) a hogback ridge just outside the Red Valley, and (*e*) a belt of small laccolithic peaks at the north edge of the uplift.

The central core, which lies slightly east of the center of the uplift, consists of a complex of Precambrian granites, schists, and meta-sedimentaries. The Limestone Plateau is underlain mainly by limestones of Paleozoic age, of which the Minnekahta limestone, of probable Permian age, is the uppermost. As a result of the asymmetry of the Black Hills uplift the Limestone Plateau is much wider on the west than it is on the east side of the uplift. On the west it is 15 to 20 miles wide and has the characteristics of a cuesta with an infacing scarp, but on the east, where dips are much steeper, instead of a cuesta it forms a homoclinal ridge.

The Red Valley is one of the most striking

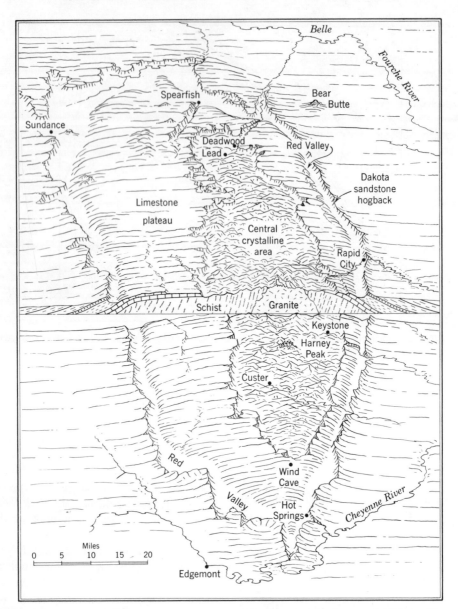

**FIG. 16.8** Diagram of Black Hills showing main topographic regions. (*After A. N. Strahler, Physical Geography, John Wiley and Sons.*)

features of the Black Hills region, because of its bright red soils developed from the Triassic Spearfish formation. This valley encircles the Black Hills but is far more striking on the east side, where it lies between the dip slope of the Minnekahta limestone homoclinal ridge and the prominent Dakota hogback east of it. The Red

Valley averages about 2 miles in width. Major streams cross rather than follow the Red Valley, and it thus appears that its development has been largely by numerous secondary streams that have developed strike valleys along the belt of outcrop of the Spearfish formation.

The Hogback Ridge or Dakota Hogback

forms the outer rim of the Black Hills. It is a true hogback on the east side but becomes a cuesta scarp on the west side, where dips are lower. Streams that emerge from the central Black Hills flow through the Dakota Hogback in narrow watergaps, but present along its crest are numerous wind gaps. These attest to stream piracies that took place as the originally radial drainage underwent change in the foothills belt to a crude annular pattern as subsequent streams worked headward along the Red Valley back of the Dakota Hogback.

Numerous laccolithic peaks at the northern edge of the uplift represent a type of topography different from any other part of the Black Hills. Peaks of this nature are Elkhorn Peak, Crow Peak, Crook Mountain, Citadel Rock, Little Sundance Mountain, and Kirk Hill (Jaggar, 1901). Bear Butte, in this area, is an igneous plug. The laccoliths responsible for the peaks are of Tertiary age.

*Geomorphic History.* Tertiary time in the Black Hills was marked by intermittent uplift. The result was development of a series of straths now represented mainly by terraces along major streams. Fillman (1929) recognized evidence for three partial cycles. These were designated as the Mountain Meadow, Rapid, and Sturgis cycles. The oldest of these, the Mountain Meadow cycle, is marked by a number of park-like tracts in the central Black Hills area. The topography had only reached late maturity when uplift occurred. The Mountain Meadow surface was dated as mid-Oligocene in age on the basis of fossils found in gravels resting upon its surface. The two later subcycles, the Rapid and Sturgis, are represented by gravel-capped terraces, about 100 and 50 feet respectively above the present stream level. They were considered Pleistocene in age.

Plumley (1948), from a study of the terrace gravels in the Black Hills and adjacent plains

FIG. 16.9   High Plains surface in Stanton County, southwestern Kansas.   (*Photo by Ada Swineford, Kan. Geol. Surv.*)

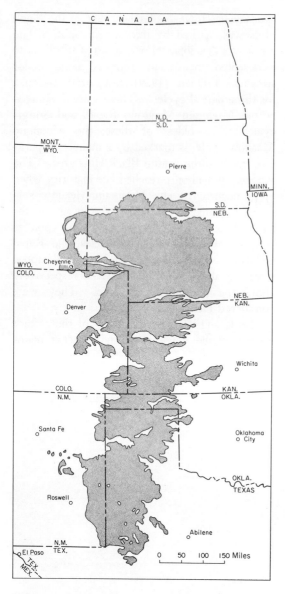

FIG. 16.10   Distribution of late Tertiary deposits over Great Plains. (*After Geologic Map of North America, Geol. Soc. Am.*)

area, concluded that evidence exists for four gravel-capped terraces younger in age than the Mountain Meadow surface. He recognized the Rapid and Sturgis terraces of Fillman, but thought that he saw evidence for two terraces below the Sturgis terrace. The upper of these two terraces he called the Bear Butte terrace and the lower

the Farmingdale terrace. Plumley attributed the terraces along the valleys leading from the Black Hills to Pleistocene changes of stream regimens of the Cheyenne and Missouri Rivers.

## High Plains Section

The High Plains section of the Great Plains stretches from southern South Dakota nearly to the Rio Grande River, in west central Texas. It comes the nearest of any part of the Great Plains province to having the monotonously flat surface which most people associate with the Great Plains (see Fig. 16.9). Even here, however, diversity of topography exists, although of a very low order of magnitude.

*Fluviatile Cover.* Much of the High Plains surface is the remnant of a great Tertiary fluviatile plain that once extended from the Rocky Mountain front to somewhat beyond the present eastern border of the Great Plains. This Tertiary mantle, which is the dominant feature of the High Plains section, consists of a number of formations ranging in age from Paleocene to Pliocene. The more widespread of the Tertiary formations are those mentioned on page 288. The uppermost formation over much of the High Plains is the Pliocene Ogallala formation. The Ogallala extends from the Pecos Valley in Texas northward across Texas, Oklahoma, Kansas, Nebraska, and into South Dakota. It is believed to have the greatest geographic extent of any nonmarine, pre-Pleistocene formation in the United States (Frye and Leonard, 1959). This formation is particularly well preserved in the area in Texas and New Mexico known as the Llano Estacado, or Staked Plains, an area of some 20,000 square miles where the High Plains have endured essentially as they were in late Tertiary time. The Ogallala formation was originally much more extensive than at present. Figure 16.10 shows the present distribution of the formation, but there is good reason to assume that it has been removed from the Pecos Lowland, Edwards Plateau, and probably the dissected part of the Missouri Plateau.

The Ogallala formation consists mainly of

sandy alluvium. Its thickness varies from a few to several hundred feet, depending on the configuration of the surface on which it was deposited. Although alluvial sands predominate, within the Ogallala are beds of gravel, silt, lacustrine clays, and even freshwater limestone.

An idea long held concerning the mode of deposition of the Ogallala sediments was that they represent a series of large coalescent alluvial fans built out from the Rocky Mountain front over a relatively flat surface. The fact that the thickness of the Ogallala formation increases away from the mountain front seems to argue against such an origin. It now appears more likely that the method of accumulation of the Ogallala sediments was one of valley alluviation along a large number of east-west valleys with initial relief of as much as 500 feet (Frye and Leonard, 1959). At first deposition was confined to the valleys but as they were filled deposition began to extend onto intervalley tracts and in time a great coalescent alluvial plain came into existence over which the streams shifted their courses laterally. What the conditions were that terminated this period of wide-scale

alluviation are not clear, but probably they were associated in some way with the climatic changes which accompanied the beginning of the Pleistocene epoch.

*Ogallala Caprock.* Geomorphically the most important part of the Ogallala formation is the upper part, in which are found over extended areas zones of massive carbonate concentration called "caprock." The caprock is from 10 to 30 feet thick and represents a zone of irregular accumulation of caliche. So resistant to erosion is the caprock that it is responsible for the development on both the eastern and western margins of the Llano Estacado of escarpments which go by the name of the Caprock Escarpments (see Fig. 16.11). Going northward from Texas caprock becomes less conspicuous, and it finally disappears in Nebraska. This decrease in the amount of caprock is partially responsible for the lack of a sharp eastern boundary to the High Plains through Kansas and Nebraska.

Elias (1931) believed that the caprock represented the final stage in the Ogallala cycle of sedimentation. He at first attributed it to depo-

FIG. 16.11   Caprock Escarpment at eastern margin of High Plains, Garza County, Texas.   (*Photo by John C. Frye.*)

FIG. 16.12 Caliche in Ogallala formation. (*Photo courtesy Ada Swineford, A. B. Leonard, and John C. Frye.*)

sition in a lake that covered the entire High Plains area, but later (1948) he modified this view and suggested that the caliche was deposited in a number of discontinuous lacustrine basins. He maintained, however, that an understanding of the caprock had been retarded by attempts to explain it as secondary enrichment and hardening of lime.

Bretz and Horberg (1949a) concluded that the caliche of the caprock (see Fig. 16.12) is a natural product of soil forming processes which brought about concentration of calcium carbonate in the B horizon of the soil profile. They believed, however, that the original caliche had undergone alteration as a result of climatic change and that the caliche as seen today displays a degraded or polygenetic profile. Brown (1956) maintained that the caliche is a normal $C^{ca}$ horizon of a pedocal and is the result of the long continued soil processes operating in an eolian aggrading profile.

The induration of the Ogallala caprock in some places has been attributed to algal bioherms and

biostromes in the top of the Ogallala formation. The term "algal limestone" has been applied to the caprock in some areas. Banded and concretionary structures are common in places but difference of opinion exists as to whether they are the result of organic or inorganic processes. Petrographic studies of 34 oriented samples of "algal limestone" from the Ogallala led Swineford, Frye, and Leonard (1958) to conclude that the structures sampled were largely the result of soil-forming processes acting on the sands and silts of the upper Ogallala rather than the product of lime-secreting algae.

*Pleistocene Sediments.*    At one time it was believed that except for glacial deposits and stream alluvium there were no Quaternary deposits on the Great Plains. It is now recognized that Quaternary materials of several sorts are present on the Great Plains surface south of the area of glaciation. Most of these are local in extent and nothing like as extensive as the Tertiary formations. Among the Pleistocene formations are such as the Odee and Kingsdown of southwestern Kansas (Smith, 1940) and the Blanco, Tule, and Tahoka formations of Texas (Evans and Meade, 1945). The Pleistocene formations in general represent accumulations in local basins on the Great Plains and consist of gravels, sands, clays, silts, and freshwater limestones that were regarded formerly as part of the Ogallala formation (see Fig. 16.13). In addition to these there are widely scattered deposits of loess, local beds of volcanic ash, Pleistocene terrace gravels, dune sands, and Recent alluvium.

In numerous areas on the High Plains there are sheets of sand lacking dunal form to which the informal name "cover sands" has been given (Frye and Leonard, 1957). These sands are everywhere found in unconformable contact with the Ogallala, as well as the Blanco and Tule formations. Their origin is not clearly understood, but their occurrence on uplands seems to preclude stream deposition, and their lack of dunal form casts some doubt upon their eolian origin, although that origin was favored by Frye and Leonard. They were believed to be Yarmouthian and Illinoian in age.

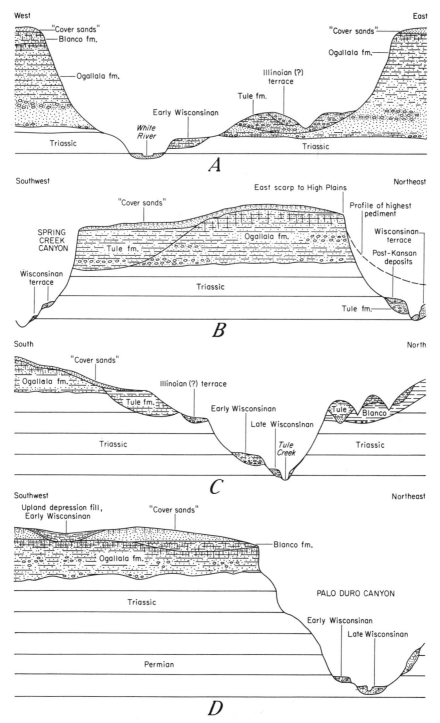

FIG. 16.13   Generalized cross-sections showing relationships of Cenozoic deposits along eastern part of High Plains of Texas.   (*After John C. Frye and A. B. Leonard, Rept. Invest. 32, Bureau Econ. Geol., Univ. Texas.*)

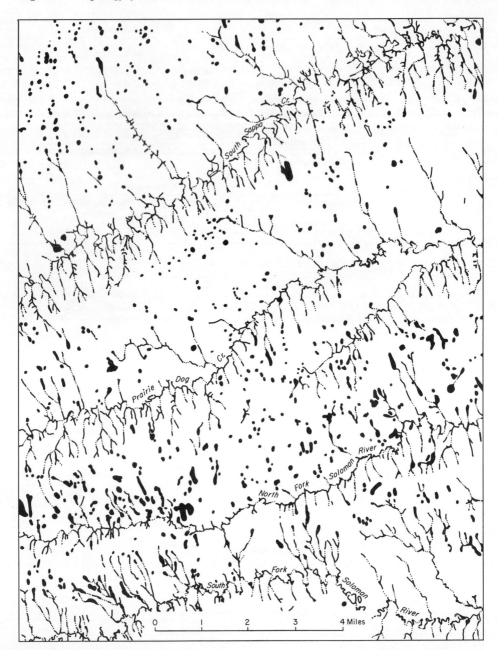

FIG. 16.14    Map showing number of depressions in area covered by the Colby, Kansas, topographic sheet.    (*After John C. Frye, Kan. Geol. Surv. Bull.* 86.)

*Great Plains Depressions.* Scattered over the Great Plains, and particularly abundant in the High Plains, are innumerable depressions whose origin has long been the cause for much speculation (see Fig. 16.14). Winn (1960) estimated that as many as 37,000 of these depressions are present in the High Plains area of Texas. In that region they average about one per square mile. The depressions range in size from mere dimples not over a foot deep and 10 feet in diameter to some that are scores of feet deep and several miles across. Many of them have permanent or intermittent lakes in them (see Fig. 16.15). It has been variously suggested that they are (1) buffalo wallows, (2) deflation basins or blowouts, (3) depressions produced by solution-subsidence, and (4) the result of differential compaction of the Tertiary sediments of the Great Plains.

Undoubtedly examples of each of these types of basins can be found, so it seems unreasonable to categorically attribute the depressions to any one process. Frye (1950) thought that an important factor in their origin and preservation was the fact that the region in which they are found lacks to a considerable degree strong stream and sheet erosion, processes that inhibit the development of shallow depressions or obscure them if formed.

Judson (1950), from a study of the depressions in eastern New Mexico, concluded that they were the result of alternate periods of leaching and wind deflation rather than collapse or local subsidence in the Ogallala formation. According to his view, leaching during wet periods

FIG. 16.15  View of lakes in Great Plains depressions near Petersburg, Texas. (*Photo by I. G. Holmes, courtesy Robert Winn.*)

destroyed the calcareous cement of the Ogallala and permitted deflation in the leached area during dry periods.

In that part of Kansas where Permian salt beds underlie the High Plains, such depressions as Big Basin (see Fig. 16.16) and Jacob's well, in western Clark County, are undoubtedly collapse

FIG. 16.16  Big Basin, a solution-subsidence basin in Clark County, Kansas. (*Photo by Ada Swineford, Kan. Geol. Surv.*)

sinks, but the Great Plains depressions are not limited to areas where soluble rocks underlie the surface, so it is illogical to attribute many of them to subsidence following solution.

The Pleistocene Blanco, Tule, and Tahoka formations, mentioned above, probably were deposited in lakes in depressions similar to those under discussion. Evans and Meade (1945), from their study of these formations, concluded that basins similar to those now found on the Great Plains have been forming and undergoing filling throughout most if not all of Quaternary time.

*Goshen Hole.* Description of the High Plains section as an essentially flat fluviatile surface holds good from the south northward to about the Platte River Valley. North of here the topography becomes less flat. A notable deviation from flat, upland, alluvial plain is found in the Goshen Hole Lowland. This is the name given to a pronounced widening of the North Platte Valley in western Nebraska and eastern Wyoming. The lowland is as much as 50 miles wide at its maximum and has been formed by north and south recession of its rim and ensuing rapid erosion of the exposed Oligocene Brule clay.

*Nebraska Sand Hills.* East and north of Goshen Hole is another area that departs notably from the typical plain-like character of the High Plains. This is the Sand Hills region of western Nebraska. Here, in an area covering some 24,000 square miles, sand dunes dominate the landscape. The topography consists of a maze of dunal mounds and ridges separated by interdunal basins (see Fig. 16.17) which are either deflation basins or the result of unequal deposition of sand. Many basins are the site of ephemeral lakes, and the drainage lines show notable lack of integration. Much of the area is drained internally and lacks surface streams, except the short, intermittent ones that flow into nearby lake basins.

The Sand Hills region is largely underlain by sediments belonging to the middle and lower Ogallala formation (Lugn, 1962). The dunes are the result of a sort of winnowing action on

the Ogallala sediments following their weathering whereby the sandy components were left behind to be built into dunes and the finer fractions were carried to the leeward and deposited as loess. That the Sand Hills region had undergone some erosion before the period of dune formation set in is evidenced by two facts: (1) the upper part of the Ogallala formation is lacking here, and (2) the Sand Hills are lower than the undissected High Plains to the west of them.

East and southeast of the Nebraska Sand Hills are extensive loess deposits. Undoubtedly deflation in the Sand Hills region contributed to their accumulation, but opinions differ as to whether this was the main source of the loess. Lugn (1962) contended that the Sand Hills region did provide most of the silts in the loess, but Frye and Leonard (1951) argued that the floodplains of the streams carrying glacial outwash were the main sources of loess. Textural and petrographic studies of the loess have led these men to different conclusions. There seems to be no question that silts from both sources are present in the loess belt, but the proportion from each is debatable.

*Aligned Drainage.* At various localities throughout the Great Plains a remarkable northwest-southeast alignment of streams may be noted (see Fig. 16.18). This shows particularly well on the Oahe, Pierre, Iona, and Chamberlin, South Dakota, quadrangle areas, but it is also found in parts of western Nebraska, western Kansas, eastern Montana, and eastern Wyoming. The alignment can hardly be explained as a result of regional tilting, for the direction of alignment does not parallel the regional slope. Neither can it be attributed to the influence of some particular geologic formation, for the aligned streams flow on rocks ranging in age from the Cretaceous Pierre shale to the Tertiary Ogallala formation.

Russell (1929) attributed the alignment to control exerted by longitudinal northwest-southeast dunes. His idea was that the streams followed the interdunal depressions, and although the dunes have largely disappeared, the pattern persists. Price (1944) has suggested a similar

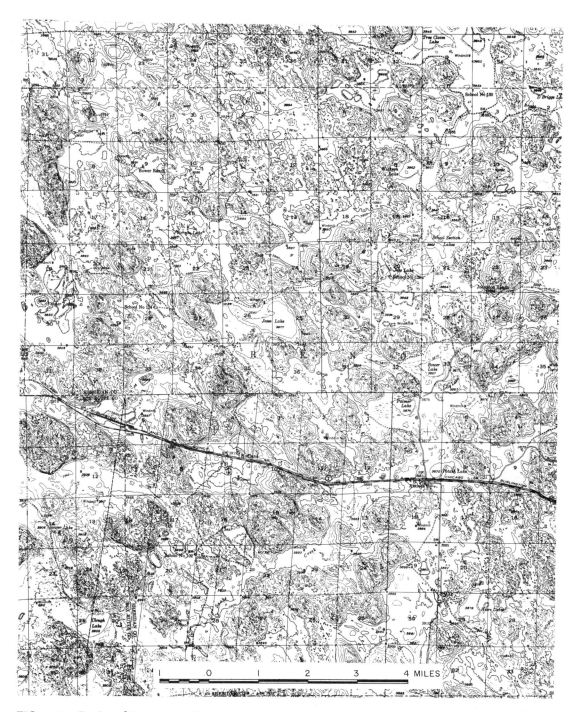

FIG. 16.17    Portion of the Antioch, Nebraska topographic sheet showing the dunal topography of the Nebraska Sand Hills.

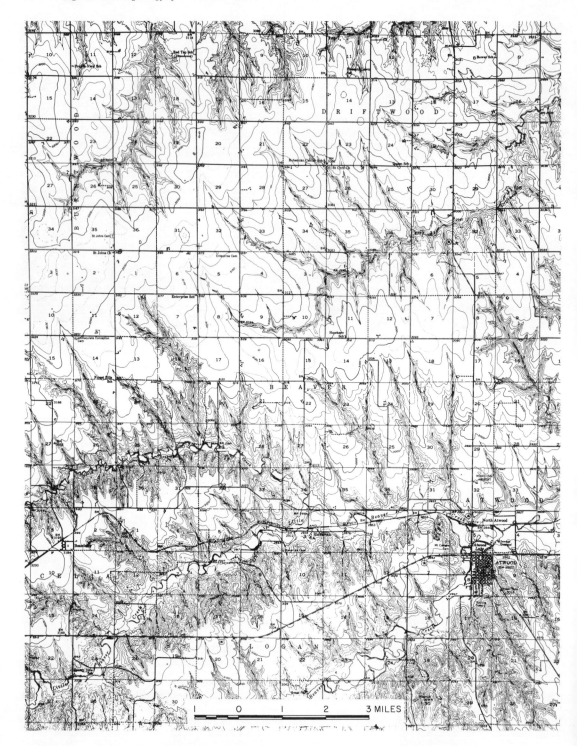

FIG. 16.18   Portion of the Atwood, Kansas, quadrangle showing aligned drainage.

origin for aligned stream courses in parts of Texas and New Mexico. Baker (1948), however, ascribed the aligned drainage to the combined effects of deflation and dunal control. He pointed out that areas of Pierre shale are commonly pitted with deflation basins which show a tendency to become ovate with axes trending northwest-southeast. Baker argued that the basins developed by deflation of shale in interdunal troughs. Drainage from one basin into another would result in the development of a parallel valley system. Flint (1955), after considering the various theories proposed to account for the aligned drainage, concluded that eolian control seemed most likely, but that the exact mechanism of development was not apparent. Crandell (1958), from his study of the aligned drainage in the Pierre, South Dakota, area, concluded that the pattern could not be explained by joint control in the Pierre shale or by differential erosion. He was thus more or less forced to the conclusion that the stream alignment was in some way related to the influence of the prevailing northwesterly winds.

*Areas of Internal Drainage.* Numerous areas in the High Plains lack external drainage. These areas vary in size from small basins, such as are common in the Nebraska Sand Hills, to areas covering many hundreds of square miles. The Scott-Finney depression in Kansas is about 40 miles long, extending from Garden City to Scott City, and has in it no throughgoing stream. Closed basins are common on the Llano Estacado, many of which are sites of salinas. They may lie a hundred feet or more below the general plains surface and encompass 50 or more square miles.

## Edwards Plateau

The Edwards Plateau is bounded on the north by the Llano Estacado of the High Plains and the Pecos Valley, on the northeast by the Central Texas uplift, on the southeast by the West Gulf Coastal Plain, and on the southwest by what is in Mexico an extension of the Mexican Highland section of the Basin and Range province. The Pecos Valley separates an area to its west known as the Stockton Plateau from the main part of the plateau. Altitudes decrease from about 4000 feet at the west and 3000 feet at the north to around 1000 feet at the eastern rim of the plateau.

*Geology and Topography.* The Llano Estacado merges at the south almost imperceptibly with the Edwards Plateau. Although no sharp line of demarcation separates the two sections, a significant difference exists between the two in that the Tertiary fluviatile cover has been removed from the Edwards Plateau. Surficial materials of the Llano Estacado are unindurated sands, marls, and loams. Hardly a stone of any size can be seen on its surface; in contrast, much of the Edwards Plateau is rough limestone country. The same Cretaceous rocks underlie both areas, but only on the surface of the Edwards Plateau do they crop out. Except for a few Permian and Pennsylvanian inliers (Cartwright, 1932), the surficial rocks of the Edwards Plateau belong to the Fredericksburg division of early Cretaceous age. The Edwards limestone of this group is the formation most commonly seen at the surface. So extensively does this limestone constitute the surficial bedrock that we must conclude that the Edwards Plateau is a stripped plain from which has been removed the Tertiary veneer that once blanketed it.

The central part of the Edwards Plateau has little relief except along major stream valleys, but along these the Edwards limestone forms bold valleyside cliffs. Dissection increases markedly toward the southeast margin of the plateau, and along with it the amount of relief. The ragged Balcones Escarpment (see p. 64), which forms the southeastern boundary of the plateau, is a prominent and striking feature.

*Karst Features.* The topography of the Edwards Plateau displays several aspects that justify describing it as being in an early phase of karst development. On the surface of the plateau are numerous small basins that are sinkholes. Many of the valleys are dry because of diversion of their waters to underground routes; these waters return to the surface as karst springs along the sides of the deeper valleys cut into the plateau.

FIG. 16.19   Rocky Mountain Front (background) and Dakota hogback (foreground) northwest of Denver, Colorado. (*Photo by John S. Shelton.*)

Caverns are fairly common in the Edwards Plateau, although none of great size is known.

### Colorado Piedmont Section

The Colorado Piedmont section differs from the High Plains to the east and north in that its former Tertiary fluviatile cover has been largely removed. Some early Tertiary rocks have been preserved, but they are either in the deeply depressed Denver basin or in the divide area between the Arkansas and Platte Rivers.

*Geology.* The major structural feature of this section is the Denver basin. This downwarp actually extends beyond the topographic boundaries of the Colorado Piedmont at the north, but its deepest part is near Denver, where a downfolding of strata of as much as 4500 feet has taken place. Exposed in the foothills at the east edge of the Colorado Front Range are Paleozoic rocks ranging in age from Cambrian to Pennsylvanian. These steeply eastward-dipping formations rapidly descend until they reach altitudes at or near sea level and then rise gently eastward, thus giving to the basin much steeper dips on the west than on the east side.

Among the Paleozoic and Mesozoic formations that dip steeply beneath the surface of the Colorado Piedmont are several which because of their great resistance produce hogbacks. The Pennsylvanian Fountain and Lyons sandstones often form hogbacks or "flatirons" where they rest against the Precambrian rocks of the Rocky

Mountain front, but by far more commonly the hogbacks are on the Cretaceous Dakota sandstone (see Fig. 16.19). Except where this formation is cut out by faults, the Dakota hogback is a distinctive topographic feature of the western edge of the Colorado Piedmont. Much of the Colorado Piedmont is underlain by shale, particularly the Pierre shale, but interbedded sandstones and limestones are responsible for numerous mesas along the western part of the section.

Tertiary volcanic rocks occur locally, but they are nothing like so conspicuous as in the Raton section to the south. The Paleocene Arapahoe and Denver formations which underlie North and South Table Mountains, near Golden, Colo-

rado, are capped with three basalt flows (see Fig. 16.20). The lowermost of the three flows apparently filled a valley cut in the Denver formation (Van Tuyl, 1938). A few dikes are present in the area, such as Valmont Butte east of Boulder, and the Ralston dike near Golden, but in general they are rare.

*Removal of Tertiary Cover.* The removal of the Tertiary cover that once extended over this area has been the work of two stream systems, the Platte and Arkansas, both of which rise to the west in the Colorado Rockies. These streams have cut valleys several hundred feet below the level at which they formerly flowed. The escarpment at the east which marks the boundary

FIG. 16.20   North Table Mountain, north of Golden, Colorado, looking west toward Colorado Front Range.   (*Photo by John S. Shelton.*)

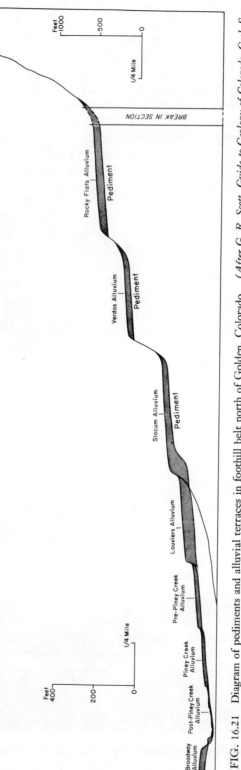

FIG. 16.21   Diagram of pediments and alluvial terraces in foothill belt north of Golden, Colorado.   *(After G. R. Scott, Guide to Geology of Colorado, Geol. Soc. Am.-Rocky Mt. Assoc. Geol.-Colo. Sci. Soc.)*

between the Colorado Piedmont and High Plains sections is now a divide area for several eastward-flowing streams.   The several small streams that unite to form the Republican River head here rather than back in the mountains.   Removal of the Tertiary cover from over much of the region has not been just the work of the Platte and Arkansas Rivers, but as much the work of their numerous laterally incoming tributaries.   Wind erosion has had a part in the removal of the Tertiary cover, but apparently a minor part.

*Regional Slope.*   The surface of the Colorado Piedmont descends eastward from altitudes ranging between 5000 and 7000 feet next to the mountains (the 7000-foot altitudes are on the divide between the Arkansas and Platte rivers) to 4000 feet near the Colorado-Kansas boundary. As can be seen from the edge of the west-facing scarp at the eastern edge of the section, the surface of much of the Colorado Piedmont is actually lower than that of the High Plains to the east.

*Geomorphic History.*   The geomorphic history of the region is closely tied in with that of the Colorado Rockies.   It does not seem unreasonable to project westward the surface on the Ogallala formation of the High Plains and connect it with the extensive erosional surface in the Rocky Mountains that is generally considered a Pliocene old-age surface.   Most of the Colorado Piedmont falls below the level of the projected Ogallala surface, indicating that a great deal of erosion has taken place since uplift of the Pliocene surface.

Numerous gravel-capped mesas are present immediately east of the foothill belt at the western edge of the Colorado Piedmont.   Fogarty (1951) described five to seven erosion surfaces in the Golden-Morrison, Colorado, area which he considered pediments.

Scott (1960) has described three alluvium-capped pediments between Boulder and Golden, Colorado, that lie below the level of the main erosion surface in the Colorado Front Range and below which are four alluvial terraces (see Fig. 16.21).   His suggested ages of the alluvium on these geomorphic surfaces are given in tabular form below. The highest pediment, the Rocky Flats pediment, lies 1650 feet below the level of the subsummit erosion surface in the Colorado Front Range (see p. 339). The second pediment, the Verdos pediment, lies 100 feet below the Rocky Flats pediment, and the third pediment is still 150 feet lower.

TABLE 16.1 Sequence of Quaternary Deposits in Colorado Piedmont (After Scott)

| System | Series | Stage or Substage | Formation |
|---|---|---|---|
| | R e c e n t | Late | Post-Piney alluvium |
| | | | Piney Creek alluvium |
| | | Early | Eolian sand |
| Q u a t e r n a r y | | | Pre-Piney Creek alluvium |
| | P l e i s t o c e n e | Wisconsin Late | Broadway alluvium |
| | | Wisconsin Early | Younger loess |
| | | | Louviers alluvium |
| | | Sangamon | |
| | | Illinoian | Older loess |
| | | | Slocum alluvium |
| | | Yarmouth | Verdos alluvium |
| | | Kansan | Rocky Flats alluvium |
| | | Aftonian | |
| | | Nebraskan | |

Eastward, in the plains area, the number of identifiable erosion levels decreases, because the diminishing interval between successive surfaces brings about a merging of topographic levels. Attempts to trace the pediments and terraces back into the mountains at the west have not proven too successful.

It may be that the gravels on the higher pediments are Pliocene in age rather than Pleistocene, but it is believed that most of the pediment and terrace veneers are of Pleistocene age. Along streams that head back in the mountains it may be possible ultimately to make a crude correlation of the gravel-capped terraces with stages or substages of glaciation. Hunt (1954) thought that he could divide the alluvial deposits of the Denver area into three ages, pre-Wisconsin, Wisconsin, and Recent.

## Raton Section

*Distinctive Features.* The Raton section stands out from the neighboring Colorado Piedmont on the north by its higher altitudes, deep canyons, and greater abundance of volcanic phenomena; it contrasts with the High Plains on the east in the lack of a fluviatile cover. On the south the Canadian Escarpment sets the section off sharply from the Pecos Valley; on the west the boundary as commonly stated is the eastern front of the Southern Rocky Mountains. This boundary, however, presents the problem of whether it should be drawn on a geologic or topographic basis. Here, Tertiary rocks are found at altitudes as high as 12,000 feet, and numerous areas that have altitudes of 10,000 feet or more might be considered mountains in terms of their topographic expression, but they are underlain by gently dipping Mesozoic and Tertiary sedimentary rocks with a Great Plains type of structure.

The oldest exposed rocks are redbeds of Pennsylvanian age which rest on Precambrian rocks in the foothills adjacent to the Sangre de Cristo Mountains. Other rocks exposed are Triassic, Jurassic, Cretaceous, Paleocene, and Pliocene in age. In addition, there are extensive Pleistocene gravels on pediment surfaces. The main Tertiary formations are the Paleocene Raton and the Pliocene Ogallala.

The Raton section as a whole may be described as a group of plateaus and mesas in advanced stages of dissection. Lava-capped mesas are common and give evidence of repeated extrusions of basalts and andesites. Topographically, the plateaus and mesas fall into three groups: the central, and highest, Raton Mesa group; the intermediate Park Plateau group at the north; and the lowest Las Vegas group at the south.

*Structure.* Structurally the Raton section can be divided into four areas (Levings, 1951): (1) a

FIG. 16.22    Fishers Peak, looking east from Starkville, Colorado.    (*Photo by Ross B. Johnson.*)

foothill belt immediately adjacent to and east of the Sangre de Cristo Range in which the rocks are rather tightly compressed; (2) a synclinal trough or basin to the east of the folded belt known as the Raton or Trinidad-Raton basin; (3) a broad northeast-southwest trending uplift east of the Raton basin known as the Sierra Grande uplift; and (4) the Apishapa uplift on the north, which extends southeastward and meets the Sierra Grande uplift.

*Features Resulting from Volcanic Activity.*    In this section, the highest and most dissected of the Great Plains sections, lava flows are widespread. It has been estimated that more than a thousand square miles are covered with lavas.    The main belt of lava-capped mesas extends from Trinidad, Colorado, and Raton, New Mexico, eastward to the Oklahoma state line.    Altitudes of the mesas

range from over 9600 feet on the west to 5000 feet on the east; and the mesas are so distributed vertically as to give to the topography a distinctly step-like arrangement.

Highest of the basalt-capped mesas are Raton, Barilla, and Johnson Mesas.    A total of eleven lava sheets can be identified on Raton and Barilla Mesas and eight sheets can be seen in Fishers Peak at the western extremity of Raton Mesa (see Fig. 16.22).    The individual lava flows vary in thickness from 100 to 500 feet.    The maximum relief that has developed since the outpouring of the lavas is about 4000 feet, which is the amount of relief between Fishers Peak and the valley of the Purgatoire River at the north.

In addition to the basalt flows, innumerable sills, dikes, and volcanic plugs may be seen. Plugs are particularly conspicuous features along the north side of the line of mesas; sills are numerous in the Park Plateau; and dikes are present in the Raton area as well as in the Spanish Peaks region. The Spanish Peaks (Knopf, 1936), lying at the north side of the Park Plateau, are two stocks of granite and grandiorite porphyry. Dikes radiate from the stocks through an arc of 360 degrees, and some are as much as 25 miles long. Hills (1901) mapped 300 dikes, and there may be as many as 500.

The age of the oldest lavas is uncertain. Those on Raton, Barilla, and Johnson Mesas rest on gravels of uncertain age. Whether these gravels are Ogallala in age or older has not been determined. Smith (1940) thought that the lava flows which reach nearest to the Kansas state boundary were post-Ogallala in age, for they rest upon a considerable thickness of Ogallala sandstone. However, he found in western Kansas exposures where basaltic pebbles are part of what appears to be typical Ogallala deposits, which may indicate that the lavas were either contemporaneous with Ogallala deposition or even antedated it. Ray and Smith (1941), from their study of the Moreno Valley in north central New Mexico, concluded that the highest basalt there must be late Miocene or early Pliocene in age.

*Erosion Surfaces.* The period of extensive vulcanism was followed by one of relative quiet during which the region was reduced to an area of low relief. An erosion surface is present in the area which may correlate with what has been called the Rocky Mountain peneplain or pediplain (see p. 339). In the Raton area, parts of this erosional surface are covered with lava flows. Regional uplift in late Tertiary time accompanied by block faulting and warping led to renewal of erosion. Three gravel-capped erosion surfaces of presumed Pleistocene age are present along the Purgatoire Valley (Levings, 1951) that have been named the San Miguel, Beshoar, and Barilla pediments. Ray and Smith (1941) recognized four erosion surfaces in the Moreno Valley just west of the Raton section in the Southern Rocky Mountains. The uppermost erosion surface, called by them the Broad

Valley stage, was correlated with the cycle of erosion that produced the Ogallala fuviatile cover in the Great Plains. The other three surfaces they considered pediments of Pleistocene age. Thus the general erosional history of the Raton section seems to correlate fairly well with that outlined for the Colorado Piedmont.

## Pecos Valley Section

The Pecos Valley section is a broad north-south asymmetric depression lying between the Llano Estacado of the High Plains on the east and the Guadalupe and Sacramento Mountains of the Basin and Range province on the west. The Ogallala formation once covered this region, as is indicated by remnants of the Ogallala west of the Pecos trough (Bretz and Horberg, 1949b). If these remnants of the Ogallala are projected eastward to similar deposits on the Llano Estacado, an average dip of 25 feet per mile is indicated. The climate of the Pecos Valley is semi-arid, like that of the adjacent High Plains to the east and Edwards Plateau to the south, but a notable contrast in the topography exists which reflects differences in the geology of the three sections. The topography of the High Plains is dominated by the Ogallala formation; that of the Edwards Plateau by resistant Cretaceous limestones; whereas the topography of the Pecos Valley reflects notably the influence of readily soluble rocks.

*Relation to Topography to Geology.* The Pecos River, which heads at the south end of the Sangre de Cristo Range, lies somewhat to the west of the center of the Pecos depression. The bedrock underlying the Pecos lowland is Triassic and Permian in age; in addition, Pleistocene and Recent alluvial deposits are widespread. The formations which have influenced the topography most are the Castile anhydrite, the Salado halite, and the Rustler limestone of the Ochoa Permian series. The region is a lowland because of the solubility of these formations, and solution phenomena are widespread (Morgan, 1942). Subterranean drainage features are common but in addition to the usual solution features there are

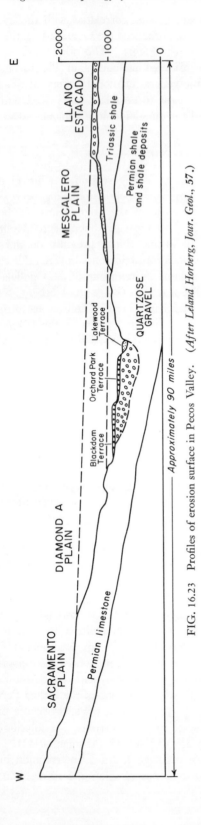

FIG. 16.23   Profiles of erosion surface in Pecos Valley.   (*After Leland Horberg, Jour. Geol., 57.*)

features that Olive (1957) has called solution-subsidence troughs. These are narrow, linear depressions that vary in width from a few hundred feet to a mile and in length from one-half mile to ten miles. They are the result of subsidence of near-surface earth blocks to fill voids dissolved by water flowing in underground channels. They are particularly common in areas underlain by the Castile formation. The troughs extend eastward parallel to the regional dip, a result of solution along eastward-trending joint systems that parallel the regional dip.

*Erosion Surfaces.* Five cyclical erosion surfaces (see Fig. 16.23) have been recognized in the area by Morgan and Sayre (1942). These in topographic order from highest to lowest are:

1. The Sacramento Plain. This is an erosional surface in the Sacramento Mountains to the west of the Pecos Lowland that is correlated with the constructional surface of the Ogallala formation in the Llano Estacado.
2. The Diamond A-Mescalero Plain. Diamond A is the name applied to the surface on the west side of the Pecos Valley and Mescalero to the corresponding surface on the east side. The Diamond A surface is a pediment that lies from 400 to 1300 feet below the level of the Sacramento Plain; the Mescalero Plain on the east side of the Pecos Valley is the much more extensive of the two pediments. It was estimated by Morgan (1942) that close to 95 per cent of the excavation that has taken place in the Pecos basin was accomplished during the Diamond A-Mescalero erosion cycle, which he believed covered a very considerable part of Pleistocene time.
3. Along the Pecos River below the Diamond A-Mescalero surface are three gravel-capped pediments named from highest to lowest the Blackdom, Orchard Park, and Lakewood terraces.

Leonard and Frye (1962) arrived at a somewhat similar interpretation of the erosion surfaces in the Pecos Valley. They recognized four pediment surfaces extending from the mountains on the west to near the river channels. These pediments with their suggested ages are:

Surface I    A pediment graded to the level of drainage lines in Ogallala time.

Surface II   An extensive pediment graded to the level of the Pecos River in Illinoian time.

Surface III  A pediment graded to the level of the Pecos River in early Wisconsin time.

Surface IV   A surface developed in late Wisconsin time and immediately below which the Pecos River is now incised.

*Pecos River Piracy.* There seems to be little question that the Ogallala formation once extended across the Pecos Valley. Removal of the Ogallala sediments from the Pecos Valley was effected by the Pecos River, and in so doing it apparently performed a notable case of progressive stream piracy (see Fig. 16.24). The original drainage of what is now the upper Pecos Valley was to the east across the High Plains. The Pecos River apparently began as a short tributary of the Rio Grande in the Edwards Plateau (King, 1948). It cut its way headward and one by one pirated the eastward-flowing streams. This task was made easier than it would have been ordinarily by the existence in what is now the Pecos Valley of a belt of easily erodible Permian rocks. It may well be that subterranean stream piracy was an important process involved in the northward extension of the Pecos River. The date of the piracies can be placed rather definitely as post-Pliocene, thus making it likely that they took place early in Pleistocene time.

## Central Texas Section

The Central Texas section, northeast of the Edwards Plateau, differs from that plateau in that it has been stripped in varying degrees of its cover of resistant Cretaceous limestone. The section can be divided into several subdivisions whose topographic characteristics are largely related to two factors, the extent to which they

have been dissected and the nature of the rocks exposed on removal of the Edwards limestone. At the east, from north to south, are the Comanche Plateau and Llano-Burnet or Central Mineral district. The boundary between these two areas is somewhat arbitrarily set at the Colorado River. West of these plateau tracts

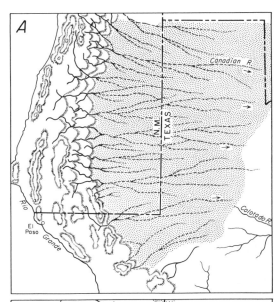

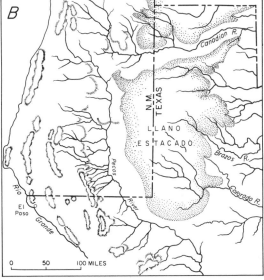

FIG. 16.24   (*A*) Postulated drainage of southern High Plains before development of Pecos Valley. (*B*) Present drainage of southern High Plains. (*After F. B. Plummer, Bureau Econ. Geol., Univ. Texas, 3232.*)

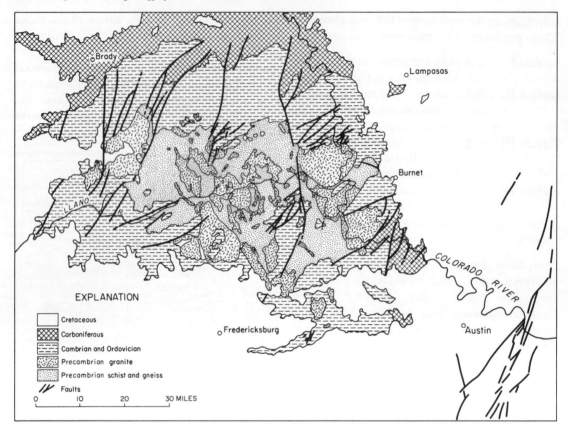

FIG. 16.25   Generalized geologic map of the Llano-Burnet or Central Mineral district.   (*After David Keppel, Geol. Soc. Am. Bull.*, **51**.)

are the lowland of the upper Colorado River, the Callahan Divide, and the Palo Pinto district.

*Comanche Plateau.*   The Comanche Plateau is a belt of submaturely dissected plateau which slopes eastward at a rate determined by the dip of the lower Cretaceous rocks. Its eastern boundary from near Waco southward is marked by the Balcones Escarpment. Relief is strongest at the west, where it amounts to several hundred feet. The name Lampasas Cut Plains is commonly applied to the higher and more deeply eroded southwestern part of the Comanche Plateau.

*Llano-Burnet Area.*   Probably the part of the Central Texas section that is most interesting geomorphically is the Llano-Burnet or Central Mineral district. Erosion on a broad domal

structure has exposed a central area of Precambrian rocks around which are encircling belts of Paleozoic and Cretaceous rocks (see Fig. 16.25). Particularly interesting is the fact that the belt of Precambrian granites, gneisses, and schists has become a topographic basin. Three rather distinct geologic and topographic belts can be recognized: (1) the central basin on Precambrian rocks, (2) a maturely dissected plateau-like tract on rocks of Paleozoic age encircling the central basin, and (3) a rim of Cretaceous rocks marked by an infacing escarpment.

The central basin on the Precambrian rocks is in a sense a basin within a basin, for the belt of Paleozoic rocks might be considered remnants of what was a basin at the time that the Cretaceous rocks were first removed from the crest of the dome. Numerous hills and ridges add relief to the central basin.   These are mainly on Precambrian rocks, but several are composed of Cambrian sandstone.  The tops of these hills are remnants of the erosion surface on which the Cretaceous rocks that once extended across the dome were deposited.

Faults are numerous in the areas of Precambrian and Paleozoic rocks but do not affect the Cretaceous beds.  Faulting has brought masses of granite or other Precambrian rocks into remarkably straight fault contact with limestones and sandstones, and these contacts are commonly marked by fault-line scarps which are most commonly on the downthrown sides of the faults (Paige, 1912).

It is possible to date fairly closely when erosion of the Cretaceous cover had penetrated deeply enough to encounter the underlying granites. This did not take place until Pleistocene time. Evidence of this is the fact that the Pliocene Uvalde formation in the Austin area does not contain any granite debris, but the gravel on the oldest Pleistocene terrace along the Colorado River does have in it granitic pebbles.

*Callahan Divide.*   The Callahan Divide, near the northwest margin of the Central Texas section, is the divide area between the Brazos and Colorado rivers.   Plateau-forming Cretaceous limestone is still preserved in part here, whereas it has been removed entirely from the lowlands to either side.   The Callahan Divide forms a connection between the Llano Estacado to the west of it and the Comanche Plateau to the east.

*Colorado River Lowland.*   The valley of the Colorado River through the Central Texas and Edwards Plateau sections presents a departure from the conventional concept that river valleys become progressively wider downstream. Through the Edwards Plateau the valley of the Colorado River is largely gorgelike; its course across the Llano-Burnet area is more open, at least that part across the central basin; northwest of the Llano-Burnet district the Colorado River flows in a broad lowland 100 miles long. The valley is narrow across the Edwards Plateau because the limestone cover is still intact here;

it is moderately open across the granites of the Llano-Burnet basin; it is wide in its upper part because here the resistant Edwards limestone has been entirely removed.

*Palo Pinto District.*   A second area in which relatively strong rock has been exposed by stripping of the Edwards limestone is in the Palo Pinto district, at the northern edge of the Central Texas section.   Exposed here are Pennsylvanian sandstones that form numerous mesas that rise above lower plains on shales where the sandstones have been removed.

### Plains Border Section

The High Plains with their alluvial cover are believed to have extended farther east formerly than they do at present.   This means that the boundary between the Central Lowlands and the Great Plains has been receding gradually westward.   Along the northern and southern contacts of the two provinces their boundary is fairly readily determinable, but in southern Nebraska, across Kansas, and in western Oklahoma it is not sharply evident.   Here a broad strip of maturely dissected topography consisting of a series of cuestas has been designated as the Plains Border section.

Difference of opinion exists as to where the boundary between this section of the Great Plains and the Central Lowlands should be drawn. Adams (1903) and Frye (1949) argued that the boundary between the two provinces should be drawn at the scarp which forms the front of the Flint Hills Cuesta.   This is farther east than drawn by Fenneman (1931, 1938).   Frye argued that the boundary used by Fenneman is unsatisfactory because it does not follow any continuous geologic or topographic contact.

Dissected topography along the eastern margin of the Great Plains is not restricted to the section under discussion.   We have already seen that it characterizes the eastern edge of the Edwards Plateau and Central Texas sections, but in the Oklahoma-Kansas-Nebraska region this type of topography forms a large enough area to justify recognition as a separate section.

REFERENCES CITED

Adams, G. I. (1903). Physiographic divisions of Kansas, *Kansas Acad. Sci. Trans.*, **18**, 109–123.

Alden, W. C. (1932). Physiography and glacial geology of eastern Montana and adjacent areas, *U. S. Geol. Survey Profess. Paper* 174, 133 pp.

Baker, C. L. (1948). The Pennington-Haakon County central boundary area, with general discussion of its surroundings, *South Dakota Geol. Surv. Rept. Invest.* 64, 28 pp.

Bretz, J H., and Leland Horberg (1949a). Caliche in southeastern New Mexico, *Jour. Geol.*, **57**, 491–511.

―――― (1949b). The Ogallala formation west of the Llano Estacado, *Jour. Geol.*, **57**, 477–490.

Brown, C. N. (1956). The origin of the caliche on the northeastern Llano Estacado, *Jour. Geol.*, **64**, 1–15.

Cartwright, L. D. (1932). Regional structure of Cretaceous on Edwards Plateau of southwest Texas, *Geol. Soc. Am. Bull.*, **16**, 691–700.

Collier, A. J., and W. T. Thom (1918). The Flaxville gravel and its relation to other terrace gravels of the northern Great Plains, *U. S. Geol. Survey Profess. Paper* 108, 179–184.

Crandell, D. R. (1958). Geology of the Pierre area, South Dakota, *U. S. Geol. Survey Profess. Paper* 307, 83 pp.

Darton, N. H., and Sidney Paige (1925). Central Black Hills, *U. S. Geol. Survey Folio* 219, 34 pp.

Elias, M. K. (1931). The geology of Wallace County, Kansas, *Kansas Geol. Surv. Bull.* 18, 254 pp.

―――― (1948). Ogallala and post-Ogallala sediments, *Geol. Soc. Am. Bull.*, **59**, 609–612.

Evans, G. L., and G. E. Meade (1945). Quaternary of the Texas High Plains, *Univ. Texas Pub.* 4401, 485–507.

Fenneman, N. M. (1931). *Physiography of Western United States*, McGraw-Hill Book Company, New York, 534 pp.

―――― (1938). *Physiography of Eastern United States*, McGraw-Hill Book Company, New York, 691 pp.

Fillman, Louise (1929). Cenozoic history of the northern Black Hills, *Univ. Iowa Studies in Natural History*, **13**, No. 1, 50 pp.

Flint, R. F. (1955). Pleistocene geology of eastern South Dakota, *U. S. Geol. Survey Profess. Paper* 262, 173 pp.

Fogarty, C. F. (1951). Pediments of the Golden-Morrison area, Jefferson County, Colorado, *Geol. Soc. Am. Bull.*, **62**, 1534 (abs.).

Frye, J. C. (1949). The Plains Border physiographic section, *Kansas Acad. Sci. Trans.*, **52**, 71–81.

―――― (1950). Origin of the Kansas Great Plains depressions, *Kansas Univ. State Geol. Surv. Bull.* 86, Pt. 1, 20 pp.

―――― and A. B. Leonard (1951). Stratigraphy of the late Pleistocene loesses of Kansas, *Jour. Geol.*, **59**, 287–305.

―――― (1959). Correlation of the Ogallala formation (Neogene) in western Texas with type localities in Nebraska, *Bureau Econ. Geol.*, *Univ. Texas, Rept. Invest.* 39, 46 pp.

Hills, R. C. (1901). Spanish Peaks, *U. S. Geol. Survey Folio* 71, 7 pp.

Horberg, Leland (1954). Rocky Mountain and continental Pleistocene deposits in the Waterton region, Alberta, Canada, *Geol. Soc. Am. Bull.*, **65**, 1093–1150.

―――― (1956). A deep profile of weathering on pre-Wisconsin drift in Glacier Park, Montana, *Jour. Geol.*, **64**, 201–218.

Howard, A. D. (1960) Cenozoic history of northeastern Montana and northwestern North Dakota with emphasis on the Pleistocene, *U. S. Geol. Survey Profess. Paper* 326, 107 pp.

Hunt, C. B. (1954). Pleistocene and Recent deposits in the Denver area, Colorado, *U. S. Geol. Survey Bull.* 996-C, 91–140.

Jaggar, T. A., Jr. (1901). The laccoliths of the Black Hills, *U. S. Geol. Survey 21st Ann. Rept.*, Pt. 3, 163–303.

Judson, S. S., Jr. (1950). Depressions of the northern portion of the southern High Plains of eastern New Mexico, *Geol. Soc. Am. Bull.*, **61**, 253–274.

King, P. B. (1948). Geology of the southern Guadalupe Mountains, Texas, *U. S. Geol. Survey Profess. Paper* 215, 183 pp.

Knopf, Adolph (1936). Igneous geology of the Spanish Peaks region, Colorado, *Geol. Soc. Am. Bull.*, **47**, 1727–1784.

Leonard, A. G. (1916). Pleistocene drainage changes in western North Dakota, *Geol. Soc. Am. Bull.*, **27**, 295–304.

Leonard, A. B., and J. C. Frye (1962). Pleistocene molluscan faunas and physiographic history of Pecos Valley in Texas, *Bureau Econ. Geol.*, *Univ. Texas, Rept. Invest.* 45, 42 pp.

Levings, W. S. (1951). Late Cenozoic erosional history of the Raton Mesa region, *Colo. School Mines Quart.*, **46**, No. 3, 111 pp.

Lugn, A. L. (1962). The origin and sources of loess, *Univ. Neb. Studies*, n.s., **26**, 105 pp.

Meneley, W. A., E. A. Christiansen, and W. O. Kupsch (1957). Preglacial Missouri River in Saskatchewan, *Jour. Geol.*, **65**, 441–447.

Morgan, A. M. (1942). Solution-phenomena in the Pecos basin, *Am. Geophys. Union, Trans. of 1942*, 27–35.

―――― and A. N. Sayre (1942). Geology and ground-water in *The Pecos River Joint Investigation*, National Resources Planning Board, 28–38.

Olive, W. W. (1957). Solution subsidence troughs, Castile formation of Gypsum Plain, Texas and New Mexico, *Geol. Soc. Am. Bull.*, **68**, 351–358.

Paige, Sidney (1912). Description of the Llano and Burnett quadrangles, *U. S. Geol. Survey Folio* 183, 16 pp.

Plumley, W. J. (1948). Black Hills terrace gravels: A study in sediment transport, *Jour. Geol.*, **56,** 526–577.

Price, W. A. (1944). Greater American deserts, *Texas Acad. Sci. Proc. and Trans.*, **27,** 163–170.

Ray, L. L., and J. F. Smith, Jr. (1941). Geology of the Moreno Valley, New Mexico, *Geol. Soc. Am. Bull.*, **52,** 177–210.

Russell, W. L. (1929). Drainage alignment in the western Great Plains, *Jour. Geol.*, **37,** 249–255.

Scott, G. R. (1960). Subdivision of the Quaternary alluvium east of the Front Range near Denver, Colorado, *Geol. Soc. Am. Bull.*, **71,** 1541–1544.

Smith, H. T. U. (1940). Geologic studies in southwestern Kansas, *Kansas Geol. Surv. Bull.* 34, 159–168.

Swineford, Ada, A. B. Leonard, and J. C. Frye (1958). Petrology of the Pliocene pisolitic limestone in the Great Plains, *Kansas Geol. Surv. Bull.* 130, Pt. 2, 97–116.

Todd, J. E. (1914). The Pleistocene history of the Missouri River, *Science*, **39,** 263–274.

Townsend, R. C., and A. L. Jenke (1951). The problem of the origin of the Max moraine of North Dakota and Canada, *Am. Jour. Sci.*, **249,** 842–858.

Van Tuyl, F. M. (1938). Guide to the geology of the Golden area, *Colorado School Mines Quart.*, **38,** 32 pp.

Willis, Bailey (1902). Stratigraphy and structure, Lewis and Livingston ranges, Montana, *Geol. Soc. Am. Bull.*, **13,** 305–352.

Winn, R. M. (1960). Classification of lake water prior to artificial recharge by wells, *Compass*, **37,** 278–298.

## ADDITIONAL REFERENCES

Alden, W. C. (1924). Physiographic development of the northern Great Plains, *Geol. Soc. Am. Bull.*, **35,** 385–424.

Collins, R. F. (1949). Volcanic rock of northeastern New Mexico, *Geol. Soc. Am. Bull.*, **60,** 1017–1040.

Flint, R. F. (1949). Pleistocene drainage diversions in South Dakota, *Geograf. Annaler*, **31,** 56–74.

Frye, J. C., and A. B. Leonard (1957). Studies of Cenozoic geology along the eastern margin of the Texas High Plains, Armstrong to Howard counties, *Univ. Texas, Bureau Econ. Geol., Rept. Invest.* 32, 62 pp.

Goddard, E. N. (1950). Structure of the Judith Mountains, Montana, *Geol. Soc. Am. Bull.*, **61,** 1465 (abs.).

Howard, A. D. (1958). Drainage evolution in northeastern Montana and northwestern North Dakota, *Geol. Soc. Am. Bull.*, **69,** 575–588.

Hurlburt, C. S., Jr., and David Griggs (1939). Igneous rocks of the Highwood Mountains, Montana, Part 1, The laccoliths, *Geol. Soc. Am. Bull.*, **50,** 1043–1112.

Johnson, R. B. (1960). Brief description of the igneous bodies of the Raton Mesa region, south-central Colorado, in *Guide to the Geology of Colorado*, Geol. Soc. Am.-Rocky Mountain Assoc. Geol.-Colo. Sci. Soc., 117–120.

Johnson, W. D. (1900). The High Plains and their utilization, *U. S. Geol. Survey, 21st Ann. Rept.*, Pt. 4, 601–741; *22nd Ann. Rept.*, Pt. 4, 631–669.

Kemp, J. F., and Paul Billingsley (1921). Sweet Grass Hills, Montana, *Geol. Soc. Am. Bull.*, **32,** 437–478.

Malde, H. E. (1955). Surficial geology of the Louisville quadrangle, Colorado, *U. S. Geol. Survey Bull.* 996-E, 217–259.

Reeves, Frank (1924). The structure of the Bearpaw Mountains, Montana, *Am. Jour. Sci.*, **208,** 296–311.

—— (1930). Geology of the Big Snowy Mountains, Montana, *U. S. Geol. Survey Profess. Paper* 165-D, 135–149.

Scott, G. R. (1963). Quaternary geology and geomorphic history of the Kassler quadrangle, Colorado, *U. S. Geol. Survey Profess Paper* 421-A, 70 pp.

Tator, B. A. (1952). Piedmont interstream surfaces of the Colorado Springs region, Colorado, *Geol. Soc. Am. Bull.*, **63,** 255–274.

Van Tuyl, F. M., and J. M. Coke (1932). The late Tertiary physiographic history of the High Plains of Colorado and New Mexico, *Colo. Sci. Soc. Proc.*, **13,** 19–25.

Wolff, J. E. (1938). Igneous rocks of the Crazy Mountains, Montana, *Geol. Soc. Am. Bull.*, **49,** 1569–1626.

# 17

# *Rocky Mountain System*

## GENERAL DESCRIPTION

What are commonly called the Rocky Mountains are more a geographic than a geomorphic entity. This name is applied conveniently to the great mountain barrier which extends from central New Mexico northwestward across the United States and into Canada. Not all of the area is mountainous, but the nonmountainous parts are so intimately associated with the mountains that they can hardly be separated from them either areally or in terms of their geomorphic histories. The Rocky Mountain system consists of a number of mountain uplifts, most of which extend in a slightly northwest-southeast direction. In most of them the ranges have been raised so high that erosion has exposed cores of Precambrian rocks along the axes of the uplifts (see Fig. 17.1). The sedimentary rocks which once extended across the uplifts are now exposed along their flanks or in downfolded or downfaulted basins within the mountain masses.

## SUBDIVISIONS

In the Fenneman classification, the Rocky Mountain system is divided into four provinces, the Southern Rocky Mountains, Wyoming Basin, Middle Rocky Mountains, and Northern Rocky Mountains. Of these four provinces the Wyoming Basin is the least mountainous topographically, but this is true only surficially, for numerous buried mountain structures are present here. Division of the Rocky Mountain system into four provinces is not merely for convenience of discussion, for fundamental differences exist

between the four provinces which justify their recognition as separate geomorphic units. Thus far subdivision of the Rocky Mountain system has not extended beyond the rank of province, although a real need for such subdivision exists.

### Southern Rocky Mountains

The southern end of the Southern Rocky Mountains lies in north-central New Mexico southeast of Santa Fe. From here this province extends northward to the northern end of the Laramie Mountains south of Casper, Wyoming. The Southern Rockies are made up mainly of a group of linear, anticlinal ranges with cores of Precambrian igneous or metamorphic rocks. Most of the ranges have an enechelon arrangement. The most notable exception to a linear shape is found in the San Juan Mountains in southwestern Colorado; sprawling, rather than linear, describes their form. Several of the ranges are separated from each other by broad intermontane basins or troughs commonly called "parks." It may be recalled that Powell was so impressed with these intermontane parks that in his physiographic subdivision of the United States (see p. 5) he applied the name Park Mountains to what is essentially the Southern Rocky Mountains province. The Southern Rocky Mountains are the highest of the Rockies; in Colorado, at least 46 peaks attain altitudes as great as 14,000 feet, and it has been estimated that there are 300 peaks in this state with altitudes as great as 13,000 feet (Fenneman, 1931). In general terms, it may be said that average altitudes in the Rocky Mountain System decrease northward and south-

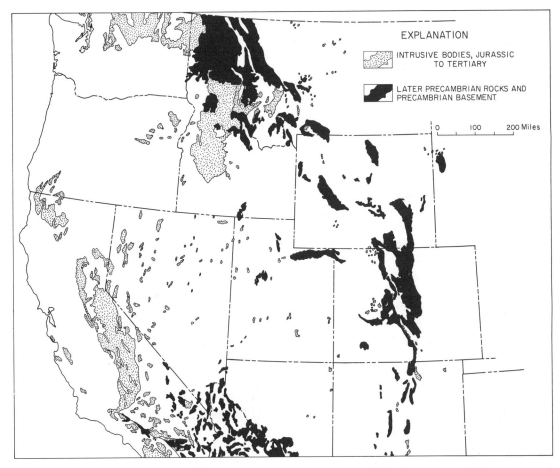

FIG. 17.1   Main igneous intrusive bodies of western United States.   (*After C. R. Longwell, Geol. Soc. Am. Bull.,* **61.**)

ward from the Colorado Rockies, although this is, of course, no regular progressive change.

### Wyoming Basin

The Wyoming Basin represents an extension of Great Plains topography into the Rocky Mountains through a break between the Laramie and Bighorn Mountains. Here all semblance of an eastern mountain front is lacking. Only the Wasatch Range and the belt of mountains in western Wyoming and southeastern Idaho known as the Wyomide Ranges interrupt an open passage from the Great Plains to the Great Basin province. At the south, through a gap east of the Uinta Mountains, the White River Plateau of the Southern Rockies connects with the Uinta

Basin of the Colorado Plateaus province. Mountains exist in the Wyoming Basin province, but in general they are buried or only partially exhumed. The extensiveness of Tertiary formations in the Wyoming Basin further attests to its affinity with the Great Plains.

### Middle Rocky Mountains

The Wyoming Basin separates the Southern and Middle Rocky Mountains. The Middle Rockies display marked diversity as to both rock types and structures. The ranges here can be divided into eastern and western groups which differ fundamentally in their characteristic structures. The eastern group, including such mountain uplifts as the Bighorn, Wind River, Beartooth, and Owl Creek, has considerable affinity with the Southern Rockies in that it consists of essentially anticlinal or domal uplifts with cores of igneous and metamorphic rocks of Precambrian age, flanked by homoclinal ridges and hogbacks on rocks of Paleozoic or Mesozoic age. The western mountain group, the so-called Wyomide Ranges along the western boundary of Wyoming and southeastern Idaho, includes the Gros Ventre, Hogback, Wyoming, Snake River, Salt, and Teton Ranges. Thrust faulting has played an important role in the development of these ranges. If it were not for the intervening Snake River Plain and the Yellowstone Lava Plateau, these ranges, because of similar structures, would probably be grouped along with those of southwestern Montana as a section of the Basin and Range province.

Certain mountain ranges in the Middle Rockies are anomalous in that they extend in an east-west direction. Most important in this group are the Uinta Mountains, but the lesser Centennial Range, west of the Montana-Idaho boundary, and the Owl Creek Range, at the south end of the Bighorn Basin, also have east-west trends. Yellowstone Plateau is anomalous in two respects; its topography is not mountainous, and it is a great pile of volcanic rocks rather than plutonic rocks flanked by sedimentaries.

*Northern Rocky Mountains*

The Northern Rockies are perhaps the least homogeneous of the four Rocky Mountain provinces as to both rock types and structure. The mountains of this province can be divided into three distinctive groups. On the west, and mainly in Idaho, the name "range" has little significance, for here the mountains are so lacking in alignment that it is difficult to say where one range ends and another begins. Lack of alignment here is related to the fact that the mountains here are developed on the Idaho batholith. The mountains of southwestern Montana have a closer structural affinity with the ranges of the Basin and Range province than with the other ranges of the Northern Rockies in that the ranges are largely bounded by high-angle normal faults. The frontal ranges in northern Montana

represent a still different type of mountain structure. Here thrust faulting, in places as highly imbricate as that found in the Alps, characterizes the frontal ranges as well as those back of them.

*Comparison of Northern and Southern Rockies*

King (1959) has pointed out some of the similarities and differences between the Southern and Northern Rockies. They are similar in that:

1. In both areas the contact between the mountainous topography and the plains topography on the east is marked by an abrupt and readily recognizable topographic front.
2. In both regions this abrupt topographic front represents a change from areas of little-deformed rocks to areas of much-deformed rocks.
3. At both the north and south, rocks that are stratigraphically lower than those underlying the Great Plains have been raised so high that they have been uncovered by erosion. These exposed rocks may be Mesozoic, Paleozoic, or Precambrian in age.

Differences between the Northern and Southern Rockies are:

1. East of the Southern Rockies the rocks of the Great Plains are little or at most mildly disturbed up almost to the mountain base, whereas in the Northern Rockies there is a belt extending a considerable distance plainsward in which the rocks of the Great Plains have been strongly folded and faulted. This is the so-called Disturbed Belt that extends along the Northern Rocky Mountain front for a distance of about 350 miles (Robinson, 1959).
2. Along the margin of the mountain uplifts in the Southern Rockies the sedimentary rocks have been upturned steeply or in some areas cut off by high-angle normal faults. In the Northern Rockies along the frontal margin the older sedimentary rocks have been carried eastward for many miles by great low-angle thrust faults onto the younger rocks of the Great Plains.
3. The Paleozoic sequence of the Southern

Rockies is a relatively thin one, whereas at the north is a thick miogeosynclinal sequence.

4. In the Southern Rockies, as well as the Middle Rockies, the Precambrian rocks are plutonic igneous rocks or metamorphic rocks; those of the Northern Rockies are the geosynclinal sedimentary rocks of the Belt Series.

## AREAS OF EXTENSIVE VOLCANIC ROCKS

Volcanic rocks are found over widely scattered parts of the Rocky Mountains, but only in two areas are they present in great quantity. One of these areas is the Yellowstone Plateau and adjacent Absaroka Mountains; the other is the San Juan Mountains. In both places great thicknesses of extrusive rocks are present. The volcanic rocks of the Yellowstone Plateau range in age from Eocene to Pleistocene, and those of the San Juan Mountains from Miocene to Quaternary. Extrusive sheets and intrusive dikes and sills are found in many parts of the Rockies and in some areas, as in western Montana and Idaho, on a rather extensive scale. In most of the mountain ranges, however, they make up a minor part of the total rock mass and are topographically inconspicuous.

## GEOMORPHIC HISTORY

### Conventional Interpretation

The present topography has developed largely since the Laramide orogeny, which initiated uplift of the present Rocky Mountains. Existing

FIG. 17.2 Flattop peneplain, looking southeast toward Longs Peak. (*Photo by John S. Shelton.*)

FIG. 17.3    Rocky Mountain peneplain, looking south toward Pikes Peak.    (*Photo by John S. Shelton.*)

land forms have long been interpreted in terms of alternating periods of peneplanation and uplift. Erosion surfaces considered peneplains have been described and named in many of the Rocky Mountain ranges. Remnants of what are presumed to be former erosion surfaces are somewhat better preserved in the Southern and Middle Rockies than in the Northern Rockies. What appear to be old erosion surfaces are particularly prominent in the Colorado Front Range, the Laramie Range, and the San Juan, Medicine Bow, Wind River, Bighorn, and Beartooth Mountains.

Preponderance of opinion seems to favor the view that possibly evidence for two major erosion cycles can be recognized in the present-day topography. In the Colorado Front Range two erosion surfaces have been described. The older of these has been called the Flattop peneplain

(see Fig. 17.2) and the younger the Rocky Mountain peneplain (see Fig. 17.3). Various other names have also been assigned to the younger of these erosion surfaces, such as the Sherman, South Park, or Green Mountain peneplain. In the Middle and Northern Rockies the two erosion surfaces are commonly called the Summit and Subsummit peneplains, but locally they have been given geographic names. Evidence for the younger of the two erosion surfaces is more convincing than for the older.

The following interpretation of Rocky Mountain geomorphic history is one that was long advocated by Atwood and Atwood (1938).

1. The Rocky Mountains came into existence during the Laramide revolution, in late Mesozoic and early Cenozoic time, as a series of

large anticlinal arches or domes, superposed on which were numerous lesser folds and faults.

2. Rise of the mountains produced a lowering of temperatures leading to mountain glaciation in Eocene time, as indicated by the Ridgway and Gunnison "tillites."

3. Erosion of the uplifted mountain structures led to development in early Tertiary time of the Flattop or Summit peneplain.

4. Uplift of this early Tertiary peneplain was followed by widespread volcanism.

5. From Oligocene to Pliocene time, erosion and basin filling went on in the Rocky Mountains, leading to near reduction of the mountains, filling of the intermontane basins, and the spreading over the Great Plains of a thick mantle of alluvial deposits. This composite erosional-depositional surface was the major geomorphic feature developed in the Rocky Mountains during Tertiary time. The erosional part of this composite surface is what has been called the Rocky Mountain, Sher-

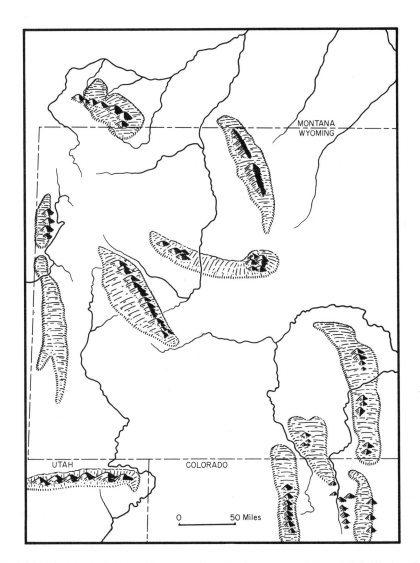

FIG. 17.4  Partially buried Rocky Mountain ranges of late Tertiary time.  (*After W. W. Atwood, Sr., and W. W. Atwood, Jr., Geol. Soc. Am. Bull.,* **49**.)

man, and Subsummit peneplains. This erosion surface merged on the east with the widespread fluviatile deposits that now constitute the Ogallala formation. Not all the mountains were destroyed during this period of erosion; some stood up as large monadnock-like tracts only partially buried in their own alluvium (see Fig. 17.4). Regional superposition of major drainage lines accompanied deposition of the great sheet of alluvium in the intermontane basins and on the mountain flanks.

6. Epeirogenic uplift of several thousand feet followed, and the superposed streams began a period of canyon cutting.
7. Increased altitude of the mountains brought about a lowering of temperatures which initiated Pleistocene glaciation.
8. Minor uplifts during the Pleistocene epoch were responsible for renewed canyon cutting, the excavation of some of the smaller parks, and the development of a series of alluvial terraces in the foothills and plains region.

With local variations, this is a pattern of geomorphic history that has been applied widely over the Rocky Mountain region. Local names have been given to the alleged peneplains, but in numerous areas two major erosion surfaces analogous to the Flattop and Rocky Mountain surfaces have been described.

Blackwelder (1915), from his study of the Wind River Mountains of western Wyoming, introduced an interpretation of their geomorphic history that has been followed by numerous geologists who have worked in areas adjacent to the Wind River Range. He recognized four erosional cycles in the degradational history of these mountains, the Pliocene Wind River cycle and three Pleistocene cycles called the Union Pass, Black Rock, and Circle cycles. The Wind River cycle presumably is represented by a summit erosion surface that has peneplain characteristics. In the succeeding Union Pass cycle a postmature, broad valley type of topography was developed, and the younger Black Rock and Circle cycles were apparently even less advanced before they were terminated.

## Pedimentation versus Peneplanation

The Atwood concept of Rocky Mountain history has been challenged by two groups of geologists, those who deny the existence of peneplains and cycles of erosion and those who believe that Rocky Mountain erosional history can be better explained in terms of pedimentation than in those of peneplanation. Mackin (1947), in interpreting the so-called Summit and Subsummit erosion surfaces in the Bighorn Mountains, found the pediment concept more applicable to them. It seemed to fit better with the semiarid climatic conditions that apparently prevailed there in late Tertiary time, and it reduces by about 6000 feet the amount of Pliocene and Pleistocene uplift that must be postulated. Mackin argued that the Atwood interpretation of Rocky Mountain geomorphic history is essentially an Appalachian Mountains-two peneplains interpretation carried into the Rocky Mountains without regard to the differences between these two parts of the United States. He doubted that any erosion surface as ancient as Eocene could be preserved except beneath a cover mass. He further doubted the occurrence of Eocene glaciation in the Rocky Mountains because the fauna and flora of early Tertiary time indicate mild, humid climates as well as altitudes that would not favor mountain glaciation.

Mackin attributed the present high regional slope of the Subsummit surface not so much to regional uplift and tilting after its formation as to original steep slopes on a pediment developed at a high altitude in relation to stream courses adjusted to late-Tertiary semi-arid conditions. The "Summit peneplain" was considered a noncyclic surface younger than the Subsummit surface, produced during Pleistocene time by the various processes encompassed under the terms altiplanation or cryoplanation. Present relief of the Bighorn Mountains was viewed as a continuation of Tertiary relief increased by the amount of regional lowering of the adjacent Great Plains and intermontane basins that has taken place and lessened somewhat by the processes which produced the Summit surface during Pleistocene and Recent time.

Rich (1938) and Howard (1941) had previously suggested that pedimentation should be given serious consideration as a possible explanation of the erosion surfaces in the Colorado Rockies, and Bradley (1936), from his study of the north flank of the Uinta Mountains, had come to the conclusion that two prominent erosion surfaces there, the Gilbert Peak and Bear Mountain surfaces, could be more logically interpreted as pediments than as peneplains. His reasons for this conclusion were that their slopes have gradients more of the order expectable on pediments than on peneplains, and the fact that their surfaces apparently never had on them the thick soil mantle expectable on a peneplain surface but had instead a thick gravel veneer, a feature expectable on the surface of a pediment.

If the concept that there developed in the Rocky Mountains in late Tertiary time a widespread composite topographic surface partly erosional and partly depositional in origin has validity, it would seem that pedimentation would more logically explain the topographic conditions that existed near the end of this cycle of erosion. Not all of the mountain masses were worn down, and surrounding the low ranges were encircling pediments and bajadas that merged into a regional gradational surface of wide extent. The deposits in the intermontane basins were definitely a bajada type and it is perhaps not extending the term bajada too much to consider the vast apron of alluvium that was spread over the Great Plains a sort of great bajada.

# GLACIAL HISTORY OF ROCKY MOUNTAINS

## Doubtful Validity of Eocene Glaciation

An integral part of the Atwood interpretation of Rocky Mountain history was belief in Eocene mountain glaciation. What were called the Ridgeway and Gunnison "tillites" were cited as evidence for this early Tertiary glaciation (Atwood, 1915; Atwood and Mather, 1932). The glacial origin of these alleged "tillites" has been pretty well disproved in recent years. Van Houten (1957) concluded that the 'Ridgway tillite" is in reality a mudflow and alluvial deposit that correlates in age with the late Cretaceous-early Paleocene Animas formation. Mather and Wengerd (1962), after careful field study of the Ridgeway area, came to the conclusion that the lower part of this deposit is truly glacial till, but of Pleistocene age and probably correlative with the Durango till in the San Juan Mountains (Atwood and Mather, 1932). The remaining part of the Ridgway deposit was believed to be landslide material and crushed Mancos shale. The "Gunnison tillite," they concluded, is all of nonglacial origin. Deposits in the Middle and Northern Rockies interpreted by Atwood as Eocene glacial materials are probably in many areas remnants of the Bishop conglomerate, a widespread Tertiary deposit (Rich, 1910). Thus the idea of Eocene glaciation as a part of Rocky Mountain geomorphic history seems to be untenable.

## Ages and Subages of Rocky Mountain Glaciation

Correlation of ages and subages of glaciation is inherently a much more difficult task in mountains than in lowlands. It may be questionable whether it will ever be possible to work out as detailed a glacial chronology for the mountains of the western United States as has already been done for the central United States, but considerable progress has been made, and gradually the broad picture is evolving, particularly for the Wisconsin glacial age.

Evidence for multiple glaciation has been described in the San Juan Mountains (Atwood and Mather, 1932; Richmond 1954), the Colorado Front Range (Ray, 1940), the Uinta Mountains (Bradley, 1936), the Beartooth Range (Bevan, 1946), the Tetons (Fryxell, Horberg, and Edmund, 1941), the Mission Range (Nobles, 1952), and the Wind River Mountains (Blackwelder, 1915).

Despite the fact that various names have been given to the ages and subages of mountain glaciation in different parts of the Rocky Mountains, the terminology that was first proposed by Blackwelder (1915) for the glaciations in the

Wind River Mountains is rapidly becoming standard for the Rocky Mountain region. Blackwelder recognized evidence for three glaciations, the Buffalo, Bull Lake, and Pinedale. The Buffalo glaciation was considered to be pre-Wisconsin in age and tentatively correlated with the Kansan; the Bull Lake was believed to be early Wisconsin and the Pinedale late Wisconsin in age.

Since Blackwelder's pioneer studies it has become recognized that the glacial sequence is somewhat more complex than first thought. Buffalo glaciation seems to have involved two ice advances, as did the Bull Lake (Richmond, 1948; Holmes and Moss, 1955). The Pinedale glaciation was at least double in nature (Moss, 1951; Holmes and Moss, 1955) and perhaps involved three stadials, as suggested by Richmond (1948). A substage in the Wind River Mountains later than Pinedale, the Temple Lake, has been suggested (Howard and Hack, 1943) on the basis of nivation hollows and secondary cirques cut in the Pinedale cirques.

Richmond (1948) believed it possible to trace seven glacio-fluviatile terraces out from the Wind River and Uinta Mountains that correlate with the seven substages of glaciation that he postulated for these two mountain ranges. The exact ages of the several glaciations are uncertain; relative ages are clearly indicated by the degree of modification of the glacial topography. The Buffalo drift is clearly the oldest drift, for it lacks fresh glacial forms and is found only on ridge crests and shoulders. There seems to be little question that the longest interval between glaciations was that between the Buffalo and the Bull Lake. The topography of both Bull Lake and Pinedale drifts has readily discernible morainal form, and the Pinedale drift particularly shows little evidence of erosion or mass-wasting. Comparison of the topography on Bull Lake and Pinedale drifts suggests that the interval between the Bull Lake II and Pinedale I was longer than between Bull Lake I and Bull Lake II or between Pinedale I and Pinedale II. Thus the Bull Lake and Pinedale are considered early and late Wisconsin glaciations respectively.

Undoubtedly the Buffalo glaciation was a pre-Wisconsin glaciation, and although it has been commonly suggested that it was Kansan in age, this is by no means established; it could very well be Illinoian or, for that matter, Nebraskan. Attempts to correlate stages of mountain glaciation, particularly pre-Wisconsin ones, with stages of continental glaciation in the central United States are at best hardly more than good scientific guesses. It is by no means certain that there were correlative glaciations in the western mountains and the Central Lowlands. Fairly good evidence exists for more than one pre-Wisconsin glaciation in the Rocky Mountain region. Richmond (1957) has described numerous areas where pre-Wisconsin drifts occur, and he thought it possible that three pre-Wisconsin glaciations could be recognized which might correlate with the Illinoian, Kansan, and Nebraskan of the Central Lowlands, but no conclusive evidence that this is true can be offered.

## PROBLEMS OF ROCKY MOUNTAIN DRAINAGE

### Tranverse River Gorges

A striking aspect of stream courses in the Rocky Mountains is the large number of streams that flow directly across mountain uplifts through deep gorges (see Fig. 17.5). Examples of such gorges are the Royal Gorge of the Arkansas River (see Fig. 17.6) through the Colorado Front Range, the Lodore Canyon of the Green River through the Uinta Mountains, the Wind River Canyon through the Owl Creek Mountains of north-central Wyoming, the gorge of the Missouri River through the Lombard overthrust block, and that of the Big Hole River through the Highland Range in southwestern Montana.

### Superposition versus Antecedence

For many years it was thought that these gorges could be most logically explained as examples of antecedent streams which maintained their courses athwart uplifts. The Lodore Canyon of Green River was Powell's type example of an antecedent stream. The Atwoods (1938)

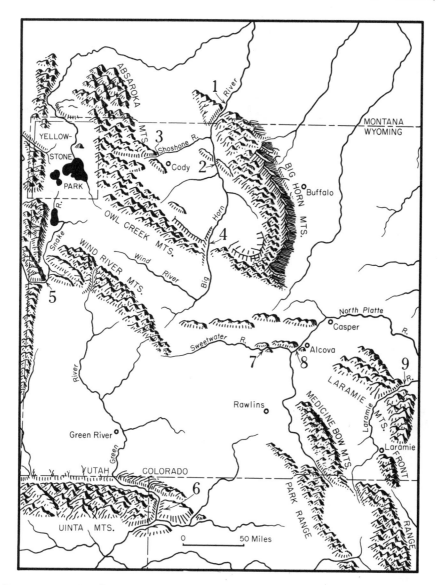

FIG. 17.5   Present topography of area covered by Fig. 17.4.   Numbers indicate sites of canyons where stream courses are superposed across mountain uplifts.   1. Bighorn Canyon through Bighorn Mountains.   2. Bighorn River near Greybull.   3. Shoshone Canyon.   4. Wind River Canyon.   5. Snake River Canyon.   6. Lodore Canyon of Green River.   7. Devil's Gate of Sweetwater River.   8. North Platte River near Alcova.   9. Laramie River.   (*After W. W. Atwood, Sr., and W. W. Atwood, Jr., Geol. Soc. Am. Bull.,* **49.**)

have particularly been responsible for showing that these unusual drainage features can more logically be explained as a result of superposition.

Whether or not we consider the major erosional cycle of late Tertiary time that produced such surfaces as the so-called Rocky Mountain peneplain as a cycle of peneplanation or one of pedimentation, there is good reason to believe that at its close not only was there a great alluvial plain built out onto the Great Plains, but many of the mountains were essentially buried in their own debris (see Fig. 17.4).

FIG. 17.6 Royal Gorge of the Arkansas River through Colorado Front Range. The suspension bridge which spans the gorge is 1053 feet above the bottom of the gorge. (*Photo courtesy Denver and Rio Grande Railway.*)

Stream courses then were largely independent of mountain structures. The conditions that existed in late Tertiary time are to some degree still reflected in the Wyoming Basin province, where several of the buried mountain structures are only now being exhumed. Strongly supporting the theory of regional superposition of Tertiary drainage lines are such examples as the Devil's Gate of the Sweetwater River in central Wyoming (see 8 of Fig. 17.5 and Fig. 19.4). Here the Sweetwater River has cut a short gorge through the nose of a partially exhumed mountain structure, whereas by merely detouring a fraction

of a mile to the east it could have avoided entirely the hard rock barrier. A similar example may be seen along the Jefferson River in Montana, where this stream cuts across the nose of a ridge of Mississippian limestone, whereas by going a short distance to the north it could have avoided the ridge (see Fig. 21.12). Stream courses of this sort are difficult to explain unless we assume that the streams have been let down from a former cover mass onto the structures through which they flow.

## REFERENCES CITED

Atwood, W. W. (1915). Eocene deposits in southwestern Colorado, *U. S. Geol. Survey Profess. Paper* 95, 13–26.

—— and Atwood, W. W., Jr. (1932). Working hypothesis for the physiographic history of the Rocky Mountain region, *Geol. Soc. Am. Bull.*, **49**, 957–980.

—— and K. F. Mather (1932). Physiography and Quaternary geology of the San Juan Mountains, *U. S. Geol. Survey Profess. Paper* 166, 176 pp.

Bevan, Arthur (1946). Three stages of Pleistocene glaciation, Beartooth Mountains, Montana, *Geol. Soc. Am. Bull.*, **57**, 1178–1179 (abs.).

Blackwelder, Eliot (1915). Post-Cretaceous history of the mountains of southwestern Wyoming, *Jour. Geol.*, **23**, 97–117, 193–217, and 307–340.

Bradley, W. H. (1936). Geomorphology of the north flank of the Uinta Mountains, *U. S. Geol. Survey Profess. Paper* 185-I, 163–204.

Fenneman, N. M. (1931). *Physiography of Western United States*, McGraw-Hill Book Company, 534 pp.

Fryxell, F. M., Leland Horberg, and Rudolph Edmund (1941). Geomorphology of the Teton Range and adjacent basins, Wyoming-Idaho, *Geol. Soc. Am. Bull.*, **52**, 1903 (abs.).

Holmes, G. W. and J. H. Moss (1955). Pleistocene geology of southwestern Wind River Mountains, Wyoming, *Geol. Soc. Am. Bull.*, **66**, 629–654.

Howard, A. D. (1941). Rocky Mountain peneplains or pediments, *Jour. Geomorph.*, **4**, 138–141.

Howard, E. B., and J. T. Hack (1943). The Finley site, *Am. Antiquities*, **8**, 224–241.

King, P. B. (1959). *The Evolution of North America*, Princeton Univ. Press, Princeton, 190 pp.

Mackin, J. H. (1947). Altitude and local relief in the Bighorn area during the Cenozoic, Wyo. Geol. Assoc. Field conference in Bighorn Basin, *Guidebook*, 103–120.

Mather, K. F., and S. A. Wengerd (1962). Pleistocene age of the "Eocene" Ridgeway till, Colorado, *Geol. Soc. Am. Spec. Paper* 73, 203 (abs.).

Moss, J. H. (1951). Late glacial advances in the southern Wind River Mountains, Wyoming, *Am. Jour. Sci.*, **249**, 865–883.

Nobles, L. H. (1952). Glacial sequence in the Mission Valley, western Montana, *Geol. Soc. Am. Bull.*, **63**, 1286–1287 (abs.).

Ray, L. L. (1940). Glacial chronology of the southern Rocky Mountains, *Geol. Soc. Am. Bull.*, **51**, 1851–1918.

Rich, J. L. (1910). The physiography of the Bishop conglomerate, southwestern Wyoming, *Jour. Geol.*, **18**, 601–632.

—— (1938). Recognition and significance of multiple erosion surfaces, *Geol. Soc. Am. Bull.*, **49**, 1695–1722.

Richmond, G. M. (1948). Modification of Blackwelder's sequence of Pleistocene glaciation in the Wind River Mountains, *Geol. Soc. Am. Bull.*, **59**, 1400–1401.

—— (1954). Modification of the glacial chronology of the San Juan Mountains, Colorado, *Science*, **119**, 614–615.

—— (1957). Three Pre-Wisconsin glacial stages in the Rocky Mountain region, *Geol. Soc. Am. Bull.*, **68**, 239–262.

Robinson, G. D. (1959). The Disturbed Belt in the Sixteenmile area, Montana, *Billings Geol. Soc. Guidebook, Tenth Ann. Field Conference*, 34–40.

Van Houten, F. B. (1957). Appraisal of the Ridgeway and Gunnison "tillites," southwestern Colorado, *Geol. Soc. Am. Bull.*, **68**, 383–388.

ADDITIONAL REFERENCES

Atwood, W. W., and W. W. Atwood, Jr. (1938). Opening of the Pleistocene in the Rocky Mountains of the United States, *Jour. Geol.*, **46**, 239–247.

Atwood, W. W. (1940). *The Physiographic Provinces of North America*, Ginn and Company, New York, Chapt. 9, 281–353.

—— and W. W. Atwood, Jr. (1948). Tertiary-Pleistocene transition at the east margin of the Rocky Mountains, *Geol. Soc. Am. Bull.*, **59**, 605–608.

Hunt, C. B., and V. P. Sokoloff (1950). Pre-Wisconsin soil in the Rocky Mountain region: a progress report, *U. S. Geol. Survey Profess. Paper 221-G*, 109–123.

Lee, W. T. (1922). Peneplains of the Front Range at Rocky Mountain National Park, *U. S. Geol. Survey Bull. 730*, 1–17.

Miller, J. P. (1958). Problems of the Pleistocene in Cordilleran North America as related to reconstruction of environmental changes that affected early man, in Smiley, T. L. Editor, Climate and man in the southwest, *Univ. Arizona Bull.*, **28**, No. 4, 19–49.

# 18

# Southern Rocky Mountain Province

## GENERAL DESCRIPTION

*Mountain Ranges.* With the notable exception of the San Juan Mountains in southwestern Colorado, the Southern Rocky Mountains consist predominately of a group of north-south mountain ranges of roughly anticlinal structure with cores of igneous and metamorphic rocks flanked by steeply dipping sedimentary rocks. The mountain ranges fall mainly into two north-south belts between which is a series of intermontane basins. The ranges in the eastern group are, from north to south, the Laramie Mountains, the Colorado Front Range, and the Wet Mountains. In the western group are, from north to south, the Park, Gore, Mosquito, Sawatch, and Sangre de Cristo ranges. The San Juan Mountains are somewhat detached from the other ranges and lie to the west of the Sangre de Cristo Mountains. In addition to lacking the north-south orientation of the other ranges the San Juans are different in that they are mainly a great pile of volcanic rocks.

Although the main mass of the Southern Rockies lies in Colorado, these mountains reach into Wyoming and New Mexico. At the north two prongs extend into Wyoming, the Laramie Mountains at the east and the Medicine Bow Mountains at the west. At the south the Sangre de Cristo Mountains continue into New Mexico.

*Intermontane Basins.* Separating the two major mountain belts are four intermontane basins which, from north to south, are North Park, Middle Park, South Park, and Wet Mountain Valley. The San Luis Valley is a similar basin farther south between the Sangre de Cristo

Range and the San Juan Mountains. These basins represent downfolded and downfaulted parts of the broad geanticlinal arch that developed when the modern Rocky Mountains came into existence. In a general way the same Paleozoic and Mesozoic rocks that are found on the eastern and western flanks of the mountain ranges may be present in the intermontane basins. This does not necessarily mean that these strata at any one time extended continuously across the entire Southern Rockies, for some likely were eroded off the rising folds about as rapidly as the folds rose, and only in the depressed sections of the geanticline did they escape erosion. Tertiary beds similar in age and origin to those found over the Great Plains are also present in the intermontane basins. They are products of the same erosion cycles during which the broad mantle of Tertiary sediments was laid down east of the Rocky Mountains and, like the Paleozoic and Mesozoic strata, were at one time more extensive than at present.

## MAJOR STRUCTURAL FEATURES

Major structural features of the Southern Rockies are products of the Laramide orogeny, which probably began in early Cretaceous time and reached its peak in Paleocene time. Figure 18.1 depicts the major structural features that may be associated with this orogeny (King, 1959). It seems likely that the pre-Tertiary topography and structure did much to localize the folding and faulting that took place during the Laramide orogeny (Lovering and Goddard,

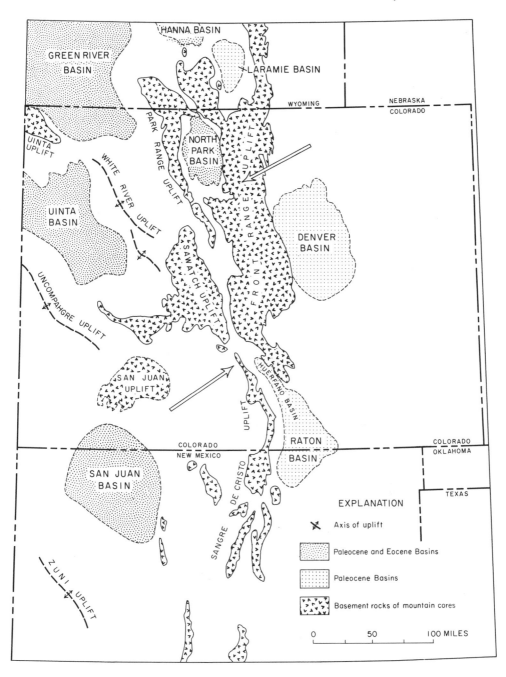

FIG. 18.1   Major structures produced by Laramide orogeny.   (*After P. B. King, The Evolution of North America, by permission of Princeton University Press.*)

1950). The site of the present Front Range seems to have been a positive area during most of Paleozoic and Mesozoic time and may have been completely covered by the sea only in Cretaceous time.

In addition to a number of major uplifts and downwarps there developed during the Laramide orogeny numerous faults whose positions may well have been influenced by structures that date back to Precambrian time. On the west side of the Colorado Front Range is a series of great overthrust faults that extend from South Park to the Wyoming border. Displacement along some of these overthrusts was as much as 4 to 6 miles. Faults later than Laramide in age are few and largely limited to areas of Miocene volcanism and to Tertiary basins close to the mountain front.

## LARAMIDE AND YOUNGER IGNEOUS ROCKS

The younger igneous rocks of the Southern Rockies can be grouped into three age groups, an early group associated with the beginning of the Laramide orogeny and ranging in age from

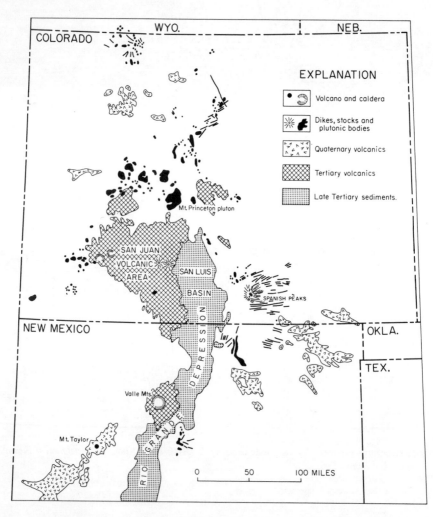

FIG. 18.2   Tertiary and Quaternary igneous rocks of Southern Rocky Mountains.   (*After P. B. King, The Evolution of North America, by permission of Princeton University Press.*)

late Cretaceous to Eocene, a mid-Tertiary group, mainly of Miocene age, and locally some igneous rocks of Pliocene-Pleistocene age. Both extrusive and intrusive rocks are present (see Fig. 18.2).

Volcanic rocks of the oldest group are represented by lava flows, andesitic conglomerates, and tuffs in the Denver and Middle Park formations of late Cretaceous-Eocene age. Flows of this age are found in South Park, Middle Park, and the Denver Basin (North Table Mountain is an example; see Fig. 16.20). Scattered dikes and plugs mark the conduits of the volcanoes of this time.

A great outpouring of volcanic rocks took place in the San Juan Mountain region in Miocene time but volcanic rocks of the same age can be found near the northwest corner of Rocky Mountain National Park, in the Cripple Creek area, and in an area between the headwaters of Arkansas and South Platte rivers near Salida, Colorado. These areas are probably the eastern outliers of the large San Juan volcanic field (Lovering and Goddard, 1950).

# FRONT RANGES

## Colorado Front Range

*Description.* The Colorado Front Range is the major range of the eastern mountain belt. It extends for approximately 185 miles from its southern end at the Arkansas River to the Colorado-Wyoming state line, north of which it becomes the somewhat subdued mountains known as the Laramie Range. The name Rampart Range is commonly applied to that part of the Front Range between the South Platte River and the Colorado Springs area. The Front Range is a mosaic of fault-bounded blocks of Precambrian granites, schists, and gneisses (Lovering and Goddard, 1950) bordered on the east by a foothill belt 2 to 4 miles wide in which Paleozoic and Mesozoic rocks dip steeply eastward into the Denver Basin (see Fig. 18.3). Along most of its margin Paleozoic beds rest on the basement complex rocks, but on the west side near Breckinridge, Colorado, steeply dipping

Mesozoic beds rest on the Precambrian rocks. Locally, the truncated edges of the Paleozoic and Mesozoic strata are covered with dipping Tertiary beds which may extend onto the Precambrian rocks. The sedimentary sequence has an aggregate thickness of at least 3 miles, and the Precambrian rocks extend from 14,000 feet above sea level in the higher peaks to 8000 feet below sea level in the Denver Basin. On the west, the Front Range is bordered by three intermontane basins, North Park, South Park, and Middle Park.

*Rocks and Structure.* The Front Range is a complexly faulted anticlinal arch on which are superposed numerous cross folds and faults that make it possible to divide it into five major fault-bounded structural belts (Boos and Boos, 1957). These structural units have the following features in common: (1) their long dimensions extend northwest-southeast; (2) they are bounded on their northeast and southwest sides by fault and shear zones; (3) in each unit there is a major granite batholith or series of stocks; and (4) the faults and shear zones are mainly of Precambrian age, but most of them were reactivated during the Laramide orogeny.

The main mass of the Front Range consists of Precambrian crystalline rocks, including high-grade meta-sedimentary beds, layered meta-igneous rocks, and quartzites which have been intruded by at least six generations of granitic rocks. Granitic rocks comprise about two-third of the Precambrian complex. Large batholiths form the north and south ends of the range. The southern batholith consists of the well-known Pikes Peak granite, and the batholith at the north end of the Front Range is composed of the hardly less well-known Sherman granite. The central part of the range has in it a complex of small plutons which are enclosed by the various gneisses, schists, and quartzites. Not all of the igneous rocks are of Precambrian age, for numerous Tertiary stocks, sills, and dikes, and locally some extrusives (see Fig. 18.2) are present.

*Topography.* The foothills belt of the Front Range with its steeply eastward-dipping Paleo-

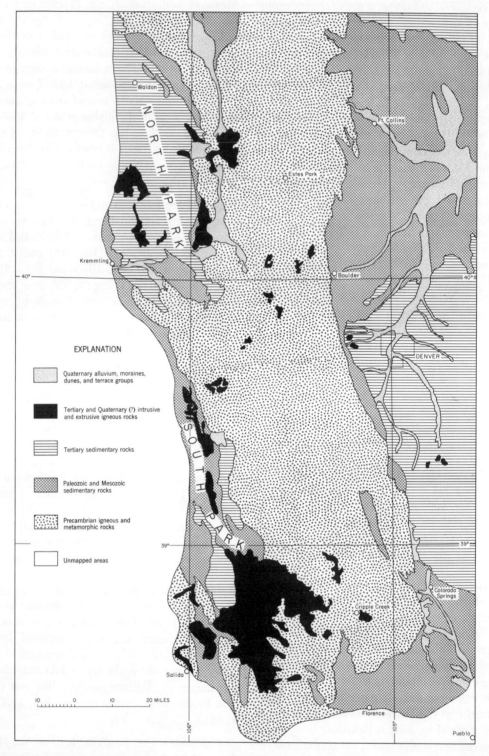

FIG. 18.3   Geologic map of Colorado Front Range and surroundings.   (*After T. S. Lovering and E. N. Goddard,*
*U. S. Geol. Survey Profess. Paper 223.*)

zoic and Mesozoic rocks, on which are developed hogback ridges and gravel-veneered pediments, has been described in the section on the Colorado Piedmont section of the Great Plains (see p. 312). At the contact of the sedimentary and igneous-metamorphic complex of the Front Range there is a sharp topographic rise from 5000–6000 feet on the plains to 8000 feet or so at the eastern edge of the Front Range. From an altitude of around 8000 feet the surface of the Front Range rises gradually westward toward the crest of the Front Range. It is this plateau-like slope that is the type area of what has been called the Rocky Mountain peneplain or pediplain (see Fig. 17.3).

Ridges extending out from the range crest that have altitudes 1500 to 2000 feet higher than the Rocky Mountain erosion surface are believed by some to represent the remnants of the Flattop "peneplain." Rising still higher than the Flattop surface are numerous axial peaks which exceed 12,000 and 13,000 feet in altitude; Longs Peak (14,255) and Mt. Evans (14,264) exceed 14,000 feet. There is a definite line of peaks along the axis of the range in the area west of Denver, but southward this line of high peaks is not continuous. Pikes Peak (14,109) is somewhat detached from the main range, and on this account stands out conspicuously above the upland tract that has been called the Rocky Mountain peneplain (see Fig. 17.3).

Glaciation has added to the sculpturing of the axial range, and most of the peaks display prominent cirques on their fronts. Actually, most of the more prominent peaks are horns along the serrate ridge that forms the crest of the Front Range. Deep glacial troughs extend down from the range crest for an average distance between 10 and 12 miles, and along these troughs may be seen numerous segments of lateral and end moraines that mark the later substages of Wisconsin glaciation.

*Erosional History.* The geomorphic history of the Colorado Front Range essentially parallels that which was outlined for the Rocky Mountain system in the preceding chapter. Van Tuyl (1955) has recognized the following major events:

1. Inception of the Front Range during the Laramide Revolution began with the formation of a broad anticlinal arch contemporaneously with downwarping of the Denver Basin to the east. This orogeny was accompanied by some volcanic activity, as represented by local dikes, sills, and extrusive sheets.

2. Truncation of the Front Range upwarp by erosion during Eocene, Oligocene, and Miocene time during periods of intermittent uplift was accompanied by deposition of the sediments in the Denver Basin and on the Great Plains to the east. It was during one of these periods of less rapid uplift that the erosion surface called the Flattop peneplain was produced.

3. During a period of essential stillstand or exceedingly slow uplift in Pliocene time, there developed the widespread erosion surface of moderate relief that has been called the Rocky Mountain peneplain. The materials removed from the mountains to produce this erosion surface were spread widely to the east and may have lapped onto the eastern edge of the Precambrian crystalline rock belt of the Front Range.

4. Widespread regional uplift initiated erosion which resulted in the removal of most of the Tertiary sediments from the Colorado Piedmont area east of the Front Range and some of the Mesozoic sediments. This same uplift initiated canyon cutting in the crystalline rock belt to the west.

5. Alternating periods of valley cutting and pedimentation in the foothills belts during Pleistocene time gave rise to several gravel-capped pediments and terraces. Erosional surfaces correlating with the pediments in the foothills can be traced back a short distance into the mountain belt.

6. Contemporaneous with development of the pediments and terraces along the eastern front of the mountains were periods of glaciation in the high mountains which produced glacial outwash that was carried into the foothills belt and deposited as gravel caps on the Pleistocene terraces.

7. Recent erosion began at the close of the Pleistocene.

## LARAMIE RANGE

A short distance south of the Colorado-Wyoming state boundary the Front Range bifurcates and becomes two ranges, the Laramie on the east and the Medicine Bow on the west; the Laramie Basin occupies the area between the two ranges. Because the Laramie Range is the frontal range in Wyoming, it is usually looked upon as the northern continuation of the Colorado Front Range. Like the Colorado Front Range, the Laramie Range is a broad asymmetrical anticlinal structure with a steeper east than west limb. The sedimentary sequence on the eastern flank of the range is similar to that for the Colorado Front Range, with one notable difference: in the Gangplank area (see p. 288) the Tertiary formations have escaped erosion and extend across the Paleozoic and Mesozoic formations onto Precambrian rocks. This is the only place along the Southern Rocky Mountains where Tertiary formations do this, and we get here a glimpse of what the relationships between the Great Plains and Rocky Mountains were at the close of the Pliocene erosion cycle. If the Tertiary formations that have been removed from the Colorado Piedmont could be restored, they would lap against and perhaps onto the Precambrian rocks of the Colorado Front Range. It appears, however, that the axial portion of the Front Range was never reduced to as low relief as is found in the Laramie Mountains.

FIG. 18.4   The Sherman peneplain of Wyoming. (*Photo by T. S. Lovering, U. S. Geol. Survey.*)

*Sherman Peneplain.* The Tertiary formations of the Gangplank merge at the west with an erosion surface cut across the Laramie Range (see Fig. 18.4), which, because of its extensive development on the Sherman granite belt, has been called the Sherman peneplain. This surface correlates with the Rocky Mountain erosion surface of the Colorado Front Range and, like this surface, has in recent years been considered by some a pediplain rather than a peneplain. Its highest elevation is around 8500 feet, and it has an eastward slope of between 90 and 100 feet to the mile, giving it an elevation at its eastern margin of about 7300 feet (Moore, 1960). Its surface in general is undulating, and over much of it is a mantle of weathered granite debris which at one place at least is 40 to 50 feet thick. It appears that a balance between erosion on the Sherman granite and deposition on the plains was attained as early as Oligocene time and continued to Pleistocene time, when dissection of the Tertiary sediments set in. The presence of Precambrian debris in rocks of Oligocene age suggests that Paleozoic and Mesozoic sediments had been stripped from the Sherman granite as early as Oligocene time. By the end of Miocene time the eastern flank of the Laramie Range probably was covered with Oligocene and Miocene sediments, and the ramp of the Gangplank had begun to develop. By the end of Pliocene time Tertiary sediments extended well onto the area of Precambrian rocks, or perhaps largely covered them. Pleistocene uplift started the stripping of Tertiary sediments that has continued to the present.

## MEDICINE BOW MOUNTAINS

The Medicine Bow Range, at the west side of the Laramie Basin, is much more rugged than the Laramie Range. A central core of Precambrian quartzite (Knight, 1953) and a high-level erosion surface at 9000 to 11,000 feet give to much of the range a plateau-like character. Rising above this surface, much like the axial peaks of the Colorado Front Range, are numerous glacially carved peaks locally known as the Snowy Range. The age of the high-level erosion surface is in dispute. Knight (1953) favored an Eocene age for it, but Steven (1956) concluded that it is late Pliocene to early Pleistocene in age on the grounds that parts of the erosion surface truncate structures that were formed in late Cenozoic time.

## SANGRE DE CRISTO RANGE

The Colorado Front Range terminates at the south at the Arkansas River. South of the Arkansas River and offset en echelon to the west are the Wet Mountains, and between them and the Sangre de Cristo Mountains farther west is Wet Mountain Valley, an intermontane valley similar to the larger South, Middle, and North Parks farther north. Although the Sangre de Cristo Mountains are the frontal range at the southern end of the Rocky Mountains, they belong with the western granite belt described above. The Sangre de Cristo Range extends from near Salida, Colorado, on the Arkansas River southeastward for 140 miles to somewhat beyond Santa Fe, New Mexico. By some, the name Sangre de Cristo is limited to the part of the range from the Arkansas River south to La Veta Pass in southern Colorado, and the name Culebra Range is applied to the continuation of the mountains into New Mexico (Gabelman, 1956).

*Rocks and Structure.* Geologically the Sangre de Cristo Range consists of a core of Precambrian schists, gneisses, pegmatites, and local bodies of granite and diorite, along with what is one of the most complexly folded belts of sedimentary rocks in the Southern Rockies on its eastern side. The sedimentary rocks range from Ordovician to Cretaceous in age (Burbank and Goddard, 1937). This belt of deformed sedimentaries comprises most of the range at the north, but at the south the sedimentary rocks are confined mainly to the foothill belt. The Precambrian rocks, which make up the western part of the range south of Blanca Peak, are partially covered with Tertiary lavas related in age and origin to the lavas of the Raton section of the Great Plains.

Although the Sangre de Cristo Range was originally considered to be essentially an anticlinal structure bordered by synclines on the east and west under Wet Mountain and San Luis valleys, it is now known that the structure of the range is rendered much more complex than this by both normal and thrust faults along the margins of the range. Downfaulting of the San Luis Valley on the west probably occurred between late Oligocene time and the close of the Tertiary period. This was at the same time that extensive outpouring of volcanic rocks took place in the San Juan Mountains region. Very likely the downfaulting of the San Luis Valley area was occasioned by withdrawal of large volumes of lava from beneath it and accompanying outpouring of the lava in the San Juan Mountains. The Sangre de Cristo Mountains were extensively glaciated during the Pleistocene epoch, and in either Pleistocene or Recent time numerous rock streams formed.

## INTERMONTANE BASINS

### San Luis Valley

The San Luis Valley is an intermontane depression having a maximum width of 50 miles and a length of 150 miles; it lies between the Sangre de Cristo Mountains on the east and the San Juan and Sawatch mountains on the west (Upson, 1939). It is open at the south, where it merges with the Rio Grande Depression (see p. 499). The San Luis Valley is one of the largest of the several intermontane basins in the Southern Rocky Mountain province. As a structural basin it is divided into two parts by the basaltic San Luis Hills. These hills rise from 500 to 1000 feet above the valley floor and are capped with volcanic andesitic rocks of the same age as those so extensively present in the San Juan Mountains to the west.

Where the Rio Grande enters the valley, near Del Norte, Colorado, it has built a large alluvial fan having a radius of about 20 miles. Other streams that come into the valley from the adjoining mountains have carried rock waste into the valley so that the structural depression has in it a great thickness of alluvial waste (Powell, 1958). The lower part of the basin fill is known as the Santa Fe formation and the upper part as the Alamosa formation. The Santa Fe formation's age is uncertain; it has been considered Miocene, Pliocene, and even as young as Pleistocene. Not much of this formation is exposed in the San Luis Valley, but farther south in the Rio Grande Depression in New Mexico it is extensively exposed.

The northern end of the San Luis Valley is a closed basin, and all the drainage into it either is lost by percolation and evaporation or forms ephemeral lakes. Viewed from a distance (see Fig. 18.5) the valley floor appears flat, except for the volcanic hills which rise above its surface. Stream erosion is not evident in the valley; even the Rio Grande has cut only a shallow trench through it.

### South Park

South Park is one of the best known of the intermontane basins of Colorado. It is a large structural basin about 45 miles long and 35 miles wide at a maximum which lies between the Colorado Front Range on the east and the Mosquito Range on the west (see Fig. 18.6). Including its foothills belt the park covers about 1400 square miles. Most of the park lies be-

FIG. 18.5    Southern San Louis Valley.    Rio Grande is at left; Ute Peak in background is capped with andesitic rocks of the same age as the volcanic rocks in the San Juan Mountains.    (*Photo by John S. Shelton.*)

FIG. 18.6   North end of South Park, looking west.   (*Photo by John S. Shelton.*)

tween altitudes of 8500 and 10,000 feet.   About four-fifths of South Park is drained by the South Platte River, which leaves the park via Eleven Mile Canyon through the Colorado Front Range; the extreme southern part of the park drains to the Arkansas River.

*Rocks and Structure.* The rocks of South Park (Stark et al., 1949) range in age from Precambrian to Pleistocene; however, rocks of Silurian, Triassic, and Jurassic age may be lacking.   With the possible exception of the Pliocene, all Tertiary epochs are represented.   The Precambrian rocks are meta-sedimentary and meta-igneous schists and gneisses.   The sedimentary rocks that are younger than Precambrian and older than Miocene have been folded into a southward plunging basin, the east limb of which has been broken by a large eastward-dipping thrust fault known as the Elkhorn fault.   This fault brings up Precambrian rocks on the east into contact with Tertiary or older rocks on the west.   The South Park structural basin is fairly well outlined by the Dakota formation on the west and north, but on the east this formation is covered by Precambrian rocks.   The general synclinal structure of South Park is complicated by a number of small domes, folds, and several faults.

*Erosional History.* Viewed from a distance the floor of South Park appears extremely flat in contrast with the surrounding mountains.   Actually much of the park does have low relief, but there is diversity of topography in the form of pediments, stream terraces, lateral and terminal moraines, and outwash plains.

Fenneman (1931) called the erosion surface

preserved in South Park at altitudes between 9000 and 10,000 feet the South Park peneplain and correlated it with the erosion surface elsewhere known as the Rocky Mountain peneplain. Stark and associates (1949) identified in the southern part of South Park an erosion surface that bevels rocks of Miocene and Pliocene age which they called the Badger pediment. This pediment slopes southward toward the Arkansas Valley rather than eastward to the South Platte. They thus concluded that during the time that the Badger pediment was being cut South Park drained to the south to the Arkansas River. Later uplift and tilting of the region caused diversion of the drainage to the present eastward route via the South Platte River. Below the Badger pediment are five sets of terraces identified from highest and oldest to lowest and youngest as Como 5, 4, 3, 2, and 1. These terraces are higher than all demonstrable glacio-fluvial terraces in the park and are considered to be pre-Illinoian in age. Late Pliocene to early Pleistocene ages seem most likely for them. Collectively these terraces comprise most of the flatland areas in the park. Below the Como terraces are two Pleistocene terraces; one may be Illinoian in age, and the other is probably of Wisconsin age. Major stages in the geologic history of South Park are suggested in Figure 18.7.

### Middle and North Parks

*Rocks and Structure.* Although Middle and North Parks are two separate topographic entities, they are structurally essentially a single unit, and for this reason they are best discussed together. The two parks are part of a synclinal basin 100 miles long and as much as 40 or 50 miles wide that lies between the Colorado Front Range and Medicine Bow Mountains on the east and the Park Range on the west. The rocks in this syncline are mainly Mesozoic and Tertiary in age, but Paleozoic strata are found at the north and south ends (Tweto, 1957). Rocks of the flanking ranges are primarily Precambrian in age. North Park and Middle Park are separated by an east-west transverse ridge known as

the Rabbit Ears Range. This low range is also a major drainage divide, for North Park is drained by the headwaters of the North Platte River, whereas Middle Park drains to the Colorado River.

Topographically Middle Park and North Park are very dissimilar. North Park is a broad, relatively flat-floored basin, whereas Middle Park possesses considerable relief and only when seen in panoramic view from the air gives the impression of being a basin. In structural details there are also differences. North Park has numerous faults and folds around its margins but in its central part displays only mild folding. Middle Park, however, has two or three overthrust belts crossing it which divide the park geologically into a series of slices and topographically into a number of subbasins. In North Park the younger sedimentary formations extend uninterruptedly for long distances, whereas in Middle Park basement rocks and older sedimentary formations protrude through the Tertiary formations as low ridges which divide the Tertiary areas into several separate units.

*Geomorphic History.* The presence of a topographic basin in the North Park area as early as late Miocene time is indicated by the presence here of the North Park formation of late Miocene or early Pliocene age (Hail and Lewis, 1960). The present topography postdates this formation, whose deposition was accompanied by some volcanic activity. Love (1939) has suggested that the park was filled to a level which made its surface coextensive with the Subsummit erosion surface in the Medicine Bow Mountains to the west. If this is true, as much as 2500 feet of sediments have been removed since Pliocene time, for the present floor has an altitude of around 8000 feet as compared with an elevation of 10,000 feet for the Subsummit erosion surface. It appears that the basin fill must at least have been thick enough to bring about superposition of the North Platte River across the western flank of the Medicine Bow Range. Numerous pediments or terraces are present in North Park, but no detailed study has been made of them; however, it is not unreasonable to assume that the

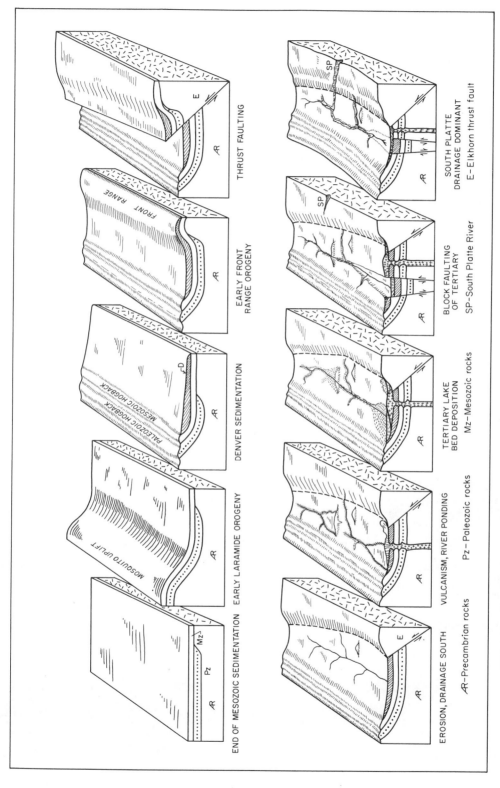

FIG. 18.7 Postulated stages in development of South Park. (*After J. T. Stark and others, Geol. Soc. Am. Memoir 33.*)

late Tertiary-Pleistocene history of North Park was not greatly different from that outlined for South Park.

## WESTERN RANGES

### San Juan Mountains

*Geology.* The San Juan Mountains in southwestern Colorado are composed predominately of Tertiary volcanic rocks (see Fig. 18.8); older bodies of Precambrian, Paleozoic, and Mesozoic rocks are exposed here, but they are of secondary importance. Volcanic activity began here in Miocene time and continued intermittently into Quaternary time. Six distinct volcanic episodes have been recognized (Larsen and Cross, 1956).

*Geomorphic History.* The San Juan Mountains are a broad domal uplift about 90 miles east-west and 70 miles north-south. Numerous peaks attain altitudes in excess of 13,000 feet (see Fig. 18.9), and the highest peak, Uncompahgre Peak, exceeds 14,000 feet in altitude. By late Pliocene

time the region was reduced to low relief; this erosion surface, which has been called the San Juan peneplain (Atwood and Mather, 1932), presumably correlates in age with the Rocky Mountain erosion surface of the Colorado Front Range. Crustal movement toward the end of the Tertiary inaugurated a cycle of erosion known as the Florida cycle and resulted in uplift to the extent of 2000 to 2500 feet.

*Glacial Features.* The earliest glaciation has been named the Cerro, and glaciers of this age not only filled the valleys but spread as piedmont glaciers into the foothills (Mather, 1957). Glacial gravels of Cerro age are found on the surface of Florida Mesa, from which the Florida cycle gets its name. Following the Cerro glaciation, canyon cutting varying from 2000 feet in the center of the mountains to a few hundred feet around their margins took place. The Durango glaciation of early Wisconsin time followed this period of canyon-cutting. Still later in Wisconsin time another episode of extensive mountain glaciation occurred. During this late Wisconsin

FIG. 18.8   Well-layered lavas of Potosi formation, looking down Rio Grande Valley, Hinsdale County, Colorado. (*Photo by Whitman Cross, U. S. Geol. Survey.*)

FIG. 18.9   San Juan Mountains, looking northwest from Weminuche Pass.   (*Photo by John S. Shelton.*)

glaciation a magnificent system of valley glaciers formed. Strong moraines and prominent valley train terraces attest to the size of these glaciers. One of the late Wisconsin glaciers, the Las Animas, was 40 miles long and was probably the longest glacier that developed in the whole Rocky Mountain system during Pleistocene time. Richmond (1954) has suggested that both the Durango and late Wisconsin glaciations consisted of two phases or advances. The two Durango advances he would correlate with Bull Lake I and II of the Wind River Mountains and the two late Wisconsin glaciations with Pinedale I and II.

*Mass-Wasting Phenomena.* The San Juan Mountains have long been famous for the striking development of various forms of mass-wasting,

including landslides, rock streams, and rock glaciers (Howe, 1909). Landslides are particularly well developed in areas where volcanic rocks overlie the Cretaceous Mancos shale. The Slumgullion mudflow, which dammed the Lake Fork of the Gunnison River to form Lake San Cristobal (see Fig. 18.10), originated in a glacial cirque at an altitude of about 11,500 feet.

## JEMEZ MOUNTAINS AND VALLES CALDERA

The Jemez Mountains are a minor mountain range at the very southern end of the western side of the Southern Rockies. They are a broad uplift composed of late Tertiary and Quaternary rocks resting upon igneous, metamorphic, and sedimentary rocks ranging in age from Pre-

FIG. 18.10    Slumgullion mudflow and Lake Cristobal behind it.    (*Photo by John S. Shelton.*)

cambrian to Tertiary.   The mountains lie at the west margin of the Rio Grande depression and are broken by a number of faults which drop mountain blocks progressively downward to the east.

At the west side of the mountain mass is one of the most unusual topographic features in the Rocky Mountains, the Valles caldera.   This caldera is 13 to 15 miles in diameter and is bounded by a number of ring faults (Smith, Bailey, and Ross, 1961).   In early Pleistocene time there occurred here a series of catastrophic eruptions which resulted in the blowing out of some 50 cubic miles of rhyolitic pyroclastic material; with the accompanying subsidence, the caldera was formed.   Subsequent to the collapse of the caldera three distinctive stages of develop-

ment ensued: (1) the eruption of rhyolitic flows and pyroclastic debris onto the floor of the caldera, (2) arching of the floor of the caldera to form a central domal structure, and (3) construction of a ring of volcanic cones around the margin of the structural dome, some of which are 2 miles in diameter and as much as 1000 feet above the floor of the caldera.   It seems likely that the central dome in the caldera and the rimming volcanic cones are surficially the equivalent of a central intrusion and associated ring dike.

### Sawatch Mountains

North of the Sangre de Cristo Range and offset to the west of it is the Sawatch Range, one of the members of the western "granite belt" of the Southern Rockies. From the Arkansas Valley on the east the Sawatch Range presents a bold front, and in this range is found Mount Elbert (14,431 feet), the highest peak in the Southern Rockies. In addition to Mount Elbert there are several other peaks that exceed 14,000 feet in altitude and a large number that exceed 13,000 feet. Thus the Sawatch Range is one of the truly alpine ranges of the Colorado Rockies. Its fame is not so great as that of the Colorado Front Range, mainly because it is not seen by so many people and because it rises from a higher base than the Great Plains east of the Front Range. The Sawatch Range has been severely glaciated, and in the Frying Pan drainage basin on its west side Nelson (1954) found evidence of six glacial advances that seemed to him to correlate with those that have been identified in the Wind River region (see Table 20.1, p. 369).

## Mosquito Range

To the east of the Sawatch Range, across the Arkansas Valley, is the Mosquito Range, which is sometimes considered the southern end of the Park Range. This range is essentially an eastward-dipping homoclinal limb of a great anticlinal structure whose axis follows the crest of the Sawatch Range (Behre, 1953).

Between the Mosquito Range and the Sawatch Range is the upper Arkansas Valley, whose floor lies some 5000 feet below the range crests. The course of the Arkansas Valley was probably influenced by downfaulting along the great Mosquito fault at the west side of the Mosquito Range, but this is not certain.

*Topographic Features.* From Leadville, Colorado, southward along the Arkansas Valley is a series of pediments, benches, and alluvial terraces. Both Behre (1933) and Powers (1935) recognized a high-level erosion surface in the mountains adjacent to the Arkansas Valley at around 12,000 feet, which they considered an age equivalent of the main erosion surface in the Colorado Front Range. Powers thought that he saw evidence for a strath some 2000 to 3000 feet below the peneplain. The upper Arkansas Valley is noted for its excellent terraces, but difference of opinion exists as to their number and age. Powers described seven terraces, two of which he considered preglacial in age, four glacial in age, and one postglacial. Behre recognized five terraces, the highest of which was considered to be preglacial and the others glacial or postglacial in age. He recognized, however, that his lowest terrace might actually represent a terrace complex.

*Origin of Royal Gorge.* A short distance south of Salida, Colorado, the Arkansas River turns east and crosses the eastern "granite belt" through the Royal Gorge (see Fig. 17.6). The course of the stream here undoubtedly antedates the uplift of the Colorado Front Range and probably represents another example of superposition, although remnants of the cover mass from which it may have been superposed are lacking. It can not therefore be cited so confidently as an example of superposition as can several other gorges in the Rocky Mountain System.

## Park Range

North of the Sawatch Range and separated from it by the valley of the upper Colorado River is the Park Range, which extends northward a considerable distance into Wyoming. The part of this range immediately west of North Park is alpine in nature, but both to the south and north of here its surface is much more plateau-like. The part of this mountain uplift south of where the Colorado River cuts through the range and north of Tenmile Creek is known as the Gore Range.

## Other Mountains

Not all of the mountains of the Southern Rocky Mountain province fall into the two north-south mountain belts. Particularly in the western part of the province are several mountain uplifts that are detached from the main mountain system. In this class are such mountains as the La Plata, San Miguel, and Rico to the west of the San Juan uplift and the Elk and West Elk mountains west of the Sawatch Range.

## REFERENCES CITED

Atwood, W. W., and K. F. Mather (1932). Physiography and Quaternary geology of the San Juan Mountains, *U. S. Geol. Survey Profess. Paper* 166, 176 pp.

Behre, C. H., Jr. (1953). Geology and ore deposits of the west slope of the Mosquito Range, *U. S. Geol. Survey Profess. Paper* 235, 176 pp.

Boos, C. M., and M. F. Boos (1957). Tectonics of eastern flank and foothills of Front Range, Colorado, *Am. Assoc. Petroleum Geologists Bull.*, **41**, 2603–2676.

Burbank, W. S., and E. N. Goddard (1937). Thrusting in Huerfano Park, Colorado, and related problems of orogeny in the Sangre de Cristo Mountains, *Geol. Soc. Am. Bull.*, **48**, 931–976.

Fenneman, N. M. (1931). *Physiography of Western United States*, McGraw-Hill Book Company, New York, 534 pp.

Gabelman, J. W. (1956). Tectonic history of the Raton Basin region, in *Guidebook to the Geology of the Raton Basin, Colorado*, Rocky Mountain Assoc. Geologists, 35–39.

Hail, W. J., Jr., and G. E. Lewis (1960). Probable late Miocene age of the North Park formation in North Park area, Colorado, *U. S. Geol. Survey Profess. Paper* 400-B, B259–B260.

Howe, Ernest (1909). Landslides in the San Juan Mountains, including a consideration of their causes and classification, *U. S. Geol. Survey Profess. Paper* 67, 58 pp.

King, P. B. (1959). *The Evolution of North America*, Princeton Univ. Press, Princeton, 190 pp.

Knight, S. H. (1953). Summary of the Cenozoic history of the Medicine Bow Mountains, Wyoming, Wyo. Geol. Assoc. and Univ. Wyo., *Guidebook, Eighth Annual Field Conference*, Laramie Basin and North Park, 65–76.

Larsen, E. S., Jr., and Whitman Cross (1956). Geology and petrology of the San Juan region, southwestern Colorado, *U. S. Geol. Survey Profess. Paper* 258, 303 pp.

Love, J. D. (1939). Geology along the margin of the Absaroka Range, Wyoming, *Geol. Soc. Am. Spec. Paper* 20, 134 pp.

Lovering, T. S., and E. N. Goddard (1950). Geology and ore deposits of the Front Range, Colorado, *U. S. Geol. Survey Profess. Paper* 223, 319 pp.

Mather, K. F. (1957). Geomorphology of the San Juan Mountains, New Mexico Geol. Soc., *Guidebook of Southwestern San Juan Mountains*, 102–108.

Moore, F. E. (1960). Summary of the Cenozoic history, southern Laramie Range, Wyoming and Colorado, Geol. Soc. Am.-Rocky Mt. Assoc. Geol.-Colo. Sci. Soc., *Guide to the Geology of Colorado*, 217–222.

Nelson, R. L. (1954). Glacial geology of the Frying Pan River drainage, Colorado, *Jour. Geol.*, **62**, 326–343.

Powell, W. J. (1958). Groundwater resources of the San Luis Valley, Colorado, *U. S. Geol. Survey Water-Supply Paper* 1379, 1–24.

Powers, W. E. (1935). Physiographic history of the upper Arkansas Valley and the Royal Gorge, Colorado, *Jour. Geol.*, **43**, 184–199.

Richmond, G. M. (1954). Modification of the glacial chronology of the San Juan Mountains, Colorado, *Science*, **119**, 614–615.

Smith, R. L., R. A. Bailey and C. S. Ross (1961). Structural evolution of the Valles caldera, New Mexico, and its bearing on the emplacement of ring dikes, *U. S. Geol. Survey Profess. Paper* 424-D, D145–D149.

Stark, J. T., et al. (1949). Geology and origin of South Park, Colorado, *Geol. Soc. Am. Memoir* 33, 188 pp.

Steven, T. A. (1956). Cenozoic geomorphic history of the Medicine Bow Mountains near the Northgate fluorspar district, Colorado, Colo. Sci. Soc., *Proc.*, **17**, 35–55.

Tweto, Ogden (1957). Geologic sketch of southern Middle Park, Colorado, Rocky Mountain Assoc. Geol., *Guidebook to the Geology of North and Middle Park Basin, Colorado*, 18–31.

Upson, J. E. (1939). Physiographic subdivisions of the San Luis Valley, southern Colorado, *Jour. Geol.*, **47**, 721–736.

Van Tuyl, F. M. (1955). Physiography, Rocky Mountain Assoc. Geol., *Field Conference Guidebook, Geology of Front Range Foothills West of Denver*, 12–14.

### ADDITIONAL REFERENCES

Atwood, W. W., and K. F. Mather (1924). Physiographic history of the San Luis Valley of Colorado and New Mexico, *Geol. Soc. Am. Bull.*, **35**, 121–123.

Behre, C. H., Jr. (1933). Physiographic history of the upper Arkansas and Eagle rivers, Colorado, *Jour. Geol.*, **41**, 785–814.

Blackstone, D. L., Jr. (1946). Origin of certain wind gaps in the Laramie Mountains, Wyoming, *Jour. Geol.*, **54**, 252–259.

Boyer, R. E. (1962). Petrology and Structure of the southern Wet Mountains, Colorado, *Geol. Soc. Am. Bull.*, **73**, 1047–1070.

Briggs, L. I., and E. N. Goddard (1956). Geology of Huerfano Park, Colorado, Rocky Mountain Assoc. Geol., *Guidebook to the Geology of the Raton Basin, Colorado*, 40–45.

Chamberlin, R. T. (1919). The building of the Colorado Rockies, *Jour. Geol.*, **27**, 145–164, 225–251.

Eschman, D. F. (1955). Glaciation of the Michigan River basin, North Park, Colorado, *Jour. Geol.*, **63**, 197–213.

Gabelman, J. W. (1952). Structure and origin of northern Sangre de Cristo Range, Colorado, *Am. Assoc. Petroleum Geologists Bull.*, **36**, 1574–1612.

Johnson, J. H. (1929). Contributions to the geology of the Sangre de Cristo Mountains of Colorado, Colo. Sci. Soc., *Proc.*, **12**, 3–21.

Litsey, L. R. (1958). Stratigraphy and structure of the northern Sangre de Cristo Mountains, Colorado, *Geol. Soc. Am. Bull.*, **69**, 1143–1178.

Rich, J. L. (1935). Physiographic development of the Front Range; Comments, *Geol. Soc. Am. Bull.*, **46**, 2046–2051.

Richmond, G. M. (1957). Three pre-Wisconsin glacial stages in the Rocky Mountain region, *Geol. Soc. Am. Bull.*, **68**, 239–262.

Siebenthal, C. E. (1910). Geology and water resources of the San Luis Valley, Colorado, *U. S. Geol. Survey Water-Supply Paper* 240, 128 pp.

Stark, J. T., and Barnes, F. F. (1932). The structure of the Sawatch Range, *Am. Jour. Sci.*, **224**, 471–480.

Van Tuyl, F. M., and T. S. Lovering (1935). Physiographic development of the Front Range, *Geol. Soc. Am. Bull.*, **46**, 1291–1350.

Wahlstrom, E. E. (1947). Cenozoic physiographic history of the Front Range, Colorado, *Geol. Soc. Am. Bull.*, **58**, 551–572.

# 19

# *Wyoming Basin*

## GENERAL DESCRIPTION

The Wyoming Basin represents a major break in the continuity of the Rocky Mountains; here an extension of Great Plains geology and topography through a gap between the Laramie and Bighorn Mountains essentially separates the Southern and Middle Rockies. Not only is the Wyoming Basin continuous with the Great Plains, but it also connects with the Colorado Plateau province through a sag east of the Uinta Mountains. The province is nearly surrounded by mountains; on the southwest are the Uinta Mountains, on the southeast the Park and Medicine Bow Ranges, on the west a group of small mountain ranges known as the Wyomide Ranges, on the northwest the Gros Ventre and Wind River Mountains, and at the north the Absaroka and Owl Creek Mountains.

Although basins are dominant in the Wyoming Basin province, buried or partially exhumed mountain structures are present and continue the Rocky Mountain structures across the province, although their trend is offset here to the west. Four prongs of the Southern Rockies extend northward toward the Wyoming Basin; these are, from east to west, the Laramie Range, the Medicine Bow Mountains, the Park Range, and the White River Plateau. The White River Plateau is not mountainous, but it does possess the anticlinal structure which characterizes most of the ranges of the Southern Rockies. Continuation of these four mountain structures may be seen in the Wyoming Basin respectively from east to west in the Rattlesnake Hills and Oil Mountain anticlines, the Ferris and Green

Mountains, the Rawlins Hills, and the Uinta Mountains.

### Geology

Rocks of early Tertiary age predominate in the Wyoming Basin (see Fig. 19.1); next in abundance are Mesozoic strata, particularly those of Cretaceous age; narrow strips of Paleozoic rocks are exposed around the flanks of a few of the basins, but their total area is not great. Although Precambrian rocks are abundant in the mountain ranges which bound the Wyoming Basin on the south and north, rocks of this age are not widespread in the Wyoming Basin proper. Exposed Precambrian rocks are found mainly in the area between the northern end of the Laramie Range and the southern end of the Wind River Mountains, where partial exhumation of buried mountain structures has exposed numerous small tracts of Precambrian rocks.

During much of Tertiary time the various basins were depositories for debris shed from the adjacent uplifts. As a result, many thousands of feet of fluviatile, paludal, and lacustrine sediments representing all epochs of the Tertiary are to be found in the various basins. Paleocene and Eocene rocks are present in all the basins, and younger Tertiary rocks are to be found in most of the basins (Thomas, 1949).

### Structure

The major structures of the Wyoming Basin are products of the Laramide orogeny. The province consists of a number of basins separated

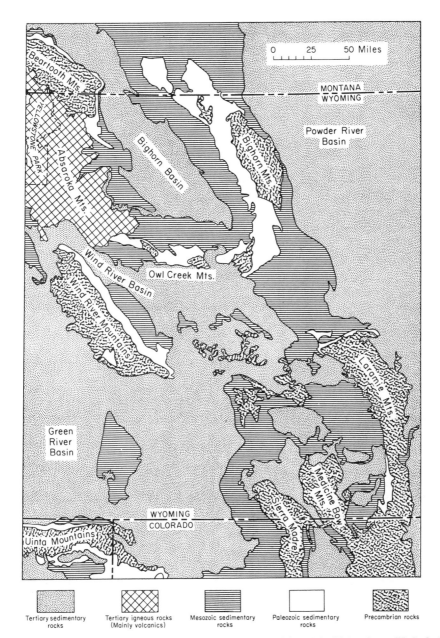

FIG. 19.1   Geology around the Wyoming Basin.   (*After Geologic Map of the United States, U. S. Geol. Survey.*)

from each other by uplifts (see Fig. 19.2) which are prominent in varying degrees.   In some of the uplifts buried mountain structures are well along toward exhumation; in others, the mountain structures are barely exposed.   Most of the uplifts, as well as the basins, are asymmetrical structures.   Superposed on the major basins are

lesser anticlines and synclines, which, too, are usually asymmetrical.   These secondary structures tend to be arranged concentrically around the basins, but they may trend at an angle to the major basin axes.

King (1959) envisioned the basins as having acted rather passively during the Laramide

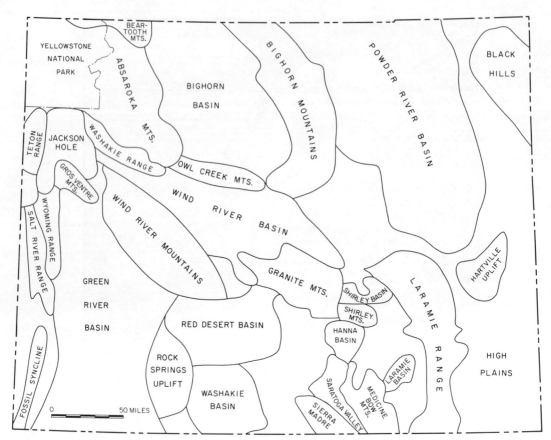

FIG. 19.2   Major basins and mountain uplifts in or adjacent to Wyoming Basin province.   (*After J. D. Love, Am. Jour. Sci., 258-A.*)

orogeny while the mountain structures rose; however, Keefer and Love (1963) did not view them as static features, but thought that they underwent active downfolding which in some of the basins may have equalled or exceeded the amount of uplift in adjacent mountain structures.

As the diastrophism increased in intensity and reached its maximum in Eocene time some of the mountain blocks were pushed basinward until they broke and were thrust onto the basins. The result is that most of the basins have their deepest parts not at their centers but marginal to adjacent major mountain uplifts.

The magnitude of movement during the Laramide orogeny is indicated by the present altitudes of Precambrian rocks in the basins and the surrounding mountains.   Estimates of the altitudes of Precambrian rocks in the uplifts and basins are given in the following table, based on data

TABLE 19.1   Estimates of Altitudes of Precambrian Rocks in Basins of Wyoming and in Adjacent Mountain Uplifts

*Basins*

| | |
|---|---|
| Wind River Basin | −14,000 to −23,000 feet |
| Green River Basin | −24,000 feet |
| Red Desert Basin | −23,000 feet |
| Great Divide Basin | −12,000 feet |
| Hanna Basin | −31,000 feet |
| Washakie Basin | −21,000 feet |

*Uplifts*

| | |
|---|---|
| Wind River Mountains | +14,000 feet |
| Owl Creek Mountains | + 9,000 feet |
| Bighorn Mountains | +13,000 feet |
| Laramie Range | +10,000 feet |
| Medicine Bow Mountains | +12,000 feet |

given by Love (1960) and Keefer and Love (1963). The difference between the altitudes of Precambrian rocks in the basins and mountain uplifts certainly does not represent the total amount of differential vertical movement, for it does not take into account the amount by which the Precambrian rocks in the mountains have been lowered by erosion.

## MAJOR BASINS

### Laramie Basin

The Laramie Basin lies between the Medicine Bow Mountains on the west and the Laramie Range on the east. It is about 90 miles long and has a maximum width of about 30 miles (Darton and Siebenthal, 1909).

*Structure and Geology.* Structurally the Laramie Basin is a north-plunging syncline involving some 8000 feet of Carboniferous and Mesozoic rocks. Tertiary rocks are not extensive, but some Paleocene beds occur toward the north end of the basin. Pleistocene terrace gravels and Recent alluvium are widespread. Four anticlines arranged en echelon at the west side of the basin expose Precambrian rocks, and at the north end of the basin is a line of folds, likewise arranged en echelon, which represents an extension southward of the Sweetwater uplift (see p. 357) into the area.

*Topography.* Altitudes on the floor of the basin are typically between 7000 and 7500 feet. Three Quaternary erosion surfaces younger than the Subsummit surface in the Medicine Bow Mountains (see p. 340) have been described (de la Montagne, 1953). These are the Table Mountain, Intermediate, and Centennial terraces, which are 80 to 200, 20 to 80, and 20 feet respectively above present valley floors. The ages of these surfaces are uncertain; the Centennial terrace is capped with glacial outwash gravels from the Medicine Bow Mountains, and patches of till that is either early Wisconsin or pre-Wisconsin in age lie on the Intermediate and Centennial terraces.

One particularly interesting topographic feature in the Laramie Basin is Big Hollow, 5 or 6 miles west of Laramie, Wyoming. This depression is about 9 miles long, as much as 3 miles wide, and 300 feet deep. It is generally considered to be a blowout produced by wind erosion on the Cretaceous Mesaverde and underlying Niobrara and Steele formations. Some deflation is still observable on the deposits in the playas in the basin. Big Basin, to the north of Big Hollow, is another, but smaller, blowout.

### Green River (Bridger) Basin

The major basin of southeastern Wyoming is the Green River or Bridger Basin. It is 170 miles long and as much as 140 miles wide and is one of the major structural basins of the Rocky Mountain region (Knight, 1950). The basin is bounded on the south by the Uinta Mountains, on the west by the Wyomide Ranges, on the north by the Wind River and Gros Ventre Mountains, and on the east by the Rock Springs uplift. A great thickness of Tertiary strata ranging in age from Eocene to Oligocene and including the well-known Eocene lacustral Green River shales is exposed within the basin.

*Topography.* The floor of the Green River Basin possesses considerable relief, as is evidenced by the fact that elevations within it range from 6000 to 8000 feet. It has undergone large-scale erosion, the result of which is a topography consisting of broad dissected lowlands interspersed with numerous ridges, mesas, and buttes. The Green River Basin is drained by the upper part of the Green River, which flows through the Uinta Mountains via the striking Lodore Canyon into the Uinta Basin of the Colorado Plateau province.

The Tertiary history of the Green River Basin can be divided into two distinctly different phases. From Eocene into Oligocene time the basin was the site of continued accumulation of fluviatile and lacustrine sediments. Following this came a period of basin excavation and stream planation (Bradley, 1936). The record of the early Tertiary period of sedimentation is fairly well preserved in the rocks in the basin, but the late Tertiary erosional history is not so readily interpreted.

TABLE 19.2  Correlation of Pleistocene Terraces in Green River Basin with Substages of Glaciation in Wind River Mountains

| *Name of Terrace* | *Glacial Substage Correlative* |
| --- | --- |
| Camp | Pre-Bull Lake (possibly Buffalo) |
| Higher Eden | Bull Lake I |
| Lower Eden | Bull Lake II |
| Upper Farson | Pinedale I |
| Lower Farson | Pinedale II |
| Parker | Temple Lake |

Long, narrow extensions of four erosion surfaces described in the Uinta Mountains by Bradley (see p. 363) can be identified in the southern part of the Green River Basin. These are the Gilbert Peak and Bear Mountain pediments and the Tipperary and Lyman fluvial terraces. In places as much as 200 feet of Bishop conglomerate (Rich, 1910) mantles the surface of the Gilbert Peak pediment. This conglomerate was deposited by the same streams which cut the Gilbert Peak pediment during middle to late Tertiary time.

Moss (1951) has described a set of Pleistocene terraces at the northeastern margin of the basin that seem to correlate with substages of glaciation in the Wind River Mountains (see p. 330) to the north. Possible correlation of these terraces is suggested in Table 19.2.

## Wind River Basin

What is commonly called the Wind River Basin is the western part of the broad depression between the Wind River Mountains on the south and the Absaroka and Owl Mountains on the north; the eastern half of this depression is usually called the Shoshone Basin. The Wind River Basin is one of the major structural basins of Wyoming (Bauer, 1934). It is asymmetrical in plan, with its deepest part at the north and northeast near the Owl Creek Mountains. The basin has a fill of 20,000 feet of sediments, most of which are fluviatile or lacustrine in origin. At the east the Casper arch, a major deeply eroded fold, is thrust southwestward onto the basin (Keefer and Love, 1963).

The larger part of the central basin area consists of low hills and ridges (Bauer, 1934) of irregular height and contour; much of this topography could be classed as badland. At the north side of the basin are numerous gravel-capped ridges which may represent surfaces produced by stream planation, but similar ridges are largely lacking on the south side of the basin. It is probable that erosion surfaces are present in the basin correlative with those that have been described in the Wind River Mountains but their existence has not been established by field studies.

## Washakie Basin

The Washakie Basin is a shallow synclinal structure that lies southeast of the Rock Springs uplift between the Great Divide Basin at the north and the Yampa Basin in Colorado at the south. The Washakie Basin is an exception to the general rule in the Wyoming Basin province that structural basins are also topographic basins (Fenneman, 1931). Its topography is that of a series of outward facing cuestas on the Wasatch, Green River, and Bridger formations of Eocene age and the Brown Park formation of probable Miocene age. The Washakie Basin is bounded at the north by a 600–700-foot-high out-facing escarpment on beds of Green River age called Laney Rim; farther south this escarpment becomes 1200 feet high and is known as Kinny Rim. The encircling escarpment is not as high at the north because numerous stream valleys have broken it down (Bradley, 1945).

## Great Divide Basin

The Great Divide Basin (Keefer and Love, 1963) lies to the east of the Rock Springs uplift. The name has a certain hydrographic implication, in that it is an area of internal drainage largely because of its low rainfall; numerous alkali lakes and playas occur within the basin. Because part of the basin is developed on red Tertiary strata, it is sometimes called the Red Desert. Something like 26,000 feet of structural relief exists between the Precambrian rocks beneath this basin and the same rocks in the mountains to the north of it.

## Other Basins

*Hanna Basin.* Lying northwest of the Laramie Basin and the north end of the Medicine Bow Mountains is the Hanna Basin. This basin is not large, but it has in it a very thick section of Paleozoic, Mesozoic, and early Tertiary rocks totaling over 35,000 feet in thickness.

*Carbon Basin.* Northwest of the Hanna Basin and separated from it by the Saddleback Hills anticline is the Carbon Basin. Dips are not steep in this basin, and the resistant sandstone beds in the Cretaceous formation have given rise to numerous homoclinal ridges, slopes, and rock benches.

*Axial Basin.* The Axial basin lies in that part of the Wyoming Basin which extends into northwestern Colorado. It is developed on an eroded anticlinal structure which connects the White River Plateau in Colorado with the Uinta Mountains. A belt of weak rock exposed by breaching of the anticline is responsible for the development here of a topographic basin.

## MAJOR UPLIFTS

### Rock Springs Uplift

The Green River Basin is separated from the Washakie Basin on the east by the Rock Springs uplift, a 40-mile-long north-south doubly plunging anticline. This is the largest anticlinal uplift in Wyoming which still has over it a sedimentary cover of Cretaceous rocks (Blackstone, 1955). This may mean that it was developed later than the other uplifts of the Wyoming Basin. Hogbacks on the west side of the uplift, where dips are steepest, and cuestas on the east side, outline the uplift. The Cretaceous Mesaverde formation is the principal ridgemaker; in places it stands 1000 feet high and encircles the elliptical Baxter topographic basin on shales at the crest of the Rock Springs uplift.

*Leucite Hills.* Lying astride the continental divide at the north end of the Rock Springs uplift is one of the two volcanic fields in the Wyoming Basin (the other is in the Elk Mountains in northwestern Colorado). The Leucite Hills cover an area about 30 by 25 miles (Carey, 1955). This area attracted much attention at the time of its discovery, because it was the first place in the United States from which the mineral leucite was reported. There are some 22 isolated exposures in buttes and mesas where igneous rocks containing leucite are found. These rocks cut through or rest on formations ranging from late Cretaceous to the Eocene Green River formation. The volcanic activity which produced these rocks was followed or accompanied by the period of erosion which produced the Bishop conglomerate; it thus appears that the volcanic activity in the Leucite Hills came somewhere between Eocene and late Miocene or early Pliocene time.

### Rawlins Uplift

The Rawlins uplift lies between the Great Divide Basin on the west and the Hanna Basin to the east. This uplift seems to align with the Park Range of the Southern Rockies and may represent a northward continuation of this positive element. The east flank of the Red Desert portion of the Great Divide Basin essentially coincides with the west flank of the Rawlins uplift (Barlow, 1955). The Rawlins uplift is a large asymmetrical anticline with steep dips on the east and moderate dips on the west. The typical Rocky Mountain "core and hogback" pattern is developed, with Precambrian rocks exposed at the center of the uplift and hogbacks on Paleozoic and Mesozoic strata on the flanks. The anticline is complicated somewhat by secondary folds and faults that have brought Precambrian rocks into contact with the Cretaceous Mesaverde formation.

### Sweetwater Uplift

Extending southeast from the end of the Wind River Mountains to the Hanna Basin at the South is an uplift known as the Sweetwater uplift or Granite Mountains uplift (see Fig. 19.2), in which numerous tracts of Precambrian "granites" have been partially exhumed (see Fig. 19.3). Included in this line of granite mountains are the Green, Ferris, Granite, Seminole, and Freezeout

FIG. 19.3    View to southeast across Granite Mountains (middle background) to Ferris Mountains in background. The Granite Mountains have been partially exhumed from a cover of Miocene and Pliocene strata.    (*Photo courtesy of P. T. Jenkins and L. P. House.*)

Mountains. In some respects this part of the Wyoming Basin throws more light on the geologic history of the province than any other part, for here can be seen the results of the depositional phase which characterized early Tertiary time as well as the erosional phase which has prevailed since late Miocene or early Pliocene time.

## GENERAL CHARACTER OF TOPOGRAPHY OF WYOMING BASIN

The most common topographic features of the Wyoming Basin are the numerous hogbacks, cuestas, and dip slopes developed on the upturned strata around the various uplifts and basins. In addition, there are numerous features that are to a considerable degree related to the fact that the climate of the Wyoming Basin is semi-arid. Features in this category are the numerous deflation basins, alkali flats and playas, local accumulations of sand and silt dunes, and badland topography.

*Deflation Basins.* When it is recalled that much of the topography of the Wyoming Basin is essentially similar to that of the western Great Plains, it is not surprising that deflation basins are common. Big Hollow in the Laramie Basin is the most striking example, but many others occur through the province, mainly in areas where shales form the surficial rock.

*Alkali Flats and Playas.* The low rainfall, particularly in the western part of the Wyoming Basin, is responsible for several area of internal drainage. These are particularly noticeable in the Great Divide Basin, but they occur locally elsewhere. The rainfall flows into small local basins that may be called playas, but the water does not overflow; as a result there develop ephemeral lakes, whose waters evaporate to form alkali deposits on the basin floors.

*Dunes.* Sand dunes are found at several localities within the Wyoming Basin; the most extensive tract is in the northern part of the Rock Springs uplift. Silt dunes are uncommon here, but they are found in the Great Divide Basin, having been derived from the silt and mud washed into local playas.

*Badland Topography.* Badland topography is found at numerous places, as would be expected in an area of weak Tertiary rocks with rainfall that frequently falls as torrential thundershowers. The badland tracts are mainly in areas of Tertiary shales; Hell's Halfacre, about 40 miles west of Casper on the headwaters of the South Fork of the Powder River, is perhaps the best known example of badland topography.

## SUPERPOSED DRAINAGE

Drainage relationships in the Wyoming Basin lend strong support to the theory of regional superposition of drainage lines in the Rocky Mountain region from a cover mass deposited in late Tertiary time. Three major streams leave the province via gorges through major mountain uplifts: the Laramie River in its gorge through the Laramie Range, the Green River through the Lodore Canyon in the Uinta Mountains, and the Wind River through a gorge across the Owl Creek Mountain uplift.

Perhaps an even more convincing argument for superposition is found in the courses of some of the lesser streams. The Devil's Gate of the Sweetwater River (see Fig. 19.4) is a striking example of a drainage relationship that can hardly be logically explained except by superposition. Here the Sweetwater River cuts through the nose of a partially exhumed mountain ridge, whereas by shifting its course about one-half mile to the south it could have avoided this ridge (see Independence, Wyoming, quadrangle). A stream free to shift its course among weak and strong rocks would not likely have chosen such a route. The North Platte River, about 13 miles west of Casper, Wyoming, cuts across the Oil

FIG. 19.4   Devil's Gate of the Sweetwater River, west of Alcova, Wyoming.   *(Photo by H. S. Palmer.)*

FIG. 19.5    Course of North Platte River through Oil Mountain anticline, 13 miles southwest of Casper, Wyoming. (*Photo by John S. Shelton.*)

Mountain anticline (see Fig. 19.5) in what also appears to represent a case of stream superposition.

## GEOMORPHIC HISTORY

In the Wyoming Basin we get a picture of what much of the topography of the Rocky Mountain region looked like in late Tertiary time. Here we find a composite topography which was produced by erosion in the mountains and deposition in the basins. In the surrounding major mountain uplifts are to be found remnants of such erosional surfaces as the Sherman peneplain of the Laramie Range, the Wind River peneplain of the Wind River Mountains, and the Gilbert Peak pediment in the Uinta Moun-

tains. Tongues of these erosional surfaces extend into the margins of the basins and there grade into depositional surfaces.

Undoubtedly most of the basins at the close of Tertiary time were filled with material removed from the mountains to form a continuous surface sloping eastward and grading into the extensive depositional surface that covered the Great Plains (see p. 300). Following uplifts of this surface in late Pliocene and Pleistocene time, part of the basin fill material has been removed. Uplift apparently was intermittent, as evidenced by the presence in the basins of rock benches and terraces. Not many of the basins have been studied in detail, but probably many of them would display erosional benches comparable to those described above for the Laramie Basin.

Just how many Quaternary subcycles of erosion are represented and whether the same number can be identified in all the major basins remain to be determined.

## REFERENCES CITED

Barlow, J. A., Jr. (1955). Structure of the Rawlins uplift, Carbon County, Wyoming, *Wyo. Geol. Assoc. Guidebook, 10th Annual Field Conference*, 138–139.

Bauer, C. M. (1934). Wind River Basin, *Geol. Soc. Am. Bull.*, **45**, 665–696.

Blackstone, D. L., Jr. (1955). Notes on a tectonic map of parts of southwestern Wyoming and adjoining states, *Wyo. Geol. Assoc. Guidebook, 10th Annual Field Conference*, 122–124.

Bradley, W. H. (1936). Geomorphology of the north flank of the Uinta Mountains, *U. S. Geol. Survey Profess. Paper 185-I*, 163–204.

———— (1945). Geology of the Washakie Basin, Sweetwater and Carbon counties, Wyoming and Moffat County, Colorado, *U. S. Geol. Survey Oil and Gas Invest. Prelim. Map 32*.

Carey, B. D., Jr. (1955). A review of the geology of the Leucite Hills, *Wyo. Geol. Assoc. Guidebook, 10th Annual Field Conference*, 112–113.

Darton, N. H., and C. E. Siebenthal (1909). Geology and water resources of the Laramie Basin, Wyoming, *U. S. Geol. Survey Bull. 364*, 81 pp.

de la Montagne, J. (1953). Geomorphology of the Centennial-Big Hollow area, southeastern Wyoming, *Wyo. Geol. Assoc. Guidebook, 8th Annual Field Conference*, 77–80.

Fenneman, N. M. (1931). *Physiography of Western United States*, McGraw-Hill Book Company, New York, 534 pp.

Keefer, W. R., and J. D. Love (1963). Vertical movements in central Wyoming, in *Contributions to Geology*, S. H. Knight Issue, Univ. Wyoming, 47–54.

King, P. B. (1959). *The Evolution of North America*, Princeton Univ. Press, Princeton, 190 pp.

Knight, S. H. (1950). Physical aspects of the Green River Basin and adjacent mountain ranges, *Wyo. Geol. Assoc. Guidebook, 5th Annual Field Conference*, 75–80.

Love, J. D. (1960). Cenozoic sedimentation and crustal movement in Wyoming, *Am. Jour. Sci.*, **258-A**, 204–214.

Moss, J. H. (1951). *Early Man in the Eden Valley*, Museum Monographs, Univ. Penn., 124 pp.

Rich, J. L. (1910). The physiography of the Bishop conglomerate, southwestern Wyoming, *Jour. Geol.*, **18**, 601–632.

Thomas, H. D. (1949). The geological history and geological structure of Wyoming, *Wyo. Geol. Surv. Bull. 42*, 28 pp.

### ADDITIONAL REFERENCES

Blackstone, D. L., Jr. (1948). The structural pattern of the Wind River Basin, Wyoming, *Wyo. Geol. Assoc. Guidebook, 3rd Annual Field Conference*, 69–78.

Eardley, A. J. (1962). *Structural Geology of North America*, 2nd ed., Harper and Row Publishers, New York, 376–388.

Kemp, J. F., and W. C. Knight (1903). The Leucite Hills of Wyoming, *Geol. Soc. Am. Bull.*, **14**, 305–336.

# 20

# *Middle Rocky Mountain Province*

## GENERAL DESCRIPTION

The Middle Rocky Mountain province is an irregular area that includes a variety of upland forms, some of which, like the Yellowstone volcanic plateau, are not even mountains. To a considerable extent this province is one of convenience. It is practically cut off from the Southern Rockies by the Wyoming Basin. The only connection between the Middle and Southern Rockies is through the White River Plateau and the anticlinal Axial Basin. This uplift, although not mountainous, does connect the Southern Rocky Mountains with the east-west trending Uinta Mountains of the Middle Rockies. At the north the Snake River High Lava Plain and the Yellowstone volcanic plateau almost separate the Middle Rockies from the Northern Rockies.

Three types of mountains are found in the Middle Rocky Mountain province. An eastern group including the Bighorn, Beartooth, Owl Creek, and Wind River Mountains consists of broad anticlinal folds with cores of Precambrian rocks about whose margins Paleozoic and Mesozoic rocks form steeply dipping homoclinal structures that pass into nearly horizontal beds in adjacent basins. A western group of mountains consisting of the Wasatch, the Teton, and the so-called Wyomide Ranges along the Wyoming-Utah-Idaho boundaries display topographic characteristics related to either thrust or normal faulting. A third type of mountain is illustrated by the Absarokas, which are essentially a great pile of volcanic rocks sculptured by erosion into mountainous relief.

## MAJOR MOUNTAIN RANGES

### *Uinta Mountains*

The Uinta Range is the largest of the few east-west trending mountain ranges in the Rocky Mountain System. This 150-mile-long range lies mainly in Utah just south of the Wyoming border, but it extends some 30 miles into Colorado. The range is about 30 to 40 miles wide, and several of its peaks attain altitudes in excess of 12,000 feet. King's Peak, the highest peak, has an altitude of 13,500 feet; the floor of Green River, to the north, has an altitude of 5000 feet, giving a regional maximum relief of 8500 feet.

*Geology and Structure.* The Uinta Mountains are a broad, arcuate anticlinal fold slightly overturned to the north and flanked on the south by the Uinta Basin and on the north by the Green River Basin (Forrester, 1937). Numerous faults are present within the range, but the three major ones are the South Flank fault, the North Flank fault, and the Uinta fault. The Uinta fault lies near the crest of the range at its west end, but at the east lies near the north flank. Rocks of the Uinta Mountains are Precambrian, Paleozoic, Mesozoic, and Cenozoic in age, giving to the mountain range a stratigraphic sequence similar to that encountered so commonly throughout the Rocky Mountain region. The core of the range consists of Precambrian rocks known as the Uinta Series. These rocks are predominantly quartzites and sandstones, but among them are some schists and shales. Along the eastern end of the Uinta fault, sedimentary rocks of Cretaceous or Tertiary age are brought into fault

FIG. 20.1    Crest of Uinta Range, showing scalloping produced by glacial cirques.    (*Photo by John S. Shelton.*)

contact with Precambrian quartzites. It has been estimated that the stratigraphic throw along this fault may be as much as 20,000 feet (Curtis, 1950), yet there has been surprisingly little deformation of rock strata.

*Geomorphic History.*  The crest of the Uinta Range lies slightly north of the central axis of the range and consists of a broad plateau-like summit deeply scalloped by glacial cirques (see Fig. 20.1) and deep glacial canyons which extend both north and south from the range crest.

The north flank of the Uinta Mountains has been carefully studied by Bradley (1936), and its geomorphic history has been worked out in considerable detail. Remnants of four erosion surfaces have been described. The oldest surface is what has been named the Gilbert Peak surface (see Fig. 20.2). This surface apparently once extended from the crest of the range into the center of the Green River Basin at the north. Its slope varies from about 400 feet per mile near the range crest to 55 feet per mile in the Green River Basin. At the time of its development the Green River Basin was filled

to a much greater height than now with sediments of Eocene age. Bradley concluded that the Gilbert Peak erosion surface was most logically explained as a pediment. Its surface was mantled with gravels, remnants of which constitute the Bishop conglomerate. Bradley further believed that the drainage at the time of development of this erosion surface was to the east, to the ancestral Platte River or some river that drained to the Gulf of Mexico, and not to the south via Green River as at present.

Lying 400 to 500 feet below the Gilbert Peak surface is the Bear Mountain erosion surface. Bradley considered it a pediment also, whose age was believed to be late Miocene or early Pliocene. If this is the correct age for the Bear Mountain surface, then the Gilbert Peak surface is probably Oligocene or early Miocene in age. Below the Bear Mountain pediment are two pediments of Pleistocene age. The older pediment, the Tipperary, lies about 150 feet below the Bear Mountain surface, and the younger Lyman pediment 50 to 75 feet below the Tipperary. Upstream these two pediments merge with present floodplains. Three glacial stages, the

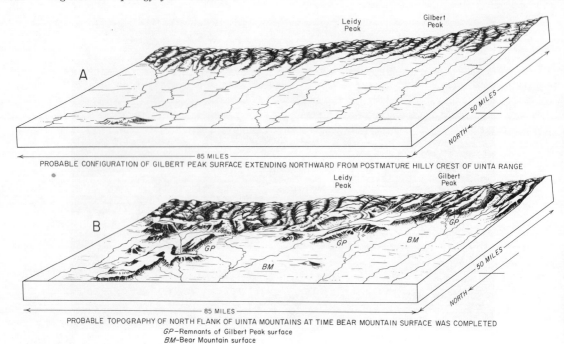

FIG. 20.2 Reconstruction of topography on north flank of Uinta Mountains: (A) at time of formation of Gilbert Peak surface; (B) at time of completion of Bear Mountain surface. (*After W. H. Bradley, U. S. Geol. Survey Profess. Paper* 185-I.)

Little Dry, Blacks Fork, and Smith Fork were recognized and thought to correlate respectively with Blackwelder's Buffalo, Bull Lake, and Pinedale glaciations in the Wind River Mountains.

### Wasatch Mountains

*Topography.* West of the Uinta Range and separated from it by a structural sag known as Kamas Prairie is the Wasatch Range. The Wasatch Mountains, along with their northern extension, the Bear River Range, form the westernmost range of the Middle Rocky Mountains. There is a notable contrast in the topographic characteristics of the east and west sides of this north-south mountain range. The west side presents a bold, straight front that has long been regarded as a fault scarp. Faceted spur ends are conspicuous along the mountain front (see Fig. 20.3). The eastern slope of the Wasatch Mountains is deeply dissected rugged topography that in no way suggests the dip slope of a tilted fault block

such as is found so commonly in the Basin and Range province.

The crest of the Wasatch Range is generally above 10,000 feet and was high enough during Pleistocene time to nourish a number of glaciers, the longest of which were on the west flank of the range. Some of the glaciers reached down to the base of the mountains, and at a few places the shoreline of Lake Bonneville (see p. 484) was etched on the moraines at the canyon mouths.

*Erosion Surfaces.* Eardley (1944) believed that there was evidence in the Wasatch Mountains of two former erosion surfaces. The higher and older of these he called the Herd Mountain surface, and the younger the Weber Valley surface. He thought it likely that these erosion surfaces correlated with the Gilbert Peak and Bear Mountain surfaces of the Uinta Mountains. A late Oligocene or Miocene age was suggested for the Herd Mountain surface, and as the Weber

Valley surface seemed to have formed before the beginning of block faulting, a late Pliocene or early Pleistocene age for it seemed probable.

### The Wyomide Ranges

*Structural Characteristics.* The Wyomide Ranges form a group of mountain ranges lying in western Wyoming, northern Utah, and southeastern Idaho. Major ranges in this group are the Snake River, Salt River, Bighole, Hoback, and Wyoming. Their outstanding characteristic is that they represent a belt of closed folds and thrust faults in which movement has been eastward along westward-dipping fault planes. The subparallel mountain ranges are bounded on the east by thrust faults which dip to the west and on the west by younger, high-angle normal faults that are down-dropped to the west. Between these marginal faults the Paleozoic and Mesozoic strata are broken by lesser faults, overturned, or torn by transverse faults. Valleys between the mountain ranges are filled with late Tertiary and Recent alluvium.

The Wyomide Ranges are geographically a part of the Middle Rocky Mountain province, but topographically and structurally they belong with the Northern Rocky Mountains. They represent an emergence south of the Snake River lava plain of a type of structure found extensively in southwestern Montana. As Rubey (1955) has stated, these mountain ranges represent "a bit of Idaho and Utah thrust eastward into the gap between the Teton and Uinta Mountains."

This mountain belt has in it a number of thrust faults of major proportions, including such

FIG. 20.3   West front of Wasatch Mountains.   (*Photo by Chicago Aerial Survey Co.*)

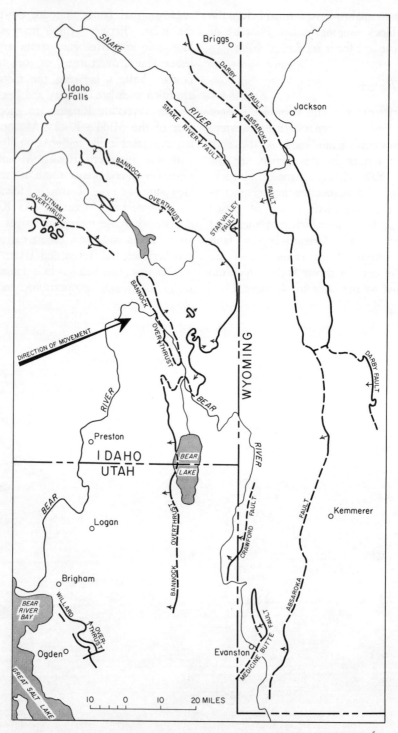

FIG. 20.4    Major faults of the Wyomide ranges.    (*After G. R. Mansfield, U. S. Geol. Survey Profess. Paper 238.*)

faults as the Bannock, Darby, Absaroka, and Putnam (see Fig. 20.4). The 150-mile-long Bannock fault was first described by Richards and Mansfield (1912) as a thrust sheet of wide proportions that was supposed to have moved eastward over 40 miles; later work (Armstrong and Cressman, 1957) has shown, however, that the Bannock fault is really a zone of imbricate faulting several miles wide extending from southwest Montana to northeastern Utah. The major faults in the Wyomide Ranges are believed to have formed during late Cretaceous or early Paleocene time. The lesser thrusts, folds, and high-angle normal faults are of mid-Tertiary age.

## Wind River Mountains

*Geology and Structure.* East of the Wyomide Ranges and across the Green River Basin lies the Wind River Range. This range is developed on an asymmetrical anticlinal uplift some 125 miles long and as much as 40 miles wide. The core of the range is mainly Precambrian granodiorite; sedimentary rocks ranging in age from Paleozoic to Cenozoic crop out on its flanks. The Wind River Range is one of rugged topography, with peaks that exceed 13,000 feet in altitude. The mountains rise 8000 feet above the Wind River Basin to the northeast. This rise is by means of a number of northeastward dip slopes and hogbacks on the Paleozoic formations that border the crystalline core. The ascent on the southwest from the Green River Basin is much more abrupt, and here there are few exposures of the Paleozoic or Mesozoic formations that are believed to be present beneath the Cenozoic sediments that lap onto the Precambrian rocks. This absence of Paleozoic and Mesozoic rocks on the southwest side of the range has been attributed to faulting, but no faults are exposed.

*Geomorphic History.* The Wind River Mountains and the Colorado Front Range have become sort of type areas for interpretation of the erosional history of the Rocky Mountains. The terminology which Blackwelder applied to the erosion surfaces in the Wind River Mountains (see p. 328) has become more or less standard for the Middle Rocky Mountain region. The erosion surface which Blackwelder (1915) described in the summit areas of the Wind River Mountains as the Wind River peneplain has been called the Fremont surface by Baker (1946) and the Summit peneplain by Westgate and Branson (1913).

The Wind River Mountains exhibit some striking glacial topography (see Fig. 20.5). Glacial cirques, glacial troughs, lateral and end moraines, and valley trains are all excellently developed. Distribution of drift and moraines indicates that during both the Bull Lake and Pinedale glaciations a mountain icecap formed in the west-central part of the Wind River Range from which piedmont glaciers extended down to the floor of the Green River (Bridger) Basin at the southwest (Holmes and Moss, 1955). In the southern part and on the east side of the range, however, the glaciers were confined to valleys. This mountain range has become a type region for stages and substages of glaciation for the Middle and Northern Rocky Mountains, and the terminology developed here (see p. 329) is being extended gradually to the whole Rocky Mountain System.

Table 20.1 gives in summary form an outline of the erosional and glacial history of the Wind River Mountains region.

It has been noted by Howard and Hack (1943) that in several of the valleys in the Wind River Mountains there are indications of a glacial readvance later than Pinedale II. Evidence for this consists of end moraines below the cirques and nivation hollows and secondary cirques in the walls of the compound Pinedale cirques. Temple Lake was suggested as a name for this advance; apparently it corresponds to Richmond's (1948) Pinedale III.

## Teton Mountains and Jackson Hole

The Teton Mountains, along with adjacent Jackson Hole, present some of the most spectacular scenery to be seen in conterminus United States. The Teton Range extends over 30 miles

FIG. 20.5   View west-northwest along crest of Wind River Range showing topographic effects of intense glacial sculpturing.   (*Photo by John S. Shelton.*)

southward from the Yellowstone Plateau and varies in width from 10 to 15 miles. It merges at the north with the Pitchstone Plateau in Yellowstone Park and at the south with the low Teton Pass Mountains. Jackson Hole, to the immediate east of the Teton Range, is a narrow intermontane basin about 48 miles long and 6 to 12 miles wide. Its floor varies in altitude from 6000 to 7000 feet. Several of the higher peaks of the Tetons exceed 12,000 feet in altitude, and Grand Teton, the highest peak, attains an altitude of 13,800 feet. Near Jenny Lake at the base of Grand Teton one of the most spectacular views in the western United States is to be seen. Here the Teton front rises 1½ miles in a horizontal distance of 3 miles. In conterminous United States only the eastern front of the Sierra Nevada and the west front of the Wasatch Mountains equal the Teton front in magnitude.

*Structure and Geology.* The Teton Range is a Tertiary fault block which has been tilted downward to the west, and thus the backslope (west side) of the Teton Range does not approach the east front in steepness (see Fig. 20.6). Upthrusting along the Teton fault at the east side of the fault block, along with erosion, has exposed a complex of Precambrian rocks along the eastern margin of the range in which gneisses, schists, granites, and pegmatites predominate. Paleozoic and Mesozoic strata form the backslope of the range.

Downfaulted Jackson Hole, at the east of the Teton Range, is floored with Cretaceous and Tertiary rocks which are covered at the north end with glacial till and outwash. The Gros Ventre Buttes in Jackson Hole (see Fig. 20.7) are smaller fault blocks which originated at the same time as the main Teton block. They are composed of Paleozoic sedimentary rocks and capped with basic lava flows, breccias, and tuffs of probable Miocene age (Scopel, 1956). Teton Basin, on the west side of the Teton fault block, is another intermontane basin similar to Jackson Hole.

The Tetons display most of the features associated with high-angle faulting; a linear mountain front, faceted spur ends, hanging valleys, and an asymmetrical cross profile (Horberg, 1938). Difference of opinion exists, however, as to the nature of the Teton frontal scarp. It has been interpreted variously as a fault scarp, fault-line scarp, and composite scarp; probably it is a composite scarp. It seems likely that faulting began along the Teton fault as early as Miocene time and continued intermittently into Pleistocene or even Recent time. Relationships of the Yellowstone volcanics to Tertiary faults in the Teton Range suggest that the major fault movements occurred in early Pliocene time following deposition of the Miocene basic volcanics and prior to outpouring of the Plateau rhyolites (Horberg, Edmund, and Fryxell, 1955). Cumulative movement of as much as 20,000 feet along the Teton frontal fault has been postulated (Love and de la Montagne, 1956).

TABLE 20.1   Summary of Geomorphic History of Wind River Mountains

| Erosion Cycles | | Glacial Stages |
|---|---|---|
| Recent | Postglacial | |
| | | Pinedale III (Temple Lake) |
| | | Pinedale II |
| | | Pinedale I |
| | Lenore | |
| Pleistocene | | Bull Lake II |
| | | Bull Lake I |
| | Circle | |
| | | Buffalo II |
| | | Buffalo I |
| | Black Rock* | |
| | Union Pass* | |
| Pliocene | Wind River (Fremont) | |

* Some difference of opinion exists as to whether the Union Pass and Black Rock subcycles took place in very late Pliocene or early Pleistocene time.

Pre-existing Laramide structures had been largely destroyed by erosion before the faulting

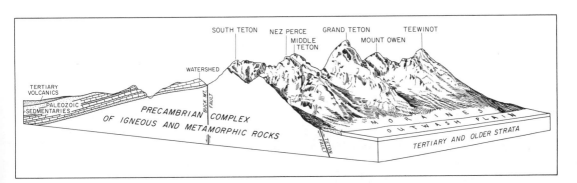

FIG. 20.6   Block diagram of Teton Range. (*After Leland Horberg, Augustana Library Pub. 16.*)

FIG. 20.7    Teton Range with East Gros Ventre Buttes in middle foreground.    Town of Jackson, Wyoming, in right foreground.    (*Photo by C. L. Haines.*)

which produced the present range occurred.    It seems probable that the site of the present Teton Range was no more than a line of low hills as late as Pliocene time when the region was covered by lavas that may have extended from the Teton Basin on the west of the Teton Range into Jackson Hole.    Later, these volcanic rocks, along with the underlying bedrock, were subjected to the faulting which produced the present Teton Range, and subsequent stripping of the volcanic rocks from the fault block has revealed the older rocks and structures (Love, 1956).

As emphasized by Horberg and others (1949) the Teton Mountains fault block, along with the adjacent downfaulted block in Jackson Hole, exhibits all the essential features of a basin-range structure.    These are (1) earlier structures (Laramide) preserved in the interior of the range, (2) an erosion surface that truncates these older structures, (3) a lava cap on the surface of erosion, and (4) tilted fault-block mountains.    It is thus mainly on the grounds of

proximity that the Tetons are included in the Rocky Mountain system rather than in the Basin and Range province.

*Geomorphic History.*    The landscape of the Teton Mountains area seems to reflect the same erosion cycles and subcycles that were recognized in the Wind River Mountains by Blackwelder, except that there is no evidence of the Wind River (Fremont) erosion surface in the Teton Range. Its former existence has been postulated, however, in order to explain the course of Webb Creek across the axis of the range as a result of superposition from the Wind River peneplain surface (Fryxell, et al., 1941).    The Union Pass and Black Rock surfaces are well represented. Possibly the mature topography in the area of Precambrian rocks may have developed during the Union Pass cycle of erosion, although the possibility exists that some of this topography may represent an older landscape that has been exhumed.    The Pleistocene Circle and Lenore terraces are present in the area, and a late Pleistocene age is suggested by the presence of glacial materials of Wisconsin age on them.

*Glacial Stages.* Three stages of glaciation are represented in the Teton Mountain region, the Buffalo, Bull Lake, and Pinedale. As the Buffalo drift is not confined to valleys but is found mainly on ridge crests and shoulders, it seems likely that the topography during the Buffalo glaciation was less rugged than during the later Bull Lake and Pinedale glaciations. Buffalo glaciers may well have been piedmont glaciers or local ice caps that extended into Jackson Hole from the Absaroka region to the east.

It should be kept in mind that the glacial materials in Jackson Hole were deposited by two sets of glaciers, the mountain glaciers from the Teton Mountains and an intermontane glacier that was a southward extension of the Upper Yellowstone Glacier of the Yellowstone Park area (see p. 373). Lakes such as Jenny, Leigh, and Phelps lie back of end moraines built by mountain glaciers from the Teton Mountains during the Pinedale glaciation. Jackson Lake, however, lies back of an end moraine of Pinedale age built by the intermontane glacier. Glacial outwash is abundant in Jackson Hole and is largely a mixture of outwash from both the mountain and intermontane glaciers. Outwash terraces of Bull Lake and Pinedale age are conspicuously developed along the Snake River (see Fig. 20.8). The Potholes, just south of Jackson Lake, is an area of pitted outwash of Pinedale age; Burned Ridge, immediately west of the Potholes, is part of an end moraine of Bull Lake age; Timbered Island, which lies southeast of Jenny Lake between Pinedale and Bull Lake outwash, is an end moraine of Bull Lake age.

FIG. 20.8  Bull Lake (upper) and Pinedale (lower) outwash terraces along Snake River in Jackson Hole.  (*Photo by J. H. Rathbone, courtesy Wyo. Geol. Assoc.*)

*Summary of Geomorphic History.* The history of the Teton Mountain-Jackson Hole area is reasonably clear as far back as the Laramide orogeny. The following events can be recognized (Edmund, 1951).

1. Laramide folding and faulting along north-south axes.
2. Extended erosion which reduced the Laramide topography to moderately low relief.
3. The outpouring of lavas onto the eroded surfaces of rocks ranging in age from Precambrian to Cretaceous. (These volcanics extended into and perhaps completely across Jackson Hole.)
4. Initiation of block-faulting and beginning of uplift of the Teton fault block in Miocene or early Pliocene time.
5. Development during Pliocene time of the Summit (Wind River) erosion surface.
6. Two subcycles of erosion that produced the Union Pass and Black Rock erosion surfaces, in either late Pliocene or early Pleistocene time.
7. Buffalo glaciation.
8. Development of the Circle erosion surface.
9. Bull Lake glaciation.
10. Development of the Lenore terrace.
11. Pinedale glaciation.
12. Postglacial erosion.

## Yellowstone Plateau Area

*Boundaries.* Although it is included in the Middle Rocky Mountain province, except for a small part of the park that is in the Gallatin Range of the Northern Rocky Mountains, Yellowstone Park is not mountainous country, but rather heavily forested volcanic plateau. The park has an area of about 3500 square miles and an average altitude around 8000 feet. The volcanic plateau is bounded on the east by the Absaroka Mountains, on the northeast by the Snowy Range (the southwest part of the Beartooth uplift), on the northwest by the Gallatin Range, on the west by the Snake River High Plains, and on the south by the Teton Mountains and lesser mountains of northwestern Wyoming.

Except for the Snake River Plains on the west, which are about 1000 feet lower than the Yellowstone Plateau, the volcanic plateau is surrounded by mountainous country.

*Geology.* Igneous activity in the Yellowstone Park area took place mainly during two periods, one in late Cretaceous-early Tertiary time and the other in middle and late Tertiary time. Rocks of the first period of volcanic activity are predominately breccias and agglomerates and basalt flows. They are most extensively exposed in the Absaroka Mountains but are found elsewhere around the margins of the younger volcanic rocks at the north, south, and northwest of Yellowstone Park (see Fig. 20.9). They probably underlie the younger rhyolites of the Yellowstone Park area. That part of Yellowstone Park commonly called the Rhyolite Plateau is believed to occupy a volcanic-tectonic depression (Hamilton, 1960) that has been filled with volcanic rocks ranging in age from Eocene to Pleistocene, if not Recent. The most famous of these volcanic rocks are the rhyolites and welded tuffs (ignimbrites) that form the surficial flows of the Rhyolite Plateau. Rimming these rocks are volcanic rocks of older age. The rhyolites and welded tuffs have commonly been considered Pliocene in age, but the finding in recent years of glacial deposits beneath volcanic rocks indicates that in part at least they are of Pleistocene age.

The Rhyolite Plateau is commonly divided into three parts, the western Madison Plateau (see Fig. 20.10), the southern Pitchstone Plateau, and the northeastern Central Plateau. Together they cover some 2000 square miles. It is believed (Boyd, 1961) that the surface of the Pitchstone Plateau near the southwest corner of the park is underlain by a single flow. Its front along the southwest margin of this flow is as much as 1000 feet high, and at its southern and eastern margins it is 300 to 500 feet high. The surface of the flow displays numerous pressure ridges 25 to 50 feet high, which on aerial photographs resemble the crevassed surface of a glacier. The pressure ridges stand out conspicuously because trees are more abundant

FIG. 20.9    Early Eocene (?) basic lava flows atop early basic breccias in Baronet Peak in northeastern Yellowstone Park.    (*Photo by David Hawley.*)

on them than in the inter-ridge swales. The surfaces of the Madison and Pitchstone Plateaus are essentially unmodified from what they were like after the deposition of the rhyolites, but the Central Plateau, northwest of Yellowstone Lake, was glaciated and has extensive glacial deposits upon it. According to Boyd (1961), several small glaciers formed along the margins of the plateau, and cirque development here has given the plateau margin a scalloped effect. Some of these small glaciers built end moraines that lie near the bases of the flows.

*Glacial History.* At least three times during the Pleistocene epoch parts of Yellowstone Park were glaciated. Glaciation of the park was largely the work of two piedmont glaciers fed by ice streams from adjacent mountains. The Lamar Glacier, which advanced onto the Yellowstone Plateau from the northeast, was fed from ice-fields in the Snowy Range and the northern part of the Absaroka Mountains. The Upper Yellowstone Glacier, which advanced from the southeast, was fed by valley glaciers in the southern end of the Absaroka Mountains. In addition, a few small glaciers formed in the Washburn Range.

At their maximum extent the Lamar and Upper Yellowstone glaciers appear to have merged in their terminal zones. Tongues of ice from the Lamar Glacier crossed the continental divide and extended into the headwater area of the Madison River drainage. Glacial deposits of this source are found in the Lower Geyser Basin.

FIG. 20.10   Madison Plateau viewed from north wall of Madison Canyon.   Cliff is the eroded front of a single rhyolite flow.   (*Photo by F. R. Boyd.*)

Similarly, ice of the Upper Yellowstone Glacier crossed the continental divide at the south and extended into Jackson Hole as far south as the south end of Jackson Lake, where it built the end moraine that forms the dam for this lake.

During final retreat of the Lamar Glacier a lake called Hayden Lake occupied Hayden Valley (really a broad basin rather than a valley) and extensive remnants of the clays and silts deposited in this lake underlie terraces around the basin. Similar lacustrine terraces, about 160 feet above present lake level, may be seen around Yellowstone Lake, but it is uncertain whether the two Pleistocene lakes were confluent. It seems likely that the basin now occupied by Yellowstone Lake was ponded several times during the Pleistocene, for each time that the Lamar Glacier moved southward into the area it would block the northward drainage.

One of the points on which there has been considerable argument is whether Yellowstone Lake in its early postglacial history drained to the north, as it now does, or to the south through so-called Outlet Channel into the Snake River. Howard (1937) was of the opinion that Outlet Channel was used only when the northern drainage route was blocked by ice; he did not believe that the field evidence supported the viewpoint that postglacial Yellowstone Lake originally drained to the Snake River and was later captured by headward erosion by a north-flowing stream, as postulated by Goode (1899).

## Absaroka Mountains

*Geology.*   The Absaroka Mountains are a highly dissected plateau composed of more than 6500 feet of early Tertiary volcanic rocks, probably of Eocene to Oligocene age.   Six volcanic units have been recognized (Rouse, 1937), which can actually be combined into two groups of three members each consisting of a lower acid breccia, an intermediate basic breccia, and an upper series of basalt flows.   The northern boundary of the

Absaroka volcanic field is at the boundary between the Absaroka Mountains and the Beartooth Mountains (see Fig. 20.11). The eastern boundary is the rugged mountain front of the Absaroka Mountains and the boundaries on the south and west are against Cretaceous and Tertiary rocks. The Absaroka volcanics are believed to have been extruded through a great number of small vents and poured out onto a landscape that possessed relief as much as 1000 to 1500 feet.

*Topography.* Although the Absaroka Mountains are bordered by the Yellowstone Plateau on the west, they differ from this plateau in three respects: they are 2000 to 4000 feet higher; the volcanic rocks are older; and what was once a volcanic plateau has been sculptured into mountainous relief (see Fig. 20.12). The Absarokas were extensively glaciated and, as previously stated, were the source area of the ice that formed the intermontane glacier in Jackson Hole.

### Heart Mountain Thrust

Lying east of the Absaroka Mountains, where the volcanic rocks of the Absaroka give way to

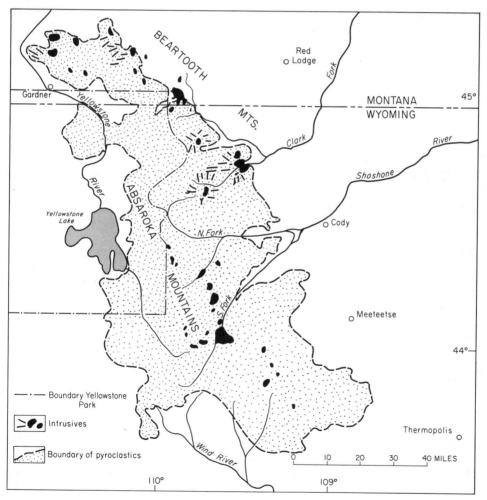

FIG. 20.11   Extent of Absaroka volcanic field.   (*After W. H. Parsons, Billings Geol. Soc. Guidebook, 9th Ann. Field Conf.*)

FIG. 20.12   Absaroka Range, looking south from over Cody, Wyoming.   *(Photo by Spence Air Photos.)*

FIG. 20.13   Heart Mountain, north of Cody, Wyoming.   *(Photo by Spence Air Photos.)*

the sedimentary rocks on the west side of the Bighorn Basin, are a number of mountain peaks such as Heart Mountain (see Fig. 20.13), Logan Mountain, Sheep Mountain, Rattlesnake Mountain, and McCullochs Peak, which have been interpreted as klippe remnants of a large thrust sheet known as the Heart Mountain thrust. At the present time some 50 separate blocks ranging from a few hundred feet to as much as 5 miles across are scattered over an area 30 miles wide and 60 miles long (see Fig. 20.14).   Dake (1920) was the first to notice these displaced blocks and map the fault surface along which they moved eastward. Not all agree as to the method by which the thrusting took place. It has most commonly been assumed that it took place along a bedding thrust similar to the Lewis thrust farther north, but Pierce (1957) and King (1960) have considered it a detachment thrust or decollement, with the blocks sliding down a basal gliding plane under the influence of gravity. Where the blocks came from presents a problem, as there is no belt of deformed rocks immediately west of the klippe unless there be such beneath the Absaroka volcanics.

Pierce (1961) has described what he believed was the "break-away" point for the Heart Mountain detachment thrust. This is near the northeast corner of Yellowstone Park, only a few hundred feet west of the park boundary. Here rocks on the west side are unfaulted and display the normal stratigraphic sequence for the Paleozoic rocks of the area. East of the presumed "break-away" point the Ordovician Bighorn dolomite and rocks above it up to and including the early acid volcanics have moved eastward and in so doing have created an open space at the bottom of which can be seen the Grove Creek limestone of Cambrian age.

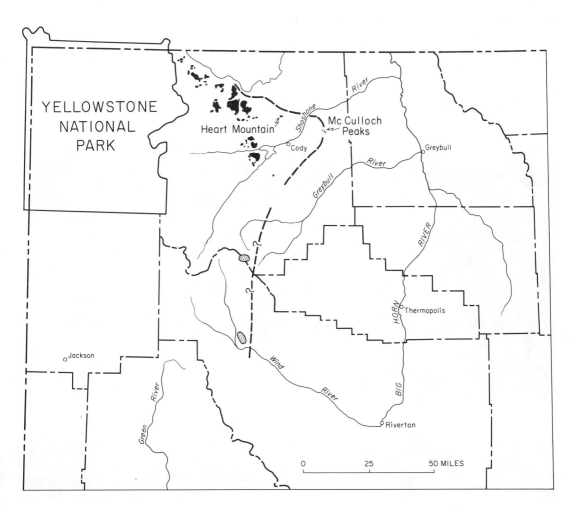

FIG. 20.14 Map showing location of remnants of Heart Mountain thrust sheet. (*After W. G. Pierce, Am. Assoc. Petroleum Geologists Bull. 25.*)

Pierce (1957) has described a second fault older and below the Heart Mountain thrust which he called the South Fork thrust. The rocks involved in the Heart Mountain thrust range from the Ordovician Bighorn dolomite at the base to the Mississippian Madison limestone at the top, including the Devonian Jefferson limestone and Three Forks shale, whereas the rocks involved in the South Fork thrust are of Jurassic and Cretaceous age. The South Fork thrust block rests on rocks of Paleocene and Eocene age. A minimum displacement of 36 miles has been estimated, but it may be greater than this, for the source area is not known.

### Bighorn Basin

Extending southeastward from the Absaroka Mountains and forming a loop that connects with the Bighorn Mountains farther east is a group of ranges that includes the Shoshone, Owl Creek, and Bridger Mountains. Along with the Absarokas and Bighorns they practically enclose a large intermontane area known as the Bighorn Basin. The Bighorn River enters this basin from the south in a deep, apparently superposed canyon cut through the Owl Creek Range (see Fig. 20.15). The small mountain mass between the Owl Creek Canyon and the southern end of the Bighorn Mountains is known as the Bridger Mountains, but it should not be confused with the larger Bridger Range in Montana.

*Geology and Structure.* The Bighorn Basin is an elliptical basin that is approximately 150 miles long and 100 miles wide. It is geologically and topographically a part of the Great Plains, but since it is so nearly enclosed by a loop of moun-

FIG. 20.15   Gorge of Wind River through Owl Creek Mountains (foreground). View is to west toward Absaroka Mountains at right and Wind River Mountains at left. *(Photo by John S. Shelton.)*

tain ranges it is included in the Middle Rocky Mountain province. The Bighorn Basin is underlain by more than 15,000 feet of Paleozoic, Mesozoic, and Cenozoic sediments (Harris, 1959). Its axis extends northwestward and passes under the overthrust southwestern corner of the Beartooth uplift.

The geomorphic history of the Bighorn Basin can be divided into two distinct phases (Mackin, 1937). The first phase was marked by uplift of the surrounding mountains accompanied by widespread fluvial aggradation of the enclosed structural depression. Aggradation of the Bighorn Basin coincided in time with the extensive alluviation on the High Plains. A later phase of Bighorn Basin history was marked by partial excavation of the previously deposited basin fill. Evidence that the basin fill was once much higher than at present is of two sorts. The Bighorn River enters and leaves the Bighorn Basin through gorges across mountain barriers; superposition from a once higher cover mass seems the most logical explanation of these transverse gorges. The presence of extensive deposits of stream gravels at altitudes higher than the present floor of the basin lends further support to the idea of a former much higher basin fill.

## Bighorn Mountains

*Geology and Structure.* The Bighorn Mountains, at the east side of the Bighorn Basin, display the structure typical of the eastern ranges of the Middle Rocky Mountain province. They consist of a granite core flanked by steeply dipping Paleozoic and Mesozoic rocks. The crystalline core is largely covered by Paleozoic rocks in both the northern and southern thirds of the range, but in the middle part Precambrian crystalline rocks are extensively exposed. This middle part of the Bighorn uplift has the simplest structure. Here Paleozoic sediments, mainly limestones and dolomites, descend in gentle dip slopes into the Bighorn Basin on the west and the Powder River Basin on the east. Here, too, extensive mountain glaciation has given to the crest of the range the distinctive biscuitboard

effect produced by cirque development on two sides of a mountain range.

*Geomorphic History.* Sizeable expanses in the Bighorn Mountains exhibit surprisingly low relief (see Fig. 20.16) and have been considered remnants of once more extensive erosion surfaces. Conventional interpretation of the geomorphic history of the Bighorn Mountains has recognized the following major events in the development of the mountain range.

1. Uplift of the range during the Laramide orogeny.
2. Reduction during early Tertiary time of the mountains to a surface of low relief called the Summit peneplain.
3. Mid-Tertiary uplift of the Summit peneplain.
4. Development during a period of essential stillstand of the Subsummit erosion surface along with filling of the adjacent Bighorn and Powder River Basins with alluvial deposits.
5. Uplift at the close of Tertiary time and during the Pleistocene epoch which produced canyon cutting and glaciation in the mountains and the development of a number of fluvial terraces in the adjacent basins.

*Mackin's Views.* As stated above (see p. 328) Mackin (1947) has interpreted the Subsummit erosion surface as a pediment developed at a high level in relation to steep stream gradients adjusted to the semi-arid climatic conditions of late Tertiary time. Interpretation of the Subsummit surface as a pediment eliminates, in Mackin's opinion, the necessity of postulating as much late Tertiary and Pleistocene uplift as is usually done, for if the usual steep slopes of pediments are taken into account, it seems likely that the Subsummit surface was formed at altitudes not more than 1000 to 2000 feet lower than present remnants of the Subsummit surface.

Even more unconventional than his explanation of the Subsummit surface is Mackin's interpretation of the Summit erosion surface as a noncyclical surface produced by the processes which have been collectively described as altiplanation (Eakin, 1916) or cryoplanation (Bryan, 1946). It is, of course, not unreasonable to assume that

FIG. 20.16   Subsummit erosion surface in Bighorn Mountains near Canyon Creek at head of Powder River.   (*Photo by N. H. Darton, U. S. Geol. Survey.*)

conditions existed in the Bighorn Mountains during Pleistocene time that favored vigorous frost action, solifluction, and the other processes which contribute to mass-wasting under severely cold climatic conditions.

One unusual aspect of Mackin's interpretation of the Bighorn erosion surfaces is that the Summit surface, even though higher than the Subsummit surface, is considered the younger of the two.   It would seem that this could only be true if numerous unreduced areas were left standing above the Subsummit pediplain that were high enough above the Pliocene pediment to induce during glacial times severe frost-climate conditions that would favor intensive mass-wasting.

### Beartooth Mountains

*Location.*   The Beartooth Mountains, or Plateau, as they are sometimes called, display some of the most interesting geomorphic features to be seen in the whole Middle Rocky Mountain province. Lying north of the Yellowstone Plateau and the Absaroka Mountains, and separated from the latter by the Clark Fork of the Yellowstone River, the Beartooth Mountains are the frontal range in this part of Wyoming and Montana. The bold eastern front of the Beartooth Mountains rises 4000 to 5000 feet above the Great Plains to the east.

*Geology and Structure.*   The Beartooth Range, like the Bighorns, consists essentially of a core of Precambrian granite and gneiss flanked by Paleozoic and Mesozoic sedimentary rocks (Foose, 1958).   The Precambrian rocks which form the main mass of the Beartooth uplift represent the largest continuous expanse of basement complex to be seen in the Middle Rocky Mountains (Spencer, 1959).   Volcanic rocks associated with those of the Absaroka-Yellowstone area are found on the south and southwest sides of the uplift.   The bold eastern front of the

Beartooth uplift is related to a fault which is generally considered a high-angle thrust fault (Hughes, 1933). Along the eastern front Paleozoic and Mesozoic sediments exhibit very steep dips and are even overturned where Precambrian crystalline rocks are thrust over them. On the southwest side the Beartooth uplift is bordered by a large normal fault known as the Dilworth or Clark Fork fault. This fault has a displacement of over 2000 feet.

*Contrasting Topography on East and West Sides.* Perhaps the most interesting aspect of the topography of the Beartooth Mountains is the striking contrast in the topography on the two sides of the uplift. The northeast side has been deeply sculptured by valley glaciers, whereas on the southwest side a local mountain icecap formed. On the northeast side, between glacial troughs, are well preserved remnants of the Subsummit erosion surface. Remnants of this erosion surface are rather smooth, commonly treeless tracts of moderate relief standing well above the deeply sunk glacial troughs. The glacial troughs divide the eastern slope into a number of small plateau-like tracts. If the glacial troughs between these upland tracts are pictured as filled with the rock debris that was removed during their cutting, it does not require much imagination to visualize the restored topography as a former erosion surface.

In contrast, on the southwest side of the Beartooth uplift little is left of the Tertiary topography that once existed. The Pleistocene icecap which mantled this side of the range scoured and abraded the surface until it produced a type of landscape that in miniature resembles very much the ice-scoured parts of the Canadian Shield. Ice-abraded rock surfaces, the roche moutonnée type of rock bosses, bedrock basins and lakes, and scarcity of glacial debris attest to the erosive effectiveness of the icecap. Probably close to two-thirds of the surface on the southwest side of the mountain range displays fresh, relatively unweathered bedrock.

*Erosion Surfaces.* Description of erosion surfaces in the Beartooth Mountains at first followed the conventional interpretation of Rocky Mountain geomorphic history. Two peneplains, the Summit at altitudes around 12,000 feet and the Subsummit some 1500 to 2000 feet lower, have been described (Bevan, 1925). The Summit peneplain was considered to be early Tertiary in age, probably no older than Oligocene, and the Subsummit peneplain to be Pliocene in age. Bevan thought that the Summit peneplain at the south passed beneath the volcanic rocks of the Absaroka Mountains and that the Subsummit surface truncated the volcanic rocks of the Absarokas.

Several geologists who have worked in the Beartooth Mountains have disagreed with this interpretation of the geomorphic history of the region. Hughes (1933) considered the southern part of Bevan's Subsummit peneplain an exhumed part of the Precambrian marine plain on which basal Cambrian sediments were deposited. Sharp (1938) doubted the existence of two peneplains and looked on the Beartooth Mountain topography as a mature topography which had developed during Pliocene time contemporaneously with the late phases of aggradation on the Great Plains.

Although no one has done so in print, the interpretation given by Mackin to the Summit and Subsummit surfaces of the Bighorn Mountains might equally well be applied to the erosion surfaces in the Beartooth Mountains. The Subsummit surface would thus be considered a pediplain of Pliocene age and the Summit surface an altiplanation surface of Pleistocene age. That climatic conditions existed here during Pleistocene time that favored solifluction and vigorous frost action is indicated by the crude patterned ground that can be seen along Highway 12 where it crosses the divide between the eastern and western slopes. Furthermore, this patterned ground has the appearance of being relict rather than active.

*Stages of Glaciation.* Little recent work has been done on the glacial history of the Beartooth Mountains. Bevan (1946) thought he saw evidence here of three stages of glaciation. The earliest glaciation is represented by extensive high-level drift near the north end of the range;

an intermediate stage was suggested to him by broad, lobate drift deposits at altitudes between 9000 and 9400 feet in the southern part of the mountains; and the latest stage of glaciation was supposed to be represented by a canyon phase of glaciation. Bevan suggested that these three glaciations might be dated as early, middle, and late Pleistocene. More work needs to be done on this aspect of the geomorphic history of the Beartooth Mountains before any firm correlation can be made between their glacial history and that of other parts of the Rocky Mountains.

## REFERENCES CITED

Armstrong, F. C., and E. R. Cressman (1957). Re-interpretation of the Bannock overthrust, southwestern Idaho, *Geol. Soc. Am. Bull.*, **68**, 1697 (abs.).

Baker, C. L. (1946). Geology of the northwestern Wind River Mountains, Wyoming, *Geol. Soc. Am. Bull.*, **57**, 565–596.

Bevan, Arthur (1925). Rocky Mountain peneplains northeast of Yellowstone Park, *Jour. Geol.*, **33**, 563–587.

———— (1946). Three stages of Pleistocene glaciation, Beartooth Mountains, Montana, *Geol. Soc. Am. Bull.*, **57**, 1178–1179.

Blackwelder, Eliot (1915). Post-Cretaceous history of the mountains of southwestern Wyoming, *Jour. Geol.*, **23**, 97–117; 193–217; 307–340.

Boyd, F. R. (1961). Welded tuffs and flows in the Rhyolite Plateau of Yellowstone Park, Wyoming, *Geol. Soc. Am. Bull.*, **72**, 387–426.

Bradley, W. H. (1963). Geomorphology of the north flank of the Uinta Mountains, *U. S. Geol. Survey Profess. Paper* 185-I, 163–204.

Bryan, Kirk (1946). Cryopedology—the study of frozen ground and intensive frost-action with suggestions of nomenclature, *Am. Jour. Sci.*, **244**, 622–642.

Curtis, B. C. (1950). Structure of the north flank of the Uinta Mountains, *Wyo. Geol. Assoc. Guidebook, Southwest Wyoming Geology*, 93–102.

Dake, C. L. (1918). The Heart Mountain overthrust and associated structures in Park County, Wyoming, *Jour. Geol.*, **26**, 45–55.

Eakin, H. M. (1916). The Yukon-Koyukuk region, Alaska, *U. S. Geol. Survey Bull.* 631, 67–82.

Eardley, A. J. (1944). Geology of the north-central Wasatch Mountains, Utah, *Geol. Soc. Am. Bull.*, **55**, 819–894.

Edmund, R. W. (1951). Structural geology and physiography of the northern end of the Teton Range, Wyoming, *Augustana Library Publication* 23, 82 pp.

Foose, R. M. (1958). Structural features of the perime-ter of the Beartooth Mountains, Billings Geol Soc., *Guidebook, 9th Annual Field Conference*, 31–35.

Forrester, J. D. (1937). Structure of the Uinta Mountains, *Geol. Soc. Am. Bull.*, **48**, 631–660.

Fryxell, F. M., Leland Horberg, and Rudolph Edmund (1941). Geomorphology of the Teton Range and adjacent basins, Wyoming-Idaho, *Geol. Soc. Am. Bull.*, **52**, 1903 (abs).

Goode, J. P. (1899). The piracy of the Yellowstone, *Jour. Geol.*, **7**, 261–271.

Hamilton, Warren (1960). Late tectonics and volcanism of the Yellowstone region, Wyoming, Montana and Idaho, Billings Geol. Soc., *Guidebook, 11th Annual Field Conference*, 92–105.

Harris, R. L., Jr. (1959). Geologic evolution of the Beartooth Mountains, Montana and Wyoming, *Geol. Soc. Am. Bull.*, **70**, 1185–1216.

Holmes, G. W., and J. H. Moss (1955). Pleistocene geology of the southwestern Wind River Mountains, Wyoming, *Geol. Soc. Am. Bull.*, **66**, 629–654.

Horberg, Leland (1938). The structural geology and physiography of the Teton Pass area, Wyoming, *Augustana Library Publication* **16**, 85 pp.

————, R. W. Edmund, and F. M. Fryxell (1955). Geomorphic and structural relations of Tertiary volcanics in the northern Teton Range, Wyoming, *Jour. Geol.*, **63**, 501–511.

Howard, A. D. (1937). History of the Grand Canyon of the Yellowstone, *Geol. Soc. Am. Spec. Paper* 6, 159 pp.

Howard, E. B., and J. T. Hack (1943). The Finley site, *Am. Antiquities*, **8**, 224–241.

Hughes, R. V. (1933). The geology of the Beartooth Mountain front in Park County, Wyoming, Nat. Acad. Sci., *Proc.*, **19**, 239–253.

King, P. B. (1960). The anatomy and habitat of low-angle thrust faults, *Am. Jour. Sci.*, **258**-A, 115–125.

Love, J. D., and J. de la Montagne (1956). Pleistocene and Recent tilting of Jackson Hole, Teton County, Wyoming, Wyo. Geol. Assoc., *Guidebook, Field Conference for 1956*, 169–178.

———— (1956). Summary of the geologic history of Teton County, Wyoming, during late Cretaceous, Tertiary, and Quaternary times, Wyo. Geol. Assoc., *Guidebook, 11th Annual Field Conference*, 140–150.

Mackin, J. H. (1937). Erosional history of the Bighorn Basin, Wyoming, *Geol. Soc. Am. Bull.*, **48**, 813–894.

———— (1947). Altitude and local relief in the Bighorn area during the Cenozoic, *Guidebook, Field Conference in Bighorn Basin*, 103–120.

Pierce, W. G. (1957). Heart Mountain and South Fork detachment thrusts of Wyoming, *Am. Assoc. Petroleum Geologists Bull.*, **41**, 591–626.

———— (1960). The "break-away" point of the Heart Mountain detachment fault in northwestern Wyoming, *U. S. Geol. Survey Profess Paper* 400-B, B236–B237.

Richards, R. W. and G. R. Mansfield (1912). The Bannock overthrust, *Jour. Geol.*, **20,** 681–709.

Richmond, G. M. (1948). Modification of Blackwelder's sequence of glaciation in the Wind River Mountains, Wyoming, *Geol. Soc. Am. Bull.*, **59,** 1400–1401 (Abs.).

Rouse, J. T. (1937). Genesis and structural relationships of the Absaroka volcanic rocks, Wyoming, *Geol. Soc. Am. Bull.*, **48,** 1257–1296.

Rubey, W. W. (1955). Early structural history of the overthrust belt of western Wyoming and adjacent states, Wyo. Geol. Assoc., *Guidebook, 10th Annual Field Conference*, 125–126.

Scopel, L. J. (1956). The volcanic rocks of the Gros Ventre Buttes, Jackson Hole, Wyoming, Wyo. Geol. Assoc., *Guidebook for 1956 Field Conference*, 126–128.

Sharp, H. S. (1938). The upland of the Beartooth Mountains, Montana, Geol. Soc. Am., *Proc. for 1937*, 113 (abs.).

Spencer, E. W. (1959). Geologic evolution of the Beartooth Mountains, Montana and Wyoming, Pt. 2, Fracture patterns, *Geol. Soc. Am. Bull.*, **70,** 467–508.

Westgate, L. G., and E. B. Branson (1913). Later Cenozoic history of the Wind River Mountains, *Jour. Geol.*, **21,** 142–159.

ADDITIONAL REFERENCES

Bauer, C. M. (1940). Discussion; Geology along the southern margin of the Absaroka Range, Wyoming, *Jour. Geol.*, **48,** 324–327.

Blackstone, D. L., Jr. (1940). Structure of the Pryor Mountains, Montana, *Jour. Geol.*, **48,** 590–618.

Branson, E. B., and C. C. Branson (1941). Geology of Wind River Mountains, Wyoming, *Am. Assoc. Petroleum Geologists Bull.*, **25,** 120–151.

Edmund, R. W. (1956). Resume of structures and physiography in the northern Teton Mountains, Wyoming, Wyo. Geol. Assoc., *Guidebook for 1956 Field Conference*, 151–157.

Foose, R. M., D. U. Wise, and G. S. Garbarini (1961). Structural geology of the Beartooth Mountains, Montana and Wyoming, *Geol. Soc. Am. Bull.*, **72,** 1143–1172.

Fryxell, F. M. (1930). Glacial features of Jackson Hole, Wyoming, *Augustana Library Publication* 13, 129 pp.

Hewitt, D. W. (1920). The Heart Mountain overthrust, *Jour. Geol.*, **28,** 536–557.

Jones, O. T., and R. M. Field (1929). The resurrection of the Grand Canyon of the Yellowstone, *Am. Jour. Sci.*, **217,** 260–278.

Love, J. D. (1939). Geology along the southern margin of the Absaroka Range, *Wyoming, Geol. Soc. Am. Spec. Paper* 20, 134 pp.

—— (1961). Reconnaissance study of Quaternary faults in and south of Yellowstone National Park, Wyoming, *Geol. Soc. Am. Bull.*, **72,** 1749–1764.

Moss, J. H. (1951). Late glacial advance in the southern Wind River Mountains, Wyoming, *Am. Jour. Sci.*, **249,** 865–883.

Parsons, W. H. (1958). Origin, age, and tectonic relationships of the volcanic rocks in the Absaroka-Yellowstone-Beartooth region, Wyoming-Montana, Billings Geol. Soc., *Guidebook, 9th Annual Field Conference*, 36–43.

Pierce, W. G. (1941). Heart Mountain and South Fork thrusts, Park County, Wyoming, *Am. Assoc. Petroleum Geologists Bull.*, **25,** 2021–2045.

Poldervaart, Arie, and R. D. Bentley (1958). Precambrian and later evolution of the Beartooth Mountains, Montana and Wyoming, Billings Geol. Soc., *Guidebook for 9th Annual Field Conference*, 7–15.

Stevens, E. H. (1938). Geology of the Sheep Mountain remnant of the Heart Mountain thrust sheet, Park County, Wyoming, *Geol. Soc. Am. Bull.*, **49,** 1233–1266.

# 21

# Northern Rocky Mountain Province

## MOUNTAIN GROUPS

That part of the Northern Rocky Mountain province which lies within the United States has a considerable degree of geographical unity, but it includes groups of mountains which have marked diversity of geology, structure, and topography. Three major and one minor mountain groups may be recognized: the central Idaho ranges, the mountains of northwestern Montana and northern Idaho, the mountains of southwestern Montana, and the Belt mountain group.

Lying mainly in Idaho north of the Snake River lava plain and extending northward to near Lake Pend Oreille is a broad mountainous mass which is so lacking in lineation that the term "range" has very little meaning here. These mountains have developed mainly on the Idaho batholith and other subsidiary intrusions; at the north, however, the rocks are those of the Precambrian Belt series, but their lithology is so uniform that their topographic expression is not greatly different from that of the "granite" batholith.

A second mountain group of distinct structure and topographic form is found in extreme northwestern Montana and in the panhandle of Idaho. These mountains extend from the frontal Lewis Range on the east to the Selkirk Mountains along the Idaho-Washington boundary. In contrast to the mountains of central Idaho these mountain ranges exhibit linear form and are separated from each other by longitudinal valleys. Their dominant structural characteristic is notable folding and faulting along north-south lines.

The mountain ranges of southwestern Montana

extend roughly to the Idaho border on the west, the Blackfoot River on the north, the Missouri River on the east, and the Snake River lava plain on the south. The ranges here are short and separated by broad intermontane valleys or basins. Mountain form and alignment are largely controlled by structures that are very similar to those found in the Basin and Range region to the southwest. If it were not for the intervening Snake River lava plain, these mountains could logically be included in the Basin and Range province.

The Big Belt, Little Belt, Castle, and Crazy Mountains are detached from the main mountain mass but are closely enough related to it geographically to be considered a part of the Rocky Mountains rather than outliers of Rocky Mountain geology in the Great Plains, as are such mountain uplifts as the Big Snowy, Highwood, Bearpaw, and others (see p. 294). The Belt Mountains are anticlinal uplifts with cores of Precambrian rocks, whereas lesser intrusives and volcanic rocks are found in the Crazy and Castle Mountains.

### Mountains of Central Idaho

*Geology.* The Idaho batholith is one of the major batholithic intrusions of North America. It covers an area of some 16,000 square miles, mainly in Idaho (see Fig. 21.1). Associated with it are other, smaller intrusive bodies, such as the Boulder batholith in Montana, which covers about 1200 square miles. The characteristic rock of the Idaho batholith is quartz monzonite of slightly gneissic texture, but associated

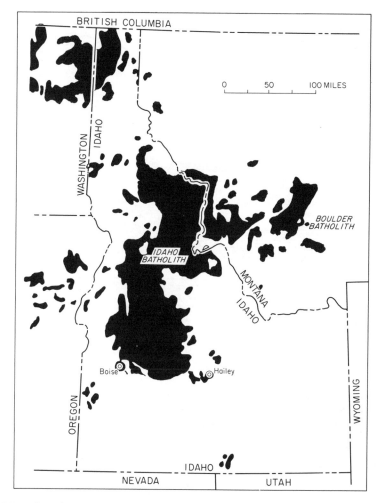

FIG. 21.1   Map of Idaho batholith and related intrusive bodies.   (*After A. L. Anderson, Jour. Geol.*, **60.**)

with it are minor facies of granodiorite and other granitic rocks (Ross, 1928, 1936). The batholith was at first believed to be Precambrian in age, but it is now known to be much younger. Anderson (1952) has shown that the batholith consists of two discrete masses of rock of different ages. The older rocks resemble those in Oregon and Washington that were emplaced during the Sierra Nevada orogeny and are considered to be of late Jurassic age; the younger rocks of the batholith apparently were emplaced early in the Laramide orogeny, in late Cretaceous time. It may well be that there are rocks of several ages in the Idaho batholith, for Knopf (1957), from a study of the nearby

Boulder batholith, concluded that it is composite in structure and displays five intrusive phases.

*Topography.*   The lithologic homogeneity of the Idaho batholith is well expressed in the mountain topography; here we find large sprawling mountains with dendritic drainage and little lineation of topography. The Bitterroot Range at the east has a marked linear form that has commonly been attributed to the presence of a marginal fault. Ross (1950), however, questioned the existence of such a fault and attributed the straightness to a gneissic slab at the base of the rocks which were intruded by the Idaho batholith. His study of the Idaho batholith indicated

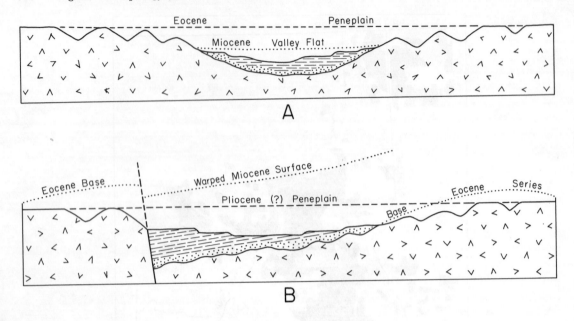

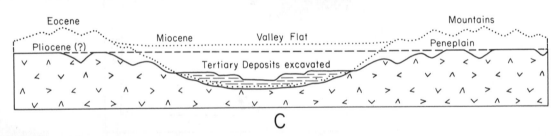

FIG. 21.2   Three possible interpretations of the relationship of basin fill deposits to the Summit erosion surface. (*After Eliot Blackwelder, Econ. Geol., 12.*)

that it was not uncommon for the batholith to have a flat roof with comparatively steeply outward-dipping beds resting against it. The Bitterroot Range is included with the mountains of Idaho more because of its contiguity than because of its similarity in geology and topography.

Major mountain groups of central Idaho are the Coeur D'Alene, Clearwater, Sawtooth, and Salmon River; boundaries between them are poorly defined. Most of the mountain valleys are narrow and gorge-like but at a few places they open up into small basins 10 to 15 miles wide and of comparable length. These basins are partially filled with Tertiary and Quaternary

deposits. Although similar in this respect to the intermontane basins in south western Montana (see p. 394), the basins in Idaho are far less numerous and much smaller in size than those of adjacent Montana.

*Idaho Peneplain Problem.*   Accordance of summit levels is not a striking attribute of the Northern Rocky Mountains, but an exception to this is found in the mountains of Idaho. Here widespread accordance of ridge crests has led to the belief that these mountains exhibit evidence of former peneplanation. This is particularly true in the Salmon River and Clearwater Mountains.

The Coeur D'Alene and Sawtooth Mountains are characterized more by sharp ridges which preserve little evidence of former erosion surfaces.

Despite the belief of some geologists that the mountains of Idaho retain evidence of a former peneplain, opinions differ as to the age of the Summit erosion surface and its relationship to the Tertiary sediments in the mountain basins. The alleged peneplain has been variously called the Summit peneplain (Atwood, 1916), the Idaho peneplain (Mansfield, 1924), and the Summit erosion surface (Anderson, 1947). Umpleby (1912) concluded that the peneplain is of Eocene age and that the basins, which contain Oligocene and Miocene sediments, were cut after development of the peneplain. This view was also held by Atwood (1916) and Kirkham (1930). Blackwelder (1912) and Rich (1918) maintained, however, that the Summit erosion surface was developed in Miocene or even as late as Pliocene time. Blackwelder pointed out that three possible interpretations may be made of the relationship of the Summit erosion surface and the Tertiary deposits below it (see Fig. 21.2): (1) An Eocene erosion surface was developed, and later broad valleys or basins were cut in it and partially filled with the Oligocene and Miocene deposits which were later partially removed by erosion. (2) An early Tertiary erosion surface, either plain-like or hilly, developed, and over it was spread a thick mantle of sediments. Faulting ensued, as a result of which some of the sediments were lifted above the local baselevel of erosion and some lowered below it. During a post-Miocene period of relative standstill erosion removed the Tertiary sediments except for those that had been downfaulted below the local baselevel of erosion; later uplift led to partial removal of those which had escaped erosion during the previous erosion cycle. (3) Broad deep valleys were cut in early Tertiary time and then more or less filled with Oligocene and Miocene sediments; the region was then uplifted, and by Pliocene time erosion had produced a topography of low relief. Part of the Tertiary deposits were preserved because they lay below the baselevel of erosion. Another uplift caused the areas of weak Tertiary formations

to be reduced to local baselevel, with the hard rock areas left standing as the present mountains.

Most recent workers have favored a Pliocene age for the Summit erosion surface in south-central Idaho, and some have thought that they saw evidence of multiple erosion levels. Anderson (1929), working in northern Idaho, came to the conclusion that here there is evidence of three erosion surfaces; the oldest he considered Cretaceous in age; the next youngest, Eocene; and the youngest, Miocene. Scholten and associates (1955) thought they saw evidence of three erosion surfaces in southwestern Montana and adjacent Idaho. The oldest surface they considered mid-Tertiary; the next youngest, late Tertiary; and the youngest, Quaternary.

## Mountains of Northwestern Montana and Northern Idaho

Lying north of the Blackfoot River and Clark Fork of the Columbia River and extending from the eastern frontal range to the Washington-Idaho boundary are a number of linear mountain ranges whose most significant structural feature is that they all display imbricate thrust faulting.

*Mountain Trenches.* The ranges are separated from each other by north-south valleys, and two of these valleys are such unusual topographic features that they have been called *trenches*. These are the Rocky Mountain Trench on the east and Purcell Trench on the west. Several other valleys between the north-south mountain ranges have linear form and may be related structurally to the trenches, but they lack the broad floors of the Rocky Mountain and Purcell trenches. It is generally believed that the trenches are the products of erosion along lines controlled by faulting, possibly block-faulting (Leech, 1959). They extend beyond the drainage basin of any single stream; eight streams drain parts of the Rocky Mountain Trench. Glacial erosion has undoubtedly contributed to their development, for they parallel the direction in which the ice moved, and each trench was the site of a major intermontane ice lobe during Pleistocene time.

The easternmost of the trenches, the Rocky

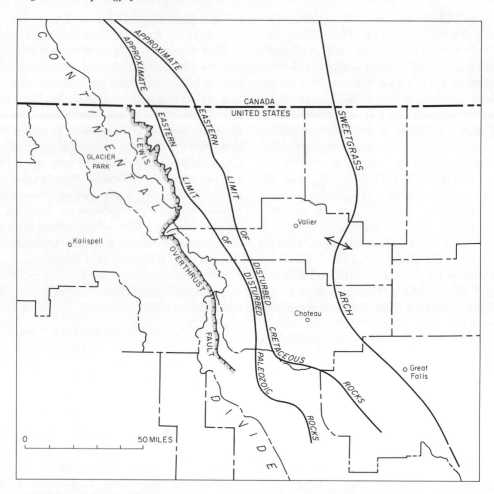

FIG. 21.3    Relation of Disturbed Belt to Lewis overthrust.    (*After G. W. Hurley, Billing Geol. Soc. Guidebook for 1959.*)

Mountain Trench, lies about 60 miles west of the Rocky Mountain front and is the more outstanding of the two. It extends north from Flathead Lake for 800 miles and might be considered as extending south from Flathead Lake another 150 miles through the Flathead and Bitterroot valleys. The Purcell Trench lies about 60 miles to the west of the Rocky Mountain Trench; this trench terminates at the south near Lake Coeur D'Alene and continues northward about 200 miles beyond the international boundary, where it intersects the Rocky Mountain Trench.

*The "Disturbed Belt."* The term "Disturbed Belt" has been applied (Robinson, 1959) to a section of the Northern Rocky Mountains extending from the Three Forks Basin northward for approximately 350 miles in Montana and Alberta (see Fig. 21.3). Included in this belt are the frontal ranges of the Northern Rockies and several ranges back of them. Structurally, the area is a zone of imbricate faults in which Paleozoic and Mesozoic strata are piled up on one another along a series of westward dipping thrust faults of Laramide age. The Disturbed Belt extends eastward into the Great Plains province as far as the Sweetgrass Arch, but the degree of deformation decreases eastward and finally plays out in a series of open folds and minor faults. An interesting aspect of the deformation is its shallowness; despite the existence of several large faults, Precambrian rocks are rarely brought to the surface. Geomorphically the mountains of the "Disturbed Belt" are sharp, linear ridges separated from each other by flat-floored, elongate valleys.

Hurley (1959) thought that the Disturbed Belt could be divided into three layers or zones of distinctly different types of structure. At the east is what he called the regional layer of relatively undisturbed rocks on the west flank of the Sweetgrass Arch. The middle layer or zone is the area of high-angle thrust faults and drag folds; this layer is best displayed in the Sawtooth Mountains (see p. 390), where a series of closely stacked thrust sheets may be seen. The third layer, the low-angle thrust layer, is the belt of the Lewis overthrust, in which a normal sequence of rocks ranging in age from Precambrian to Mississippian was thrust eastward over Cre-

taceous sediments. West of the Continental Divide this layer is marked by high-angle block faulting of both normal and reverse types. Stages in the development of these three structural zones are suggested in Figure 21.4.

*Lewis Overthrust.* Most famous of the faults in the disturbed belt is the Lewis overthrust (see Fig. 21.3). This thrust is at least 135 miles and perhaps as much as 300 miles long; it has been traced for 50 miles south of the international boundary and 85 miles north of it. How far westward beneath the Rocky Mountain ranges the Lewis fault extends is unknown, but a well drilled in the Flathead Valley went through 4500 feet of Beltian rocks and then entered Mississippian strata below the level of the fault (Hume, 1957). Willis (1902), who named the fault, thought that Precambrian Beltian rocks had

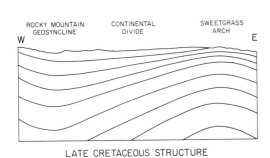

LATE CRETACEOUS STRUCTURE

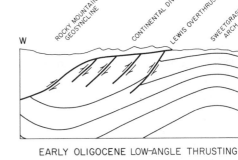

EARLY OLIGOCENE LOW-ANGLE THRUSTING

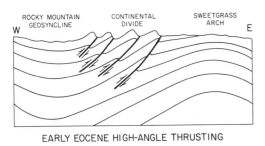

EARLY EOCENE HIGH-ANGLE THRUSTING

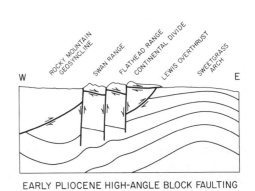

EARLY PLIOCENE HIGH-ANGLE BLOCK FAULTING

FIG. 21.4  Postulated stages in development of structures in Disturbed Belt.  (*After G. W. Hurley, Billings Geol. Soc. Guidebook for 1959.*)

ridden eastward along an ancient erosion surface. Billings (1938), however, concluded that the erosion surface described by Willis is younger than the thrust and that the thrust developed during the Laramide orogeny.

The erosion surface over which Willis thought the Lewis thrust sheet moved is known as the Blackfoot peneplain. This surface can be recognized in the plain region immediately east of the mountains and to a limited degree in the mountains. Billings considered it to be late Miocene or younger in age and probably equivalent to the Flaxville Plain or Number 1 Bench of Alden (see p. 292). Willis, however, considered the Blackfoot surface to be of early Tertiary age, and he thought that the Lewis thrust movement over this erosion surface was in mid-Tertiary time.

The plane of the Lewis overthrust has an average dip of 7 degrees to the west-southwest, but locally its dip is as much as 50 degrees. There is a maximum stratigraphic throw of 40,000 feet, and the net slip may be as much as 15 miles. In Glacier National Park, the Precambrian Altyn formation has been thrust over Cretaceous shales and sandstones. Throughout its length the trace of the Lewis thrust has an irregularly scalloped plan. Displacement of as much as 40 miles has taken place (Ross, 1959).

*Front Ranges in Montana.* The Rocky Mountain front in Montana does not consist of a single range; it is made up of several mountain units differing considerably in their structure and geomorphic expression (Bevan, 1929). The general trend of the mountains is northwestward, but there is a broad, elongate salient extending plainsward consisting of the Big Belt and Little Belt Mountains. Associated with this salient are such mountain uplifts as the Crazy, Highwood, Bearpaw, and Little Rocky Mountains, which are usually considered a part of the Great Plains. As several of these mountains are the result of igneous intrusions or extrusions, they are not typical of the type of mountain structure which marks the contact between the Great Plains and Rocky Mountains.

From the international boundary southward as far as Marias Pass the front range is the Lewis Range. This range presents an abrupt frontal scarp composed of Beltian rocks of the Lewis thrust plate. South of Marias Pass the Sawtooth Range becomes the front range. Both structurally and topographically it differs from the Lewis Range. The Sawtooth Range consists of a series of imbricate thrust slices of Paleozoic beds usually separated by Mesozoic beds. The fault planes dip to the west, and the thrust slices are arcuate in plan and convex toward the plains (see Fig. 21.5).

Deiss (1943) divided the Sawtooth Range into three north-south structural provinces in terms of degrees of intensity of deformation, with most intense deformation being on the west and the least intense on the east. The eastern province is marked by a series of en echelon high-angle to moderately low-angle westward-dipping thrusts or soles; the central province is characterized by intense imbricate structures and associated drag folding; and the western province displays a series of low-angle thrust sheets and open, closed, and overturned folds. The structures of the Sawtooth Range give a clue to the mechanics of mountain building in the area. According to Alpha (1955), most of the thrusts started as anticlinal flexures which, as their magnitude increased, overturned, steepened toward the plains, and finally broke with ensuing thrusting.

In most of the thrusts the Hannan (Mississippian) limestone was pushed over Mesozoic shale and sandstone (commonly the Cretaceous Kootenai shale) and forms parallel ridges steep-walled toward the east (see Fig. 21.6), which repeat themselves as many times as there are thrust sheets. Viewed from the east these ridges present sheer walls, and the succession of ridges and intervening valleys gives the Sawtooth Mountains their name.

South of the Sawtooth Mountains the Lewis and Clark Range, whose northern end lies west of the Sawtooths, becomes the frontal range. The Lewis overthrust terminates at the south in this range of predominantly Precambrian Beltian rocks. South of the Lewis and Clark Range is the eastward-extending Big Belt-Little Belt salient. The southernmost frontal range

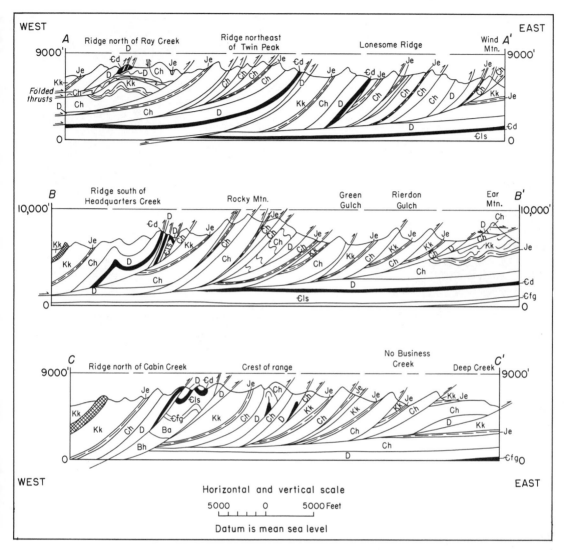

FIG. 21.5   Structure sections across central Sawtooth Range, Montana.   Kk, Cretaceous Kootenai formation; Je, Jurassic Ellis formation; Ch, Mississippian Hannan limestone; D, unnamed Devonian formation; €d, Cambrian Devil's Glen dolomite; €ls, undifferentiated Cambrian limestone; €fg, Cambrian Flathead sandstone and Gordon shale; Ba, Precambrian Belt Ahorn quartzite; Bh, Precambrian Belt Hoadley formation; cross-hatched pattern, diorite sill. (*After C. A. Deiss, Geol. Soc. Am. Bull.,* **54.**)

of the Northern Rocky Mountains is the Bridger Range, which consists of Precambrian metamorphic rocks and arkoses on the west flanked on the east by steeply-dipping Paleozoic and Mesozoic sedimentary rocks (McMannis, 1955).

*Topography of Glacier Park Area.*   The mountain ranges of the Glacier National Park area are the Lewis Range on the east and the Clark Range on the west.   These ranges form the two sides of a broad synclinal structure that has moved eastward along the Lewis fault.   Although not so high as the ranges of the southern and middle Rockies, these ranges exhibit some of the finest glacial topography to be seen in the Rocky Mountain system.   The much lower snowline

FIG. 21.6   Castle Reef Mountain thrust sheet (left background) in Sawtooth Mountains.   Mississippian Hannan limestone is thrust over Cretaceous formations, which are also deformed by imbricate thrusts.   Along the bank of the Sun River in the foreground can be seen multiple thrust slices in rocks of the Colorado group.   (*Photo by David Hawley.*)

here than that farther south accounts for their extensive glaciation. The fact that rocks here are layered sedimentary rocks gives to the glacial topography a unique topographic aspect not found in the "granite" ranges of the southern and middle Rockies. We find here a type of glacial topography which has been described as having an "architectural effect" and which is the type of glacial topography described by Hobbs (1910) as monumented upland. Most of the erosional landforms produced by mountain glaciation can be seen in this area, ranging from glacial cirques, horns, and arêtes along the range crests to trough lakes in the lower parts of the glaciated valleys. It is rather surprising, however, that in this area, where the effects of glaciation are so evident, very little detailed work has been done on the stages and substages of mountain glaciation.

Richmond (1960), from field studies in this area, concluded that the Kennedy drift (see p. 293), just east of Glacier National Park, can be divided into three tills correlative with the Nebraska, Kansan, and Illinoian of the central United States. He further believed that there is evidence of two phases of Bull Lake glaciation and three advances during the Pinedale subage. Moraines marking two minor advances of the ice in the cirques were correlated with the Temple Lake stadial in the Wind River Mountains. Such perfect correlation of glacial history in the northern Rockies with that elsewhere in the Rockies and Central Lowlands may exist, but acceptance of it should remain in abeyance until publication of the field evidence for it.

*Erosional History.* The preglacial erosional history of the Glacier Park region has been studied by a few geologists. No remnants of a summit erosion surface have been recognized in the Lewis and Clark ranges, but both Willis (1902) and Alden (1932) regarded the relatively flat-topped ridges east of the main mountain mass as remnants of an erosion surface. Willis named this surface the Blackfoot peneplain and correlated it with Alden's Flaxville Plain or Number 1 Bench on the Great Plains. Ross (1959), who has devoted many years of study to the Northern Rockies, did not consider the Blackfoot erosion surface a peneplain, but rather a surface of late maturity which developed in late Tertiary or possibly early Pleistocene time. Contrary to Willis' views, he considered this erosion surface younger than the Lewis thrust. Ross further thought that the gravel-capped terraces east of the mountains seemed to fit better with an interpretation of the Blackfoot erosion surface as a pediment rather than a peneplain. There seems to be no evidence that the mountains were destroyed or even extensively subdued in relief

during the Blackfoot cycle, as would seem necessary if the Blackfoot surface were to be considered a peneplain.

*Lake Missoula.* At least once, if not several times, a lobe of Cordilleran ice moved down the Purcell Trench and dammed the Clark Fork of the Columbia River and thus formed an extensive ice-marginal lake known as Lake Missoula (Pardee, 1910). This elongate and branching lake (see Fig. 23.11) is estimated to have covered as much as 3300 square miles (Alden, 1953). Its highest shoreline attained an altitude of 4200 feet, which is 1000 feet higher than the lake terrace on which the city of Missoula, Montana, is situated. The depth of the lake at its lower end may have been as great as 2000 feet.

Faint traces of its shorelines may be seen along numerous valley sides (see Fig. 21.7), but none is prominent topographically, and many are so faint that they show only when the lighting is right. This suggests that Lake Missoula did

FIG. 21.7   Telephoto of Lake Missoula shorelines taken from campus of Montana State University. *(Photo by David Hawley.)*

not occupy any of its shorelines for long but rather fluctuated in level. Fluctuation in level must have been related to change in height of the obstruction which created Lake Missoula. It is uncertain whether this dam was moraine or glacial ice. The impermanence of the lake levels suggests that it is more likely that it was an ice dam.

Terraced lacustrine silts and clays may be seen along the floors of many of the valleys which were occupied by Lake Missoula, but sand and gravel are not particularly abundant among the lake deposits. The age of Lake Missoula is uncertain; Alden (1953) thought that it obtained its maximum extent in pre-Wisconsin time. Shorelines cut on the Polson moraine south of Flathead Lake suggest, however, that there was a lake here in late Wisconsin time, as this moraine is believed to correlate with the Pinedale glaciation (de la Montagne, 1959). It may well be that there were several Lake Missoulas. The conditions which produced the Cordilleran glacial complex with lobes extending down the Purcell and Rocky Mountain trenches very likely repeated themselves a number of times during the Pleistocene.

### Belt Mountain Group

The easternmost extension of the Northern Rocky Mountains is formed by the Big Belt and Little Belt Mountains (Alpha, 1955). These mountains, along with the Castle Mountains and Crazy Mountains, form a group of mountains somewhat apart from the main Rocky Mountain mass. There may be some question as to whether the Castle and Crazy mountains should be included in this group, for geologically they are different from the Belt Mountains, but geographically it seems more logical to include them in the Rocky Mountains than to class them as outliers of Rocky Mountain geology in the Great Plains.

The Little Belt and Big Belt mountains are anticlinal uplifts with Precambrian batholithic cores and Paleozoic and Mesozoic sedimentary rocks on their flanks. In this respect they resemble geologically more the ranges of the Middle and Southern Rocky Mountains than those of the Northern Rockies.

The Crazy Mountains (Wolff, 1938) are composed of late Cretaceous and Eocene sandstones and shale which have been intruded by three stocks and thousands of associated sills, laccoliths, and dikes. The Castle Mountains are of volcanic origin.

### Mountains and Basins of Southwestern Montana

*Nature of Topography.* Numerous short mountain ranges and associated intermontane basins dominate the topography of southwestern Montana and adjacent Idaho. Commonly the intermontane depressions are called valleys, despite the fact that they are essentially structural rather than erosional in origin. Pardee (1950) listed 56 basins (see Fig. 21.8), and Alden (1953) identified 27 in this area. The difference in number is related primarily to how detailed a subdivision of major units is made. The basins are commonly irregular in outline, although some are subellipsoidal in shape. They exist singly or in chains connected by gorges or low mountain passes. Basins range in length from a few miles to 50 or 60 miles and in width from 2 or 3 miles to as much as 20 or 30 miles. In area they vary from a few square miles to as much as 1000 square miles. Most basins are fairly well enclosed by mountain walls, which may rise as much as 5000 to 6000 feet above their floors. Both the geomorphic and structural patterns of the mountain basins lead to the conclusion that the topography and structure here are similar to that which is found in the Basin and Range province.

*Date of Origin of Major Land Forms.* It is rather generally agreed that evidence exists in the area for three major periods of diastrophism datable as Precambrian, Laramide, and Tertiary. Precambrian folds and faults are evident as part of the internal structure of the mountain ranges, but very rarely do they seem to control features of the present-day topography.

Unquestionably the effects of the Laramide orogeny are reflected in the present topography.

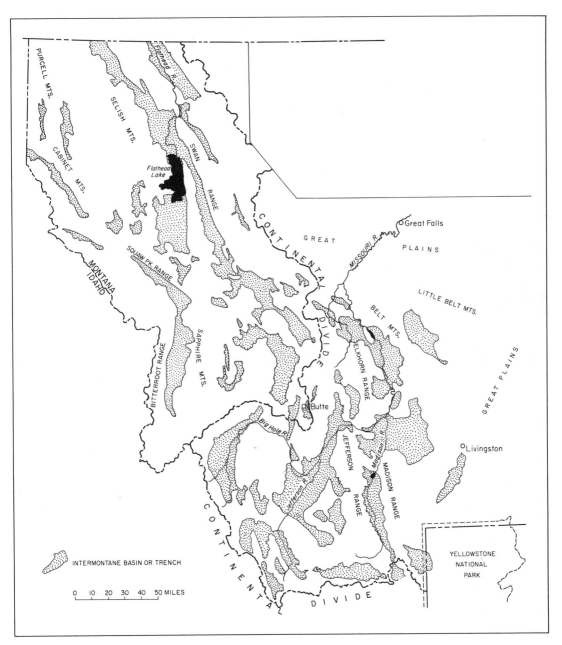

FIG. 21.8   Tertiary basins of western Montana.   (*After J. T. Pardee, Geol. Soc. Am. Bull.*, **61**.)

Some, such as Lowell (1957), would argue that the mountains and basins were essentially outlined during this orogeny and that later Tertiary faulting has largely been along older Laramide structures.   Others, such as Horberg (1940),

Pardee (1950), and Hackett et al. (1960), would assign a major role to late Cenozoic (Miocene to Pliocene) faulting in the outlining of the present mountains and basins.   There can be little question about the importance of late Tertiary diastrophism, for there was notable uplift of the region in late Tertiary time. The major question is whether late Tertiary block faulting was largely responsible for outlining of the existing mountains and basins or whether this was essentially done much earlier during the Laramide orogeny.

*Relation of Faults to Topography.* Whether or not the existing topography is primarily fault controlled or the product of differential erosion has been the subject of much argument. Even if it is admitted that faulting has played an important role in outlining the ranges and basins, there remains the question of whether the frontal scarps are fault scarps or fault-line scarps. It is particularly on this point that there is wide divergence of opinion. In part this is a result of failure to appreciate fully the difference between a fault scarp and a fault-line scarp and to recognize that topographically they may be similar in appearance. Proof from surface phenomena of the existence of a bounding fault is not always possible, for faults are not too commonly exposed. Geophysical rather than geomorphic information is likely to be more definitive in determining the existence of a fault, but little geophysical work has been done in the area.

*Date of Faulting.* That wide-scale faulting has occurred in southwestern Montana and adjacent areas in Idaho can hardly be doubted. Dislocated structures and stratigraphy show that both thrust and normal faulting have taken place. It is generally assumed that the thrust faulting occurred during the Laramide orogeny and the normal faulting later, in middle or late Tertiary time. Probably most of the normal faulting did occur after the thrust faulting, but in some ranges they may have been closely associated. Several generations of normal faults may be present in the area, some of which are still active, as was shown by the Lake Hegben earthquake in 1959 (Witkind, 1960).

The basin stratigraphy has not been studied in detail in many areas, but such information as is available points to the conclusion that the basins formed rather early in Tertiary time. Oligocene, Miocene, and Pliocene beds are rather commonly present, and in some basins beds as old as Eocene have been found. The Three Forks Basin has been studied in detail in recent years, and at least five Tertiary and five Quaternary sedimentary units have been recognized there (Robinson, 1961), including sediments as old as Eocene. Sedimentary rocks of Eocene age are not abundant in the basins, but such rocks of Oligocene and Miocene age are (Lowell, 1957).

Even if it be granted that the mountains and basins were outlined roughly as they are today as early as Eocene time, this does not preclude the occurrence of block faulting late in Tertiary time; it does, however, seem to render very dubious the conclusion drawn by some that the mountains and basins were not outlined until as late as Pliocene time.

*Origin of Basins.* The question of to what degree the basins are diastrophic in origin and to what extent erosional cannot be answered with any degree of certainty. Undoubtedly both diastrophism and erosion have contributed to the outlining of the basins as they exist today. Figure 21.9 shows a gravimetric anomaly parallel to the west side of the Tobacco Root Mountains that logically may be considered an indication of the presence of a range-marginal fault. If a fault does exist, it now underlies the Jefferson Valley several miles removed from the western front of the Tobacco Root Range. This probably means that the mountain front has receded several miles from an original position near the fault. Thus considerable widening of the Jefferson Valley has been brought about by the processes of degradation. But even admitting that the basins have been modified considerably by erosion throughout Tertiary time, it is difficult to escape the belief that in their broad outlines they are more structural than erosional features.

*Nature of Basin Fills.* The intermontane basins have been filled in varying degrees with sediments ranging in age from Eocene to Recent (see Fig. 21.10). The present thickness of the basin fills is considerably less than it was at its maximum because of erosion during Pliocene, Pleistocene, and Recent time. Not many accu-

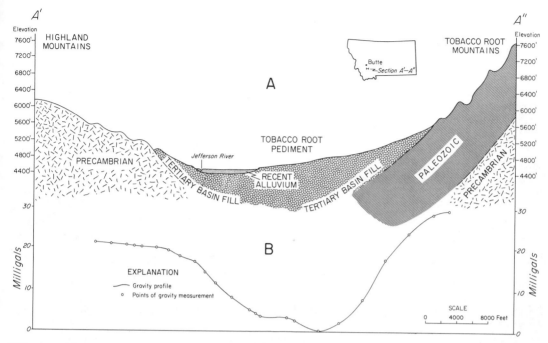

FIG. 21.9    Topographic-geologic (A) and gravity (B) profiles across Jefferson Basin west of Tobacco Mountains. (*Gravity profile after Walter Burfiend, unpublished Ph. D. thesis.*)

rate determinations of the thickness of the basin sediments have been made, but those that are available indicate that in some basins the thickness is several thousand feet. Robinson (1961) estimated the thickness of fill in the Three Forks Basin to be 3500 feet or more.

Unfortunately the terms "Tertiary lake beds" and "Bozeman lake beds" have been widely applied to the deposits in the intermontane basins. Some lacustrine materials are present among the basin fill materials, and in a few basins they even constitute a major part, but regionally lacustrine deposits constitute a minor part of the basin fills. The fills consist of a variety of materials whose proportions vary from basin to basin. Floodplain sediments, alluvial fan deposits, paludal materials, bajada type of deposits, eolian silts, colluvial materials, glacial outwash, or volcanic debris including ash, pumice, agglomerates, and flows may be found among the basin deposits. It would certainly make for a better understanding of the nature of the basin fills if the term "lake beds" were abandoned

except where applied to specific deposits of demonstrable lacustrine origin and if the far more appropriate term "basin fill" were used instead. Only a beginning has been made in the study of the nature and age of the basin fills.

*Erosion Surfaces in Basins.* The basin floors have been eroded in varying degrees, and erosion surfaces, some of which are pediments and some fluvial terraces, have developed across them. Most of these erosion surfaces are Pliocene or Pleistocene in age. It thus seems likely that the Eocene (to a certain extent), Oligocene, and Miocene epochs were times when deposition predominated over erosion in the intermontane basins, and the Pliocene and Pleistocene epochs were times when the opposite was true.

The relationship of erosion surfaces in the intermontane basins to alleged erosion surfaces in adjacent mountains represents a major geomorphic problem in southwestern Montana. Correlation of erosion surfaces in the intermontane basins with comparable surfaces in the Great

FIG. 21.10   Basin fill deposits resting unconformably on Belt rocks, near Whitehall, Montana.

Plains immediately east of the Rocky Mountain front is another problem that awaits solution. As in south-central Idaho, at least three interpretations have been given of the relationships of the basin fill deposits and basin erosional surfaces to presumed erosion surfaces in adjacent mountains (see p. 386).

*Major Tertiary Erosion Cycle.* Evidence in southwestern Montana of an Eocene peneplain is not very convincing. However, there is strong evidence of a late Miocene or early Pliocene surface of moderately low relief which came into existence as a result of degradation of the mountains and aggradation of the intermontane basins. The mountains were notably reduced in relief, but not destroyed, and the basins were aggraded to levels accordant with graded stream valleys

through the mountain uplifts. Such a regional surface can not properly be called a peneplain. In the first place, it possessed too much relief to be so called, and secondly, it was only partially degradational in origin. It may best be pictured as a series of interconnecting pediments and bajadas developed with respect to varying local baselevels. Development of this composite degradational-aggradational topographic surface appears to have been the major geomorphic event in southwestern Montana during later Tertiary time. Its culmination appears to have come in late Miocene or early Pliocene time.

*Late Tertiary-Quaternary Subcycles.* Following the period of relative crustal stability described above, renewal of uplift took place and continued intermittently through late Pliocene and Pleistocene time. Robinson (1961) estimated that in the Three Forks area this uplift amounted to at least 1000 feet. Not all of the late Pliocene-Pleistocene movement was positive. In some areas there is evidence that while the mountains were being further elevated, parts of some basins underwent deepening. Robinson cited as evidence of Pleistocene deepening of the Three Forks Basin the fact the alluvium of the Jefferson, Madison, and Gallatin rivers, which converge in this basin to form the Missouri River, extends well below the bedrock surface at the outlet canyon where the Missouri River leaves the Three Forks Basin. The result of these uplifts was partial removal of the previously deposited basin fills and the cutting of river gorges across the mountain uplifts. That this uplift was intermittent rather than continuous is indicated by the presence in most, if not all, of the basins of multiple erosional surfaces, attesting to partial cycles of erosion.

Two or three erosion surfaces can be identified in most of the basins (see Fig. 21.11). The oldest and uppermost surface is probably a pediment of late Pliocene or early Pleistocene age. Such a surface in the Madison Valley has been named the Cameron pediment (Paul and Lyons, 1960) and a similar surface can be identified in the Jefferson Valley and the Three Forks Basin. Even more extensive pediments can be seen flanking the Ruby Mountains farther south.

Below the widespread Pliocene pediment surface are usually one or two narrow benches that seem to be stream-cut terraces veneered with alluvium. They are most certainly Pleistocene in age, but as yet cannot be dated more specifically than that.

Any attempt at the present to correlate topographic surfaces in the intermontane basins with those farther east on the Great Plains is based on uncertain grounds. It seems logical to assume that the regional erosional-depositional surface described above would correlate in age with similar surfaces in the other parts of the Rocky Mountains, such as the Subsummit surface in the Bighorns and the Rocky Mountain

FIG. 21.11   View northwest across North Boulder Valley, Montana, showing pediment surfaces.   The pediments are developed mainly across Mio-Pliocene beds, but near the mountains they extend across rocks of Paleozoic age.   (*Photo by David Hawley.*)

FIG. 21.12    Watergap of Jefferson River through ridge of Mississippian limestone, near Sappington Junction, Montana.

surface of the Colorado Front Range. If such an assumption is correct, the Cameron pediment and its equivalent in other basins may correlate with the Flaxville Plain or Number 1 Bench of Collier and Thom (1918) on the Great Plains. Similarly, correlation of the alluvial terraces below the Cameron pediment with the number 2 and Number 3 Benches on the Great Plains would seem logical, but such correlation is highly speculative.

*Drainage Problems*

The drainage lines of southwestern Montana present two interesting problems. Some have thought that originally the drainage was internal, into a series of closed basins such as we have today in the Great Basin region. Assuming that such a condition did exist one problem is

ascertaining when integrated external drainage developed. A second problem is the question of how the numerous river gorges through the mountain ranges can best be explained. The Jefferson, Bighole, Beaverhead, Madison, and Missouri Rivers, as well as other lesser streams, flow from one intermontane basin to another through gorges.

*Date of Integration of Drainage.* The question of whether or not the drainage originally was largely internal is the more difficult of the two to answer, for the reason that we are dealing with a condition much more remote in geologic time than the development of the gorges through the mountain uplifts. Possibly the idea of original internal drainage was an outgrowth of two closely related concepts: the structural and topographical similarity of this region to the Basin

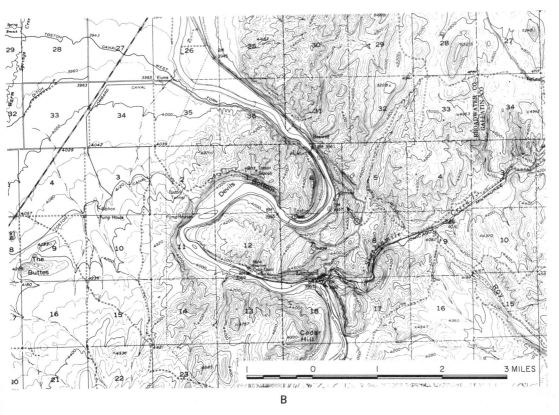

FIG. 21.13   (A) View of horseshoe bend of Missouri River through Lombard thrust sheet.   (B) Portion of Toston, Montana, topographic sheet showing course of Missouri River across Lombard thrust sheet and point from which (A) was taken.

and Range province, where there is considerable internal drainage, and the idea that long persisted that the basin fills consist largely of lacustrine deposits. Lakes unquestionably existed at times in various basins, but there is little evidence to suggest that the lakes lacked outlets and were saline or brackish in nature. The internal drainage of the Basin and Range province is as much a result of inadequate rainfall as it is of topographic conditions. If the rainfall of the Basin and Range province were appreciably increased, drainage to the sea would be established for most of the province. Such information as exists regarding climatic conditions in Montana during early Tertiary time indicates that the area was more humid then than now, or at least more humid than it was in late Tertiary time. This does not fit in well with the idea of a region with internal drainage. If a series of separate basins lacking drainage connections did exist originally, their integration must have come about as a result of rising basin fills which caused drainage from the higher basins to spill over into the lower ones and thus develop in time a system of through drainage.

*Superposition of Drainage versus Antecedence.* If the interpretation made above that in southwestern Montana a Miocene-Pliocene regional topographic surface of moderately low relief developed, it is only logical to explain the numerous river gorges through the present mountain ranges as a result of superposition from this late Tertiary surface. That this could have happened does not seem unreasonable, for at several places remnants of the basin fills can be found at altitudes as high as the top of the river gorges through the mountains. As Lowell (1957) has pointed out, where the Jefferson River leaves the Jefferson Valley (Basin) and flows through the Mt. Doherty-London Hills uplift through a gorge 1400 feet deep into the Three Forks Basin, basin fill materials can be found adjacent to the gorge at altitudes that indicate that the Jefferson Valley was filled to a level as high as the top of Jefferson River gorge.

Two examples of unusual drainage relationships may be cited in support of the theory of regional superposition of drainage in south-

western Montana. About 2 miles below where the Jefferson River leaves its gorge through the London Hills and enters the Three Forks Basin it flows through a watergap cut in Mississippian limestone (see Fig. 21.12), when by changing its course less than a mile to the northwest it could have avoided the ridge. Perhaps a more striking argument for superposition is found where the Missouri River leaves the Clarkston Basin and flows into the Townsend Basin through a meandering gorge cut into the Lombard thrust sheet (see Fig. 21.13). It seems much more logical to explain such a meandering gorge course as one let down from a cover mass than one developed athwart a structural barrier.

## Glacial History

Little study has been made of the glacial history of southwestern Montana and adjacent areas in Idaho. Evidence of glaciation can be seen in many of the ranges in the form of cirques, moraines, and outwash plains extending down the mountain valleys, but thus far little detailed mapping of these features has been done. Nobles (1952) made a study of the glacial deposits of the Mission Valley and found there what he believed to be evidence of three Wisconsin advances of the intermontane lobe that extended down the Rocky Mountain trench. He correlated these advances with early, middle, and late Wisconsin time. South of the area, in the Teton Mountains, a detailed sequence of mountain glaciation has been described (see p. 371), but whether this same sequence is represented in southwestern Montana can not be stated at present.

## REFERENCES CITED

Alden, W. C. (1932). Physiography and glacial geology of eastern Montana and adjacent areas, *U. S. Geol. Survey Profess. Paper* 174, 133 pp.
—— (1953). Physiography and glacial geology of western Montana and adjacent areas, *U. S. Geol. Survey Profess. Paper* 231, 200 pp.
Alpha, A. G. (1955). Tectonic history of north central Montana, Billings Geol. Soc., *Guidebook, 6th Annual Field Conference*, 129–142.

Anderson, A. L. (1929). Cretaceous and Tertiary planation in northern Idaho, *Jour. Geol.*, 37, 747–764.

—— (1947). Drainage diversion in the northern Rocky Mountains of east-central Idaho, *Jour. Geol.*, 55, 61–75.

—— (1952). Multiple emplacement of the Idaho batholith, *Jour. Geol.*, 60, 255–265.

Atwood, W. W. (1916). The physiographic conditions at Butte, Montana, and Bingham Canyon, Utah, when the copper ores in these districts were enriched, *Econ. Geol.*, 11, 697–740.

Bevan, Arthur (1929). Rocky Mountain Front in Montana, *Geol. Soc. Am. Bull.*, 40, 427–456.

Billings, Marland (1938). Physiographic relations of the Lewis overthrust in northern Montana, *Am. Jour. Sci.*, 235, 260–272.

Blackwelder, Eliot (1912). The old erosion surface in Idaho: a criticism, *Jour. Geol.*, 20, 410–414.

Collier, A. J., and W. T. Thom (1918). The Flaxville gravel and its relation to other terrace gravels of the northern Great Plains, *U. S. Geol. Survey Profess. Paper* 108, 179–184.

Deiss, C. F. (1943). Structure of the central part of the Sawtooth Range, Montana, *Geol. Soc. Am. Bull.*, 54, 1123–1168.

de la Montagne, J. (1959). Comments on late Pleistocene features of western Montana, Geol. Soc. Am., Rocky Mt. section, *Guidebook, 12th Annual Meeting*, 66–70.

Hackett, O. M., F. N. Visher, R. G. McMurtrey, and W. L. Steinhilber (1960). Geology and groundwater resources of the Gallatin Valley, Gallatin County, Montana, *U. S. Geol. Survey Water-Supply Paper* 1482, 282 pp.

Hobbs, W. H. (1910). Studies of the cycle of glaciation, *Jour. Geol.*, 29, 370–386.

Hume, G. S. (1957). Fault structures in the foothills and eastern Rocky Mountains of southern Alberta, *Geol. Soc. Am. Bull.*, 68, 395–412.

Hurley, G. W. (1959). Overthrust faulting and Paleozoic gas prospects in Montana's disturbed belt, Billings Geol. Soc., *Guidebook, 10th Annual Field Conference*, 98–108.

Kirkham, V. R. D. (1930). Old erosion surfaces in southwestern Idaho, *Jour. Geol.*, 38, 652–663.

Knopf, Adolph (1957). The Boulder batholith of Montana, *Am. Jour. Sci.*, 255, 81–103.

Leech, G. B. (1959). The southern part of the Rocky Mountain trench, *Canadian Mining and Metal. Bull.*, 52, 327–333.

Lowell, W. R. (1957). Tertiary geologic history of the Rocky Mountains in Montana, U. S. A., *Rept. 20th Int. Geol. Congress, Proc. Section 5*, 455–467.

Mansfield, G. R. (1924). Tertiary planation in Idaho, *Jour. Geol.*, 32, 472–487.

McMannis, W. J. (1955). Geology of the Bridger Range, Montana, *Geol. Soc. Am. Bull.*, 66, 1385–1430.

Nobles, L. H. (1952). Glacial sequence in the Mission Valley, western Montana, *Geol. Soc. Am. Bull.*, 63, 1286–1287 (abs.).

Pardee, J. T. (1910). The glacial Lake Missoula, *Jour. Geol.*, 18, 376–386.

—— (1950). Late Cenozoic block faulting in western Montana, *Geol. Soc. Am. Bull.*, 61, 359–406.

Paul, H. P., and S. A. Lyons (1960). Quaternary surfaces along the Madison Valley floor from Ennis Lake to English George Creek, Montana, Billings Geol. Soc., *Guidebook, 11th Annual Field Conference*, 170–173.

Rich, J. L. (1918). An old erosion surface in Idaho: Is it Eocene? *Econ. Geol.*, 13, 120–136.

Richmond, G. M. (1960). Correlation of alpine and continental glacial deposits of Glacier National Park and adjacent High Plains, *U. S. Geol. Survey Profess. Paper* 400-B, B223–B224.

Robinson, G. D. (1959). The disturbed belt in the Sixteenmile area, Montana, Billings Geol. Soc., *Guidebook, 10th Annual Field Conference*, 34–40.

—— (1961). Origin and development of the Three Forks Basin, Montana, *Geol. Soc. Am. Bull.*, 72, 1003–1014.

Ross, C. P. (1928). Mesozoic and Tertiary granitic rocks in Idaho, *Jour. Geol.*, 36, 673–693.

—— (1936). Some features of the Idaho batholith. *Rept. 16th Int. Geol. Congr.*, 1, 369–385.

—— (1950). The eastern front of the Bitterroot Range, Montana, *U. S. Geol. Survey Bull.* 974, 135–175.

—— (1959). Geology of Glacier Park and the Flathead region, northwestern Montana, *U. S. Geol. Survey Profess. Paper* 296, 125 pp.

Scholten, R. K., K. A. Keenmon, and W. O. Kupsch (1955). Geology of the Lima region, southwestern Montana and adjacent Idaho, *Geol. Soc. Am. Bull.*, 66, 345–404.

Umpleby, J. B. (1912). An old erosion surface in Idaho: its age and value as a datum plane, *Jour. Geol.*, 20, 139–147.

Willis, Bailey (1902). Stratigraphy and structure, Lewis and Livingstone ranges, Montana, *Geol. Soc. Am. Bull.*, 13, 305–352.

Witkind, I. J. (1960). The Hebgen Lake, Montana, earthquake of August 17, 1959, Billings. Geol. Soc., *Guidebook, 11th Annual Field Conference*, 31–44.

Wolff, J. E. (1938). Igneous rocks of the Crazy Mountains, Montana, *Geol. Soc. Am. Bull.*, 49, 1569–1626

ADDITIONAL REFERENCES

Alpha, A. G. (1960). Tectonic history of Montana, in *Montana Oil and Gas Fields—A Symposium*, Billings Geol. Soc., 10–31.

Chapman, R. W., David Gottfried, and C. L. Waring (1955). Age determinations on some rocks from the Boulder batholith and other batholiths of western Montana, *Geol. Soc. Am. Bull.*, 66, 607–610.

Deiss, C. F. (1943). Stratigraphy and structure of the southwest Saypo quadrangle, Montana, *Geol. Soc. Am. Bull.*, **54**, 205–262.

de la Montagne, J. (1960). Geomorphic problems in the Madison Valley, Madison County, Montana, Billings Geol. Soc., *Guidebook, 11th Annual Field Conference*, 165–169.

Eakin, G. R., and F. S. Honkola (1952). Cenozoic history of Missoula Valley, Missoula County, Montana, *Geol. Soc. Am. Bull.*, **63**, 1361 (abs.).

Eardley, A. J. (1947). Late Cenozoic trenches of the Rocky Mountains, *Geol. Soc. Am. Bull.*, **58**, 1176 (abs.).

Freeman, V. L., E. T. Ruppel, and M. R. Klepper (1958). Geology of part of the Townsend Valley, Broadwater and Jefferson counties, Montana, *U. S. Geol. Survey Bull.* 1042-N, 481–556.

Honkola, F. S. (1960). Structure of the Centennial Mountains and vicinity, Beaverhead County, Montana, Billings Geol. Soc., *Guidebook, 11th Annual Field Conference*, 107–113.

Klepper, M. R. (1951). A geologic reconnaissance of parts of Beaverhead and Madison counties, Montana, *U. S. Geol. Survey Bull.* 959-C, 55–85.

——, R. A. Weeks, and E. T. Ruppel (1957). Geology of the southern Elkhorn Mountains, Jefferson and Broadwater counties, Montana, *U. S. Geol. Survey Profess. Paper* 292, 82 pp.

Langton, C. M. (1935). Geology of the northeastern part of the Idaho batholith and adjacent region in Montana, *Jour. Geol.*, **43**, 27–60.

Lindgren, Waldemar (1904). A geological reconnaissance across the Bitterroot Range and Clearwater Mountains in Montana and Idaho, *U. S. Geol. Survey Profess. Paper* 27, 123 pp.

Lorenz, H. W., and R. G. McMurtrey (1956). Geology and occurrence of ground water in the Townsend Valley, Montana, *U. S. Geol. Survey Water-Supply Paper* 1360-C, 171–273.

Mansfield, G. R. (1927). Geography, geology and mineral resources of part of southeastern Idaho, *U. S. Geol. Survey Profess. Paper* 152, 409 pp.

—— (1952). Geography, geology and mineral resources of the Ammon and Paradise Valley quadrangles, Idaho, *U. S. Geol. Survey Profess. Paper* 238, 92 pp.

McMannis, W. J. (1959). Salient tectonic features of western Montana, Geol. Soc. Am., Rocky Mt. Section, *Guidebook, 12th Annual Meeting*, 72–75.

Ross, C. P. (1930). Erosion surfaces in Idaho [with discussion by G. R. Mansfield and A. L. Anderson], *Jour. Geol.*, **38**, 643–650.

—— (1938). Geology and ore deposits of the Bayhorse region, Custer County, Idaho, *U. S. Geol. Survey Bull.* 877, 161 pp.

—— (1947). Geology of the Borah Peak quadrangle, Idaho, *Geol. Soc. Am. Bull.*, **58**, 1085–1160.

—— and J. D. Forrester (1958). Outline of the geology of Idaho, *Idaho Bur. Mines and Geol. Bull.* 15, 74 pp.

Umpleby, J. B. (1913). The old erosion surface in Idaho, *Jour. Geol.*, **21**, 224–231.

# 22

# Colorado Plateau Province

## GENERAL DESCRIPTION

The Colorado Plateau province covers approximately 150,000 square miles and includes parts of the states of Arizona, New Mexico, Utah, and Colorado. About 90 per cent of the province is drained by the Colorado River and its tributaries. The province would probably be more appropriately designated as the Colorado Plateaus province, for there is variety among its parts, and individual plateaus have their distinctive characteristics. This is a notable area in American geomorphology, for here many of the basic concepts of geomorphology were first grasped. Reports by Powell (1875), Gilbert (1877), and Dutton (1882) based on work done in this province are among the classics of American geology.

Province boundaries are distinct except on the southeast. On the west and south the province stands well above its neighboring province, the Basin and Range province, but on the north and northeast the Rocky Mountains rise above the plateaus. The characteristic topography is that of broad plateaus bounded by receding escarpments and dissected in varying degrees by great canyons. Here are found the highest plateaus in the United States; the Aquarius Plateau of Utah exceeds 11,000 feet in altitude.

### Major Distinguishing Characteristics

A number of distinctive features give this province a high degree of individuality; among the most outstanding are:

a. Despite the existence locally of a high degree of structural relief (see Fig. 22.1), gently dipping sedimentary rocks characterize much of the province.

b. Altitudes exceed 5000 feet over most of the province and attain maxima of more than 13,000 feet in some of the mountains.

c. Deep canyons are more common here than in any other part of the United States. Although a part of the Snake River Canyon is actually deeper than the Grand Canyon, the Snake River lacks the large number of deep tributary canyons that the Grand Canyon has.

d. Except at high altitudes the climate is semi-arid to arid. Spasmodic rainfall makes for maximum runoff and sheetwash erosion. Major streams, such as the Green, Colorado, and San Juan, are maintained by rainfall in the boundary mountains on the north and east.

e. Erosion on strong and weak rocks has produced innumerable escarpments and structural benches. Angularity of topography is conspicuous as a result of the arid climate and horizontality of rocks. Retreating escarpments might be considered the most characteristic features of much of the province. Pediments in front of and structural benches back of the escarpments account for the step-like nature of much of the topography.

f. In contrast to the adjacent Rocky Mountain and Basin and Range provinces, the great relief is more the result of the incision of deep canyons below moderately flat terrain than of upstanding mountain ranges above adjacent plains or basins. Mountain peaks of volcanic origin exist within the province, but mountain ranges are lacking.

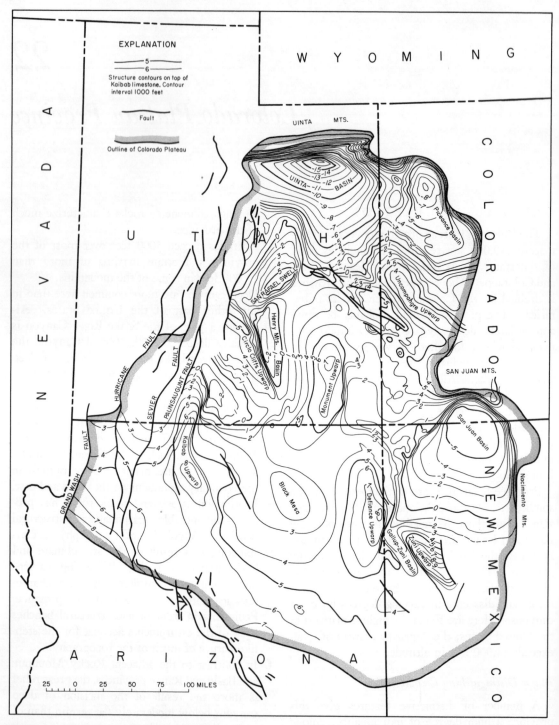

FIG. 22.1   Structural map of Colorado Plateau province.   (*After C. B. Hunt, U. S. Geol. Surv. Profess. Paper 279.*)

# BEDROCK GEOLOGY

Exposed rocks of the Colorado Plateaus range in age from Precambrian to Recent. Exposures of Precambrian rocks are limited to five small areas. Early Paleozoic rocks (Cambrian to Devonian) are in general thin or lacking; this is in contrast to the Basin and Range province, where such rocks have thicknesses of 10,000 to 20,000 feet. In general, late Paleozoic rocks (Mississippian to Permian) are not so thick as in the Basin and Range province, but in the Paradox Basin there is a Pennsylvanian section of at least 7000 feet. Rocks of Mesozoic age, particularly Triassic and Jurassic, are thin compared with adjacent areas to the west, but there are thick sections of Cretaceous rocks in the southeastern and northwestern parts of the province. During most of the Paleozoic and Mesozoic eras the Colorado Plateau was a shelf area; only during the Pennsylvanian period did it develop deep synclinal basins.

Early Cenozoic rocks are widespread in the Colorado Plateau, but middle and late Cenozoic sedimentary rocks are scarce or lacking. This is in striking contrast to the Basin and Range province, where the reverse is true. Late Tertiary deposits are fairly common around the margins of the Colorado Plateau but are scarce within the Plateau. Cenozoic igneous rocks cover roughly 10 per cent of the Colorado Plateau (Hunt, 1956) and form stocks, laccoliths, bysmaliths, volcanoes, and extrusive sheets (see Fig. 22.4).

## MAJOR STRUCTURAL FEATURES

The Colorado plateaus display a striking structural control of their larger topographic features. At least seven major types of structure have topographic expression (Kelley, 1955a; Kelley and Clinton, 1960; and Hunt, 1956). These are basins, uplifts or upwarps, monoclines, fault blocks, salt structures, igneous domal uplifts, and so-called intermediate structures.

### Basins

Seven major basins make up about one-third of the Colorado Plateau province (see Fig. 22.1).

The following tabular summary indicates the size and approximate structural relief of these seven basins estimated from the top of the Triassic Chinle formation (Kelley, 1955a).

TABLE 22.1    Area and Structural Relief of Major Colorado Plateau Basins

| Name of Basin | Area in Square Miles | Structural Relief in Feet |
|---|---|---|
| Uinta | 9,750 | 14,000 |
| San Juan | 10,600 | 6,000 |
| Piceance | 5,800 | 11,000 |
| Black Mesa | 7,000 | 800 |
| Kaiparowits | 4,200 | 1,000 |
| Henry | 2,100 | 4,000 |
| Blanding | 2,500 | 700 |

### Upwarps

Upwarps or uplifts of tectonic origin, as well as those produced by igneous intrusions, are conspicuous in the Colorado plateaus. Those of tectonic origin are much more extensive and have stronger topographic expression than the associated with igneous intrusions. The major tectonic upwarps are shown in Figure 22.1

TABLE 22.2    Area and Structural Relief of Major Colorado Plateau Uplifts. (Structural relief as estimated from top of Triassic Chinle formation by Kelley).

| Name of Uplift | Area in Square Miles | Structural Relief |
|---|---|---|
| San Rafeal Swell | 2,600 | 4,000 |
| Circle Cliffs | 1,300 | 500 |
| Monument | 2,500 | 3,000 |
| Uncompahgre | 3,500 | 2,500 |
| Defiance | 3,450 | 3,000 |
| Kaibab | 2,500 | 3,000 |
| Zuni | 1,800 | 500 |
| Echo Cliffs | 1,300 | 500 |

### Monoclines

According to Kelley (1955b), monoclines are the most distinctive and diagnostic type of structure found in the Colorado Plateau province. He estimated their aggregate length at 2500 miles; the longest one, the Grand-Axial-Uinta,

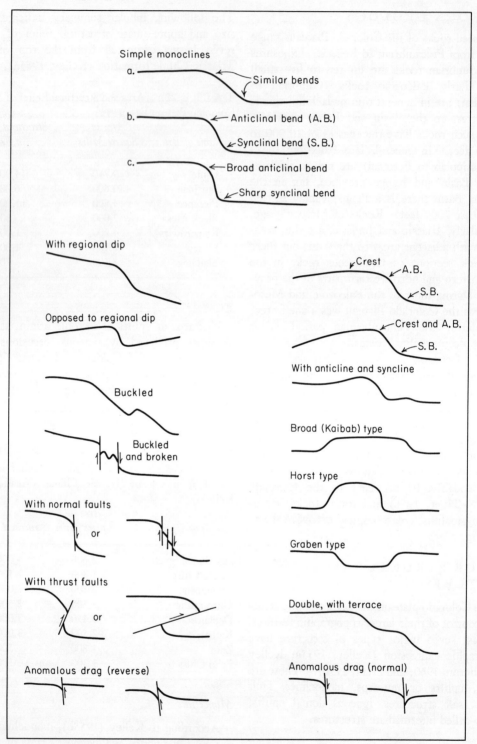

FIG. 22.2   Variations in character of Colorado Plateau monoclines.   (*After V. C. Kelley, Geol. Soc. Am. Bull.,* **66.**)

is about 300 miles long. Most of the deformation that produced the upwarps and basins has taken place along the monoclines, as is indicated by the fact that the structural relief in the monoclines is commonly five to ten times as great as it is in bordering upwarps and basins. The monoclines show variations in character (see Fig. 22.2) from broad, gently dipping flexures to very sharply overturned and thrust-faulted structures. They vary in length from 10 miles to 300 miles; their heights range from 200 to 14,000 feet; maximum rock dips in them range from 10 to 85 degrees. The monoclines and related upwarps and basins are believed to be of Laramide age, but only a few have been accurately dated.

*Faults*

Many varieties of faults exist in the Colorado plateaus, but they are predominantly steeply dipping or nearly vertical. Major faults are located on the east, north, and west margins of the province. Faults along the boundary of the Southern Rockies and the Colorado Plateau are the White River, Elk, and Nacimiento faults, and along the Uinta Mountains, at the north, the South Flank fault is of major proportions. However, the best known and topographically the most striking faults are those that bound the various fault blocks of the High Plateaus of Utah and the lower plateaus just north of the Grand Canyon (see Fig. 22.10). Included in this group are the Grand Wash, Hurricane, Toroweap, Sevier, Paunsaugunt, Paradise, and Pleasant Valley faults. A striking feature of this set of faults is their en echelon arrangement, with offsetting to the east going northward.

*Grand Wash Fault.* The westernmost of the great faults is the Grand Wash. The scarp formed along this fault forms the boundary at the southwest between the Colorado Plateau and the Basin and Range provinces; the Shivwits Plateau on the east of the fault stands above the Grand Wash, a dry drainage course in the Basin and Range province. The scarp along the Grand Wash fault is about 4000 feet high at its maximum. The throw of the fault is between 6000

and 7000 feet, and where it crosses the lower end of the Grand Canyon it brings lower Triassic rocks into contact with lower Carboniferous rocks. The displacement diminishes to the north, and the fault and associated scarp end near Saint George, Utah, where the boundary between the Colorado Plateau and the Basin and Range provinces becomes the scarp along the Hurricane fault.

*Hurricane Fault.* The Hurricane fault can be traced, according to Gardner (1941), from 25 miles northeast of Cedar City, Utah, at least as far south as the Colorado River, a distance of 170 miles. Along most of its course it is a zone of fractures as much as a mile wide, but south of the Virgin River it appears to be a single fracture and is marked by a scarp 100 to 1400 feet high known as the Hurricane Ledge (see Fig. 22.3). Stratigraphic displacement along this fault ranges from 1500 to as much as 10,000 feet. Typical basin-range topography lies west of the Hurricane Ledge at the north, but at the south the Shivwits Plateau, the most westerly of the Colorado plateaus, adjoins it on the west.

Gardner concluded that the Hurricane Ledge is composite in nature; the part bounding the Shivwits Plateau he considered a fault-line scarp and the part north of here, a fault scarp. He recognized evidence of movement along the fault during (1) the Laramide revolution, (2) post-Eocene–pre-Miocene time, (3) post-Miocene–pre-Quaternary time, and (4) Quaternary time.

*Toroweap Fault.* The Toroweap fault separates the Kanab and Uinkaret Plateaus. Upthrow along this fault is on the east side. North of Grand Canyon the Toroweap fault is marked by Toroweap Valley, and south of the canyon by Prospect Valley. At the north, about 1½ miles north of Findley Knolls, the fault makes an angular junction with the Sevier fault, and 5 miles from here grades into a monoclinal flexure.

*Sevier Fault.* From its junction with the Toroweap fault the Sevier fault extends northeastward into Utah, forming the boundary between several

FIG. 22.3    Hurricane Ledge, looking south toward Mount Trumbull.    (*Photo by John S. Shelton.*)

of the high plateaus (see Fig. 22.10).  To the east of the Sevier fault lie the Wasatch, Sevier, Paunsaugunt, and Kanab Plateaus; to the west of it are the Gunnison, Tushar, Markagunt, and Uinkaret Plateaus.

*Paunsaugunt Fault.*  The easternmost of the five great faults, the Paunsaugunt, has broken Paleozoic, Mesozoic, and Cenozoic formations.  It is most conspicuous topographically near the bend in the Paria River, where the upthrown Aquarius Plateau on the east (see Fig. 22.13) stands as much as 2000 feet above the downthrown side on the west.  However, it is not everywhere so strikingly displayed in the topography.

### Salt Structures

Possibly the most unique structural features of the Colorado Plateau province are the so-called salt structures of the Paradox Basin in southeastern Utah and southwestern Colorado.  Here subsurface flowage of salt and gypsum has produced a series of elongate folds which as a result of solution have been modified by collapse and by faulting.

### Igneous Domal Uplifts

In addition to the tectonic uplifts there are a number of domal structures produced by intrusion of stocks and laccoliths.  These are found mainly in the central and east-central part of the province and include the Henry, La Sal, Abajo, Navajo, Carrizo, and El Late Mountains (see Fig. 22.8).  The degree of doming varies from moderate uplifts in which the igneous rocks are not yet exposed to more pronounced ones, such as Mount Hillers in the Henry Mountains, where the structural relief is as much as 8000 feet and the stock exposed at the center is a mile wide (Hunt, 1956).

*Intermediate Structures*

What Kelley (1955a) termed intermediate structures make up about 50 per cent of the Colorado Plateau area. These include the nu-

merous benches, sags, and arches that represent areas of only mild deformation.

### VOLCANIC AREAS

Something like 15,000 square miles of the Colorado plateaus are covered with eruptive igneous rocks (Hunt, 1956). The three major areas lie around the margins of the province

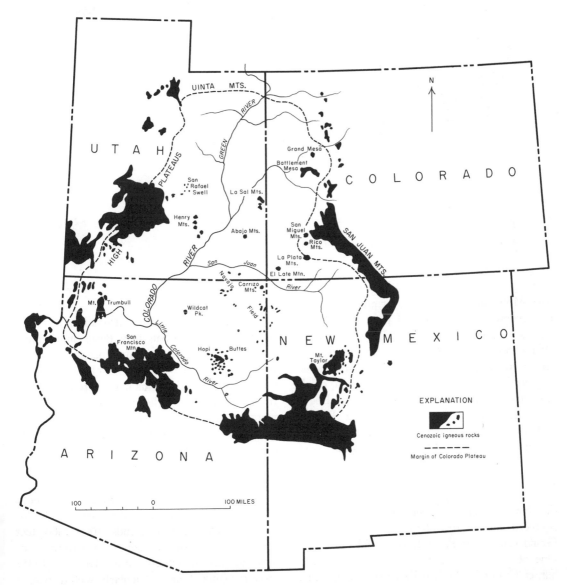

FIG. 22.4   Distribution of Cenozoic igneous rocks in Colorado Plateau province.   (*After C. B. Hunt, U. S. Geol. Surv. Profess. Paper 279.*)

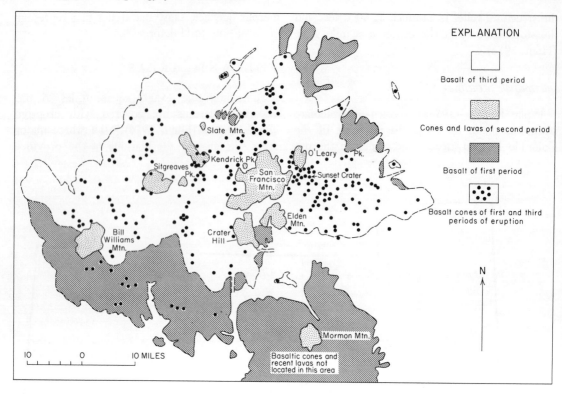

FIG. 22.5    San Francisco volcanic field.    (*After C. B. Hunt, U. S. Geol. Surv. Profess. Paper 279.*)

(see Fig. 22.4) in the High Plateaus, San Francisco Mountain, and Mt. Taylor areas, but there are several other centers; of particular interest are the diatremes of the Hopi Buttes country. Of the several volcanic peaks particularly well known are San Francisco Mountain and Mount Taylor; less famous are Mt. Dillenbaugh, on the Shivwits Plateau, and Mt. Emma, Mt. Logan, and Mt. Trumbull, on the Uinkaret Plateau. Volcanic eruptions have occurred from Miocene to historic times. Quaternary basalt flows occupy present-day valleys along the San Jose River south of Mount Taylor, south of the Zuni Plateau, near the edge of the Mogollon Rim, in the San Francisco Mountain region, in the southern part of the High Plateaus, along the Grand Canyon at Peach Spring, and elsewhere. One of the most recent eruptions was that at Sunset Crater in the San Francisco field, which has been dated at about A.D. 1190.

## Mt. Taylor Volcanic Field

The Mt. Taylor volcanic field is located on the south flank of the San Juan Basin and extends into the Basin and Range province at the south. It covers an area of approximately 2000 square miles. Most of the lavas here were poured out from central vents rather than from fissures and were spread over an erosion surface that had developed across the Cretaceous rocks of the area. According to Hunt (1938) there is evidence of three major periods of eruption ranging in time from Miocene to Recent. Mt. Taylor (altitude 11,390 feet) stands prominently above a broad lava-capped mesa called the Mt. Taylor Mesa, which in turn stands 1000–2000 feet above the valley of the Puerco River to the east. Volcanic necks, whose nature Dutton (1885) early recognized, are particularly well displayed in the valley of Puerco River. Here, the volcanic necks have been brought into strong relief by erosion of the Cretaceous strata surrounding them.

## San Francisco Volcanic Field

The San Francisco volcanic field is located mainly on the Coconino Plateau south of the Grand Canyon and covers an area of about 3000 square miles. The center of the field (see Fig. 22.5) lies about 50 miles south of the Grand Canyon and takes its name from San Francisco Mountain, the most prominent volcanic cone in the area. Colton (1937) mapped 388 vents and recognized evidence of three periods of volcanic activity in this field. The first period of activity was marked by the eruption of several basaltic flows; during the second period acid or intermediate lavas were extruded (San Francisco Peak belongs to this period of eruption); and during the third period, which extends to the present, basaltic extrusions again took place. Hundreds of the cinder cones in the area belong to this latest period of activity. The topography of the lava flows varies from those which show no appreciable erosion to some that have been so eroded that their original extent is hardly determinable. A characteristic feature of this volcanic field is the presence of many basins whose drainage was blocked by the surrounding cinder cones and lava flows and at times contained temporary lakes.

## Volcanic Area North of Grand Canyon

According to Koons (1945), lava flows from over 100 craters can be identified on the Uinkaret Plateau; similar flows are found on the Shivwits Plateau. Also in the High Plateaus are many cones and lava flows; lavas are present on the Fish Lake, Awapa, Paunsaugunt, Sevier, and Markagunt Plateaus and the Pavant Range, Antelope Range, and Tushar Mountains (see Figs. 22.4 and 22.12). The highest of the High Plateaus, the Aquarius, is basically a great lava-capped plateau. The volcanic rocks appear to be mainly of early Tertiary and late Tertiary age. This volcanic field extends beyond the

Colorado Plateau into the Basin and Range province at the west.

## Navajo-Hopi Volcanic Field

In some respects the most interesting of the volcanic fields is the Navajo-Hopi volcanic area, which lies northeast of the San Francisco field and northwest of the Mt. Taylor field. Three major parts can be identified, the Hopi Buttes, the Monument Valley, and Chuska Mountains areas. The volcanoes in this region were mainly an explosive type known as diatremes. According to Shoemaker (1953), there are approximately 250 necks and diatremes in the Navajo-Hopi Indian reservation. About 200 of these are in the Hopi Buttes field, 20 in the Monument Valley field, and 36 in the Chuska Mountains area. The diatremes are funnel-shaped vents that flare at the top to widths of as much as a mile or more (see Fig. 22.6). Hack (1942), who first described the detailed structure of the diatremes, stated that they are distributed over an area of some 800 square miles and are, along with lava-capped mesas and buttes, the most distinctive features of the Hopi-Buttes country. The volcanic necks stand like giant towers above the present topography; Shiprock, in northwestern New Mexico, is the most famous example. Presence in many of the diatremes of such materials as bedded chert, bedded tuffs, limestones, and varved clays give evidence of deposition in lakes that occupied the vents in the diatremes.

## GLACIATION IN THE COLORADO PLATEAU

Search for evidence of Pleistocene glaciation in the Colorado Plateau province has not been so detailed as in some other parts of the west, particularly the Rocky Mountains and the Sierra Nevada, but enough is known to indicate that Pleistocene glaciers did exist on some of the volcanic mountains and several of the plateaus.

Evidence of Wisconsin glaciation has been reported from the Markagunt Plateau (Gregory, 1949), Grand Mesa (Reitzer, 1954), the Aquarius Plateau (Flint and Denny, 1958), Fish

FIG. 22.6   Western Hopi Buttes, looking northwest.   (*Photo by John S. Shelton.*)

Lake Plateau (Hardy and Muessig, 1952), San Francisco Mountain (Sharp, 1942), and the Wasatch Plateau (Spieker and Billings, 1942); probably there are other areas where Wisconsin glaciers existed that have not been reported.

### Glaciation on Grand Mesa

In some areas the effects of Wisconsin glaciation are very conspicuous. This is true on Grand Mesa (see Fig. 22.7), a lava-capped plateau that attains altitudes of as much as 11,000 feet. At least 400 glacial rock basin lakes dot the mesa's surface. Evidence for at least three glacial advances has been recognized and two of these advances are marked by end moraines on the top of the mesa and the third by

a moraine down Kannah Creek Valley. Reitzer (1954) concluded that one of the glaciations was pre-Wisconsin in age and the other two Wisconsin. The glaciers on Grand Mesa were ice caps which had local extensions down the flanks of the plateau.

### Glaciation of Aquarius Plateau

Boulder Mountain, the northeast part of the Aquarius Plateau, exceeds 11,000 feet in altitude. It has a fairly flat summit area of about 70 square miles, with steep bounding side slopes. Ice caps developed several times atop this plateau during Wisconsin time (Flint and Denny, 1958), and the ice drained off the plateau into broad glacial troughs extending down its sides. During the most extensive glaciation (thought to correlate probably with the Bull Lake glaciation in the Rockies) the glaciers descended to altitudes as low as 6600 feet. Glaciers of the presumed Pinedale substage were much less extensive. The effects of glacial erosion are very conspicuous on the top of the plateau.

*Scarcity of Pre-Wisconsin Glaciations*

A rather puzzling aspect of glaciation in the Colorado Plateau is the meager evidence for pre-Wisconsin glaciation in the High Plateaus. Evidence of pre-Wisconsin glaciation has been found in the La Sal Mountains (Richmond, 1952) and on San Francisco Mountain (Sharp, 1942), but glacial materials of pre-Wisconsin age appear to be largely lacking in the High Plateaus, whereas evidence for multiple Wisconsin glaci-

ation is abundant. Hunt (1956) has suggested that the scarcity of pre-Wisconsin glacial deposits in the High Plateaus may be attributable to the fact that they did not attain their present altitudes until Pleistocene time. He cited several sorts of evidence to support the idea that elevation of the High Plateaus has taken place recently and is even continuing at present. He did not consider it unreasonable to postulate as much as 2000 feet of uplift in the High Plateaus during Pleistocene time. It might be argued that because the glaciers in the High Plateaus were ice caps they likely would have destroyed all evidence of earlier glaciations. Actually, however, in several areas tongues of ice extended down the plateau flanks as valley glaciers, and it would seem that here pre-Wisconsin glacial moraines, if such existed, would stand a chance of being preserved.

FIG. 22.7   West end of Grand Mesa, western Colorado, looking southeast.   (*Photo by John S. Shelton.*)

## SECTIONS OF COLORADO PLATEAU PROVINCE

The Colorado Plateau province has been divided into six sections (Fenneman, 1931).

These sections (see Fig. 22.8) and their outstanding characteristics are:

1. Grand Canyon section. Structurally this is the highest part of the Colorado Plateau prov-

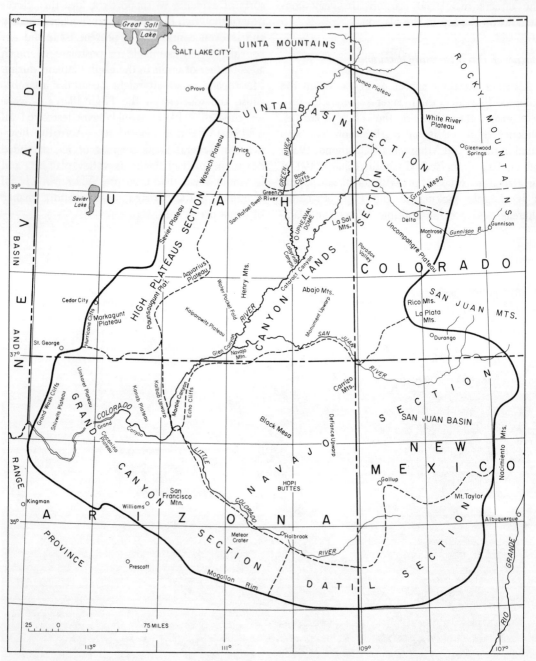

FIG. 22.8   Index map of Colorado Plateau province with sectional boundaries.   (*After C. B. Hunt, U. S. Geol. Surv. Profess. Paper* 279.)

ince, and Carboniferous rocks predominate at the surface except where covered by volcanic rocks. The great trench of the Colorado River is the dominant topographic feature. North of the Grand Canyon are several high, block plateaus that are bounded by fault or fault-line scarps.

2. High Plateaus section. This section is characterized by exceptionally high north-trending plateaus separated from each other by fault or fault-line scarps and fault-controlled valleys. Early Tertiary rocks cap the northern and southern parts of the section and volcanic rocks the central part. Terraced step-like rises mark the more southerly of these plateaus.

3. Uinta Basin. The Uinta Basin is structurally the lowest part of the Colorado Plateau province. As a consequence, it still retains a thick section of Tertiary rocks which topographically have the aspects of dissected plateaus.

4. Canyon Lands section. Deeply incised canyons cut in rocks of pre-Tertiary age are the distinctive features of this section. Superposed on the broad epeirogeic uplift are numerous large folds and laccolithic mountains.

5. Navajo section. The Navajo section is a somewhat poorly defined area of scarped plateaus nearly as high as those of the Canyon Lands section but much less dissected. Numerous volcanic vents and associated flows and pyroclatic materials add variety to its topography.

6. Datil section. The topography of this section is largely volcanic in origin. Much of the area was covered with lava flows, and extensive lava-capped mesas and benches abound throughout the section. Hundreds of volcanic necks add diversity to the landscape.

### Grand Canyon Section

The boundaries of the Grand Canyon section are fairly readily recognizable. On the south the Mogollon Rim (see Fig. 22.9), a south-facing scarp, overlooks Basin and Range structure and topography, as do the Grand Wash Cliffs on the west. The eastern boundary essentially follows the Little Colorado River, and the Vermillion Cliffs, developed on the Wingate sandstone of Jurassic age, form the northern boundary.

*Grand Canyon.* The dominant topographic feature of this section, although by no means the only interesting one, is the Grand Canyon of the Colorado. The term "Grand Canyon" is applied to that portion of the gorge of the Colorado River between Lees Ferry, where the Colorado River cuts through the Echo Cliffs on the Jurassic Navajo sandstone, and the Grand Wash Cliffs, where the canyon ends. Words can hardly do justice to this masterpiece of erosion, but perhaps the description of it by Dutton (1882) gives some idea of why, despite the existence of innumerable other deep canyons in the Colorado Plateau province, the Grand Canyon stands out preeminently.

The observer who visits its commanding points with the expectation of experiencing forthwith a rapturous exaltation, an ecstasy arising from a degree of grandeur and sublimity never felt before, is doomed to disappointment. Supposing him to be but little familiar with plateau scenery, he will be simply bewildered . . . .

If its sublimity consisted only in its dimensions, it could be sufficiently set forth in a single sentence. It is more than 200 miles long, from 5 to 12 miles wide, and from 5,000 to 6,000 feet deep. There are in the world valleys which are longer and a few which are deeper. There are valleys flanked by summits loftier than the palisades of the Kaibab. Still the Grand Canyon is the sublimest thing on earth. It is so not alone by virtue of its magnitudes, but by virtue of the whole—its *ensemble* . . . .

It is perhaps in some respects unfortunate that the stupendous pathway of the Colorado River was ever called a cañon, for the name identifies it with the baser conception. But the name presents as wide a range of signification as the word house. The log cabin of the rancher, the painted and vine-clad cottage of the mechanic, the home of the millionaire, the places where parliaments assemble, are all houses. Yet the contrast between Saint Mark's and the rude dwelling of the frontiersman is not greater than that between

FIG. 22.9    Mogollon Rim, looking west-northwest.    (*Photo by John S. Shelton.*)

the chasm of the Colorado and the trenches in the rocks which answer to the ordinary conception of cañon.   And as a great cathedral is an immense development of the rudimentary idea involved in the four walls and roof of a cabin, so is the chasm an expansion of the simple type of drainage channels peculiar to the Plateau Country.   To the conception of its vast proportions must be added some notion of its intricate plan, the nobility of its architecture, its colossal buttes, its wealth of ornamentation, the splendor of its colors, and its wonderful atmosphere.   All of these attributes combine with infinite complexity to produce a whole which at first bewilders and at length overpowers.

A number of factors combine to make the Grand Canyon "grand," most important of which are: the height of the Kaibab Plateau above sea level, the lithological variety in the rocks through which it is cut, the near horizontality of the successive rock formations, a semi-arid climate with

resulting sparsity of vegetation and dominance of physical weathering, and sources of the Colorado River in mountains to the east and north where the rainfall is adequate to maintain a sizeable permanent stream across the Colorado plateaus.

The character of the Grand Canyon changes considerably as its course successively borders the Kaibab, Kanab, Uinkaret, and Shivwits plateaus.   Differences in the altitudes of these plateaus and the positions of particular geological formations with respect to river level are responsible for the varying aspects of the canyon. The part of the canyon that most people see is that cut through the Kaibab uplift; here it is deepest and widest.

The Grand Canyon is cut in rocks ranging in age from Precambrian to Permian, with rocks of Ordovician and Silurian age being absent.   The Kaibab, Toroweap, or Coconino formations, of Permian age, commonly form the uppermost of the succession of cliffs by which the canyon walls rise from the inner gorge cut in Precambrian rocks. Despite the striking evidence of valley deepening, valley widening has exceeded many times the amount of deepening. Cliff recession, not lateral stream planation, has been the major process involved in valley widening.

The terraced or tabulated form of the upper Grand Canyon is one of its most striking aspects. Four geological formations are the main cliff formers, the Cambrian Tapeats sandstone, the Redwall limestone of Mississippian age, the Supai sandstone of early Permian age, and the Kaibab limestone of middle Permian age. At the bases of the cliffs are broad aprons of talus, and extending canyonward from these are benches or platforms of varying widths. Two platforms with notable longitudinal and horizontal extent are the Tonto Platform and the so-called Esplanade. The Tonto Platform is a prominent bench, more than a mile wide in places, along the Kaibab section of the Grand Canyon; it is underlain by the Cambrian Tapeats sandstone. The Esplanade is an equally prominent bench along the Kanab stretch of the canyon which is underlain by the Permian Supai sandstone. Certain geologists (see p. 437) interpreted these benches as former baselevels of erosion or strath terraces, but it seems more likely that they are structural benches controlled by the geological formations that underlie them. The Tonto Platform is lacking along the Kanab section of the canyon because here the Tapeats sandstone is below stream level. The Esplanade is lacking along the Kaibab section because the Hermit shale, which lies between the Cocinino sandstone and the Supai sandstone, has thinned so much here that the interval between the two formations is too small to permit stripping of the Supai formation and resulting development of the Esplanade.

*Plateaus North of Grand Canyon.* The Colorado River divides the Grand Canyon section into two distinctly different parts. On the north side of the river is a series of north-south trending plateaus whose boundaries and outlines are determined mainly by a series of faults and flexures beginning with the Grand Wash fault on the west and ending with the East Kaibab monocline at the east. South of the Colorado River is the Coconino-San Francisco plateau area, in which faults and folds are relatively unimportant.

The plateaus north of the Grand Canyon are, from west to east, the Shivwits, Uinkaret, Kanab, and Kaibab (see Fig. 22.10). Structurally these plateaus belong more with the Basin and Range province, but topographically they are a part of the Colorado Plateaus. Their average height increases from west to east roughly 1000 feet for each plateau ascent until in the Kaibab Plateau altitudes exceeding 9000 feet are attained. Lava flows and volcanic cones add diversity to the surfaces of the Shivwits and Uinkaret plateaus but such features are lacking on the Kanab and Kaibab plateaus.

The Shivwits Plateau is bounded on the west by the Grand Wash fault and on the east by the Hurricane fault; the Uinkaret Plateau on the west by the Hurricane fault and on the east by the Toroweap fault; the Kanab Plateau on the west by the Toroweap fault and on the east by the West Kaibab monocline and fault zone; the Kaibab Plateau on the west by the West Kaibab monocline (Strahler, 1948) and three normal faults, all downthrown on the west, and on the east by the East Kaibab monocline.

*East Kaibab Monocline.* The Kaibab Plateau is developed on the major structural uplift of the Colorado Plateau province, the Kaibab uplift. On the crest of this, the westernmost of the great north-south uplifts (see Fig. 22.1), the Permian Kaibab limestone attains altitudes of better than 9000 feet; from its crest strata descend to the east in the East Kaibab monocline, a compound flexure with structural relief of 2000 to 5000 feet. The East Kaibab monocline extends approximately 150 miles from the San Francisco Mountain volcanic field on the south to Bryce Canyon at the north. It ranges in width from 20 to 30 miles. The monocline varies from a single to a triple flexure and is broken in places by faults (Babenroth and Strahler, 1945).

The topography on the monocline has much

**FIG. 22.10**  Map of part of western Colorado Plateau province showing faults, plateaus, and northward-receding cliffs. (*a*) Chocolate Cliffs, (*b*) Vermillion Cliffs, (*c*) White Cliffs, (*d*) Gray Cliffs, and (*e*) Pink Cliffs.  (*After P. B. King, The Evolution of North America, by permission of Princeton University Press.*)

diversity, but over an extensive area its surface coincides with the upper part of the Kaibab limestone, and its slopes parallel the dips of this formation.  The east side of the Kaibab Plateau is marked by a monoclinal scarp that descends 3000 feet from the level of the Kaibab Plateau to that of the Marble Platform.  From its crest the Kaibab Plateau surface descends gently to the west for about 10 miles and then drops

abruptly to the level of the Kanab Plateau through the multiple West Kaibab faults.

One especially interesting aspect of the topography of the Kaibab Plateau is the presence of numerous valleys or basin-like areas called "parks" (Strahler, 1944).  These are shallow valleys whose floors are undulating or nearly flat and are underlain by fills of waste across which streams rarely flow.  When followed down valley they become narrower and eventually grade into v-shaped canyons which are undergoing active deepening. Theories as to their origin are discussed on p. 437.

*Area South of Grand Canyon.* South of the Grand Canyon is a plateau tract with a general altitude between 7000 and 7500 feet which in general lacks the faulting and folding that marks the region north of the Grand Canyon. The area immediately south of the canyon is commonly called the Coconino Plateau and the remaining part the San Francisco Plateau, although the whole area is by some called the San Francisco Plateau. The boundary between the two plateaus is somewhat indefinite, but it is a boundary between an area in which volcanic rocks are important and one in which they are not. The San Francisco Mountain volcanic field is the dominant feature south of the Grand Canyon.

The Coconino Plateau is a southern continuation of the Kaibab Plateau, separated from it by the Grand Canyon. It is mainly a regional slope coincident with the dip of the Kaibab limestone. It is lower than the Kaibab Plateau and slopes gradually downward on the west and south. Gently rolling topography is characteristic of most of the Coconino Plateau, and here are found several parks similar to those that are particularly numerous in the Kaibab Plateau.

*Meteor Crater.* Probably the most unique topographic feature in the whole San Francisco Plateau is Meteor Crater, near its southeast edge. The origin of this feature, which at times has been called Coon Butte, Crater Mound, and Barringer Meteorite Crater, has been much debated, but evidence for a meteoritic impact now seems to be very strong, particularly since the finding of coesite, a high pressure polymorph of $SiO_2$ (Chao et al., 1960) in the rimrock of the crater. Coesite is a mineral produced by the polymorphic transformation of quartz by shocks such as meteoritic impacts would produce.

The average width of Meteor Crater is about 570 feet, and its floor lies some 600 feet below the highest point on its encircling rim. This rim is composed of upturned strata of the Triassic Moenkopi formation and the Kaibab, Toroweap, and Cocinino formations of Permian age. The floor of the crater is underlain by Pleistocene and Recent talus, alluvium, and lacustrine silts and clays. The time of the meteoritic impact is uncertain but it likely took place very late in geologic time. Blackwelder (1932) concluded that the Pleistocene lacustrine deposits in the crater suggested that it may have formed during the Tahoe glacial stage some 40,000 years or so ago, but this is largely conjecture.

## High Plateaus of Utah Section

*General Description.* Located near the northwest corner of the Colorado Plateau province are the High Plateaus of Utah. These plateaus resemble the group of plateaus immediately north of the Colorado River in that their outlines and boundaries are primarily fault-controlled, but they differ in three respects: they are notably higher; they are aligned in a north-south rather than an east-west direction; and they are underlain by rocks of Mesozoic and Cenozoic rather than Paleozoic age.

Surface altitudes ranging from 9000 to more than 11,000 feet truly justify their designation as "high plateaus." Lava flows cap several of the plateaus (see p. 413 and Fig. 22.4), and, as pointed out above, several of the plateaus were sites of local icecaps during at least Wisconsin time.

The High Plateaus can be divided into three south-north groups that are separated from each other by two major structural trenches (see Fig. 22.11). The main plateaus of the western strip, from south to north, are the Markagunt, Tushar, Pavant, and Gunnison; the plateaus of the middle strip are the Paunsagunt and Sevier; those of the eastern strip are the Aquarius, Awapa, Fish Lake, and Wasatch. The depression which divides the western and middle plateau groups is the Sevier-San Pete (also spelled San Pitch) Valley. This depression is largely controlled by the Sevier fault at its east side (see Fig. 22.10). The middle and eastern plateau strips are separated by Grass Valley, another fault-controlled depression, and by the

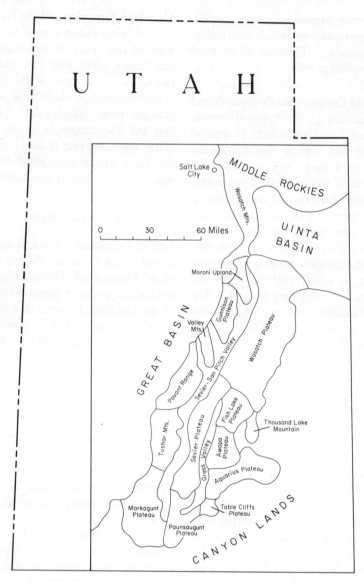

FIG. 22.11    Map of the High Plateaus.    (*After Eugene Callaghan, Trans. Am. Geophys. Union for* 1939.)

Paunsagunt fault. The western boundary of the High Plateaus section also follows a fault, the northern part of the Hurricane fault. With few exceptions, the throw along the faults is to the west, and thus the altitudes of the plateaus increase from west to east and attain their greatest magnitudes in the Wasatch, Fish Lake, and Aquarius (see Fig. 22.12) plateaus, where altitudes better than 11,000 feet are reached. Al-

though most of the plateaus are bounded by fault scarps, not all the scarps are such. Some, as at Bryce Canyon on the southeast edge of the Paunsagunt Plateau, are fault-line scarps.

Locally, the faults which bound the plateaus grade into monoclines. One of the most striking of these monoclines is the 7000 foot monocline which forms the west wall of the Wasatch Plateau for a distance of over 50 miles and provides the descent from this plateau to the floor of the San Pete Valley.

*South-Facing Cliffs.* Although the general outlines of the High Plateaus are determined by a series of northeast-southwest-trending faults, their rise from the levels of the plateaus immediately north of the Grand Canyon to the highest of the High Plateaus takes place through a series of cliffs and associated rock terraces which have been named according to the predominant colors of the geological formations responsible for them. This ascent takes place over a distance of 40 to 50 miles. The cliffs have a general east-west trend, in contrast to the faults of the area, and are outstanding examples of receding escarpments. Five cliffs have widespread regional extent; they are in order from south to north the Chocolate, Vermillion, White, Gray, and Pink cliffs (see Fig. 22.10). Each cliff is developed on a resistant geological formation; these formations range in age from Triassic to Eocene. The Chocolate Cliffs are developed on the Triassic Shinarump formation, the Vermillion Cliffs on the Jurassic Navajo sandstone, the Gray Cliffs on Cretaceous sandstone, and the Pink Cliffs on the Eocene Wasatch formation (see Fig. 22.13).

The cliffs are cuesta scarps developed on northward-dipping resistant formations and are in this respect quite different from the scarps that form the east and west sides of the High Plateaus. The formations which underlie the rock terraces bounded by the cliffs once extended farther south than at present and were stripped during the period of erosion which Dutton called the "Great Denudation" (see p. 436.) The cliffs are marked by many indentations, projecting spurs, and outliers. Locally, they exhibit a high degree of dissection such as is

FIG. 22.12 Aquarius Plateau, looking toward the northwest. The shadow of the north end of the Henry Mountains may be seen at the extreme left. (*Photo by John S. Shelton.*)

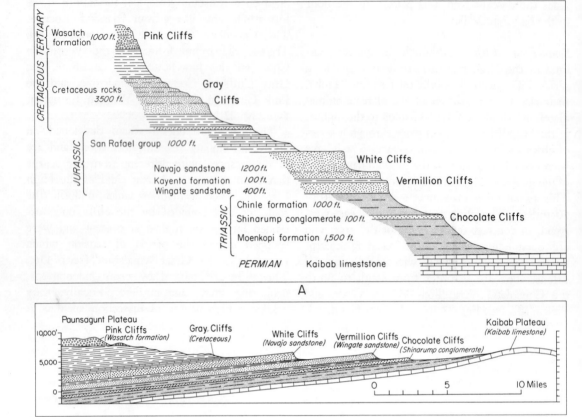

FIG. 22.13    (A) Columnar section showing sequence of rocks north of Grand Canyon and their usual topographic expression.    (B) Sequence of erosional cliffs north of Grand Canyon.    (*After P. B. King, The Evolution of North America, by permission of Princeton University Press.*)

seen at the Bryce Canyon and Cedar Breaks portions of the Pink Cliffs near the southeast corner of the Paunsagunt Plateau.

*Transitional Nature of High Plateaus.*    The nature of the High Plateaus section, both structurally and topographically, can perhaps be best understood if we recognize that it is essentially a transitional zone between the geology and topography of the Colorado Plateau and that of the Basin and Range province to the west (Spieker, 1949).

In the Colorado Plateau, folds are typically fairly simple, open ones, and the faults are normal.    Rock strata, except in the major monoclines and on the immediate flanks of the stronger

folds, approach horizontality over wide areas. In contrast, in the Basin and Range province the geological structure is highly complex.    It is a type of structure that has resulted from a series of compressive movements followed later by block faulting.    The diastrophism that affected the Basin and Range province did not produce broad, smooth plateaus but rather short block-faulted mountain ranges separated by broad basins which served as areas of accumulation for waste shed from the bounding mountains.    The High Plateaus display a mixture of the two types of structure and topography.    The plateau type of topography is dominant, but structures resemble more those found in the Basin and Range province than those of the Colorado Plateau.    Such features as Sevier, San Pete, and Grass valleys are controlled by the Basin and Range type of structures. The Joes Valley graben in the Wasatch Plateau is another Basin and Range type of structure.

Thus the fault and fault-line scarps and the grabens of the High Plateaus, typical of the Basin and Range type of structure and topography, combine with the receding cliffs on the south side of the High Plateaus, strictly erosional features, to give to the High Plateaus the composite topography expectable along the margin of two provinces having distinctly different types of geologic structure.

### Uinta Basin Section

The Uinta Basin, despite the fact that its average altitude is over 5000 feet, is both structurally and topographically a basin. It is structurally the lowest part of the Colorado Plateau province. However, not all of the Uinta Basin section is basin topography, for in the Tavaputs Plateau at its southern margin altitudes between 10,000 and 11,000 feet are attained. In general the Uinta Basin is bordered by higher topography, the Uinta Mountains on the north, the Wasatch Mountains and High Plateaus on the west, the White River Plateau and West Elk Mountains on the east, and the Uncompahgre Plateau on the southeast. Only on the south does the Uinta Basin section look down on its adjoining section. Here, in a double escarpment, there is a descent of some 3000 feet from the Uinta Basin section to its neighboring section at the south.

*Geology and Topography.* The Uinta Basin is a great east-west asymmetrical syncline near the base of the Uinta Mountains. A thick section of more than 9000 feet of early Tertiary rocks is exposed here (Childs, 1950). The rocks are mainly Paleocene and Eocene in age and consist of lacustrine, fluviatile, and deltaic continental deposits, most famous of which are the lacustrine Green River beds. Limited exposures of Mesozoic and Paleozoic formations appear around the flanks of the basin. Steeply dipping Mesozoic formations on the southern flank of the Uinta

Mountains form prominent hogbacks, and the Grand Hogback on the Dakota sandstone along the boundary between the Uinta Basin and the White River Plateau of the Southern Rocky Mountains attains locally a height of 1500 feet.

The south-facing escarpment at the southern edge of the Uinta Basin section consists of two parts, the upper Roan Cliffs on rocks of Eocene age, an eastern equivalent of the Pink Cliffs of the High Plateaus, and the lower Book Cliffs on rocks of Cretaceous age. Locally these two escarpments are close enough together to form a single escarpment, but they may be as much as 10 miles apart. The name Tavaputs Plateau is most commonly applied to the plateau (cuesta backslope) north of these cliffs. This plateau is cut midway by the north-south Desolation Canyon of the Green River, a 3000-foot gorge. The Book Cliffs differ notably in character on the two sides of Green River. East of Green River they are highly irregular, with many salients and canyons which give the cliffs a very irregular outline. West of Green River, the Book Cliffs present a fairly unbroken front.

Despite the synclinal structure of the Uinta Basin much of its topography is rugged, intricately dissected plateau with broad tabular upland tracts between valleys. Large-scale, coarse-textured topography of this sort is particularly common in the Tavaputs Plateau. At the south base of the Uinta Mountains are numerous broad benches that are probably pediments, but not enough geomorphic work has been done to say with certainty whether they are pediments or structural benches. It seems likely that surfaces correlative with the Gilbert Peak and Bear Mountain pediments of the Uinta Mountains (see p. 363) may be present here. Badland topography is extensively developed in the central part of the Uinta Basin.

*Geomorphic History.* Clark (1957) tentatively suggested the following major events in the geomorphic history of the part of the Uinta Basin immediately south of the Uinta Mountains.

1. Laramide uplift of the Uinta Range resulted in damming of westward drainage and formation of a lake in the Uinta Basin.

2. Continued blockage of drainage led to the deposition of several thousand feet of Paleocene and Eocene sediments in the Uinta Basin lake.
3. Upwarping of the basin was accompanied by the development of numerous local structures such as are found at Split Mountain, Blue Mountain, and elsewhere.
4. By early Pliocene time the Gilbert Peak and Bear Mountain pediments had developed in the Uinta Mountains, with extensions into the Uinta Basin.
5. Erosional excavation of the basin has continued to the present time, interrupted by at least three episodes of glaciation in the Uinta Mountains during which outwash from the glaciers reached the Uinta Basin.

*Canyon Lands Section*

The Canyon Lands section is bounded on the west by the High Plateaus, on the north by the Book Cliffs, on the south by the San Juan River, and on the east by the San Juan and other mountains of the Southern Rockies. The region has been epeirogenically uplifted and has had superposed on it a number of structural features that are strongly reflected in its topography. These structures include various local upwarps, monoclines on the flanks of the upwarps, salt structures in an area of salt intrusion, and local domal uplifts produced by igneous intrusions. Topographically the structures are marked by hogbacks, homoclinal ridges, or cuestas on their flanks, depending on the degree of deformation.

It may seem inconsistent to apply the name Canyon Lands to a particular section of the Colorado Plateau province when canyons are common throughout the province and when the section so named lacks the greatest of the canyons. Yet the name is appropriate because canyons are more numerous and extensive in this section than in any other part of the Colorado Plateaus. Although the Grand Canyon is outside this section, there are numerous canyons of respectable magnitude within it. In this section are several canyon segments of the Colorado River, including the Marble Canyon, which extends from the junction of the Little Colorado

River northeast to Echo Cliffs; Glen Canyon, which extends northeastward from Echo Cliffs to the Henry Mountains; and Cataract Canyon, which extends from the Henry Mountains region to the junction of the Green River (see Fig. 22.8). Other sizeable canyons are the Labyrinth Canyon of Green River and the Canyon of the San Juan River.

Not all of the Canyon Lands section is intricately dissected by canyon networks; broad, nearly flat, interstream tracts in southeastern Utah and southwestern Colorado are so extensive that canyons seem of secondary importance here. One such area is the so-called Great Sage Plain, an area of some 1200 square miles east of the Monument Upwarp and the Abajo Mountains and north of the San Juan River (see Fig. 22.8). This plain viewed from a distance has the appearance of a limitless sea of sagebrush. Actually it is difficult to traverse, as there are numerous valleys 100 to 500 feet or more deep cut in it. The plain is a structural slope underlain throughout by the Dakota sandstone. Its east-west slope is very slight, but it has a descent to the south of about 40 feet to the mile.

The master stream of the Canyon Lands section is still the Colorado River, but the San Juan, Green, Gunnison, Dolores, San Rafael, Dirty Devil, Escalante and many other rivers have cut the country into a series of tabular blocks separated from each other by what are for the most part nontraversable canyons. The area is noted for its incised meanders, particularly those of the San Juan River.

*San Rafael Swell.* One of the better known uplifts of the Canyon Lands section is the San Rafael Swell, near its northwest corner (Gilluly, 1929; Baker, 1946). This asymmetrical anticline has a maximum width of 50 miles and a length of about 100 miles and extends in a northeast direction. Dips on the northwest side are only 4 or 5 degrees, but on the southeast side they are as much as 85 degrees (see Fig. 22.14). Structural relief on the southeast side of the uplift reaches a maximum of 4000 feet (see Fig. 22.1). An open, gently domed area about 10 miles wide and 40 miles long near the center of the San Rafael Swell is

FIG. 22.14   View southwestward across southern margin of San Rafael Swell to Aquarius Plateau.   (*Photo by John S. Shelton.*)

known as the Sinbad.   The Sinbad is rimmed by a steep escarpment called The Reef.   Locally The Reef rises as much as 2000 feet above the adjacent Sinbad, but heights of 800 to 1000 feet are more common.   The oldest rocks exposed in the San Rafael Swell are sandstones and limestones of the Pennsylvanian Hermosa formation. Permian Coconino and Kaibab limestones form a floor for a large part of its eastern flank, but Triassic and Jurassic rocks form narrow outcrop bands along The Reef.   The Jurassic Navajo sandstone is the main resistant formation in The Reef.

*Monument Upwarp.*   The Monument Upwarp is the most centrally located uplift of the Colorado Plateau province and is exceeded only by the East Kaibab uplift in the amount of structural relief.   This upwarp trends north about 10 degrees east and is over 100 miles long and up to 50 miles wide (Gregory, 1938).   Like the San Rafael Swell, it is an asymmetrical structure with steepest dips on its east side.   It resembles the East Kaibab uplift in that its internal geology is well exposed, in this case by the canyon of the San Juan River.   Along this canyon beds of the Pennsylvanian Hermosa formation crop out, but over much of the crest of the structure the surficial rocks are of Permian age, as is true in the Kaibab uplift.   Locally, however, rocks of Triassic and Jurassic age are exposed.   Like the East Kaibab uplift, it has been stripped of most of its former cover of Mesozoic rocks.

On the west side of the Monument Upwarp dips rarely are as much as 2 degrees, but in the

Comb monocline on the east side they may be 50 degrees. The topography on the west side of the uplift is one of gently sloping cuestas, but on the east hogback ridges are characteristic. The most prominent of these ridges is Comb Ridge, on the Jurassic Wingate and Navajo sandstones. This ridge is as much as 1000 feet high, and between it and the main part of the uplift is Comb Wash, a subsequent strike valley bordered on the west by the Permian Cedar Mesa sandstone and on the east by the Triassic Chinle formation.

*Henry Mountains.* The Henry Mountains region of southeastern Utah is one of the classical areas of American geology (see Figs. 22.1 and 22.4). Made famous by Gilbert's study (1877) and more recently by that of Hunt and associates (Hunt et al., 1953), the Henry Mountains are one of several groups of igneous uplifts in the Colorado Plateaus that are commonly referred to as "laccolithic mountains." Other mountains in this category are the La Sal, Abajo, El Late, and Navajo Mountains in the Canyon Lands section, the Carrizo Mountains of the Navajo section and the La Plata, Rico, and San Miguel Mountains just beyond the eastern edge of the Colorado Plateaus on the western flank of the San Juan Mountains (see Fig. 22.4). The designation "laccolithic mountains" is hardly correct, for the major updoming was not produced by laccoliths, as suggested by Gilbert (1877), but by small stocks. Laccoliths are present around the stocks, but mainly on the flanks of the uplifts rather than at their centers.

Various stages of intrusion and subsequent erosion are displayed by the several mountain groups (Hunt et al., 1953). The least advanced stage is represented by Navajo Mountain; here no igneous rocks are exposed, but the similarity of this domal structure to that where igneous rocks are exposed makes it appear certain that this is the same type of structure. From Navajo Mountain there is a gradation in the amount of doming and exposure of the stocks and associated dikes, sills, and laccoliths to the advanced stage represented by Mount Hillers in the Henry Mountains. Here there is structural relief of

8000 feet, and a stock, more than a mile wide with numerous tongue-shaped laccoliths radiating from it, is exposed.

The Henry Mountains uplift extends in a northwest-southeast direction near the center of a broad regional basin called the Henry Basin. The Henry Mountains form an irregular arch about 40 miles long and 10 miles wide. Paralleling the Henry Basin on the west is the Circle Cliffs uplift, which connects with the Henry Basin through the Waterpocket monocline, one of the major structures of southern Utah. Beds in this flexure have dips that range from 15 to 75 degrees; in areas of steepest dips there is exposed in a distance of 2 miles a stratigraphic section 9000 feet thick including rocks ranging in age from Permian to latest Cretaceous.

Each of the Henry Mountains is a structural dome, 6 to 10 miles in diameter, at the center of which is a stock. Mt. Ellen, Mt. Ellsworth (see Fig. 22.15) Mt. Holmes, Mt. Hillers, and Mt. Pennell are five peaks developed on the stocks. Laccoliths, dikes, and sills associated with the stocks are found around their margins (see Fig. 22.16); typically they have minor topographic expression. Laccoliths have formed particularly in the Jurassic Morrison formation and the Mancos shale of Cretaceous age. The intrusions are probably mid-Tertiary (Miocene) in age. Each dome is marked by radial drainage, encircling hogbacks on the upturned sedimentary rocks, and pediments and rock fans at their bases that extend into the Henry Basin.

*Paradox Salt Basin.* Located in southeastern Utah and southwestern Colorado is an area known variously as the Paradox Salt Basin, the Paradox Fold and Fault Belt, and the Pennsylvanian Paradox Evaporite Basin. The Paradox Salt Basin lies west of and parallel to the Uncompahgre Plateau and forms a rectangular tract about 150 miles long and 60 to 70 miles wide (Dane, 1935). The laccolithic La Sal Mountains lie slightly west of the center of the basin, but except for these mountains the major structural and topographic features are all related to flowage or solution of masses of salt and gypsum. Instead of domes, similar to those in the Gulf Coastal Plain,

FIG. 22.15   Mount Ellsworth, viewed from the north.   (*Photo by R. C. Frampton and John S. Shelton.*)

the structures here are mainly anticlines and synclines. The eight major anticlinal structures of the area have been modified in varying degrees by collapsed folds and faults attendant on solution of salt at depth. The Mesozoic rocks in the anticlines are pierced irregularly by salt from the Paradox Evaporite member of the Pennsylvanian Hermosa formation. Individual salt plugs range from one half mile to a mile in diameter.

The eight major anticlinal structures are all known as "valleys" because they have been breached by erosion to form anticlinal valleys (see Fig. 22.17). Best known of these anticlinal valleys are Salt, Paradox, and Gypsum valleys. Collapse features or grabens resulting from solution of salt are particularly well developed in Gypsum Valley, but are present elsewhere (Stokes, 1948). The synclinal areas between the anticlines have given rise to flat-topped mesa-like tracts that contrast strikingly with the anti-clinal valleys.

Opinions differ as to the date of the salt intrusions. One interpretation of the history of the area is given in Figure 22.18. Some geologists maintain that the structures are a product of intermittent growth through a period extending from Permian into Tertiary or even Recent times; still another theory is that the salt was intruded during the Laramide deformation of the region.

*Upheaval Dome.* One of the most unusual features of the Colorado Plateaus is Upheaval Dome. This structure lies west of the salt structures in the angle between the junction of the Colorado and Green rivers (see Fig. 22.8). It consists of a conical dome surrounded by a ring syncline. The dome is about 2 miles wide and the encircling syncline is one-half mile wide, giving to the whole structure a diameter of about 3 miles. Strata involved in the structure (see Fig. 22.19) extend from the White Rim sand-

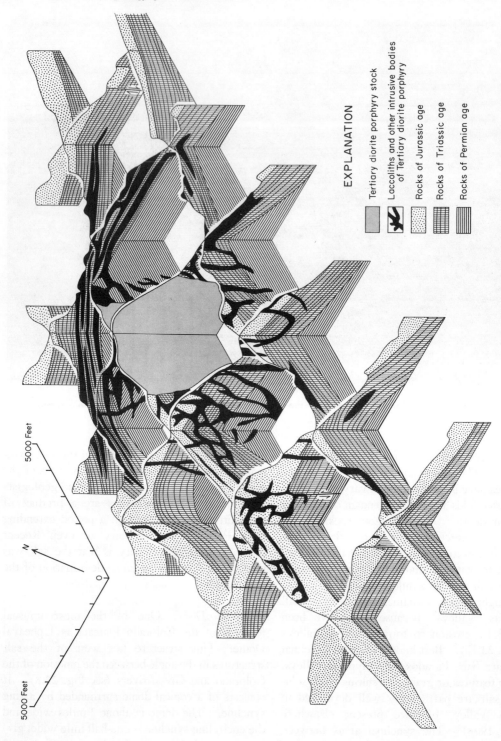

EXPLANATION

Tertiary diorite porphyry stock

Laccoliths and other intrusive bodies
of Tertiary diorite porphyry

Rocks of Jurassic age

Rocks of Triassic age

Rocks of Permian age

5000 Feet

N

5000 Feet

FIG. 22.16 Fence diagram showing structural relations of the intrusions in and adjacent to Mount Ellsworth. *(After C. B. Hunt, U. S. Geol. Survey Profess. Paper 228.)*

stone member of the Permian Cutler formation, at the center, to the Jurassic Navajo sandstone around the rim. Outward dips in the central dome range from 30 to 90 degrees but more commonly are 40 to 60 degrees. Inward dips at the outer edge of the rimming syncline are from 15 to 30 degrees. In form, Upheaval Dome resembles more the salt domes of the Gulf Coastal Plain than the salt structures of the Paradox Salt Basin. Bucher (1936) interpreted Upheaval Dome as a cryptovolcanic structure, but most geologists are inclined to look on it as a salt dome. So considered, the encircling syncline would be a result of subsidence caused by removal of salt either by plastic flowage or solution and analogous to the grabens in the salt anticlines east of Upheaval Dome.

## Navajo Section

The Navajo section, south of the Canyon Lands section, is nearly as high as the Canyon Lands section but not so deeply or intricately dissected. Valleys here are more commonly broad and open than canyon-like; dry washes are very characteristic of this section; locally, streams are deeply incised, but this is the exception rather than the rule. Scarcity of deep canyons is not so much because of lack of height above regional baselevel as it is because of lack of permanent, through-flowing streams. Only the San Juan River, which rises in highlands outside the region, receives sufficient runoff to maintain itself as a permanent stream. The rocks of this section have not been deformed so much as in adjacent

FIG. 22.17   Gypsum Valley anticline, looking southeast.   (*Photo by John S. Shelton.*)

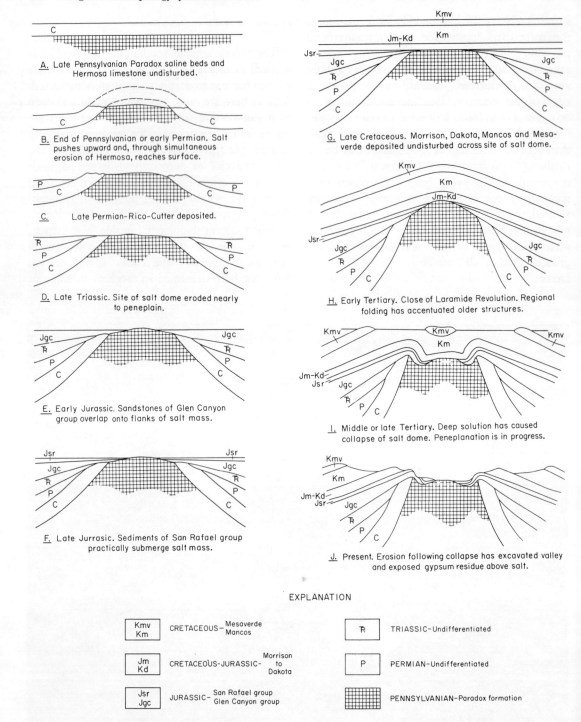

A. Late Pennsylvanian Paradox saline beds and Hermosa limestone undisturbed.

B. End of Pennsylvanian or early Permian. Salt pushes upward and, through simultaneous erosion of Hermosa, reaches surface.

C.    Late Permian-Rico-Cutter deposited.

D. Late Triassic. Site of salt dome eroded nearly to peneplain.

E. Early Jurassic. Sandstones of Glen Canyon group overlap onto flanks of salt mass.

F. Late Jurrasic. Sediments of San Rafael group practically submerge salt mass.

G. Late Cretaceous. Morrison, Dakota, Mancos and Mesaverde deposited undisturbed across site of salt dome.

H. Early Tertiary. Close of Laramide Revolution. Regional folding has accentuated older structures.

I. Middle or late Tertiary. Deep solution has caused collapse of salt dome. Peneplanation is in progress.

J. Present. Erosion following collapse has excavated valley and exposed gypsum residue above salt.

EXPLANATION

| | | |
|---|---|---|
| Kmv / Km | CRETACEOUS— Mesaverde / Mancos | |
| Jm / Kd | CRETACEOUS-JURASSIC— Morrison to Dakota | |
| Jsr / Jgc | JURASSIC— San Rafael group / Glen Canyon group | |
| Ŧ | TRIASSIC–Undifferentiated | |
| P | PERMIAN–Undifferentiated | |
| | PENNSYLVANIAN–Paradox formation | |

FIG. 22.18   Postulated sequence in development of salt structures.   (*After W. L. Stokes, Guidebook to Utah Geology, No. 3.*)

areas, hence mesas, buttes, cuestas, and rock terraces are more common than hogbacks and homoclinal ridges. This is not to say that this section lacks strong structural deformation, for the Defiance monocline near its center has a maximum structural relief of 8000 feet and a maximum topographic relief of 6000 feet. More commonly, however, the structures are not of this magnitude. As Gregory (1917) stated, "Synclines and anticlines, both broad and narrow, sharply delineated monoclines, and domical upwarps follow one another in succession or abut against one another like waves in a choppy sea. In one feature only—their general trend—do the flexures displayed in the Navajo country simulate those of the region farther west." The diversity of the topography in this section is suggested by the fact that Gregory in his discussion of the Navajo country divided it into twenty geomorphic divisions.

The Navajo section is bounded on the west by the Little Colorado River and the Echo Cliffs monocline, a long north-trending monocline which is delineated by an eastward dip slope on the top of the Navajo sandstone (see Fig. 22.20). East of Echo Cliffs is the well-known Painted Desert on colorful Triassic and Jurassic formations. The three major structures of the section are the Black Mesa Basin on the west, the San Juan Basin on the east, and the intermediate Defiance uplift (see Fig. 22.1). Black Mesa Basin is a shallow basin about 90 miles in diameter with rocks of Permian to Tertiary age. Its outstanding topographic feature is Black Mesa, which is capped with the Cretaceous Mancos shale and Mesaverde sandstone. The Defiance uplift is a very sinuous north-trending asymmetrical fold about 100 miles long and 30 miles wide marked on the east by the steeply eastward-dipping Defiance monocline. Rocks ranging from Permian to late Cretaceous age are exposed in the Defiance uplift.

*San Juan Basin.* The San Juan Basin at the east side of the Defiance uplift, alone comprises nearly half of the Navajo section. It is a structural depression of the order of 5000 feet and contains a deep Tertiary fill resting on rocks of late Cretaceous age. Cretaceous rocks crop out around the margins of the basin and Tertiary rocks at the center, giving to the area a topographic expression similar to that of the Uinta Basin.

*Volcanic Features.* Instead of laccolithic domal uplifts similar to those of the Canyon Lands section, igneous activity in the Navajo section is reflected in a notable assemblage of volcanic necks, dikes, lava flows, and other phenomena associated with volcanic eruptions. The diatremes of the Navajo-Hopi volcanic field have

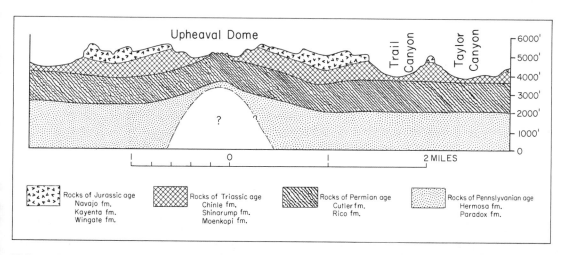

FIG. 22.19 Cross section across Upheaval Dome. (*After E. T. McKnight, U. S. Geol. Survey Bull. 908, as modified by W. L. Stokes.*)

FIG. 22.20   Echo Cliffs monocline, looking north-northwest.   Paria Plateau is visible in distance.   (*Photo by John S. Shelton.*)

been previously discussed (see p. 413).   A striking feature associated with one of the diatremes is Buell Park (Allen and Balk, 1954), near the northeast corner of the Defiance Plateau.   It is a circular diatreme caldera that is about 2 miles by 2½ miles in dimension.   It is a basin because the lapilli tuff in it has been more readily eroded than the surrounding rim rock of the Permian Cutler formation.   In the diatreme basin is a ring dike that extends through an arc of about 115 degrees; several plugs of basic igneous rocks rise above the floor of the basin.   Although there are many other diatremes in the area, the Buell Park diatreme is unusual for its size and topographic expression.

Volcanic necks are present in this area in great number, most famous of which is Shiprock, located about 80 miles north of Gallup, New Mexico, near the northwest corner of New Mexico.   It stands some 1400 feet above its surroundings and has several dikes radiating from it.   Another striking volcanic neck is Agathla Peak in northeastern Arizona; it rises over 1200 feet above its base and is considered by some even more striking than Shiprock.

### Datil Section

The Datil section lies at the southeast edge of the Colorado Plateau province and its boundary with the Rio Grande Depression of the Mexican Highland section of the Basin and Range province is sharply marked by the westernmost fault of the Rio Grande Depression.   Except in the Zuni Plateau at the north the Datil section is marked by extensive, thick lava flows.   The southern part of the section is particularly a land of lava-capped mesas and buttes.   Hundreds of volcanic necks of the Mount Taylor volcanic field (see p. 412) add striking variety.   Dutton (1885) was deeply impressed by the change noted in the terrain on entering the Plateau country from the east, and he described the topography of the Datil section as follows:

> Thin sheets of basalt are seen covering limited areas. Sometimes it mantles the soil of a valley bottom, sometimes it is the cap-sheet of some mesa. It is scattered about in an irregular way, as if the molten stuff had been dashed over the country from some titanic bucket, and lies like a great inky slop over the brightly colored soils and clays. There is often no trace of a vent or circular cone marking the spot whence it issued from the earth, and until we reach Mount Taylor we find noting to remind us of our old conventional ideas of a volcanic mountain.

*Zuni Uplift.* One of the most prominent parts of the Datil section is the Zuni uplift, also called the Zuni Plateau or Zuni Mountains, at the northwest edge of the section. This is one of the major upwarps of the Colorado plateaus; it is 75 miles long and 30 miles wide (see Fig. 22.1) and has a structural relief of at least 5000 feet (Kelley, 1960). The uplift is bounded on the southwest by the Nutria monocline, which locally is called The Hogback. Topographically The Hogback consists of two ridges, an eastern ridge on the Dakota sandstone and a western ridge on the Gallup member of the Mesa Verde formation.

The Zuni uplift differs from most of the upwarps of the Colorado Plateau in that Precambrian igneous and metamorphic rocks are exposed at its center. Above the Precambrian rocks lie some 6000 feet of sediments ranging in age from Permian to Pleistocene. Maximum elevations in the Zuni uplift exceed 9000 feet and the central core of crystalline rocks is encircled by alternating lowlands or valleys and cuestas or mesas on the sedimentary rocks.

# GEOMORPHIC HISTORY OF COLORADO PLATEAU PROVINCE

## Dating of Diastrophic Events

The geomorphic features of the Colorado Plateau province are largely the product of processes that operated during Tertiary and Quaternary time. Its erosional history cannot be separated from its diastrophic history or from the intrusion and extrusion of great quantities of igneous rocks, and locally the intrusion of salt and gypsum. All present problems, the answers to which are not yet entirely clear. Certainly the diastrophic history of the region must be taken into account, for the Colorado Plateau province is one in which major structural features are strikingly developed and the upwarps, downwarps, monoclinal flexures, faults, and lesser structural features are strikingly reflected in the topography. When these structures were produced is a major question. As work has progressed in the area, it has become more and more apparent that they cannot all be attributed to a single period of diastrophism. It does seem, however, that the major orogenic structures, the great uplifts, downwarps, and monoclines mainly developed during the Laramide revolution and were largely completed before late Tertiary time (Miocene or Pliocene). There is stratigraphic evidence, for example, that the East Kaibab monocline is of early Tertiary age, for at Canaan Peak the Eocene Wasatch formation rests unconformably on beveled Cretaceous strata involved in the monoclinal fold. It thus appears likely that the monoclines developed during the Laramide revolution, although they cannot all be so accurately dated as the East Kaibab monocline. On the other hand, the horsts, grabens, and faults at the western edge of the Colorado Plateau are younger than the monoclines and date from the middle or late Tertiary diastrophism that was particularly significant in the Basin and Range province. Faulting in the High Plateau region continued into Quaternary time, for here lava flows considered Pleistocene in age are faulted. As stated above (see p. 409), Gardner (1941) concluded that there is evidence for four periods of faulting along the Hurricane fault. Probably in the interior of the province the effects of late Tertiary diastrophism were limited mainly to local warping of preexisting structures.

## Evidence of Great Erosion

Epeirogenic uplift can not be separated completely from orogenic movements but elevation of the plateau area has been a major factor in the cutting of the deep canyons and the widespread stripping by erosion of the major structures. The present extent of Eocene sedimentary deposits in the northern plateau area, along with outliers of possible Eocene beds as far away as the Chuska Mountains, suggests that Eocene beds were originally very extensive. It is thus logical to conclude that the Colorado Plateau area was a low-lying area at the beginning of Tertiary time. Apparently conditions changed at the close of the Eocene period, for aggradation ceased to be dominant and degradation set in. This implies epeirogenic uplift of the region. Thus it seems likely that by mid-Tertiary time the Colorado Plateau had attained considerable height, permitting the inauguration of the degradation that has continued to the present.

*Magnitude of Erosion.* Probably the one outstanding fact about the Colorado Plateau province is that here erosion has been carried on on a scale unmatched in any other part of the United States. Striking diastrophic and igneous structures exist, but they have been brought into relief by degradation on a grand scale. It is impossible to state accurately how many feet of strata have been eroded from the Colorado Plateau, but estimates run as high as 10,000 feet. Hunt (1956) estimated that 80 per cent of the province has been eroded to formations below the middle of the Upper Cretaceous; that 60 per cent has been eroded below the base of the Cretaceous; that 35 per cent has been stripped below the base of the Jurassic; and that 25 per cent has been eroded below the base of the Triassic.

Many people, if asked to give the most striking evidence for profound erosion in the Colorado Plateau province, would doubtless cite the Grand Canyon and other canyons. Actually the amount of rock material removed from the canyons is relatively insignificant compared with that which has been removed from the broad upland plateaus. This fact was early recognized by the geologists who first mapped in this area. Newberry (1861) recognized that the wide open valleys on the uplands and the receding cliffs were "a much grander monument of the power of aqueous action than

even the stupendous cañon of the Colorado," and Powell (1875) stated that "the carving of the cañon . . . is insignificant when compared with the denudation of the whole area, as evidenced in the cliffs of erosion."

*Various Interpretations of Erosional History*

*Dutton's Views.* Dutton, first in 1880, in his "Geology of the High Plateaus of Utah," and later, in 1882, in a more elaborate presentation, "Tertiary history of the Grand Canyon district," was the first to attempt a systematic interpretation of the geomorphic history of the Colorado plateaus. According to him, following a long period during Paleozoic and Mesozoic time when the region was the site of extended sedimentation, the area acquired a positive tendency and began to rise. Irregular warping accompanying the rise resulted in a series of basins in which Eocene sediments accumulated. A drainage system developed across the rising terrain, and under humid climatic conditions throughout early and middle Tertiary time denudation proceeded to remove an average thickness of 10,000 feet of sediments. This extended period of erosion was Dutton's "Great Denudation." Presumably in Pliocene time the region underwent uplift of 2000 to 3000 feet, and intense local warping produced the East Kaibab and other monoclines, as well as the system of north-south faults north of the Grand Canyon. This widespread Pliocene uplift was accompanied by climatic change from humid to more arid conditions. The Pliocene uplift inaugurated the Canyon cycle of erosion, during which the Grand Canyon and other canyons were cut. According to Dutton, it was during a pause in the Pliocene uplift that the Esplanade of the Uinkaret and Kanab plateaus was cut. He believed that the outer gorge of the Grand Canyon developed during a partial erosion cycle whose baselevel is represented by the Esplanade. Uplift terminated this cycle of erosion and inaugurated the present cycle, during which the inner gorge has been cut. Thus two cycles of erosion were thought to be represented in the Grand Canyon area. The first cycle, inaugurated by broad uplift in Eocene time, had advanced well toward old age under humid climatic conditions when it was terminated by uplift and climatic change toward aridity. The uplift which initiated the Canyon cycle was temporarily interrupted by a pause during which a mature valley stage was attained, the baselevel of which is now marked by a strath terrace called the Esplanade. Renewal of uplift permitted the canyon cutting to continue.

*Davis' Views.* W. M. Davis visited the Colorado Plateau in 1900, and in a paper published in 1901 entitled "An excursion to the Grand Canyon of the Colorado" he expressed his views on the geomorphic history of the region. He recognized evidence of two major cycles of erosion, which he called the Plateau and the Canyon cycles. The Plateau cycle was essentially the equivalent of Dutton's "Great Denudation," except that Davis thought that the "Great Denudation" might have been complicated by intermittent uplifts after each of which the topography might have reached a rather advanced stage of development. Davis concluded that the "Great Denudation" was in reality the sum total of degradation accomplished during several partial cycles. Davis thought that the monoclines, major faults, and other structures antedated the Plateau cycle rather than postdated it, as Dutton thought. He further concluded that the Canyon cycle need not be divided into two partial cycles, for he interpreted the Esplanade as a stripped structural bench rather than a former baselevel of erosion.

*Other Interpretations.* The idea that the topography of the Colorado plateaus is a product of two major periods of erosion, one of which preceded the cutting of the canyons and another which produced the canyons, has pervaded geomorphic thought for many years. Minor departures from this interpretation have been expressed. Robinson (1910), for example, thought that the parks of the Kaibab and Coconino plateaus were evidence of an extra cycle between the Plateau and Canyon cycles which had attained a stage of maturity before the uplift that inaugurated the Canyon cycle.

Dutton (1882) was the first to offer an explanation of the parks. According to his theory the Kaibab and Coconino plateaus were denuded of their Mesozoic cover during the Pliocene period of erosion called by him the "Great Denudation," with resulting exposure of the Permian limestones. With change to more humid conditions during the Pleistocene epoch many stream valleys were cut in the limestone plateaus, but with return of more arid conditions at the end of the Pleistocene the streams disappeared or decreased notably in size, as a result of which the valleys began to fill with waste from their walls; thus in time they came to have smooth, alluviated floors.

Davis' (1901) interpretation of the parks was that they simply represent mature valleys near the heads of drainage that developed during the Plateau cycle and which have not yet been reached by headward erosion during the Canyon cycle.

Strahler (1944) thought that the parks could be explained as monocyclic rather than multicyclic phenomena. He attributed them to drainage abandonment resulting from limestone solution beneath their floors. He viewed the parks as essentially elongate, closed basins which are drained mainly through numerous sinks on their floors. Thus, according to his view, the parks represent former stream-cut valleys which were deepened and enlarged by solution of the limestones beneath alluvial fills on their floors.

Conventional interpretations of the geomorphic history of the Colorado Plateaus have assumed that the processes which lead to peneplanation were dominant during Tertiary and Quaternary time. It might well be argued that the surfaces which have been interpreted as former peneplains can be viewed more logically as pediments. In a region of arid to semi-arid climate where the stratigraphy and geologic structure are conducive to the development of retreating escarpments, pedimentation rather than peneplanation may be the dominant process.

Regardless of whether the present topography of the Colorado Plateau province is a product of peneplanation, pedimentation, or noncyclical erosion, it does appear that the gradational history of the area can be divided into two rather distinct episodes, one during which wide-scale regional stripping and accompanying cliff recession predominated and another during which canyon cutting came to have regional significance, although cliff recession and accompanying stripping by no means ended.

## History of the Colorado River

Accompanying any satisfactory explanation of the landscape of the Colorado Plateaus must be an interpretation of its drainage history, and this involves primarily the Colorado River and its tributaries. Interpretation of Colorado River history calls for answers to several questions. How old is the Colorado River? Is it an antecedent stream? A superposed stream? A consequent stream? Was the drainage of the province originally interior drainage? If so, when did it become integrated and find an outlet to the sea?

*Antecedent Theory.* Powell, Dutton, and others considered the Colorado River an antecedent stream older than the major structures which it crosses. The course of the Green River through the Uinta Mountains was Powell's type example of an antecedent stream. Most geomorphologists today, however, are likely to believe that the Green River can be explained better as a superposed stream.

*Consequent Theory.* Gilbert was not so certain as Powell and Dutton that the Colorado River is an antecedent stream, and he thought that much further study would be necessary before its true nature could be ascertained. Davis (1901) concluded that for the most part the stream was not following a course that developed in Eocene time and persisted despite the great flexures that rose athwart its course; rather, he thought that its course is one mainly consequent on the surface of the mid-Tertiary peneplain that developed during the Plateau cycle. He believed that the Colorado River had been able to maintain this consequent course despite the diastrophic movements of late Tertiary time.

It is now fairly well established that the East Kaibab monocline and other major structures of the Colorado plateaus that are crossed by Colorado River date back to the Laramide Revolution and hence most likely antedate the Colorado River. This is not to say that the Colorado River may not be antecedent along some parts of its course to structures that developed in late Tertiary time. Many persons who have studied the distribution of Tertiary strata over the Colorado Plateaus have been inclined to favor the idea that the Colorado River was superposed from Tertiary strata onto the structures that it crosses. This conclusion, of course, presumes that Tertiary beds formerly were far more extensive than they are today.

*Anteposition Theory.* Hunt (1956) has attempted to account for the course of the Colorado River by a process which he called "anteposition"; this, as the word suggests, represents a combination of antecedence and superposition. According to this theory, arching of the canyon part of the stream's course resulted in ponding upstream from the site of the upwarping and consequent deposition of sediments in the lake thus formed. Deposition continued in the lake until its floor had risen to the level of the up-arched canyon below, and then the dammed portion of the valley spilled down the canyon below the crest of the arch. Thus the part of the valley upstream from the spillway would be superposed and the part below the spillway would be antecedent.

*Age of Colorado River.* An even more difficult question than the relationship of the course of the Colorado River to the structures which it crosses is the question of when the Colorado River came into existence as a through stream with an outlet to the Gulf of California. Most students of the area seem to believe that the region did not have exterior drainage at the beginning of the Cenozoic era, but there is wide difference of opinion among them as to when integration of drainage into a system with an outlet to the sea took place. Suggested dates for integration of drainage range from early Eocene to as recently as the Pleistocene.

The great abundance of lacustrine deposits among early Tertiary formations in the Colorado plateaus suggests that the region may have consisted then of a series of enclosed basins similar to those in the Great Basin portion of the Basin and Range province today. The major question is when these basins became connected and obtained an outlet to the sea. Most geologists have assumed that this took place fairly early in Tertiary time, probably no later than Miocene time. Blackwelder (1934) and Longwell (1946) thought that the establishment of the Colorado River as a through stream took place considerably later than commonly assumed. Longwell believed that this might have occurred as recently as late Miocene or early Pliocene time, and Blackwelder suggested the possibility that it had been as recently as Pleistocene time.

Longwell arrived at his conclusion from two sorts of evidence. The youngest known interior-basin deposits west of the Colorado Plateau province through which the Colorado River has cut its valley is the Muddy Creek formation. The age of this formation is uncertain. Longwell at first considered it to be of Pliocene age but later concluded that it might be as old as Miocene. The oldest known fluviatile deposits in the Basin and Range province that contain suites of pebbles and cobbles indicating derivation from within the Colorado Plateau province are likewise of uncertain age. Originally interpreted as Pleistocene in age on the basis of limb bones of a camel found in them, it now seems possible that they may be as old as Pliocene. These two lines of evidence suggested to Longwell that establishment of a through course by the Colorado River took place considerably later than envisaged by early workers in the region.

Blackwelder, although admitting that his idea of Colorado history was highly theoretical, concluded that during most of Tertiary time the Colorado Plateau region was an area of arid to semi-arid climate with drainage into local basins. It was not until uplift of the Rockies to the east during late Pliocene or early Pleistocene time that there was enough precipitation to give to the Colorado River the volume necessary for it to escape from the Plateau region to the sea.

Assumption that the Colorado Plateau region did not have exterior drainage until as late as Pliocene or Pleistocene time presents problems. Dutton and others assumed that during the period of the "Great Denudation" base level control was that of the ocean, which implies exterior drainage.

If it is assumed that this great period of degradation went on within a series of interior basins, the problem arises of what became of all the material that was eroded. There are not enough middle and late Tertiary deposits within the Colorado plateaus to represent the great volume of material that was removed during degradation of the plateaus. Furthermore, real doubt must exist as to whether there would be sufficient time since the Pliocene or early Pleistocene for the amount of erosion to take place that apparently has, even if we take into account the rapidity of erosion in an area of high relief.

## REFERENCES CITED

Allen, J. E., and Robert Balk (1954). Mineral resources of Fort Defiance and Tohatchi quadrangles, Arizona and New Mexico, *Bur. Mines and Mineral Resources, N. M. Inst. Mining and Tech., Bull.* 36, 192 pp.

Babenroth, D. L., and A. N. Strahler (1945). Geomorphology and structure of the East Kaibab monocline, Arizona and Utah, *Geol. Soc. Am. Bull.*, **56,** 107–150.

Baker, A. A. (1946). Geology of the Green River Desert-Cataract Canyon region, Emery, Wayne, and Garfield counties, Utah, *U. S. Geol. Survey Bull.* 951, 122 pp.

Blackwelder, Eliot (1932). The age of Meteor Crater, *Science,* **76,** 557–560.

—— (1934). Origin of the Colorado River, *Geol. Soc. Am. Bull.*, **45,** 551–566.

Bucher, W. H. (1936). Cryptovolcanic structures in the United States, *Rept. 16th Int. Geol. Cong.*, 1055–1084.

Chao, E. C. T., E. M. Shoemaker, and B. M. Madsen (1960). First natural occurrence of coesite, *Science,* **132,** 220.

Childs, O. E. (1950). Geologic history of the Uinta Basin, Utah Geol. and Mineralogical Survey, *Guidebook to the geology of Utah, No.* 5, 49–59.

Clark, John (1957). Geomorphology of the Uinta Basin, Intermountain Assoc. Petroleum Geol., *Guidebook, 8th Annual Field Conference,* 17–20.

Colton, H. S. (1937). The basaltic cinder cones and lava flows of the San Francisco Mountain volcanic field, Arizona, *Museum of Northern Arizona Bull.* 10, 50 pp.

Dane, C. H. (1935). Geology of the Salt Valley anticline and adjacent areas, Grand County, Utah, *U. S. Geol. Survey Bull.* 863, 179 pp.

Davis, W. M. (1901). An excursion to the Grand Canyon of the Colorado, *Harvard Mus. Comp. Zool. Bull.* 38, 106–201.

Dutton, C. E. (1880). Report on the geology of the High Plateaus of Utah, *U. S. Geog. and Geol. Survey of Rocky Mountain Region (Powell)* 32, 307 pp.

—— (1882). Tertiary history of the Grand Canyon district, *U. S. Geol. Survey Mon.* 2, 264 pp.

—— (1885). Mount Taylor and the Zuni Plateau *U. S. Geol. Survey, 6th Annual Rept.*, 105–198.

Fenneman, N. M. (1931). *Physiography of Western United States*, McGraw-Hill Book Co., New York, 534 pp.

Flint, R. F., and C. S. Denny (1958). Quaternary geology of Boulder Mountain, Aquarius Plateau, Utah, *U. S. Geol. Survey Bull.* 1061-D, 103–164.

Gardner, L. S. (1941). The Hurricane fault in southwestern Utah and northwestern Arizona, *Am. Jour. Sci.*, **239**, 241–260.

Gilbert, G. K. (1877). Report on the geology of the Henry Mountains, *U. S. Geog. and Geol. Survey Rocky Mountain Region*, 160 pp.

Gilluly, James (1929). Geology and oil and gas prospects of part of the San Rafael Swell, Utah, *U. S. Geol. Survey Bull.* 806-C, 69–130.

Gregory, H. E. (1917). Geology of the Navajo country: a geographic and hydrographic reconnaissance of parts of Arizona, New Mexico, and Utah, *U. S. Geol. Survery Profess. Paper* 93, 161 pp.

—— (1938). The San Juan country, *U. S. Geol. Survey Profess. Paper* 188, 123 pp.

—— (1949). Geologic and geographic reconnaissance of eastern Markagunt Plateau, Utah, *Geol. Soc. Am. Bull.*, **60**, 969–998.

Hack, J. T. (1942). Sedimentation and volcanism in the Hopi Buttes, Arizona, *Geol. Soc. Am. Bull.*, **53**, 335–372.

Hardy, C. T., and S. Muessig (1952). Glaciation and drainage changes in the Fish Lake Plateau, Utah, *Geol. Soc. Am. Bull.*, **63**, 1109–1116.

Hunt, C. B. (1938). Igneous geology and structure of the Mount Taylor volcanic field, New Mexico, *U. S. Geol. Survey Profess. Paper* 189-B, 51–80.

—— (1956). Cenozoic geology of the Colorado Plateau, *U. S. Geol. Survey Profess. Paper* 279, 99 pp.

——, Paul Averitt, and R. L. Miller (1953). Geology and geography of the Henry Mountains region, Utah, *U. S. Geol. Survey Profess. Paper* 228, 234 pp.

Kelley, V. C. (1955a). Regional tectonics of the Colorado Plateau and relationship to origin and distribution of uranium, *Univ. New Mexico Publ. Geol.*, No. 5, 120 pp.

—— (1955b). Monoclines of the Colorado Plateau, *Geol. Soc. Am. Bull.*, **66**, 789–804.

—— and N. J. Clinton (1960). Fracture systems and tectonic elements of the Colorado Plateau, *Univ. New Mexico Pub. Geol.*, No. 6, 104 pp.

Koons, E. D. (1945). Geology of the Uinkaret Plateau, *Geol. Soc. Am. Bull.*, **56**, 151-180.

Longwell, C. R. (1946). How old is the Colorado River?, *Am. Jour. Sci.*, **244**, 817–835.

Newberry, J. S. (1861). Geological report, in Ive, J. C., Report upon the Colorado River of the West, *U. S. 36th Cong., 1st Sess., S. Ex. Doc. and H. Ex. Doc.* 90, Pt. 3, 154 pp.

Powell, J. W. (1875). *Exploration of the Colorado River and Its Tributaries*, Smithsonian Institution, Washington, 291 pp.

Reitzer, J. L. (1954). Glacial advances and soil development, Grand Mesa, Colorado, *Am. Jour. Sci.*, **252**, 26–37.

Richmond, G. M. (1952). Quaternary stratigraphy of the La Sal Mountains, Utah, *Geol. Soc. Am. Bull.*, **63**, 1368–1369.

Robinson, H. H. (1910). A new erosion cycle in the Grand Canyon district, Arizona, *Jour. Geol.*, **18**, 742–763.

Shoemaker, E. M. (1953). Collapse origin of the diatremes of the Navajo-Hopi reservation, *Geol. Soc. Am. Bull.*, **64**, 1514 (abs.).

Spieker, E. M. (1949). Transition between the Colorado plateaus and the Great Basin in central Utah, *Utah Geol. Soc. Guidebook to Geology of Utah*, 4, 3–82.

—— and M. P. Billings (1940). Glaciation in the Wasatch Plateau, Utah, *Geol. Soc. Am. Bull.*, **51**, 1173–1198.

Stokes, W. L. (1948). Geology of the Utah-Colorado salt dome region with emphasis upon Gypsum Valley, Colorado, *Utah Geol. Soc. Guidebook to the Geology of Utah*, 3, 3–40.

Strahler, A. N. (1944). Valleys and parks of the Kaibab and Coconino plateaus, Arizona, *Jour. Geol.*, **52**, 361–387.

—— (1948). Geomorphology and structure of the West Kaibab fault zone and Kaibab Plateau, *Geol. Soc. Am. Bull.*, **59**, 513–540.

ADDITIONAL REFERENCES

Appledorn, C. R., and H. E. Wright, Jr. (1957). Volcanic structures in the Chuska Mountains, Navajo reservation, Arizona-New Mexico, *Geol. Soc. Am. Bull.*, **68**, 445–468.

Baker, A. A. (1935). Geologic structure of southeastern Utah, *Am. Assoc. Petroleum Geologists Bull.*, **19**, 1472–1507.

Blackwelder, Eliot, and Dorsey Hager (1953). Crater Mound-Meteor Crater, *Am. Assoc. Petroleum Geologists Bull.*, **37**, 2577–2580.

Childs, O. E. (1948). Geomorphology of the valley of the Little Colorado River, *Geol. Soc. Am. Bull.*, **59**, 353–388.

Darton, N. H. (1945). Crater Mound, Arizona, *Geol. Soc. Am. Bull.*, **56**, 1154 (abs.).

Gould, L. M. (1939). Glacial geology of Boulder Mountain, Utah, *Geol. Soc. Am. Bull.*, **50**, 1371–1380.

Gregory, H. E. (1947). Colorado drainage basin, *Am. Jour. Sci.*, **245**, 694–705.

—— (1951). The geology and geography of the

Paunsaugunt region, Utah, *U. S. Geol. Survey Profess. Paper* 226, 116 pp.

——— (1952). Geology and geography of the Zion Park region, Utah and Arizona, *U. S. Geol. Survey Profess. Paper* 220, 200 pp.

——— and R. C. Moore (1931). The Kaiparowits region, *U. S. Geol. Survey Profess. Paper* 164, 161 pp.

Hager, Dorsey (1953). Crater Mound (Meteor Crater), Arizona, a geologic feature, *Am. Assoc. Petroleum Geologists Bull.*, **37,** 821–857.

Hunt, C. B. (1958). Structural and igenous geology of the La Sal Mountains, Utah, *U. S. Geol. Survey Profess. Paper* 294-I, 305–364.

Johnson, D. W. (1907). Volcanic necks of the Mount Taylor region, New Mexico, *Geol. Soc. Am. Bull.*, **18,** 303–324.

Kelley, V. C. (1958). Tectonics of the Black Mesa region of Arizona, Ariz. Geol. Soc., *Guidebook, 9th Field Conference*, 137–144.

McCann, F. T. (1938). Ancient erosion surface in the Gallup-Zuni area, New Mexico, *Am. Jour. Sci.*, **236,** 260–278.

McKnight, E. T. (1940). Geology of area between Green and Colorado rivers, Grand and San Juan counties, Utah, *U. S. Geol. Survey Bull.* 908, 147 pp.

Maxey, G. B. (1946). Geology of part of the Pavant Range, Millard County, Utah, *Am. Jour. Sci.*, **244,** 324–356.

Maxson, J. H. (1950). Lava flows in the Grand Canyon of the Colorado, Arizona, *Geol. Soc. Am. Bull.*, **61,** 9–16.

Robinson, H. H. (1913). The San Francisco volcanic field, Arizona, *U. S. Geol. Survey Profess. Paper* 76, 213 pp.

Shoemaker, E. M. (1954). Structural features of southeastern Utah and adjacent parts of Colorado and Arizona, *Utah. Geol. Soc., Guidebook to geology of Utah,* **9,** 48–69.

———, J. E. Case, and D. P. Elston (1958). Salt anticlines of the Paradox basin, Intermountain Assoc. Petrol. Geol., *Guidebook to the Geology of the Paradox Basin,* 39–59.

Williams, Howel (1936). Pliocene volcanoes of the Navajo-Hopi country, *Geol. Soc. Am. Bull.*, **47,** 111–172.

# 23

# Columbia Intermontane Province

## INTRODUCTION

What is here called the Columbia Inter-montane province is in Fenneman's classification known as the Columbia Plateau province. The author is using for this province the classification of Freeman, Forrester, and Lupher (1945) because it seems to represent an improvement over Fenneman's (1931) subdivisions. The term "Columbia Plateau" has become so identified with the basaltic plateau of eastern Washington that its use as a province name commonly leads to the erroneous belief that this type of geology and topography characterizes the whole province. The term "intermontane" rather appropriately describes relationships of the province to surrounding areas, for it is bounded by mountainous topography on all sides except the south.

The Columbia Intermontane province is bounded on the west by the Cascade Mountains, on the north and east by the Rocky Mountains, and on the south by the Basin and Range province. Location of the western, northern, and eastern boundaries presents no serious problem, for there are fairly sharp contrasts between the topographies of adjacent provinces along these boundaries. Drawing the boundary on the south is not so easy, for, despite the fact that the topographic characteristics of the Columbia Intermontane and Basin and Range provinces are very different, there is no sharp boundary between them. A considerable area of basaltic rocks lying mainly in southern Oregon is included in the Great Basin section of the Basin and Range province mainly because faulting has produced here types of structure and topog-

raphy similar to those of the Basin and Range province.

The popular picture of the province as one vast stretch of lava plains or plateaus is by no means correct. Although this type of topography may be the most distinctive, included in the province are mountainous tracts of complex geology and structure; there are also areas of fault-block topography. Even the lava plains vary in their characteristics, depending on the age of the lavas.

## GEOLOGY OF PROVINCE

### Rock Types

The rocks of this province are to a large degree lava flows, with a predominance of basalts, that range in age from Eocene to Pleistocene. Two main outpourings of basalt occurred, the Columbia River basalt of Miocene age (called the Yakima basalt by the United States Geological Survey) and the Snake River basalt of Pliocene-Pleistocene-Recent age. Interbedded with the basalts are various sedimentary formations of fluvatile or lacustrine origin consisting of mud, silt, sand, gravel, and volcanic debris. In this category are such formations as the Ellensburg, of Miocene or Pliocene age, the Latah formation, of Miocene age, the Ringold formation, of Pleistocene age, and the Touchet and Nespelem silts, of Pleistocene age.

*Columbia River Basalts.* I. C. Russell (1893) originally applied the term "Columbia lavas" to the great mass of lavas east of the Cascade Range. In 1901, he changed the name to "Columbia

River lavas" to avoid confusion with the Columbia formation of the Atlantic Coastal Plain. At the same time he extended this term to include lavas ranging in age from Eocene to Recent which had been spread over much of eastern Washington, eastern Oregon, the plains of southern Idaho, and the plateaus of northern California. Smith (1901) introduced the name "Yakima basalt" for the flows of Miocene age which are typically exposed between Yakima and Ellensburg in Yakima canyon. The term "Columbia River basalt" as generally used includes basalts that are both older and younger than Miocene. The United States Geological Survey recognizes Columbia River basalt as a convenient blanket term but uses the term Yakima basalt to designate those of Miocene age.

The Columbia River lavas represent one of the great lava extrusions of geologic time. They cover an area of some 200,000 square miles in Washington, Oregon, and Idaho. The maximum thickness of the basalts is unknown, but a well at the eastern end of the Rattlesnake Hills was reported to have gone 10,655 feet without reaching pre-basalt rocks (Waters, 1961). The Columbia River basalts are only one of four rather distinct Tertiary volcanic sequences in the Pacific Northwest; the other three are the Eocene basalts of the Olympic Mountains and Puget-Williamette trough, the andesite complex of the Cascade Range, and the lavas of the Snake River plains (Waters, 1955a).

Individual flows average close to 100 feet in thickness and may extend for over 100 miles in a nearly horizontal attitude (see Fig. 23.1). However, at the western edge of the plateau the basalts are notably folded. The flows do not appear to have come from central vents but more likely from extended fissure systems, although few of these have been recognized. A few dike swarms that may represent the feeders to basalt flows are the Grande Ronde dike, swarm in the northeast corner of Oregon; the Cornucopia swarm, in the eastern Wallowa Mountains; the

FIG. 23.1  Lava flows at east side of Steamboat Rock, upper Grand Coulee, resting on granite.  (*Photo by John S. Shelton.*)

Monument swarm, in the John Day River Basin in Oregon; and the Tieton dike swarm, west of Yakima, Washington (Waters, 1961). However, most of the huge lava flows show no evidence of a connection with dikes.

*Snake River Basalts.*   Russell (1902), proposed the name Snake River basalts for the basaltic rocks which underlie most of the Snake River plains. They were considered by him to be Pliocene and Pleistocene in age. It is now recognized that some of them are even Recent in age (Stearns et al., 1938). In addition to the Snake River plains area, basalts of Pliocene to Quaternary age are found east of the Cascades in south-central Oregon (Piper et al., 1939).

*Pre-lava Rocks.*   Older igneous, metamorphic, or sedimentary rocks are exposed at numerous localities within the Columbia Intermontane province. Such exposures are particularly common in the Blue Mountains and Wallowa-Seven Devils region to the east of the Blue Mountains. The sedimentary rocks of the Blue Mountains are Paleozoic and Mesozoic in age. Igneous and metamorphic rocks are exposed along the Snake River canyon and locally as peaks projecting through the basalt, such as Steptoe Butte north of Colfax, Washington.

*Pre-lava Topography.*   Probably because locally rocks of the prebasalt topography project through the basalt flows, it is often assumed or stated that the topography over which the basalts spread was everywhere very irregular, if not mountainous. Actually this may have been true more at the eastern margin of the province near the Rocky Mountains than at the west. The idea that such mountainous areas as the Blue Mountains stood as high at the time of extrusion of the basalt as they do today is open to question. At least part of their mountainous height has been attained through uplifts that postdated extrusion of the Miocene basalts, and part of the granite core of the Blue Mountains has been exposed by erosion following post-basalt uplift. Evidence that the mountains were uplifted after extrusion of the basalt is found in the presence of remnants of basalt in the Seven Devils Mountains of Idaho

up to elevations of 7500 feet (Livingston, 1928). However, the mountains extend at least 2000 feet above this altitude, so it appears that they did project as islands above the basalt flows, although probably not so much as their present altitudes might suggest.

## GEOMORPHIC SUBDIVISIONS

The division of the Columbia Intermontane province into geomorphic units by Freeman, Forrester, and Lupher (1945) departs from the conventional procedure of dividing provinces into sections by recognizing a category between province and section which they call subprovince. They recognize thirteen distinct geomorphic units, versus five in the Fenneman classification. Following is the classification of the Columbia Intermontane province as proposed by Freeman, Forrester, and Lupher[1] (see Fig. 23.2).

Columbia Intermontane Province
   Columbia Basin Subprovince
      1. Central Plains section
      2. Yakima Folds section
      3. Waterville Plateau section
      4. Channeled Scablands section
      5. Palouse Hills section
      6. North Central Oregon Plateau section
   Central Highlands Subprovince
      7. Blue Mountains section
      8. Wallowa-Seven Devils section
      9. Tristate Uplands section
   High Lava Plains Subprovince
      10. Snake River Plain section
      11. Malheur-Boise Basin section
      12. Harney-High Desert section
   Owyhee Upland Subprovince

## COLUMBIA BASIN SUBPROVINCE

The Columbia Basin subprovince includes the area east of the Cascades, west of the northern

---

[1] One departure from this classification made by the author involves use of the term Central Highlands Subprovince rather than Central Mountains Subprovince. The reason for this change is explained on p. 458.

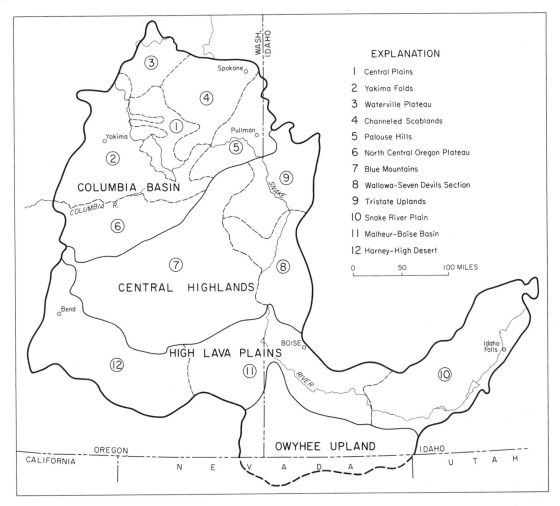

FIG. 23.2 Divisions of Columbia Intermontane province. *(After O. W. Freeman, J. D. Forrester, and R. L. Lupher, Annals, Assoc. Am. Geog., 35.)*

Rockies, and north of the Blue Mountains and thereby roughly correlates with Fenneman's Walla Walla Plateau section. This subprovince has unity in that (1) it is structurally a basin, (2) it is surrounded by mountains, and (3) most of its surface is covered with basalt flows of Miocene age. The Columbia Basin subprovince includes nearly two-thirds of eastern Washington and is one of the most distinctive geomorphic divisions of the state. Its topography is gently undulating to moderately hilly, and most of it lies between altitudes of 1000 and 2000 feet. Annual rainfall for much of the area is less than 10 inches,

and as a consequence much of it is treeless. Streams that originate within the basin are few and generally intermittent. The Columbia, Snake, and Spokane rivers, which border or flow through the region, have their sources outside the Columbia Intermontane province.

*Central Plains Section*

The Central Plains section has a nearly central position in the Columbia Basin subprovince and represents a region of major downwarping. Rocks here are basalts and related fluviatile, lacustrine, and eolian sediments. Two major structural basins lie within the section, the Quincy Basin at the north and the Pasco Basin at the south. These basins are separated from each other by two eastward-projecting anticlinal ridges, Frenchman Hills and Saddle Mountain, that are part of the so-called Yakima Folds. The Pasco Basin is the lower of the two basins; several hundred square miles of its surface lie below the 500-foot contour. In Pleistocene time the two basins were important areas of sedimentation of glacial outwash that was carried through the Channeled Scablands section at the northeast, and as a result large quantities of silt, sand, and gravel accumulated in the basins. Locally, sand dunes derived from the glacial outwash are extensive. Moses Lake, in the southern part of the Quincy Basin, was formed by damming of an abandoned drainage channel by shifting barchan dunes.

Although it is in the realm of speculation, it would not be unreasonable to suppose that the Pasco and Quincy Basins are the result of subsidence resulting from isostatic adjustment accompanying withdrawal of large volumes of lava from beneath their floors.

### Yakima Folds Section

Lying west of the Central Plains is the Yakima Folds section, so named because the dominant topographic features of this section are a series of high, broad, anticlinal ridges and intervening synclinal valleys (see Fig. 23.3).

These structures, originally interpreted by Russell (1893) as fault blocks analogous to the tilted lava blocks in southern Oregon and northwestern Nevada, have been shown to be fundamentally anticlinal and synclinal folds (Smith, 1903; Calkins, 1905), although it is recognized that small breaks involving 10 to 20 feet of displacement do occur in the folds (Waters, 1955b). Folding postdated deposition of the Miocene basalt and Ellensburg formation and was so recent that there is a very close correspondence between structure and topography. Anticlinal ridges rise as much as 1700 feet above adjacent synclinal troughs or valleys. Practically all the lesser

streams flow in synclinal valleys, and this is true of the Yakima River along much of its course, but this stream does cut through several anticlinal ridges in gorge-like stretches as its course leads from one syncline to another.

The southernmost and most easterly extending of the anticlinal ridges is the Horse Heaven Hills, a broad-topped ridge 1000 to 1500 feet high and several miles wide. The Columbia River cuts through the eastern end of the Horse Heaven Hills in a narrow 1000-foot-deep gorge called the Wallula Gap or Wallula Gateway. This gap is not so striking now as it once was, for construction of the McNary Dam below it has formed a lake which has reduced considerably the height of the gap above water level.

### Waterville Plateau Section

At the northwest corner of the Columbia Basin subprovince is the Waterville Plateau section. Unlike the basalts in the Yakima Folds section, those of the Waterville Plateau are relatively undisturbed from their originally nearly horizontal position. It might be argued that this section, as well as the Central Plains section, could logically be included in the Channeled Scabland section, for a number of coulees cut by glacial meltwaters extend across it, including the prominent and well-known Grand Coulee and Moses Coulee. However, the Waterville Plateau is separated from the Quincy Basin to the south by a large monoclinal fold, and its resulting greater altitude seems to justify its recognition as a separate geomorphic unit.

The Columbia River at the north and the Grand Coulee on the southeast divide the section into three units. Moses Coulee almost succeeds in making another incision through the section but does not quite do so. The present course of the Columbia River, which is mainly north and west of the Waterville Plateau, essentially skirts the edge of the basalt flows. However, a small part of this section lies north of the Columbia River. This lava-capped tract is known as the Okanogan Plateau and is a part of an upland area lying east of the Cascade Mountains and North

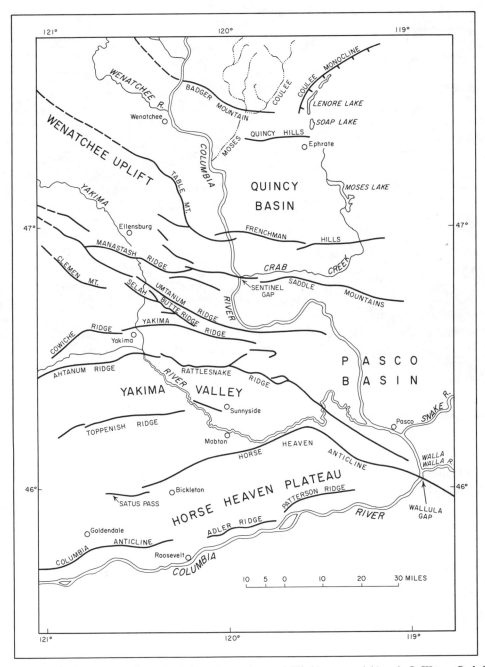

FIG. 23.3   Map showing axes of anticlinal ridges in southcentral Washington.   (*After A. C. Waters, Geol. Soc. Am. Bull.*, **66**.)

FIG. 23.4   End moraine marking limits of glaciation on Waterville Plateau, looking northwest.   (*From Geology Illustrated by John S. Shelton, copyright by W. H. Freeman and Company.*)

of the Columbia and Spokane rivers known as the Okanogan Highlands.

*Effects of Glaciation.*   The mass of ice in Canada which Johnston (1926) described as the "Cordilleran system of intermontane, piedmont, and valley glaciers" sent a large tongue of ice called the Okanogan lobe (Flint, 1935) across the Columbia River onto the Waterville Plateau for a distance of some 30 miles.   The end moraine which marks the southern limits of this glaciation extends from Chelan to the Grand Coulee near Coulee City (see Fig. 23.4).   Freshness of the glacial topography suggests that it is Wisconsin in age.

The Grand Coulee was cut by the Columbia River while temporarily displaced southeastward by the Okanogan lobe.   Grand Coulee is 50 miles long, nearly 1000 feet deep at its head, and one-half to 4½ miles wide, and is one of the most

striking features of the whole Columbia Intermontane province.   No stream flows through it at the present time, but a number of rock basin lakes lie along its course, many of which were cut as plunge basins at the base of former waterfalls (see Fig. 23.7).   At the north end the coulee is cut through the basalt and exposes the granite surface on which the basalt was laid down (see Fig. 23.1).

Ice-marginal constructional terraces are abundant in the Okanogan Plateau stretch of the Columbia River, particularly along the tributaries of the Columbia.   The ice dam that diverted the waters of the Columbia through the Grand Coulee formed a lake in the Columbia Valley above Grand Coulee that reached eastward as far as the mouth of the Spokane River.   The silts deposited in this lake are known as the Nespelem silts (Flint, 1935), and they form what at places is a very prominent terrace along the Columbia

Valley. It appears that as the ice in the Columbia valley wasted, the lake in which the Nespelem silts accumulated extended itself below Grand Coulee and eventually found an outlet over the residual ice via the present route of the Columbia.

The most prominent terrace along the Columbia River is one that extends downstream from the mouth of the Okanogan River to below the town of Chelan at the southern end of Lake Chelan. This terrace was named by I. C. Russell (1893) "The Great Terrace of the Columbia" and is now simply called the Great Terrace. It stands several hundred feet above the Columbia River and is underlain by silt, sand, and gravel. It is discontinuous, as are most terraces, but locally expands into very extensive flats. Russell thought that it represented the remnants of a great delta that had been built into a lake in the Columbia Valley. More recent studies by Waters (1933) and Flint (1935) seem to indicate that although there is a predominance of lacustrine material beneath the Great Terrace, there are also fluviatile deposits and locally even

glacial till. Notable variations in the altitude of the terrace suggest that, rather than being fill in a single lake, it is a combination of deltas, alluvial fans, and glacial outwash having varying local levels of deposition that was smoothed out to some extent by a final flood of glacial meltwater (Waters, 1933). It differs from the Nespelem terrace in that instead of being a lacustrine terrace it is essentially a kame terrace.

### Channeled Scabland Section

*Characteristics of Scabland Topography.* Lying southeast of the Waterville Plateau section and east of the Central Plains section is the Channeled Scabland section (see Fig. 23.5). The terms "scabland" and "scabrock" have long been applied in eastern Washington to areas where erosion by vast melt-water floods has exposed bare tracts of the Columbia River basalt. The term "scab" is particularly appropriate, for when viewed from the air these areas have the appear-

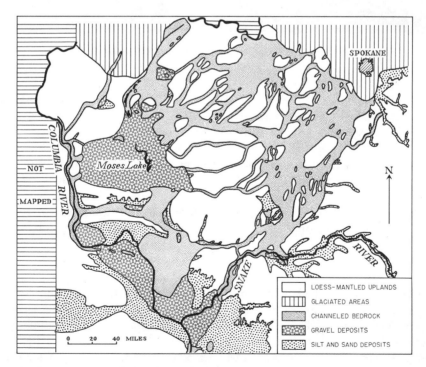

FIG. 23.5 Map of scabland area of eastern Washington. (*After J Harlen Bretz, Geog. Rev.*, **18**, *courtesy American Geographical Society.*)

FIG. 23.6   Drumheller Channels spillway plexus.   (*Photo by John. S. Shelton.*)

ance of great wounds or scars on the surface of the basalt plateau. Because the scars form conspicuous channels across the plateau of eastern Washington, Bretz (1923) applied the name "Channeled Scabland" to this area. Individual members of the scabland system are called coulees, a term used widely in northwestern United States and western Canada to designate valleys that are dry most of the time.

This is not the only region in the world where scabland topography exists, if by scabland we mean areas of bare rock which have been swept over by glacial meltwaters, but nowhere in the world does it exist on the scale and in the grandeur of that in eastern Washington. The plateau in which the scabland is cut covers some 12,000 square miles, and Bretz estimated that at least 2000 square miles are scabland.

To a large degree the Channeled Scabland section and the Palouse Hills section southeast of it interpenetrate each other. The interscabland upland tracts veneered by palouse soil (see p. 456) might well be considered western extensions of the Palouse Hills topography. Channeling of the basalt is such a distinctive characteristic of the section that it seems justifiable to recognize it as a distinct geomorphic region, despite the fact that such outstanding meltwater channels as the Grand Coulee, Moses Coulee, and the Drumheller Channels are in other sections.

The most outstanding features of the scabland region (Bretz, 1928a) are the elongated, interlocking, braided, or anastomosing coulees. Individual coulees are several hundred feet deep and as much as 5 miles wide. They cut the basalt plateau into a maze of intercoulee buttes, mesas, and plateau tracts, varying in size from less than 40 acres to more than 40 square miles.

Along the scabland channels are numerous topographic features that further support the belief that the Channeled Scablands are unusual in origin. These include dry waterfalls and cataracts, steep-walled midchannel buttes and mesas of bare basalt, rock-rimmed basins that may or may not have lakes in them, interchannel islands with cappings of silt, gravel terraces, large bar-like deposits the nature of which is in dispute, slackwater deposits in some tributary valleys, hanging channels above the main coulees which leave them to return farther downstream, valleyside scarps cut in both basalt and silts, divide crossings and trenched spur ends, and at the distal ends of the coulees spillway plexuses of amazing complexity (see Fig. 23.6). An abandoned waterfall in Grand Coulee is 400 feet high (see Fig. 23.7); numerous others of slightly lesser magnitude are present. The rock basins

along the coulees vary from tiny dimples to the large one in which Rock Lake lies, which is 7 miles long and reported to have a maximum depth of 250 feet (Bretz, 1928a). Despite this great display of features that attest to unusual erosion by running water, the scabland region today has insufficient rainfall to maintain a single permanent and continuous stream across it.

*Theories as to Origin of Scablands.* Leighton (1919) apparently was the first to suggest that the Channeled Scablands were a product of glacial meltwaters. Real interest in their origin began with the publication of Bretz's 1923 paper, which interpreted both the depositional and erosional features along the scabland coulees as the product of a brief but gigantic flood which he called the Spokane Flood. The coulees were interpreted as channels cut by this enormous flood; the gravels deposits along the channels were interpreted as giant river bars. Bretz maintained

FIG. 23.7   Dry Falls in Grand Coulee, looking northeast.   (*Photo by Spence Air Photos.*)

that all the topographic evidence indicated that great volumes of water hundreds of feet deep had coursed through the channels for a brief period of time rather than normal streams for a long period of time. Bretz's 1923 paper started a debate that has continued to the present.

Bretz's idea of the Spokane Flood represented in a sense a return to catastrophism; his ideas were quickly challenged, and other theories were proposed which attempted to account for the scabland features by more "normal" events. It has been suggested that they are the product of (1) glacial erosion (Hobbs, 1943, 1947), (2) alternate deposition and erosion by glacial streams of normal size (Flint, 1938), and (3) the bursting of a temporary lake produced by a blockade of the Columbia River gorge (Allison, 1933).

It is probably true that no one today gives serious consideration to the theory that the scablands are a product of glacial erosion. Field evidence does not seem to support Hobbs' belief that an ice lobe crossed the scablands area.

Allison (1933) agreed with Bretz that there is evidence of a "flood" but he suggested that this flood was produced by ponding of the Columbia River by an ice blockade in the Columbia gorge, and that this blockade grew headward along the Columbia, attaining higher and higher levels until the meltwater from the Cordilleran ice sheet at the north was "diverted by the ice of accessory blockades into a succession of routes across secondary drainage divides at increasing altitudes, producing scabland and perched gravel deposits along the diversion routes . . . ." Allison recognized the difficulty of explaining an ice blockade that would hold back waters that must have attained depths in excess of 1000 feet, but he favored the idea that the blockade was initiated by landslides in the Columbia gorge. He felt that this interpretation of the origin of the "flood" avoided the necessity of postulating a short-lived catastrophic flood. According to this theory the scablands can be explained as the result of a moderate flow of water over an extended period of time.

Flint (1938), after studying particularly the Cheney-Palouse Scabland tract at the east, con-

cluded that it was not necessary to postulate a great flood in order to explain the scabland features. He believed that they could be explained as the work of streams whose volumes were even less than that of the Snake River of today. His explanation was that meltwater of normal volume from the Cordilleran glacier discharged across the scabland tract along preglacial drainage lines and scoured the basalt to form the coulees. These meltwater streams were supposed to have discharged into a body of ponded water in the Pasco Basin called Lake Lewis. The streams gradually filled the coulees with glacial outwash gravel, sand, and silt as the level of Lake Lewis rose. Subsequently a lowering of the level of Lake Lewis allowed the streams in the coulees to excavate partially the previously deposited fills (see Fig. 23.8). According to Flint's views the so-called "giant bars" (see Fig. 23.9) that Bretz interpreted as alluvial bars made by streams several hundred feet deep (Bretz, 1928b) are terrace remnants of the fill deposited along the coulees when Lake Lewis was at its maximum height. Ultimately, backwasting of the Cordilleran ice caused the scablands to run dry.

*Points of Agreement and Disagreement.* Despite pronounced differences of interpretation as to how the scablands evolved, there are numerous points on which there has been fairly general agreement and which must be explainable by any acceptable theory of scabland origin. If we exclude the view of Hobbs that the scablands are the product of glacial erosion, we find the following points of general agreement:

1. The Palouse soil of the interscabland tracts and of the Palouse Hills section to the southeast is older than the scabland.
2. The scabland complex is a product of erosion by glacial meltwaters.
3. The rock basins along the coulees are products of glacio-fluviatile erosion.
4. The cross cliffs along many of the coulees represent sites of former falls or cataracts in the coulees.
5. The so-called Palouse scarps (loessial scarps)

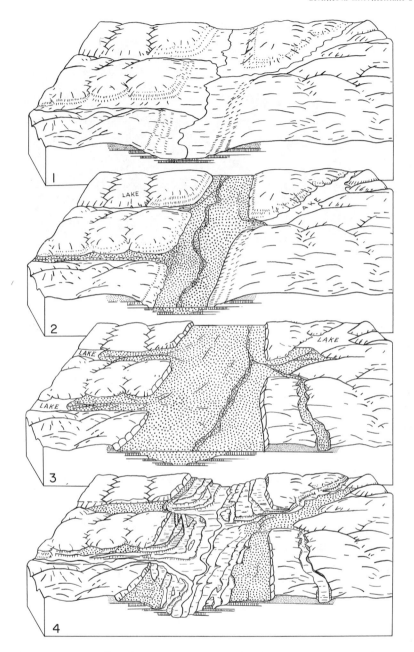

FIG. 23.8 Flint's interpretation of scabland history. (1) Preglacial valleys were cut in Palouse soil and basalt. (2) Meltwater streams initiated valley fills. (3) Valley fills are completed, and lateral planation has developed the Palouse scarps. (4) Postglacial erosion has left remnants of fills as terraces along coulees.

FIG. 23.9    A so-called "giant bar" in upper Crab Creek Valley.    (*Photo by H. T. U. Smith.*)

bordering scabland channels were cut by glacial meltwater.

6. Most, if not all, members of the anastomosing scabland channels were occupied contemporaneously by glacial meltwaters.

7. Backwater lakes occupied many of the valleys tributary to the scabland channels, and fine-grained lacustrine sediments accumulated in these lakes.

Major points on which there is marked difference of opinion are:

1. Were the scabland gravel deposits formed contemporaneously with the cutting of the channels?

2. Do the structure, composition, and topographic form of the gravel deposits in the scabland channels resemble river bars of gigantic size?

3. Did the Spokane "flood" occur only during the Wisconsin glaciation?

4. Must waters of abnormal volume and depth and of short duration be postulated in order to explain the scabland phenomena?

*Origin of the Spokane Flood.*    Numerous geologists have thought that Bretz was essentially correct in his contention that the geomorphic features in the channeled scablands support the belief that they were produced by enormous volumes of water,

but no adequate explanation of an unusual flood seemed available until Pardee (1942) called attention to features which appeared to be giant ripple marks (see Fig. 23.10) that might be logically explained as the result of sudden emptying of Lake Missoula (see p. 393) with the resultant release of a great volume of water across the scablands (see Fig. 23.11).    Pardee estimated that as many as 9½ cubic miles of water per hour might have discharged from Lake Missoula if its dam was suddenly removed, as might have happened if the dam was glacial ice rather than end moraine.

Bretz has, in recent years, although still maintaining that all the topographic evidence pointed to cutting of the scablands by enormous volumes of water of short duration, modified his theory to allow for several such floods which could be explained by repeated damming of the Clark Fork by glacial ice and subsequent dam failures (Bretz et al., 1956).

Although the origin of the channeled scablands is by no means clear, the general thesis that the channeled scablands were produced by unusual volumes of water seems to be getting more favorable consideration.    The draining of Lake Missoula provides what is a not unreasonable source for such volumes of water.    Bretz has modified his theory to allow for more than one

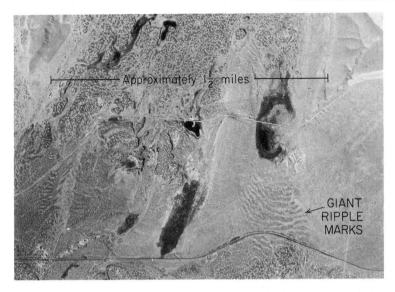

FIG. 23.10    Vertical photo showing giant ripple marks near center of Cheney-Palouse scabland tract.    (*Production and Marketing Administration photo.*)

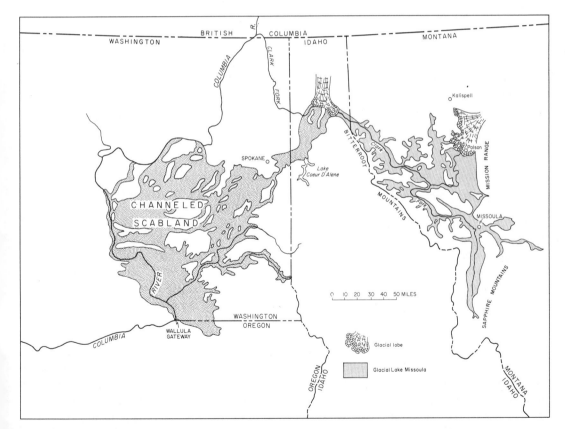

FIG. 23.11    Map showing relation of Lake Missoula to Channeled Scablands.    (*After J Harlen Bretz and others, Geol. Soc. Am. Bull.,* **67,** *and J. T. Pardee, Geol. Soc. Am. Bull.,* **53.**)

flood; he believed that there was evidence in the Grand Coulee-Quincy Basin area of at least seven floods, but he still maintains that they all occurred during Wisconsin time. Certainly meltwater during the Wisconsin glaciation put the finishing touches to the scablands, but it seems reasonable to suppose that these were in reality only "finishing touches." The events that have been postulated to produce the flood of waters from Lake Missoula could have occurred equally well during one or more pre-Wisconsin glaciations, and thus the scablands as we see them today may well be the cumulative work of meltwaters from several glaciations.

Three separate glacial drifts have been described in the area, an old drift considered Kansan in age (Leverett, 1917), the Spokane drift (Bretz, 1923) or intermediate drift (Bryan, 1927), and Wisconsin drift. Flint (1937) was doubtful, however, as to whether these were separate drifts and thought it possible that they were all Wisconsin in age. This did not imply, however, that he thought the basalt plateau was glaciated only once, for he recognized that evidence north of the area suggested that there had been more than one glaciation in the region.

## Palouse Hills Section

Southeast of the Channeled Scablands section is the Palouse Hills section, a region of maturely dissected hills with an average relief of 200–250 feet, but in places as much as 400 feet. Altitudes vary from around 2500 feet at the Idaho-Washington boundary to as low as 1000 feet at the western margin. As stated above (p. 450), there is a gradation of Palouse topography on the east into Channeled Scabland topography on the west, and the easternmost of the interscabland tracts resemble in many respects the Palouse Hills. The eastern margin of this section is very sinuous, as numerous embayments of Palouse topography extend into the western edge of the Northern Rocky Mountain province.

Lewis (1960) has called attention to differences in the topography of the northeast and southwest parts of the Palouse Hills section. At the northeast the topography is typical of an area having a dendritic drainage system which has reached a mature stage of development. At the southwest, the topography shows a distinct alignment with hills trending roughly north 30 degrees east. Lewis attributed the linear arrangement of the hills here to deposition by southwest winds of loess to the leeward of basalt ridges which taper to the east.

Striking asymmetry and a thick veneer of loessial silts distinguish the Palouse Hills from ordinary hills of mature aspect. Slopes of 30 to 35 per cent or more on the northeast side contrast with slopes of 20 to 25 per cent on the southwest sides. This asymmetry at first was attributed to eolian action, and the crests of the hills were considered to be essentially dunal in form with steep northeast slip faces. A more recent interpretation is that the steeper slopes are a result of nivation (Kirkham et al., 1931). Rockie (1934) pointed out that snowdrifts as much as 10 feet deep commonly accumulated during the winter months on the northeast sides of the hills, and he believed that the concavities observed here were really shallow nivation depressions resulting from erosion beneath the snow banks.

The Columbia River lavas extend into the Palouse Hills section, but are not exposed extensively because of the fairly thick cover of silt. It is difficult to determine the maximum thickness of this silt cover, but according to some estimates it may be as great as 200 feet; sections 40 to 60 feet thick actually have been observed. Bryan (1927) applied the name "Palouse soil" to this silt veneer. In a way this is a poor name, for the material is not soil in the sense of the pedologist, and furthermore what Bryan called "Palouse soil" has been shown to consist of two materials of different ages. The upper part consists of a thin veneer of recent loess beneath which is an older weathered silt. Difference of opinion exists as to the origin of the lower portion of the "Palouse soil." It was originally considered a weathering product of the basalt on which it rests, but petrological studies (Krynine, 1937) indicated that the silts are mainly eolian in origin, although they do include a small percentage of volcanic ash; its age, however, is still uncertain.

FIG. 23.12   Steptoe Butte, north of Colfax, Washington, a quartzite hill that projects above the lavas of the Columbia Plateau, and surrounding Palouse hills topography.   (*Photo by John S. Shelton.*)

Considering the nearness of the Palouse Hills section to the mountainous topography of the northern Rockies it is not surprising that the pre-basalt topography of this area was hilly and that several of the hills project through the basalt and its loessial veneer.   One of these, Steptoe Butte (see Fig. 23.12), has been mentioned above. Others less well known are Kamiak Butte and Smoot Hill. Unlike Steptoe Butte, they are granite rather than quartzite hills.

### North Central Oregon Section

The North Central Oregon section is an extension into Oregon of what is popularly called the Columbia Plateau.  It is a region of moderately dissected basaltic plateau that rises in altitude from a few hundred feet near the Columbia River to around 3000 feet where it abuts against the Blue Mountains.  Although some Tertiary rocks are found in the section, particularly along the middle courses of the Deschutes and John Day Rivers, the most common surficial rock is basalt.  The Deschutes and John Day Rivers have cut deep canyons through the plateau near its western margin, and other streams, such as the Umatilla, have done likewise along its eastern edge.  The canyons of these northward-flowing tributaries of the Columbia divide the section into a number of distinct plateau blocks.

## CENTRAL HIGHLANDS SUBPROVINCE

Extending from the Cascade Mountains on the west to the Rocky Mountains on the east is a belt of highlands which are here designated as the

Central Highlands subprovince.[1] This subprovince, which is narrow at the west and wide at the east, is a complex of mountains and dissected plateaus along with a few expansive valleys that may be considered local lowlands. Although basalt is the predominant rock in this region, extensive exposures of Paleozoic and Mesozoic sedimentary, igneous, and metamorphic rocks may be seen. Most of the areas of granite and Paleozoic sedimentary rocks which project through the basalts are tracts that stood above the uppermost lava flows, for the relief on the prebasalt topography was as much as 2000 or 3000 feet. However, some of the basement rocks have been exposed as a result of erosion following deformation (King 1959), most of which was probably prior to the Pleistocene (Freeman et al., 1945).

## Blue Mountains Section

The Blue Mountains section is a complex of mountain ranges and dissected plateaus. Major mountain ranges are the Ochoco, Aldrich, and Strawberry Mountains at the southwest and south, the Greenhorn and Elkhorn Mountains near the center of the section, the Umatilla Range on the northwest, and the Blue Mountains proper at the northeast. The various mountain ranges are largely warped or tilted basaltic plateaus or ridges that have been deeply dissected (Livingston, 1928). Maximum altitudes exceed 9000 feet; Strawberry Butte in the Strawberry Mountains has an altitude of 9600 feet.

Downwarping has produced several basins in and at the margin of the Blue Mountains section. Grand Ronde Valley and Baker Valley on the east are marginal basins that form the boundary

---

[1] As stated on p. 444, the classification followed for the Columbia Intermontane province is with one exception that proposed by Freeman, Forrester, and Lupher in 1945. The one departure consists of designating the particular area under discussion the Central Highlands subprovince rather than Central Mountains subprovince. This is the terminology used by Freeman and Martin in their book *The Pacific Northwest*, 2nd edition, 1954. Because the topography of part of this subprovince is better described as plateau than mountain, the general term highland seems more appropriate.

between the Blue Mountains section and the Wallowa-Seven Devils section to the east. Probably the most famous of the intermontane basins is the John Day Basin north of the Strawberry and Aldrich Mountains. Here a succession of colorful tuffaceous beds deposited mainly under lacustrine and fluviatile conditions during late Oligocene and early Miocene time have become famous for the fossil vertebrates and plants found in them.

## Wallowa-Seven Devils Section

The Wallowa Mountains rise above the mile-high lava plateau of northeastern Oregon to a maximum altitude of 10,033 feet in Sacajawea Peak. The mountains are composed of greenstone (altered lavas, tuffs, and sediments) of probable Permian age, late Triassic sediments, and Mesozoic batholithic intrusions of granodiorite, overlain by the Columbia River basalts (Smith et al., 1941). The pre-basalt rocks were intensely folded and faulted before extrusion of the basalt. Apparently the Columbia River basalts extended across the site of the Wallowas, for basalt remnants are found on peak crests ranging in altitude from 6000 feet to 9600 feet on Aneroid Peak.

The mountains have been so intricately sculptured by streams that sharp ridges are common. Major valleys were sites of valley glaciers in Pleistocene time, and three of the larger glaciers extended down to or beyond the mountain front.

The Seven Devils Mountains, across the Snake River canyon in Idaho, although similar in a general way, differ from the Wallowa Mountains in two respects. Their topography reflects to a greater extent the effects of block faulting, and the basalt cover was thicker and more complete here than in the Wallowa Mountains. As a consequence, the older rocks (essentially the same rocks found in the Wallowa Mountains) are not so extensively exposed. Exposures are limited mainly to the lower canyon walls of the Snake and Salmon rivers and to the lower fronts of the tilt blocks (Anderson, 1941). The topography of the Seven Devils Mountains, as pointed out by Anderson, displays the following characteristics: (1) the fault blocks are elongated in a north-south direction and are marked by steep scarps on their eastern sides, and gentle to moderate backslopes on their western sides; (2) basins make up a small part of the total area, but several of the faulted blocks have partially filled basins between them; (3) the fault-block topography differs from that of the Basin and Range province in that there is external drainage and fault blocks are not bounded by pediments and bajadas as in the Basin and Range province. The faulted structures at the southern end of the Seven Devils Mountains plunge beneath the Snake River lavas of the High Lava Plains to reappear south of these plains in the Owyhee Mountains.

## Tristate Uplands Section

The Tristate Uplands section (Freeman et al., 1945) is an upwarped lava plateau which includes parts of Idaho, Washington, and Oregon. Altitudes are lower than in the Seven Devils, Wallowa, and Blue Mountains to the south and southwest but greater than in the Palouse section to the north. The uplands are high enough that the Snake, Salmon, Clearwater, and Grande Ronde rivers have all cut deep canyons into the plateau that vary from 2000 to 4000 feet in depth. Altitudes reach 5000 feet in a central, flat-topped, plateau-like bulge known as Craig Mountain. The upland surface slopes outward from here and on the north descends by a great monoclinal fold from 5000 feet on Craig Mountain to only 500 feet above sea level in the east-west depression in which Lewiston, Idaho, is located. The Craig Mountain bulge has influenced the courses of the Clearwater and Salmon Rivers, causing the Clearwater River to be deflected to the east and north and the Salmon River to the south and west.

## THE HIGH LAVA PLAIN SUBPROVINCE

The High Lava Plain subprovince is a crescent-shaped belt convex to the south that extends from the Teton Mountains on the east to the Cascade Mountains on the west. In some respects it is the southern counterpart of the Columbia Basin subprovince to the north of the Central Highlands. However, the High Lava Plains subprovince differs from the Columbia Basin subprovince in several significant ways. Most important differences are: (1) the lavas of the High Lava Plains are younger than those of the Columbia Basin; (2) the topography of the High Lava Plains has been less modified by post-lava erosion and is to a large degree the original constructional topography, except in the Malheur-Boise section, where considerable erosion has taken place; (3) fluviatile and lacustrine sediments are more commonly interbedded with the lavas than in the Columbia Basin; (4) except in the Harney Basin, the lavas of the High Lava Plains are less commonly veneered with terrestrial sediments such as the Palouse soil, Ellensburg, Ringold, and other formations of the Columbia Basin; (5) the lava beds of the High Lava Plains subprovince have been much less deformed than those of the Columbia Basin and largely retain their original attitudes; and (6) youthful cinder cones are far more common on High Lava Plains, particularly near their eastern and western margins.

## Snake River Plain Section

The Snake River Plain section occupies the easternmost part of a broad structural depression termed by Kirkham (1931) the Snake River downwarp. Much of this section is underlain by lavas so recent that a soil cover adequate to grow sufficient grass for grazing has not yet developed; probably 90 per cent of this section is covered with Quaternary lavas (see Fig. 23.13). These lavas are known as the Snake River lavas (Russell, 1902), and they cover an area of approximately 14,000 square miles in parts of Idaho, Oregon, and Nevada. In addition to being more youthful they are more variable in composition than the Columbia River lavas. They seem to have been extruded under more variable conditions, as some were poured out of fissures and others from central vents.

FIG. 23.13    East edge of a lava flow on Snake River Plain, 10 miles west of Idaho Falls, Idaho.    View is to the north-west.    (*From Geology Illustrated, by John S. Shelton, copyright by W. H. Freeman and Company.*)

The Snake River Plain lava plain is dissected appreciably only at its western margin, where the Snake River has incised itself a few hundred feet (Stearns et al., 1938).    The lava plain slopes to the west and descends from an altitude of around 6000 feet at its northeast margin to around 3500 feet at the west.

The Snake River lies fairly well toward the southern margin of the lava plain and, except for it, streams are very scarce.    In a stream distance of approximately 350 miles the Snake River receives only one tributary from the north (Russell, 1902).    This scarcity of northern tributaries is attributable to the high permeability of the lavas; in this area are numerous so-called Lost Rivers, so named because of their disappearance into the permeable basalts.

*Large Springs and Alcoves.*    Springs which represent the return to the surface of waters that have entered the basalts exist at numerous places along the Snake River.    The largest and best known group, the so-called Thousand Springs, is located on the north side of the Snake River between Twin Falls and Bliss, Idaho.    Eleven of these springs rank among the largest springs in the United States.    Total discharge of the Thousand Springs is estimated at 5000 cubic feet, or nearly 40,000 gallons, per second (Stearns, 1936).    Most of the springs emerge from pillow lavas at the base of basalt flows at points where the Snake River canyon intersects lava-filled buried ancestral valleys.    Nearly all of the springs below American Falls are on the north side of the Snake River valley.

Along the same stretch of the Snake River where the large springs have developed are found numerous spring alcoves. In fact, several of the springs issue from the heads of alcoves. The alcoves are box-canyon-shaped features similar to the so-called steepheads of Florida, except that they are in basalt rather than limestone. They have nearly vertical walls which in places are as much as 300 feet high; the larger alcoves are as much as 2000 feet wide and 2 miles long (Stearns, 1936). They are believed to be the product of headward extension by spring sapping through solution of the basalt.

*Volcanic Features.* Cinder cones are scattered throughout the Snake River Plains section; the most outstanding group is that known as the Craters of the Moon (see Fig. 23.14). Washington Irving (1868) described this as "an area of about sixty miles in diameter, where nothing meets the eye but a desolate and an awful waste;

where no grass grows nor water runs, and where nothing is to be seen but lava." Cinder cones and associated craters, hornitos, ash cones, and lava flows of both aa and pahoehoe types of lava are common (Stearns, 1924). There is a striking alignment of cones along a 14-mile-long fracture called the Great Rift.

### Malheur-Boise Section

The Malheur-Boise section, middle section of the High Lava Plains subprovince, differs from the Snake River Plains to the east in three major respects: it is lower in altitude; it is considerably more dissected; and lacustrine and fluviatile sediments are more commonly interbedded with the lava flows. This interbedding of weak and strong beds is largely responsible for the more advanced stream dissection. Plain-like expanses do exist, but they are the exception, whereas they are the rule in the Snake River Plains section.

FIG. 23.14    Part of the Craters of the Moon, northwest of Pocatello, Idaho.   (*Photo by Spence Air Photos.*)

Numerous mesa-like tracts occur where Quaternary basalts cap the lacustrine sediments.

## Harney-High Desert Section

In most respects the western counterpart of the Snake River Plain is the Harney-High Desert section. It is characterized by flatness of topography and, except at the northwest along the Deschutes River, very slight dissection; stream courses are few because of the low rainfall and permeability of the lava surface; recent lava flows, ash deposits, and cinder cones are common.

*Relation to Basin and Range Province.* In two important respects, the Harney-High Desert section differs from the Snake River Plain and shows a closer affinity with the Basin and Range province to the south (Fenneman, 1931). A considerable part of the area has internal drainage, and faults similar to those in the Basin and Range province are present. Ephemeral lakes develop seasonally in the areas of closed drainage. Two of these lakes, Harney and Malheur (Piper et al., 1939), usually receive enough runoff to maintain themselves through the year, although like all lakes in arid climates they vary greatly in depth and area. Lake Harney, the sump for much of the drainage, is a saline lake, but Lake Malheur, because it overflows into Lake Harney, is fresh.

The boundary between the Harney-High Desert section and the Great Basin province to the south is a transitional one, but the line as drawn attempts to mark the change from a topography that is not fault controlled to one which is, and from a region where individual mountain ranges with intermontane basins are essentially lacking to one where they are characteristic features. The boundary between the Harney-High Desert section and the Basin and Range province is drawn just north of Steens Mountain, Hart Mountain, Abert Rim, and Winter Rim, all typical tilt-block ranges of the Basin and Range type.

*Great Sandy Desert.* A notable feature of the Harney-High Desert section is the Great Sandy Desert. This desert extends southeastward from near Bend, Oregon, for approximately 150 miles. It is 30 to 50 miles wide, and its surface is remarkably smooth, except for numerous low volcanic cones. Although the surficial material is called "sand," it actually is disintegrated pumice derived from the many volcanic cones that dot the desert's surface.

*Newberry Caldera.* Most of the volcanic cones or buttes, as they are locally named, are small, but toward the western end of the section and some 30 miles south of Bend, Oregon, is an exceptionally large volcanic form, the Newberry caldera (Williams, 1935). This feature is really an outlier of Cascade Mountains geology in the Columbia Intermontane province and is only 35 miles east of the crest of the Cascade Range. Newberry volcano was a large, circular shield volcano approximately 20 miles in diameter at its base. The caldera at its summit is 5 miles long and 4 miles wide and is bounded by precipitous in-facing scarps as much as 1500 feet high on all but the western side. The highest point on Newberry volcano has an altitude of 7985 feet, which is about 4000 feet above the adjacent plateau surface. Williams (1935) estimated that the volume of material in Newberry volcano is close to 80 cubic miles and thereby equals in size Mount Shasta, the largest of the Cascade volcanoes. Some 150 small cinder cones dot the flanks of the volcano, and located in the caldera of Newberry volcano are two lakes, Paulin Lake and East Lake.

*Deschutes River.* The only part of the Harney-High Desert section that exhibits marked stream dissection is at the northwest along the Deschutes River. The Deschutes River rises in this section, and the beginning of its canyon (see Fig. 23.15) is within the section, but its more spectacular parts lie north of the Harney-High Desert. The Deschutes River is remarkable for its constancy of flow, which is attributable to the fact that it is fed mainly by springs from the porous basalts. The water which maintains the springs is meltwater from glaciers in the High Cascades to the west. Some of the water issuing from the lavas actually has flowed as underground streams in

FIG. 23.15  Beginning of the canyon of Deschutes River, northwest of Redmond, Oregon.  The Three Sisters volcanoes show in the background.  (*Photo courtesy Oregon State Highway Department.*)

lava tubes similar to those in which the interesting ice caves of the region are developed.

## OWYHEE UPLAND SUBPROVINCE

The Owyhee Upland subprovince takes its name from the Owyhee Mountains at its north-western margin.  This geomorphic unit presents two problems.  Its small size makes it appear illogical to consider it a subprovince; it would seem more logical to give it sectional rank.  However, the classification being used for the Columbia Intermontane province provides no subprovince of which it might be considered a section, so it is designated a subprovince despite its small size.  It might seem that this dilemma could be avoided by putting the Owyhee Upland

in the Basin and Range province.  However, it does not fit well into this province, for it lacks the characteristic topographic assemblage of isolated mountain ranges and adjacent inter-montane basins with their alluvial fills and ephemeral lakes.  Nor is the structure typical Basin and Range structure, for doming is more common than faulting in the Owyhee Upland.

The Owyhee Upland contrasts with the High Lava Plains to the north in that its lavas are older and to a large degree different in type.  Much of the area is underlain by rhyolites and quartz latites (Anderson, 1941) rather than basalts.  Structurally it is an upwarped area rather than a downwarped one.  Furthermore, dissection is more advanced than in the High Lava Plains, and in numerous places erosion has removed the lavas and exposed the underlying granites.

Most of the Owyhee Upland may be described as upwarped plateau which locally possesses considerable relief. Two areas rise appreciably above the general plateau level, the Owyhee Mountains at the north and South Mountain about 20 miles to the south of them. These two mountain uplifts are separated by a broad sag of lava-covered plateau. The Owyhee Mountains stand some 5000 feet above the Snake River lava plains to the north of them. Maximum altitudes in these mountains exceed 8000 feet, whereas in South Mountain maximum altitudes are slightly under 8000 feet. In both of these mountain upwarps the lavas have been removed from their crests to expose the pre-lava meta-sedimentary and igneous rocks.

## DRAINAGE HISTORY

### Columbia River History

The Columbia River has had an interesting geomorphic history. For the purpose of discussion we may divide its course into three parts, that part in the Columbia Intermontane Plateau, the gorge through the Cascade Mountains, and the part west of the Cascades. We will here consider only the Columbia River east of the Cascade Mountains.

*Course of Columbia East of Cascades.* From about 50 miles west of Spokane to Wenatchee, Washington, the Columbia River essentially follows the margin of the basalt plateau. At Wenatchee, however, the river turns from its marginal route and flows southeastward to near the center of the basalt plateau at Pasco, Washington. In its course from Spokane to Wenatchee the Columbia River essentially follows the northern margin of the basalts and undoubtedly has this course as the result of diversion from an unknown pre-basalt route to its present one by the northward-spreading basalt flows.

At Wenatchee, the Columbia changes direction from a southwestward to a southeastward course. There has been considerable speculation as to the cause of this change in direction. It might be thought that the Columbia at one time continued

from Wenatchee in a southwesterly direction, but no channel suggesting such a route has been found. Two theories have been suggested for the bend at Wenatchee (Chappell, 1936): (1) that the river was diverted from a more westerly route by the rise of the anticlinal Wenatchee Mountains, and (2) that there has been no change in the course of the Columbia since it took a southeasterly course determined by the line of lowest altitude between the basalt flows which came from the west and those which came from the east, a view favored by Chappell.

The Columbia River flows south from Wenatchee to the Pasco Basin and then turns west and crosses the southeast end of the Horse Heaven Hills through Wallula Gap. In doing so it crosses the anticlinal Saddle Mountains through a gorge that was cut as this anticline rose athwart the river's course. Warren (1941a, 1941b) has suggested that the present Wallula Gap route represents a diversion of the Columbia from an earlier more westerly course through Sentinel Gap, Satus Pass, and Goldendale to Hood River (see Fig. 23.3). This route was postulated from the distribution of the quartzite-bearing Hood River conglomerate. Warren attributed the diversion of the Columbia to the Wallula Gap route to defeat by the rising Horse Heaven anticlinal fold.

Flint (1938) held a view similar to that of Warren. He believed that growth of the Horse Heaven structure ponded the Columbia River and that it ultimately overflowed at Wallula Gap.

Waters (1955b) has presented evidence which to him indicated that the Columbia River did not flow through the Satus Pass route. Rather, he interpreted Satus Pass as a wind gap produced by piracy of a local stream. Waters believed that the Columbia River has had its course through Wallula Gap since early in Ellensburg time. He postulated an early period of Columbia River history during which much shifting of its course took place. Later volcanoes broke out in the highlands to the west of the river and contributed great showers of andesitic, pyroclastic debris to the headwater portions of the eastward-flowing tributaries of the Columbia. Gradually a compound alluvial fan or bajada slope was built eastward onto the basalt plain. Waters thought that possibly synchronous subsidence in the Yakima and Pasco Basins might have contributed to this eastward shifting of the Columbia.

As Mackin (1961) has pointed out, about the only evidence bearing on early Columbia River drainage is found in rather widespread gravels at the base of the Ellensburg formation. Among these gravels are pebbles of Belt quartzite from the Northern Rockies, which seems to indicate that they were deposited by a throughgoing stream. It appears that prior to the rise of the Yakima folds the Columbia River shifted its course laterally over a rather wide belt between the east flank of the Cascades and its present route. With the rise of the Yakima folds only the Columbia and the Yakima Rivers were able to maintain transverse routes. Mackin believed that the distribution of the quartzitic gravels supported Warren's contention that the ancestral Columbia River flowed southwestward across the present site of the Horse Heaven Hills.

## Snake River History

*Course of the Upper Snake River.* After the Snake River crosses the Snake River Range south of Jackson Hole (see p. 331), it turns north and enters the eastern end of the Snake River Plain section. Because of its small volume and youthfulness the Snake River has incised itself very little in the upper part of the Snake River Plain. Incision starts at American Falls and takes place through a series of waterfalls and cataracts; the river drops 50 feet at American Falls, 180 feet at Twin Falls, and 200 feet at Shoshone Falls. From here on to about 15 miles below Weiser, Idaho, the Snake River is incised only 600 to 700 feet below the lava plain.

*Snake River Canyon.* From the point below Weiser, where the Snake River makes a bend to the northeast, the river flows through a rugged canyon that is nearly 200 miles long. The deepest part of this canyon begins a few miles below Homestead, Oregon, and in the 40-mile stretch of canyon which has been cut between the

Wallowa Mountains of Oregon and the Seven Devils Mountains of Idaho the depth averages 5500 feet. This canyon is actually deeper than the Grand Canyon of the Colorado, but not nearly so scenic, because of the somber black color of the basalt in which it is cut. Freeman (1938), in comparing depths of the Snake and Colorado canyons, pointed out that from Devil Peak, 7 miles east of the Snake Canyon, to the river's edge there is a descent of 7900 feet, whereas from Bright Angel Point, an equal distance from the Colorado River, the descent is only 5650 feet.

The deep canyon ends at Lewiston, Idaho, where the Clearwater River joins the Snake. In places the canyon exposes as much as 6000 feet of basalts, and locally it has been cut as much as 1000 feet into the crystalline rocks underlying the basalt. The unconformity between the basement rocks and the basalts at places is marked by considerable relief. At a place known as Buffalo Rock, about 15 miles upstream from Asotin, Washington, the schists which underlie the basalts rise at least 2000 feet into the horizontal lava sheets (Russell, 1897).

*Possible Earlier Routes of Snake River.* The Snake River undoubtedly has had a complicated history involving changes in course produced by lava dams and structural uplifts. It is probably too much to hope that the early or even mid-Tertiary courses of the Snake River can ever be worked out in any detail. Suggestions of pre-basalt and inter-basalt river channels are found in the sedimentary or basalt valley fills beneath or in the basalt, but these are too few and widely scattered to be joined into an integrated river system. An example of these buried valleys is the one described by Lupher and Warren (1942) in the Lewiston Basin. This valley, which they designated as the Asotin stage of the Snake River, is cut as much as 1200 feet in the Columbia River lavas and is filled with younger lavas of probable Pleistocene age.

There is a possibility that the late Pliocene-early Pleistocene history of the Snake River may be worked out ultimately; to do this a correct interpretation must be given to certain lacustrine deposits found mainly in the Malheur-Boise Basin. These are the so-called "Payette" and "Idaho" formations. Differences of opinion have developed around the age and stratigraphic relationships of these formations, but they need not be considered here.

In 1883, Cope described fish remains from lacustrine deposits at a Castle Creek, Idaho, locality; he called the sediments from which the fish remains came, along with intercalated basalts, the Idaho group, and the lake in which they accumulated, Idaho Lake (see Fig. 23.16).

The beds were dated as early or middle Pliocene in age. In 1898, Lindgren gave the name Payette formation to a large thickness of lacustrine deposits in the same region. Lindgren recognized that the beds were probably not the same as those described by Cope as the Idaho formation, but he thought it probable that the two formations represented successive stages of a lake that existed in southern Idaho and adjacent Oregon in Miocene and Pliocene time as a result of a lava dam or dams across the Snake River. Lindgren believed that Lake Payette overflowed

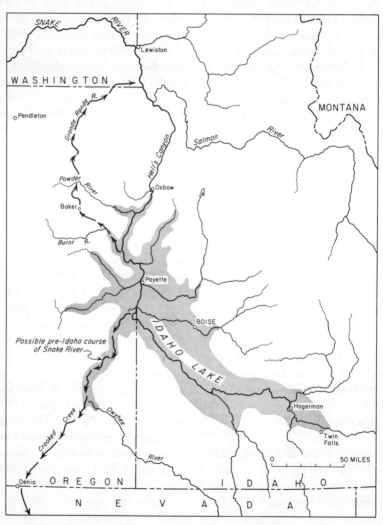

FIG. 23.16    Approximate extent of Idaho Lake with two suggested possible outlets.    (*After H. E. Wheeler and E. F. Cook, Jour. Geol.,* **62.**)

its lava barrier and established an outlet to the north and that in time the lake was drained as a result of downcutting of its outlet.

Livingston (1928), believing in the reality of Lake Payette, suggested that the Snake River prior to establishment of its present course along the Idaho-Oregon boundary had a route across northeastern Oregon. He further thought that Lake Payette might have been a series of connected bodies of water occupying intermontane basins which overflowed via the Grande Ronde River to the Columbia. He suggested that a large tributary of the Grande Ronde cut headward along the present route of the Snake River between the Wallowa Mountains and Seven Devils Mountains and eventually tapped Lake Payette and short-circuited the drainage of the Grande Ronde route to the present canyon route of the Snake River. It would seem rather unusual for a tributary of the Grande Ronde to capture the upper drainage of the Grande Ronde. If Lake Payette was drained as the result of headward erosion of some stream, the pirating stream would seem more likely to have been a tributary of the Salmon River than of the Grande Ronde.

Wheeler and Cook (1954) proposed a different theory to account for the present canyon route of the Snake River. They recognized the role that ponding of drainage had played but attributed this ponding more to warping or folding than to lava dams. The ponding, in their opinion, which led to the development of the present canyon route of the Snake River was that which produced Idaho Lake; this was believed to have taken place in late Pliocene or early Pleistocene time, considerably later than the ponding of Lake Payette.

Wheeler and Cook recognized that evidence as to where Snake River route was prior to formation of Idaho Lake is very meager, but they suggested that the Snake River might have flowed from Idaho in a southwesterly course across Nevada to the Feather River in northern California (see Fig. 23.16). The present canyon route along the Idaho-Oregon boundary was believed to have come into existence when Idaho Lake established an outlet to the north

either through simple spillover or through capture by headward erosion of a northward-flowing tributary of the Salmon River. Then, for the first time, according to their theory, the Snake River drained to the Columbia.

## GEOMORPHIC HISTORY OF PROVINCE

The geomorphic history of the Columbia Intermontane province is not to be written so much in terms of erosion cycles or subcycles that have produced erosion surfaces as in terms of the constructional processes of volcanic extrusion and glacio-fluviatile, lacustrine, eolian, and stream deposition. Numerous features within the region, such as the scablands, great river canyons, and deeply dissected mountains and plateaus, attest to the effectiveness of the erosional processes, but these are but youthful scratches on a landscape that is primarily depositional in origin. Nowhere have the fluviatile processes advanced beyond youthful conditions, and over much of the province the surface is still fundamentally a depositional surface.

*Pre-basalt Erosional History.* Suggestions of the pre-basalt erosional history of the Columbia Plateau region can be obtained from the known or inferred geomorphic history of the Rocky Mountains to the east and the Cascades to the west. The interpretation of the erosional history of the mountains of Idaho has been much debated (see p. 386), but most geologists who have worked in the area agree that there is evidence here of one or more erosional surfaces, although they do not agree upon their ages. Anderson (1929) thought he saw evidence in northern Idaho, in the Clearwater and Coeur d'Alene Mountains, of three erosion surfaces, called by him the Summit, Subsummit, and Old Valley surfaces, and dated as pre-Eocene, Eocene, and post-middle Miocene. His view was that the outpouring of the basalts postdated the Old Valley surface, for reentrants of basalt extend into the Coeur d'Alene Mountains in young, narrow valleys cut about 800 feet below the Old Valley level. Pardee and Bryan (1925) found that beneath a tongue of basalt that flowed up the Spokane Valley into the Purcell Trench the relief was as much as 1500 feet, which suggested to Anderson that between the time of cutting of the Old Valley surface and the outpouring of the basalts the region must have been elevated and entrenched by stream erosion. This conclusion seems to fit in with the finding in places of relief of as much as 2000 to 3000 feet on the basement rocks.

It has been suggested (Smith et al., 1941) that there is evidence in the Wallowa Mountains of extensive erosion that stripped much of the area of its sedimentary cover and reduced the region to one of low relief. This was thought to have occurred during late Cretaceous and early Tertiary time. Presumably this erosion surface might be correlated with the Summit surface in the Idaho mountains.

What was called the Cascade (Russell, 1901) or Methow (Willis, 1903) peneplain was postulated in the Cascade Mountains (see p. 526). However, Waters (1939), from his studies in the Wenatchee-Chelan district at the western border of the Columbia Intermontane province, has presented evidence which casts serious doubt on the reality of such an erosion surface; it appears more likely that what were considered remnants of this surface are really outliers of the Columbia basalt or structural benches on gneiss. At the same time that he proposed the Methow peneplain Willis described a mature erosional topography which he designated as the Entiat surface or matureland. Waters concluded that evidence for such a topography is recognizable in areas of resistant granodiorites and gneiss. Remnants of this topography were interpreted as largely resurrected parts of a once widespread late mature erosion surface which was buried beneath the Columbia River basalts and associated sediments. Waters found no evidence for a peneplain surface cut across the basalts and believed that areas which had been so interpreted were local in extent and probably pediments.

Thus evidence on the erosional history of the Columbia Intermontane province is very fragmentary. Possibly it will never be worked out in detail; if it ever is, it will likely be done, as Mackin (1961) suggested, through a study flow-by-flow of the stratigraphy of the basalts and their associated sediments.

## REFERENCES CITED

Allison, I. S. (1933). New version of the Spokane flood, *Geol. Soc. Am. Bull.*, **44**, 675–722.

Anderson, A. L. (1929). Cretaceous and Tertiary planation in northern Idaho, *Jour. Geol.*, **37**, 747–764.

——— (1941). Physiographic subdivisions of the Columbia Plateau in Idaho, *Jour. Geomorph.*, **4**, 206–222.

Bretz, J H. (1923). Channeled scablands of the Columbia Plateau, *Jour. Geol.*, **31**, 617–649.

——— (1928a). The channeled scabland of eastern Washington, *Geog. Rev.*, **18**, 446–477.

——— (1928b). Bars of channeled scablands, *Geol. Soc. Am. Bull.*, **39**, 643–702.

———, H. T. U. Smith, and G. E. Neff (1956). Channeled scabland of Washington; New data and interpretations, *Geol. Soc. Am. Bull.*, **67**, 957–1049.

Bryan, Kirk (1927). The "Palouse soil" problem, *U. S. Geol. Survey Bull.* 790-B, 21–46.

Calkins, F. C. (1905). Geology and water resources of a portion of east-central Washington, *U. S. Geol. Survey Water-Supply Paper* 118, 96 pp.

Chappell, W. M. (1936). The effect of Miocene lavas on the course of the Columbia River in central Washington, *Jour. Geol.*, **44**, 379–386.

Cope, E. D. (1883). On the fishes of the Recent and Pliocene lakes of the western part of the Great Basin, and of the Idaho Lake, Acad. Nat. Sci. Philadelphia, *Proc. for 1883*, 134–166.

Flint, R. F. (1935). Glacial features of the southern Okanogan region, *Geol. Soc. Am. Bull.*, **46**, 169–194.

——— (1937). Pleistocene drift border in eastern Washington, *Geol. Soc. Am. Bull.*, **48**, 203–231.

——— (1938). Origin of the Cheney-Palouse scabland tract, Washington, *Geol. Soc. Am. Bull.*, **49**, 461–523.

Freeman, O. W. (1938). The Snake River canyon, *Geog. Rev.*, **28**, 597–608.

———, J. D. Forrester, and R. L. Lupher (1945). Physiographic divisions of the Columbia Intermontane Province, Assoc. Am. Geog., *Annals*, **35**, 53–75.

———, H. H. Martin (1954). *The Pacific Northwest*, 2nd edit., John Wiley and Sons, New York, 53–87.

Hobbs, W. H. (1943). Discovery in eastern Washington of a new lobe of the continental Pleistocene glacier, *Science*, **98**, 227–230.

——— (1947). *The Glacial History of the Scabland and Okanogan Lobes, Cordilleran, Continental Glacier*, J. W. Edwards, Ann Arbor, 36 pp.

Irving, Washington (1868). *The Adventures of Captain*

Bonneville, *U. S. A.*, Peoples edit., G. P. Putnam and Son, New York, 191.

Johnston, W. A. (1926). The Pleistocene of Cariboo and Cassiar districts, British Columbia, Royal Soc. Canada, *Trans.*, Sect. 4, **20**, 137–147.

King, P. B. (1959). *The Geological Evolution of North America*, Princeton Univ. Press, Princeton, 190 pp.

Kirkham, V. R. D. (1931). Snake River downwarp, *Jour. Geol.*, **39**, 456–481.

———, M. M. Johnson, and Joseph Holm (1931). Origin of the Palouse Hills topography, *Science*, **73**, 207–209.

Krynine, P. D. (1937). Age of till on "Palouse soil" from Washington, *Am. Jour. Sci.*, **233**, 205–216.

Leighton, M. M. (1919). The road building sands and gravels of Washington, *Wash. Geol. Surv. Bull.* 22, 307 pp.

Leverett, Frank (1917). Glacial formations in the western United States, *Geol. Soc. Am. Bull.*, **28**, 143–144 (Abs.).

Lewis, P. F. (1960). Linear topography in the southwestern Palouse, Washington-Oregon, Assoc. Am. Geog., *Annals*, **50**, 98–111.

Lindgren, Waldemar (1898). The mining district of the Idaho Basin and the Boise Ridge, Idaho, *U. S. Geol. Survey 18th Annual Rept.*, Pt. 3, 617–719.

Livingston, D. C. (1928). Certain topographic features of northeastern Oregon and their relation to faulting, *Jour. Geol.*, **36**, 694–708.

Lupher, R. L., and W. C. Warren (1942). The Asotin stage of the Snake River Canyon near Lewiston, Idaho, *Jour. Geol.*, **50**, 866–881.

Mackin, J. H. (1961). A stratigraphic section in the Yakima basalt and the Ellensburg formation in south-central Washington, *Wash. Div. Mines and Geol. Rept. Invest.* 19, 45 pp.

Pardee, J. T. (1942). Unusual currents in glacial Lake Missoula, *Geol. Soc. Am. Bull.*, **53**, 1569–1600.

——— and Kirk Bryan (1925). Geology of the Latah formation in the lavas of the Columbia Plateau near Spokane, Washington, *U. S. Geol. Survey Profess. Paper* 14, 1–16.

Piper, A. M., T. W. Robinson, and C. F. Park, Jr. (1939). Geology and ground-water resources of the Harney Basin, Oregon, *U. S. Geol. Survey Water-Supply Paper* 841, 189 pp.

Rockie, W. A. (1934). Snowdrifts and the Palouse topography, *Geog. Rev.*, **24**, 380–385.

Russell, I. C. (1893). A geological reconnoissance in central Washington, *U. S. Geol. Survey Bull.* 108, 108 pp.

——— (1897). A reconnoissance in southeastern Washington, *U. S. Geol. Survery Water-Supply Paper* 4, 96 pp.

——— (1901). Geology and water resources of Nez Perce County, Idaho, Part I, *U. S. Geol. Survey Water-Supply Paper* 53, 85 pp.

——— (1902). Geology and water resources of the Snake River Plain of Idaho, *U. S. Geol. Survey Bull.* 199, 192 pp.

Smith, G. O. (1901). Geology and water resources of a portion of Yakima County, Washington, *U. S. Geol. Survey Water-Supply Paper* 55, 68 pp.

——— (1903). Anticlinal mountain ridges in central Washington, *Jour. Geol.*, **11**, 166–177.

Smith, W. D., J. E. Allen, L. W. Staples, and W. R. Lowell (1941). Geology and physiography of the northern Wallowa Mountains, Oregon, *Oregon Dept. Geol. Min. Industries Bull.* 12, 64 pp.

Stearns, H. T. (1924). Craters of the Moon National Monument, *Geog. Rev.*, **14**, 362–372.

——— (1936). Origin of the large springs and their alcoves along the Snake River in southern Idaho, *Jour. Geol.*, **44**, 429–450.

———, L. Crandall, and W. C. Stewart (1938). Geology and ground-water resources of the Snake River plain in southeastern Idaho, *U. S. Geol. Survey Water-Supply Paper* 774, 268 pp.

Warren, C. R. (1941a). Course of the Columbia River in south central Washington, *Am. Jour. Sci.*, **239**, 106–127.

——— (1941b). The Hood River conglomerate in Washington, *Am. Jour. Sci.*, **239**, 209–232.

Waters, A. C. (1933). Terraces and coulees along the Columbia River near Lake Chelan, *Geol. Soc. Am. Bull.* **44**, 783–820.

——— (1939). Resurrected erosion surface in central Washington, *Geol. Soc. Am. Bull.*, **50**, 638–659.

——— (1955a). Volcanic rocks and the tectonic cycle, in *Crust of the Earth*, Arie Poldervaart, Editor, *Geol. Soc. Am. Spec. Paper* 62, 703–722.

——— (1955b). Geomorphology of south-central Washington, illustrated by the Yakima East quadrangle, *Geol. Soc. Am. Bull.*, **66**, 663–684.

——— (1961). Stratigraphic and lithologic variations in the Columbia River basalt, *Am. Jour. Sci.*, **259**, 583–611.

Wheeler, H. E., and E. F. Cook (1954). Structural and stratigraphic significance of the Snake River capture, Idaho-Oregon, *Jour. Geol.*, **62**, 525–536.

Williams, Howel (1935). Newberry volcano of central Oregon, *Geol. Soc. Am. Bull.*, **46**, 253–304.

Willis, Bailey (1887). Changes in river courses in Washington Territory due to glaciation, *U. S. Geol. Survey Bull.* 40, 10 pp.

ADDITIONAL REFERENCES

Allison, I. S. (1941). Flint's fill-hypothesis for channeled scabland, *Jour. Geol.*, **49**, 54–73.

Bretz, J H. (1925). The Spokane flood beyond the channeled scabland, *Jour. Geol.*, **33**, 97–115.

——— (1929). Valley deposits east of the channeled scabland, *Jour. Geol.*, **37**, 393–427.

——— (1930). Valley deposits west of the channeled scablands, *Jour. Geol.*, **38**, 385–422.

———— (1932). The Grand Coulee, *Am. Geog. Soc. Spec. Pub.* 15, 89 pp.

Flint, R. F. (1936). Stratified drift and deglaciation of eastern Washington, *Geol. Soc. Am. Bull.*, **47**, 1849–1884.

———— (1938). Summary of the late-Cenozoic geology of southeastern Washington, *Am. Jour. Sci.*, **235**, 223–230.

———— and W. H. Irwin (1939). Glacial geology of the Grand Coulee Dam, Washington, *Geol. Soc. Am. Bull.*, **50**, 661–680.

Freeman, O. W. (1926). Scabland mounds of eastern Washington, *Science*, **64**, 450–451.

Hodge, E. T. (1934). Origin of the Washington scabland, *Northwest Science*, **8**, 4–11.

Jenkins, O. P. (1925). The Spokane flood; a discussion, *Jour. Geol.*, **33**, 747–748.

McKnight, E. T. (1927). The Spokane flood; a discussion, *Jour. Geol.*, **35**, 453–460.

Newcomb, R. C. (1958). Ringold formation of Pleistocene age in type locality, the White Bluffs, Washington, *Am. Jour. Sci.*, **256**, 328–340.

Olmsted, R. K. (1963). Silt mounds of Missoula flood surfaces, *Geol. Soc. Am. Bull.*, **74**, 47–54.

Piper, C. V. (1905). The basalt mounds of the Columbia lava, *Science*, **21**, 824–825.

Stearns, H. T. (1963). *Geology of Craters of the Moon*, Craters of the Moon Nat. Hist. Assoc., 34 pp.

Trimble, D. E., and W. J. Carr (1961). Late Quaternary history of the Snake River in the American Falls region, Idaho, *Geol. Soc. Am. Bull.*, **72**, 1739–1748.

Waters, A. C., and C. W. Flagler (1929). Origin of the small mounds on the Columbia River Plateau, *Am. Jour. Sci.*, **218**, 209–224.

# 24

# *Basin and Range Province*

## GENERAL DESCRIPTION

The Basin and Range province extends through approximately 17 degrees of longitude and 12 degrees of latitude (actually considerably more than this if its continuation southward into Mexico is included). The province is approximately 500 miles wide between the Wasatch Range and the Sierra Nevada, narrows to about 225 miles between the Grand Wash Cliffs and the front of the Sierra Nevada at Owens Valley, and expands to nearly 700 miles along the southern border of the United States.

### *Distinguishing Characteristics*

It is to be expected that in a province as extensive as the Basin and Range province there will be considerable variety in geology and topography. In detail this is true, but despite the fact that its rocks range in age from Precambrian to Quaternary and include most rock types, there is surprising homogeneity of topography. This can be attributed primarily to the overall similarity of geologic structure and climate. Taken as a whole this is the most arid geomorphic region in the United States; most of the province has an annual rainfall less than 10 inches. Internal drainage characterizes much of the northern part of the province and is prevalent locally in the southern part. Although geologic structures are variable within the province, one particular type, commonly referred to as block faulting, is so prevalent that it has notably influenced topographic characteristics. The mountains contrast sharply with those of other parts of the western United States; they are typically isolated, subparallel ranges that rise abruptly above adjacent desert plains. The desert plains over much of the province are essentially debris-filled intermontane basins, but in some areas they are more erosional than depositional surfaces.

### *Province Boundaries*

Despite the fact that the Basin and Range province stands out as an area of distinctive topography, in a sense its boundaries on the west, north, and east are transitional in nature. The Sierra Nevada contrasts notably in size and height with the ranges of the Basin and Range province, yet structurally it is a fault block similar basically to many of the mountain ranges east of it. Major differences are in size, height, and the fact that its core is a great granite batholith. On the north are basalts similar in age and origin to those of the Columbia Intermontane province that are included in the Basin and Range province because they have the fault structures similar to those found in this province; here, again, the boundary is transitional. The Wasatch Mountains on the east contrast topographically in size and height with ranges of the Basin and Range province, but structurally this mountain range is a large fault block. As indicated on p. 409 there is a rather sharp topographic break between the Colorado Plateaus and the Basin and Range province, but structurally there is a transitional zone between the two. The southern boundary of the province lies outside the United States.

## Climatic Influence on Topography

Except for the higher mountain slopes, most of the province is very dry, largely as a result of the rain shadow effect of the Sierra Nevada. Numerous weather stations average less than 5 inches of rain per year. The rainfall is notably sporadic in occurrence and variable from year to year. The showers are often torrential, but the idea commonly encountered that some of the heaviest individual rains of the western United States occur here is far from being true. Rainfall maps of the region show that rarely do rains exceed 4 inches within a 24-hour period. More significant is the fact that with a sparse vegetal cover torrential rainfall produces maximum runoff. This helps to account for the seemingly paradoxical fact that running water rather than the wind is the dominant geomorphic agent. Desert streams, however, are notably intermittent and discontinuous in nature; streamfloods

which form suddenly and abate equally rapidly are common phenomena. Sheetflood erosion is probably even more significant here than streamflood erosion. Both streamfloods and sheetfloods move great quantities of rock debris downslope; thus basin filling is a dominant process in much of the Basin and Range province.

Lack of external drainage is particularly common in the northern part of the Basin and Range province in what is known as the Great Basin; however, a small portion of the Great Basin section has external drainage through California to the Pacific via the Klamath and Pitt rivers. External drainage is more common in the southern part of the province via the Colorado River and Rio Grande and their tributaries.

## Distinctive Topographic Characteristics

A geologist transplanted from almost any other mountainous portion of the United States to the

FIG. 24.1    Arrow Canyon Range, southern Nevada, an example of the type of mountain ranges found in the Basin and Range province.    (*Photo by John S. Shelton.*)

FIG. 24.2    Slightly dissected Pleistocene (?) pediment and bajada sloping from Quartzite Mountain to Mohave River, east of Oro Grande, California.    The piedmont slope has been stripped and eroded because of Recent regional uplift. (*Photo by John S. Shelton.*)

Basin and Range province should recognize at once that he is in a distinctly different type of mountains from that to which he has been accustomed.    The mountain ranges are short and rise precipitously to heights of 3000 to 5000 feet above encircling piedmont slopes (see Fig. 24.1); some mountains attain altitudes of more than 10,000 feet and were high enough to nourish Pleistocene glaciers.    When depicted by hachures on a physiographic map the mountains resemble, as Dutton is reported to have said (King, 1959), "an army of caterpillars crawling northward out of Mexico."    There are more than 150 mountain ranges in the Basin and Range province.    Their axes, in general, extend north-south; east-west ranges are practically lacking.

The mountain ranges are typically asymmetrical in cross profile; the steeper or scarp slope is commonly fairly straight, but it may be sinuous. Scarps may bound both sides of a range, but more characteristically they are confined to one side. Range crests may be jagged, but usually they are continuous rather than being cut into numerous segments.    Some of the range have lava caps, called by Davis (1930) louderbacks (see Fig. 24.9).

The description of mountain ranges given above applies particularly to those in the Great Basin section at the north.    An appreciable difference in appearance exists between the ranges in the northern and those in the southern parts of the province.    Particularly in the Sonoran Desert section at the southwest the ranges are smaller, lower, comprised of older rocks, and fringed by more extensive piedmont slopes than in the Great Basin section.

Typically, the mountain ranges are bordered by smooth piedmont slopes that extend into the basins (see Fig. 24.2). These slopes may be a few or many miles wide, and their gradients are measured in hundreds of feet per mile. They typically make a sharp angle with the mountain front. As the piedmont slopes are more commonly associated with the basins than the mountains, this further adds to the idea that basins more than mountains characterize the province.

Typically the piedmont slopes consist of two parts, a pediment on the side adjacent to the

mountain and a bajada on the basin side. These usually merge imperceptibly with each other. However, not all piedmont slopes have a pediment portion. If uplift of the mountain range by faulting has gone on rather continuously, there will have been no opportunity for a pediment to form; under such circumstances the piedmont slope will be all bajada. This seems to be true of the striking piedmont slopes that descend from the east side of the Panamint Range into Death Valley.

Blackwelder (1931) estimated that three-fourths of the province consists of plains of one type or another. He distinguished five types of plains: pediments, bajadas, lake bottom plains, including playas, structural plains, and river

FIG. 24.3   Playa at north end of Panamint Valley.   Note fine texture of drainage lines on alluvial slopes leading to the playa.   (*Photo by John S. Shelton.*)

FIG. 24.4  Dune field in the vicinity of Delta, Utah.  (*Photo by Fairchild Aerial Surveys, Inc.*)

floodplains. The most common of these are pediments, bajadas, and playas.

Many of the intermontane basins are closed and have playas at their centers (see Fig. 24.3). According to Hubbs and Miller (1948) the Basin and Range province has in it at least 141 closed basins, and Flint (1957) indicated that at least 119 of them display evidence of having been sites of lakes during pluvial Pleistocene time. The basin fills commonly exhibit two lithologic facies, a coarse and commonly conglomeratic bajada type that was deposited around the outer margins of the basins, and a finer lacustrine facies deposited in the central parts of the basins.

Most landscapes that are regional in extent are to varying degrees the product of multiple geomorphic processes; this is particularly true in the Basin and Range province. At one time the intermontane basins were attributed in varying degrees to wind erosion (Keyes, 1908; Blackwelder, 1928a). It is now generally believed that running water has played a greater role in developing the existing landscape than the wind, but locally the wind is an effective agent. Although one may traverse much of the province without seeing a sand dune, locally they are conspicuous features (see Fig. 24.4). All of the geomorphic processes, with the possible exception of solution by groundwater, have operated in the Basin and Range province, but four in particular have produced the land forms that constitute the major part of the present landscape. These are erosion and deposition by both concentrated and unconcentrated running water, wind erosion and deposition, volcanism, and diastrophism. Their relative importance varies from place to place. More local in importance than the others are volcanism and wind action.

## Geology of Basin and Range Province

*Rocks.* It should be emphasized, as stated by King (1959), that the distinctive Basin and range topography has been developed on a variety of rocks and structures. As stated above, rocks in the province range in age from Precambrian to Quaternary. Precambrian granites and gneisses are more extensively exposed in the southern than in the northern part of the province. In contrast to the Colorado Plateau, where a thick Paleozoic sequence is found only in the Paradox Basin, numerous localities in the Basin and Range province display thick Paleozoic sections; this is particularly true at the north and in the latitude of Las Vegas, Nevada (Longwell, 1952).

In further contrast with the Colorado Plateau, Mesozoic rocks are sparingly present in the Basin and Range province, are notably discontinuous in extent, and seem to have been deposited in a number of separate basins. In still further contrast with the Colorado Plateau province, late, instead of early, Tertiary rocks predominate in the Basin and Range province. South of the latitude of Lake Mead thick sections of Paleozoic, Mesozoic, and Cenozoic sedimentary rocks are notably lacking, and in their place Precambrian igneous and metamorphic rocks, younger intrusive rocks, and thick sections of volcanic rocks intercalated with clastic sediments are more characteristic (Longwell, 1952). This difference is probably attributable to the fact that the southern part of the province has had a more persistent positive tendency, and continuing uplift has allowed erosion to remove the Paleozoic and Mesozoic rocks. Igneous intrusive activity seems to have affected the southern area more than the northern, or perhaps it is more correct to say that because erosion has extended more deeply into the stratigraphic section intrusive bodies are more widely exposed.

At the extreme northwest, in southern Oregon, northeastern California, and northwestern Ne-

vada, there is an almost continuous cover of sheets of late Tertiary basalts of the same age and kind as those of the Harney-High Desert section of the Columbia Intermontane Plateau province. Because these basalts are intricately faulted (see Fig. 24.5), this area is included in the Basin and Range province. Elsewhere, volcanic rocks of Tertiary and Quaternary age are more discontinuous. The volcanics are predominately basaltic flows, but in addition there is a considerable volume of silicic rocks that are to be classed as welded ash flows or ignimbrites (Mackin, 1960).

*Structure.* The Basin and Range province has become the type area for a structural pattern commonly called basin-range, tilt-block, or fault-block structure. Actually, what is commonly referred to as the basin-range type of structure is only one of various types of structure found in the province, for structures are variable from place to place, commonly complex, and usually the product of more than one period of diastrophism. Both high- and low-angle normal faults are common; overturned folds and thrust faults that produce an imbricate type of structure are also present; and horst and graben types of structures characterize particularly the Oregon portion of the province (Fuller and Waters, 1929) and the Rio Grande trough (Fitzsimmons, 1959).

The structural picture may be simplified somewhat if we consider separately what we may call the external and internal structures of the ranges. By external structures we refer to the "boundary faults" that are presumed by many to control the outlines of the ranges. These faults are supposed to be normal faults along which there has been movement resulting in the development of a number of tilted fault blocks. Few, if any, such faults have actually been observed, but the forms of the ranges and intervening basins and displacement of geological formations suggest that such faulting has taken place, as may geophysical data (see Fig. 24.6). As Mackin (1960) has stressed, the one thing that characterizes basin-range faulting more than any other is that the normal faulting is antithetic, i.e.,

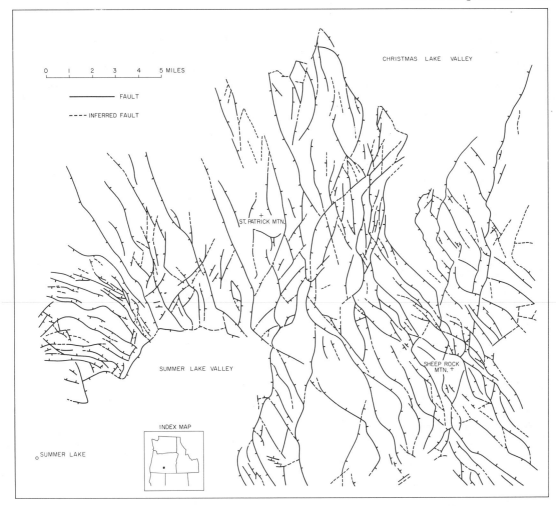

0   1   2   3   4   5 MILES

——————— FAULT

- - - - - INFERRED FAULT

ST. PATRICK MTN.

SUMMER LAKE VALLEY

SHEEP ROCK
MTN.

INDEX MAP

SUMMER LAKE

**FIG. 24.5**  Fault distribution in part of central Lake County, Oregon.  (*After F. A. Donath, Geol. Soc. Am. Bull., 73.*)

the faults dip opposite to the direction in which the strata dip.  Thus the same stratigraphic units along a profile at right angles to the faults may repeat themselves several times.

Internal range structure is commonly complex and exhibits folds, some of which are overturned, thrust faults (see Fig. 24.6), high-angle normal faults, and igneous intrusive masses.  The existence within the ranges of thrust faults and folds suggests that more than one period of diastrophism has occurred within the Basin and Range province.  It is believed that some of the folds and thrust faults date back to Cretaceous time and the Laramide revolution; others may be

later in age.  One of the most striking of the thrust faults is the Keystone thrust (Hewett, 1931).  This thrust is located near the southeast end of the Spring Mountain Range west of Las Vegas, Nevada.  In this thrust the middle Cambrian Goodsprings dolomite has been thrust over the Jurassic (?) Aztec sandstone (see Fig. 24.7).  Another well-known thrust is the Muddy Mountain thrust (Longwell, 1928) along which Paleozoic limestones and dolomites have been thrust onto rocks of Jurassic age.

High-angle and low-angle normal faults are also a part of the internal range structure (see Fig. 24.6).  Whether the normal faults within the ranges are of the same age as the "boundary faults" is uncertain. It is common practice to postulate two major periods of orogenic activity, an early one, presumably Laramide in age, during which there was compression of the region resulting in the development of folds and thrust faults, and a later one, which was dominantly tensional in nature, resulting in the development of normal faults. Longwell (1945) argued that this concept needed reexamination, as it seemed to him unlikely that all the normal faulting took place late in Cenozoic time.

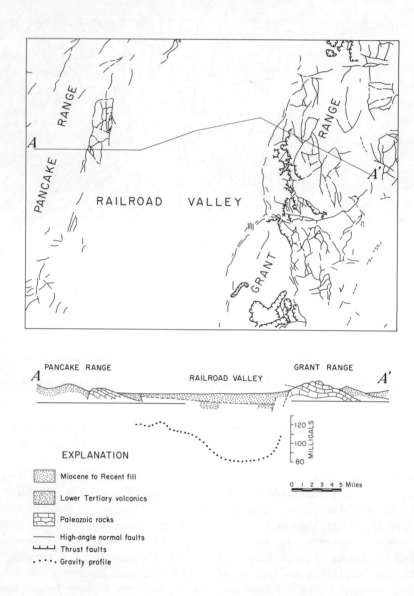

FIG. 24.6   Map of Pancake and Grant ranges and enclosed Railroad Valley showing traces of internal range faults, along with diagrammatic geologic cross-section and a gravity profile along the line *AA'*.   (*After J. C. Osmond, Mining Engineering,* **12.**)

FIG. 24.7   View of Keystone thrust at southeast end of Spring Mountain Range, west of Las Vegas, Nevada.   The middle Cambrian Goodspring dolomite is thrust over the Jurassic (?) Aztec sandstone.   Vegetation contrasts mark the dolomite-sandstone contact.   Pinyon and pine grow profusely on the dolomite and sparingly or not at all on the sandstone.   (*Photo by John S. Shelton.*)

## THE BASIN-RANGE PROBLEM

### Historical Sketch

One of the problems that has engaged the attention of numerous American geomorphologists is the "basin-range problem." The following brief historical sketch merely points out some of the more significant aspects of this perplexing problem. For a more detailed summary the reader should consult the discussion by Nolan (1943).

Clarence King, in 1870, interpreted the mountains as erosional remnants of folds which were presumed to have developed in late Jurassic time. This represented an interpretation of the topography in terms of the then familiar Appalachian type of mountains. He recognized that the mountains of the Basin and Range province were unlike the Appalachian Mountains in appearance, but he attributed this to the different climatic conditions under which the two mountain areas developed.

Gilbert (1874, 1875) concluded that the geomorphic evidence suggested that the mountains instead of being anticlinal structures were really faulted monoclinal blocks that had been raised above the intervening basins along range-front faults. Thus the mountain ridges were not looked on as remnants of folds or the basins as valleys cut by erosion on weaker rocks, as they were considered by King. Gilbert's views were

FIG. 24.8   View looking east to Sheep Range, near Las Vegas, Nevada.   Repetition of strata is produced by four normal faults (indicated by dashed lines).   Strata dip to east and faults dip to west.   (*Photo by Spence Air Photos; geology after C. R. Longwell, Trans. Am. Geophys. Union, 26.*)

supported by Powell (1877) in a report which included, among other things, a classification of mountain types.

Powell (1877) and King (1878) called attention to evidence that indicated two distinct times and types of diastrophism within the province, an earlier one marked by folding and thrust faulting and a later one characterized by block faulting. Dutton (1880) accepted this idea of two types and ages of mountain structures and added to it the concept that the relief produced by the early period of folding and thrust faulting had been obliterated largely by erosion before the block faulting took place.

Spurr (1901) expressed opposition to this viewpoint and contended that the topography could be adequately explained as a result of erosion of folds, without later block faulting. He maintained that (*a*) although high-angle faults do exist within the ranges, they lack topographic expression; and (*b*) many of the ranges lack boundary faults. There can be little argument on Spurr's first contention; there are indeed many normal faults within the ranges which displace older structures but lack topographic expression. This is true mainly because they do not bring together rocks of unequal resistance to erosion. Some of the intra-range faults may bring about repetition at the surface of resistant strata and in that way have topographic expression (see Fig. 24.8).

Spurr's paper brought forth vigorous defense of the block-faulting concept, particularly from Davis (1903, 1905). Davis not only defended

Gilbert's ideas, but he presented geomorphic criteria for the recognition of range-marginal faults.

Keyes, in 1909, presented a paper in which he essentially followed the view of King that the mountains are residual features resulting from the erosion of the basins in areas of weak rocks. However, he attributed the major part of the development of the basins to wind erosion.

Davis, in 1930, presented a summary of the history of the Basin and Range province that has been repeated many times. He recognized the following stages in the development of the present topography:

1. Growth of the ancestral folds during the Laramide orogeny, followed by dissection, to form the *King Mountains*.

2. Reduction by erosion of the *King Mountains* during early Tertiary time to form the *Powell surface*.

3. Local extrusion of lavas onto the *Powell surface*, which, following stage 4, became louderbacks (see Fig. 24.9) on the *Gilbert fault blocks*. (The name louderback was used in recognition of G. D. Louderback (1923) who was the first to recognize the significance of the lava caps.)

4. Block faulting that produced the *Gilbert fault blocks*.

The above outline of the history of the Basin and Range province is useful in presenting a general sequence of events, but it represents oversimplification of the history of an area with diverse features and histories.

FIG. 24.9   A basin range, some 40 miles west-southwest of Gila Bend, Arizona, with a louderback lava cap on it. (*Photo by R. C. Frampton and John S. Shelton.*)

Mackin (1960) has presented well the status of the basin-range problem during the early part of the present century as follows:

> If to the many oversimplifications . . . such as those given above by Davis . . . one more is added to the effect that block faulting began or occurred chiefly in late Cenozoic time, then we have the version of basin-range theory expressed by the familiar Davis diagram showing a tilted block consisting of folded strata, bounded on one or both sides by faults, in process of burial by up-building basin fills of its own detritus. This picture may be thought of as representing the gen-eneral consensus at the end of the heroic period—the Gilbert-Powell-Dutton period—of develop-ment of the basin-range concept. It is difficult, looking back over the years, to grasp fully the impact of the new, much needed, and obviously good idea which was the crux of that concept, i.e., that the origin of a range as a topographic feature may be an entirely different matter from the origin of its internal structures.

Blackwelder (1928a), long a student of western desert land forms, questioned the then prevailing idea that the basin-ranges were produced directly by faulting. He granted the existence in the western part of the province of topography of this origin but believed that elsewhere it was rare. He maintained rather that "the visible topo-graphic forms of both mountains and plains have been carved largely by stream erosion on a heterogeneous mass in which there were many old faults." Thus he recognized that faults may influence the configuration of the topography indirectly rather than directly. Most of the scarps associated with faults he would interpret as fault-line scarps rather than fault scarps. Blackwelder suggested that only a small part of the detritus removed from the mountains by erosion remains in the basins, but he recognized that it was difficult to explain how the greater part was removed. Two possible explanations were suggested: (1) the detritus was carried to the sea by river systems that were later dis-membered, or (2) most of the detritus was eventually reduced to dust-size particles and then exported by wind.

*Fault Scarps versus Fault-Line Scarps.* Probably Blackwelder's most important contribution to the basin-range problem was a paper (1928b) which pointed up the similarities and differences be-tween fault scarps and fault-line scarps and presented geologic and geomorphic criteria for distinguishing them. Much of the confusion regarding basin-range topography has come from a lack of understanding of the difference in origin of fault scarps and fault-line scarps and an appreciation of the implied differences in geomorphic histories represented by the two types of scarps. They may have many features in common, but there are certain diagnostic characteristics of each; if these are applied care-fully, much of the confusion, though not all, between the two types of scarps can be avoided, along with many of the conflicting interpretations of basin-range topography. The assumption often made, particularly by earlier workers but also by some modern geologists, that the presence of a range-front scarp is proof that the scarp was produced by faulting is certainly fallacious. This assumption leads to the type of reasoning strongly condemned by Threet (1960) as follows:

> Confusion has arisen with an unwarranted exten-sion of the view that basin-range physiography is fault-block physiography and must, therefore, be related to direct effects of faulting. Range-marginal faults have often been mapped *because* of range-marginal scarps, and the height of the supposed fault scarp, plus the depth of "alluvium" in the adjacent basin, has been taken as a minimum measure of fault throw . . . . This sort of circular reasoning makes an unbeatable system—using the range-marginal scarps to prove the existence of a "basin-range fault" and then using the fault thus established to substantiate a pre-conceived notion of "basin-range" structure. Again Blackwelder's admonition is appropriate—structural and topographic or geomorphic terms must be kept separated.

It has gradually become apparent that in addi-tion to the Laramide and perhaps a pre-Laramide period of folding and thrust faulting expressed in the internal structure of the basin-ranges, there have been two or more episodes of normal faulting. Normal faults exist within some ranges to such an extent as to make the ranges mosaics bounded by normal faults whose trends do not coincide with the range-marginal faults. These internal normal faults may or may not have topographic expression, as is true of the range-marginal faults.

It is therefore becoming apparent that some of the range-front scarps are true fault scarps; others are fault-line scarps; furthermore, range-marginal faults may exist without being expressed topographically by scarps. Each individual range must be interpreted in terms of its own geomorphic history and no unqualified sweeping statements can be made that apply to all ranges.

As Mackin (1960) has again pertinently stated, "The fact that Great Basin block faulting may have no topographic expression raises a question as to whether 'basin-range structure' should be restricted to what seems to have been its original meaning, i.e., the block-fault structure that produced the present ranges as suggested by Gilbert, or whether it should be explicitly broadened to conform with what it means to most people working in the Great Basin, i.e., block faulting without regard for the relationship of the faulting to topographic form." To further clarify our thinking on the basin-range problem we might add to the above statement the fact that a fault may have topographic expression as the result of differential erosion on its two sides rather than because of differential uplift along the fault. Use of the expression "basin-range structure" in this sense carries no implication as to the age or origin of the topography but refers rather to block-fault structure which may be of early or late Tertiary age and which may or may not be strongly evident in the present topography.

## SECTIONS OF THE BASIN AND RANGE PROVINCE

The Basin and Range province is divided into five sections (Fenneman, 1931): the Great Basin, Sonoran Desert, Salton Trough, Mexican Highland, and Sacramento sections. Their major distinguishing characteristics are:

GREAT BASIN SECTION. This section is marked by numerous short mountain ranges and intermontane aggradational plains in about equal proportions. Most of the section has internal drainage.

SONORAN DESERT SECTION. Altitudes are lower, aggradional plains less common, and mountain areas proportionately less extensive here than in the Great Basin section.

SALTON TROUGH SECTION. This is the lowest part of the province, and except for a small area at the north it is occupied by the Gulf of California.

MEXICAN HIGHLAND SECTION. Geologic structure is more variable here than in most of the province; high desert valleys and mountain ranges occur in about equal proportions; most of the section has external drainage.

SACRAMENTO SECTION. Faults are common here, but they have not produced the pronounced tilt blocks found elsewhere; cuestaform and plateau-like topography is more characteristic of this section.

### Great Basin Section

The Great Basin section probably most nearly fits the conventional picture of Basin and Range geology and topography. It is not a single topographic basin but rather a collection of mountains and intermontane basins in roughly equal proportions. Most of the Great Basin has internal drainage, but it is not a true hydrographic basin any more than it is a simple topographic basin. Internal drainage is partly a result of geomorphic configuration, but it is more a result of the arid climate; if the rainfall were greater, many basins would discharge from one to another and eventually to the sea.

Here more than anywhere else in the province do we find the "typical" basin-range topography. Here, too, the geologic structure fits fairly well the concept of fault-blocks bounded by high-angle normal faults. The rocks of the ranges are in general younger than those in the Sonoran section to the south, and the ranges are not so maturely eroded.

The lavas in the northwestern part of the section have been intricately faulted (Donath, 1962) to form a series of horsts, grabens, and tilt blocks. Here range scarps such as that of Steens Mountain are unquestionably fault scarps, and depressions occupied by such lakes as Lake Abert and Summer Lake are grabens (Fuller, 1931). If the sections of the Basin and Range province are ever divided into smaller geomorphic units, this northern area will undoubtedly become one of the distinctive subdivisions of the Great Basin section.

*Internal Drainage.* Few of the intermontane basins in the Great Basin section contain permanent lakes, but such lakes as Pyramid, Winnemucca, and Great Salt are permanent, even though they fluctuate notably in level. A few freshwater lakes exist, such as Klamath Lake, which has an outlet through the Pitt River, and Utah Lake, which drains to Great Salt Lake, but most of the lakes are brackish or salty. The basins have more playas in them than intermittent lakes, but the runoff varies so markedly from month to month and year to year that it is difficult to draw a line between the two. Lakes of one type or another are more numerous along the western and eastern margins of the Great Basin section than elsewhere. Those on the west are maintained by runoff from the Sierra Nevada and Cascade Mountains, and those on the east by rainfall in the Wastach Mountains and High Plateaus of Utah. The mountain ranges in the central part of the Great Basin in general are not high enough to induce sufficient rainfall to maintain permanent lakes.

### Pleistocene Lakes

It has long been recognized that most of the individual basins of the Great Basin section during pluvial Pleistocene times were sites of lakes much larger than any that exist today. Figure 24.10 shows the positions of the Pleistocene lakes, approximately 100 of which were in the Great Basin section. Some lakes were a result of direct emptying into their basins of glacial meltwater from nearby mountains, but the majority of them formed because the climate during glacial time was rainier and cooler, with consequent greater runoff and less evaporation than now.

Most of the lake histories have not been worked out, but four in particular have been studied enough that general outlines of their histories can be given; these are Lakes Bonneville, Lahontan, Russell, and Manly.

*Lake Bonneville.* The largest and by far the best known of the Pleistocene Great Basin lakes was Lake Bonneville, whose history was first discussed in a classical paper by G. K. Gilbert (1890). This name is applied to the Wisconsin phases of what likely was a succession of Pleistocene lakes, for sediments beneath its basin floor suggest that at least three pre-Wisconsin

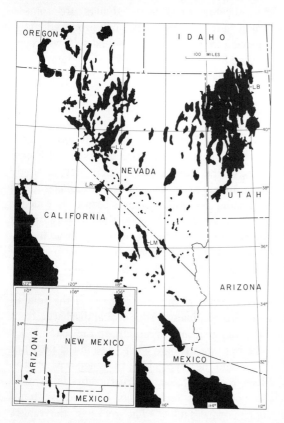

FIG. 24.10  Sites of Pleistocene lakes in the Basin and Range province. (*After R. F. Flint,* Glacial and Pleistocene Geology, *John Wiley and Sons, Inc.*)

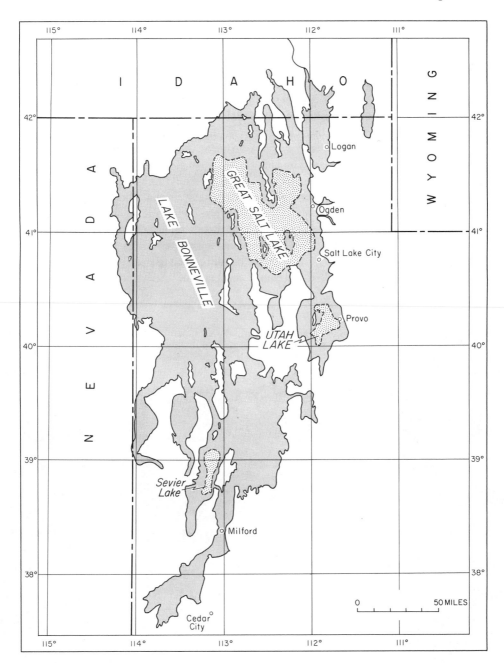

FIG. 24.11 Comparison of extent of Lake Bonneville and its present-day remnants, Sevier, Utah, and Great Salt Lakes. (*After C. B. Hunt, H. D. Varnes, and H. E. Thomas, U. S. Geol. Survey Profess. Paper 257-A.*)

lakes may have preceded Lake Bonneville (Flint, 1957). Lake Bonneville occupied a number of coalescent basins in parts of Utah, Idaho, and Nevada (see Fig. 24.11); at its maximum extent if covered over 20,000 square miles and was thus about the size of the present Lake Michigan. Several mountain ranges in the area formed islands or peninsulas in the lake and divided it into a number of irregular bodies connected by narrow straits. Present-day remnants of Lake Bonneville are Great Salt Lake, Sevier Lake, and Lake Utah. At its highest stand Lake Bonneville stood about 1000 feet above the present Salt Lake, at which time it had an outlet to the north to the Snake River via Red Rock Pass (see Fig. 24.12). According to data obtained by radiocarbon dating of calcareous

tufa (Broecker and Orr, 1958), the Red Rock Pass outlet appears to have been cut more recently than 16,000 years ago and perhaps during a 11,500 B.P. high-level stand of the lake.

Former levels of Lake Bonneville are indicated by shorelines (see Fig. 24.13) and associated deltas, bars, deposits of calcareous tufa, wave-cut niches in bedrock, and other shoreline features, as well as sedimentary deposits consisting of gravel, sand, silt, and clay. Four distinct strand lines have been identified, formed presumably in the following chronological order: the pre-Bonneville at an altitude of 5100 feet, the Bonneville at 5135 feet, the Provo at 4800 feet, and the Stansbury at 4500 feet. Considerable difference of opinion exists as to the time and sequence of the various lake phases. This is

FIG. 24.12   Red Rock Pass outlet of Lake Bonneville looking north toward Cache Valley.   (*Photo by J. S. Williams.*)

FIG. 24.13   Lake Bonneville shoreline on north flank of Traverse Mountains, north of Utah Lake.   (*Photo by John S. Shelton.*)

particularly true with respect to where the Stansbury shoreline fits into the sequence. One view regarding the Stansbury shoreline is that it was formed during a low-water stand between the Bonneville and Provo phases; another interpretation is that it was occupied twice, first between the Bonneville and Provo phases and later after the Provo phase.

Antevs (1945) suggested that the Bonneville phase could be correlated with the Tahoe glaciation and the Provo phase with the Tioga glaciation of the Sierra Nevada (see p. 512), but even assuming that such a correlation is correct, there is still some uncertainty as to the time of these glaciations. Radiocarbon dating of wave-formed tufas taken from various shorelines (Feth and Rubin, 1957) are difficult to correlate with postulated lake level successions. Tufa from the Bonneville shoreline gave an age of 11,330 ± 300 years, whereas tufa from the Provo level gave more than 32,000 years. Still more puzzling is the fact that other Provo-level tufas gave ages ranging from 11,650 ± 450 years to 14,389 ± 500 years. Four tufas collected at the Stansbury level gave ages ranging from 14,000 ± 400 years to 18,000 ± 1000 years. This may mean that the tufas were deposited at different times and hence cannot be used to date accurately the time at which the lake level stood against a particular shoreline. It is evident that much more work remains to be done before a reliable chronology for the phases of Lake Bonneville can be worked out.

*Lake Lahontan.* Lake Lahontan, first recognized and described by Russell (1885), lay mainly in northwestern Nevada, but it extended a short distance into California and Oregon (see Fig. 24.10). Its maximum length and width were 250 miles and 180 miles respectively; its maximum area was a little over 8000 square miles. As in Lake Bonneville, mountain ranges formed islands or peninsulas in the lake and divided it into a number of irregular sections connected by straits. The lake had two main parts, an eastern and a western; present North Carson, South Carson, and Walker lakes are remnants of the eastern water body, and Honey, Pyramid, and Winnemucca lakes are remnants of the western portion. Lake Lahontan at no time had an outlet to the sea, if the geomorphic evidence is to be given first consideration, but Miller (1946) thought that data on Recent and fossil fish distribution supported the belief that Lake Lahontan had a connection with a system of Pleistocene lakes in California (see p. 490) that terminated in Lake Manly in Death Valley, or perhaps had an outlet to the south into the Colorado River.

The history of Lake Lahontan has not been worked on as much as Lake Bonneville's, but the lake appears to have had a maximum depth of at least 500 feet, and Russell (1885) recognized three lake levels marked by what he called the Lithoid, Thinolite, and Dendritic terraces, at altitudes above sea level of 4367, 3977, and 4187 feet respectively. These names were given the three terraces because of differences in the type of calcareous tufa deposited at each level.

Radiocarbon dating of freshwater carbonates from Lake Lahontan (Broecker and Orr, 1958) suggest two high-water-level periods in its history, one from 24,000 to about 14,000 years B.P. and the other close to 11,500 years ago; there is a suggestion of a third maximum about 10,000 years B.P., but the evidence for it is not conclusive. Preceding the first maximum was a period of moderately low water level that apparently extended back to 34,000 years B.P.; following recession to a moderately low level about 13,000 years B.P., Lake Lahontan rose to its maximum level about 11,700 years ago. The lake has apparently remained at a low level since about 9000 years ago.

*Lake Russell.* Putnam (1949) proposed the name Lake Russell for the Pleistocene predecessor of present Mono Lake. Two shorelines at altitudes of approximately 7180–7190 feet and 7070 feet have been correlated respectively by him with the Tahoe and Tioga stages of glaciation in the Sierra Nevada. The higher shoreline is 754 feet above the 1947 level of Mono Lake and the lower is 654 feet above it. Below the highest Tioga shoreline Putnam (1950) identified 38 shorelines that represent waning phases of Lake Russell during late Pleistocene and Recent time. These shorelines vary in strength from broad treads to mere watermarks. It seems probable that Lake Russell during Tahoe, but not Tioga, time had an outlet to the south into Owens Valley and thus was the northernmost of a chain of lakes (see p. 493) that ultimately drained into Lake Manly in Death Valley. Kesseli (1948) agreed with Putnam that Lake Russell reached its maximum level during the Tahoe glaciation and that during the Tioga glaciation Lake Russell stood about 250 feet lower. The very prominent shoreline that is about 650 feet above Mono Lake, and which marks the most prolonged stand of Lake Russell, Kesseli considered as having developed during an intermediate phase between the Tahoe and Tioga phases rather than during the Tioga phase.

One interesting aspect of Lake Russell history is that in the Mono Lake district we have one of only two places in the Great Basin where Pleistocene lake shorelines have been cut into Pleistocene glacial moraines (see Fig. 24.14). The other place is at the foot of the Wasatch Mountains, where Lake Bonneville shorelines are etched into end moraines built by mountains glaciers from the Wasatch Mountains. Lake Russell shorelines are cut in moraines of both Tahoe and Tioga age.

### Death Valley Region

The Death Valley region is one of the most interesting portions of the Great Basin section, both historically and for its striking geomorphic features. The region is one of the least alluviated parts of the Great Basin section and hence is an

FIG. 24.14   Lake Russell shorelines etched on end moraine deposited by glacier from Sierra Nevada.   View is to the southwest from near shore of Mono Lake at Leevining, California.   (*Photo by John S. Shelton.*)

excellent area for study of basin-range structure. Death Valley is bounded on the west by the eastward-tilted Panamint Range and on the east by the eastward-tilted Funeral and Blacks Mountains, and is thus essentially a fault trough or graben, formed in late Pliocene or Pleistocene time (see Fig. 24.15). Recency of faulting is evidenced by numerous alluvial scarps and displacement of Pleistocene basalt flows. Rocks of the Death Valley region (Noble and Wright, 1954) are Precambrian, Paleozoic, Mesozoic, and Tertiary in age. Present are granitic intrusions of uncertain age and Quaternary fanglomerates, playa and lake deposits, dunal sands, and basalt cinder cones and flows. The Ubehebe Craters (Von Engeln, 1932) at the

north end of Death Valley are almost perfect examples of craters and are so recent they have undergone little erosion.

According to Maxson (1950), the Panamint Range displays many of the geomorphic features associated with the basin ranges. The faulting which produced this range was in part normal and in part strike-slip. The Wildrose graben along its west face attests to the recency of the faulting. This graben is about 3 miles long, nearly a mile wide, and has a maximum depth of about 400 feet. A stream which formerly flowed west across its present site was beheaded when the faulting occurred and now flows southward, lengthwise of the graben, at the base of the fault scarp at its west side.

*Lake Manly.* It has been recognized by geologists for a long time that a lake or a succession of lakes existed in Death Valley during Pleistocene time. Gilbert on Plate II of his monograph on Lake Bonneville indicated the existence of a lake in Death Valley, although he does not in the text state the evidence for such a lake. Apparently Noble (1926) was the first to point out specific geomorphic evidence for such a lake when he called attention to strand lines at two localities in Death Valley, one near the mouth of Wingate Pass and the other in an embayment north of Mormon Point. Noble described the strand lines at both localities as being between 400 and 500 feet above the valley floor. Later, the name Lake Manly was suggested for the Pleistocene lake (Means, 1932). Blackwelder (1933) described Lake Manly as approximately 90 miles long and 6 to 11 miles wide. He considered its maximum depth to have been about 585 feet, and thus its surface was approximately 310 feet above sea level. Clements and Clements (1953)

thought they found evidence of strand lines as high as 550 feet above sea level. Wave-formed terraces are visible at numerous places (see Fig. 24.16). The north side of Shoreline Butte is marked by 10 or 12 shoreline benches. The discrepancies in the altitudes given for the highest strand lines are probably due to a combination of three factors, the reconnaissance nature of some of the work, the fact that the highest strand lines impressed on the mountains surrounding Death Valley do not everywhere represent the same lake level, and the vagueness of the strand lines in some localities.

Lake Manly's chief influent probably was the Amargosa River but it has been suggested (Gale, 1915) that it was also supplied with water via Wingate Pass from Lake Panamint in Panamint Valley, immediately west of Death Valley (see p. 493). The topographic evidence seems to indicate that Lake Manly had no outlet. Alternation of salt and clay deposits beneath the surficial saline deposits on the floor of Death

FIG. 24.15   Death Valley, looking south from Furnace Creek Ranch.   (*Photo by Spence Air Photos.*)

FIG. 24.16 Lake Manly shorelines in Death Valley. *(Photo by R. C. Frampton and John S. Shelton.)*

Valley suggest that Lake Manly was only the latest in a series of lakes that occupied Death Valley during pluvial Pleistocene time.

Clements (1952) has described dissected lacustrine beds at the north end of Death Valley which mark the existence of a separate lake in this part of the Death Valley graben that was contemporaneous with Lake Manly at the south. This lake was named Lake Rogers.

### Sonoran Desert Section

The Sonoran Desert section takes its name from the Sonora Desert of northwestern Mexico. The part of this geomorphic unit in the United States consists primarily of the Mohave Desert of southeastern California and the Gila Desert of southwestern Arizona.

*Contrasts with Great Basin Section.* The Sonoran Desert section has certain features that are similar to those described above for the Great Basin section, but there are several distinct differences between the two sections both geologically and geomorphically. As stated above, the rocks of the Sonoran Desert section as a whole are older than those in the Great Basin. Precambrian granites and gneisses are much more widely exposed than at the north, and thick sections of Paleozoic, Mesozoic, and Cenozoic rocks are notably scarce. This difference is probably the result of two factors: first, that this region has been uplifted more than at the north, thus permitting erosion to penetrate more deeply into the geologic section, and second, that it is in a more advanced stage of arid land pedimentation. The landscape here is also characterized by mountain

FIG. 24.17   Cima Dome, looking to the south.   (*Photo by John S. Shelton.*)

ranges and intervening basins, commonly called bolsons, but typically the ranges are smaller, lower, and less extensive than in the Great Basin section.   It may well be said that pediments and bajadas dominate the topography.   Much of the section has internal drainage, but because of the aridity more than lack of outlet to the sea. Closed basins are less common east of the Colorado River than west of it.   On the east two rivers, the Williams and Gila, carry water derived from the Colorado Plateau into the Colorado River, whereas none of importance enters the Colorado River from the west.

The portion of this section in southeastern California and southwestern Arizona has seen to a considerable degree the type area in this country for study of the process of pedimentation.   Many of the pioneer papers in this phase of geomorphology dealt in part or whole with features found in the Sonoran Desert section

(McGee, 1897; Bryan, 1923; Blackwelder, 1931; and Davis, 1936).   Cima Dome in the Mohave Desert of California (see Fig. 24.17) has often been cited as the nearest thing in the United States to the end product of pedimentation. Sharp (1957), however, interpreted it as a regraded portion of a once extensive late Pliocene-early Pleistocene erosion surface named by Hewett (1956) the Ivanpah Upland.   Cima Dome may have been a residual feature upon the Ivanpah surface, or it may have been produced as the result of deformation of this surface.

*Pleistocene Lakes.*   Considerable geomorphic and geologic evidence indicates that there existed in the Mohave Desert region of southeastern California during one or more of the pluvial Pleistocene ages a number of lakes now represented by playas or salines.   Two or perhaps three such systems existed (see Fig. 24.18).

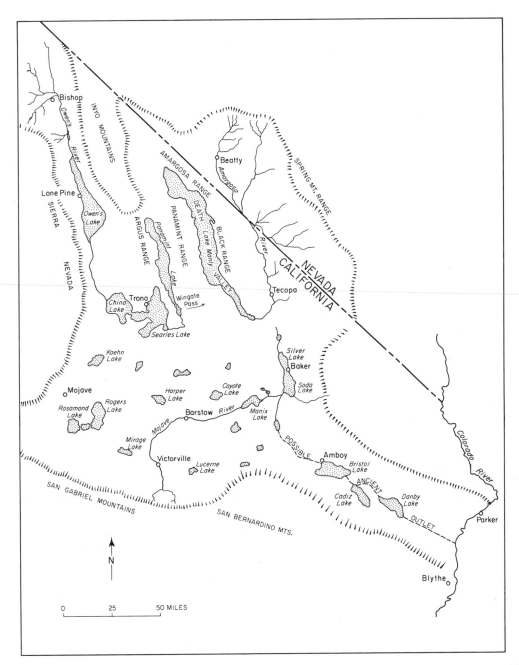

FIG. 24.18   Map of Pleistocene lakes in southeastern California.   (*After Eliot Blackwelder, Calif. Bureau Mines Bull.* 170.)

One system began with Owens Lake, which was fed by glaciers in the Sierra Nevada, and terminated in either Lake Panamint or Lake Manly. When Owens Lake rose to a level about 200 feet higher than its present level, it overflowed southward into Indian Wells Valley and formed a lake about 35 feet deep called China Lake (Blackwelder, 1954). This lake in turn overflowed into the much lower Searles Lake basin to the east of it. It is possible that at the time of maximum high water Searles Lake and China Lake merged (Droste, 1961). During the early Wisconsin Tahoe glaciation the lake in the Searles basin was as much as 640 feet deep and overflowed eastward into Panamint Valley to form Lake Panamint. Lake Panamint at this time was about 60 miles long and 930 feet deep. Blackwelder (1934) and Gale (1915) believed that it overflowed eastward through Wingate Pass into Lake Manly, but there is some uncertainty about this, for Wingate Pass is a narrow pass that displays little topographic evidence to suggest that it acted as a spillway for the waters of Lake Panamint.

Blackwelder believed that during Tioga time Searles Lake was the final sump for the Owens River drainage, because Searles Lake did not reach a high enough level to overflow into Panamint Valley. Evidence points toward the existence of a lake in Panamint Valley during Tioga time, but it apparently was fed only by streams from the surrounding mountains.

The present Searles Lake is a dry lake or playa covering about 60 square miles, whose surface is about four-fifths covered with salt, sand, silt, and clay. Its upper strata give evidence (Flint and Gale, 1958) of two deep lakes, each of which was followed by dessication and precipitation of evaporites. Carbon 14 dating indicates that the first of the two lakes formed over 46,000 years B.P. and began to wane somewhat before 32,000 years B.P. The life of the later lake extended from sometime before 23,000 years B.P. to sometime before 10,000 B.P.

A second system of Pleistocene lakes was that represented by present Bristol, Cadiz, and Danby dry lakes (see Fig. 24.18). These dry lakes or playas occupy a northwest-trending trough that is divided into separate basins by projecting mountain ranges. Lake Danby presumably was the sump for this chain of lakes. A large lava flow from Amboy Crater (see Fig. 24.19) has divided the Bristol Lake Basin into two parts, Bristol Dry Lake on the east and Alkali Dry Lake on the west. Thompson (1929) proposed the name Amboy Lake for a large lake which he believed existed in the Bristol-Cadiz basins in Pleistocene time. Danby Lake probably was also the sump for a lake that existed in Ward Valley, although it was suggested by Thompson (1929) that Lake Ward may have overflowed into the Colorado River through a pass near Rice, California. As mentioned above, a connection of the Pleistocene lakes in the Mohave Desert region with the Colorado River and Lake Lahontan was suggested by Miller (1946) on the basis of fossil and Recent fish distribution. Miller believed that the Owens Valley system of lakes terminated in Death Valley and that this line of lakes was connected with the Colorado River, through a chain of basins consisting the Soda-Silver Lake, Ludlow, Bristol-Cadiz, and Danby basins. Water connections based on the distribution of fish are at best uncertain in view of the fact that fish can be carried by birds from one lake basin into another. Lack of topographic evidence of spillways to the south for either chain of lakes makes a connection with the Colorado River highly questionable.

### Salton Trough Section

*Geology and Topography.* The Salton Trough section is a wedge-shaped depression extending for over 200 miles from the Gulf of California on the south to San Gorgonio Pass at the north. Structurally it is a complexly faulted graben. Several of the well-known faults of southern California, such as the San Andreas, San Jacinto, and Elsinore, extend into the trough. Topographically the region is a basin bounded on the west by the Peninsular Ranges (see p. 546) and on the north and east by the San Bernardino Mountains and Chocolate Mountains. A portion of the trough, about 85 miles long and 30 miles wide, is below sea level and has a

FIG. 24.19 Amboy Crater, south central San Bernardino County, California. (*Photo by R. C. Frampton and John S. Shelton.*)

minimum altitude of −273 feet. From north to south the Salton Trough may be divided into the Coachella Valley, Salton Sink, Imperial Valley, and Colorado River delta. Seismic data suggest thicknesses of ˙sediments in excess of 20,000 feet in the Imperial and Coachella valleys.

Conventional interpretation of the origin of Salton Sea is that the Gulf of California formerly extended into the area and subsequent construction of the delta of the Colorado River across the trough separated the Salton Sea area from the Gulf of California. Buwalda and Stanton (1930) have questioned this interpretation, however, and have argued that depression of the Salton Sea area took place during or since construction of the Colorado delta. They based this conclusion on the following lines of evidence: (1) the Colorado delta is much younger than the youngest marine strata in the area, which are Pliocene; (2) freshwater lake terraces are found around the Salton sea, but no marine terraces or strand lines; (3) marine strata several hundred feet above sea level and strongly folded and faulted as well as beveled by erosion were evidently deposited during an earlier depression of the Salton Sea area; and (4) recent earthquakes and faulting lend support to the plausibility of recent depression of the area.

*Lake Cahuilla.* Mollusks found in beach deposits indicate that prior to development of the present Salton Sea there existed in the Salton Trough a

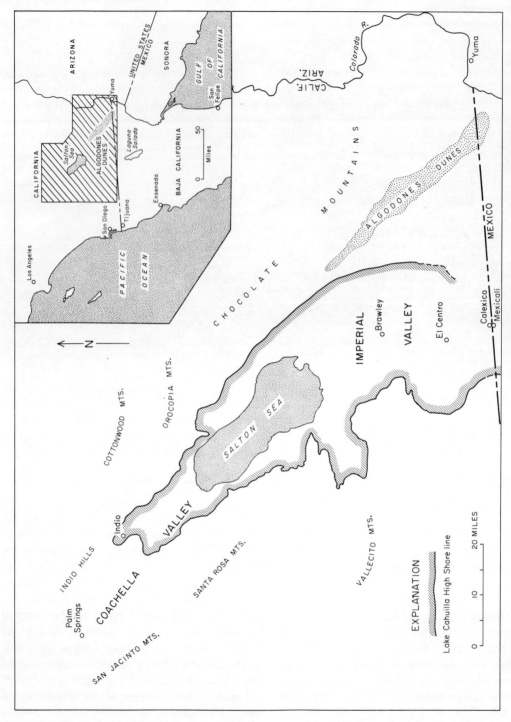

FIG. 24.20   Comparison of extent of Lake Cahuilla and Salton Sea.   (After R. M. Norris and K. S. Norris, Geol. Soc. Am. Bull., 72.)

freshwater lake that was named by Blake (1907) Lake Cahuilla (see Fig. 24.20). A shoreline 40 to 50 feet above sea level encircles the Imperial Valley, Salton Sea, and the southern part of the Coachella Valley (Brown, 1923). At places this strand line is marked by deposits of travertine (see Fig. 24.21) and on the east side of the Imperial Valley the Algodones Dunes (Norris and Norris, 1961), which extend for over 40 miles in a belt 3 to 6 miles wide, represent material derived from the beach of Lake Cahuilla. Radiocarbon dates on beach materials of Lake Cahuilla give ages that range from 1580 $\pm$ 200 years B.P. to 300 $\pm$ 100 years B.P. No lake existed in the Salton Sink at the time of the Spanish occupation. It appears likely that the lake may have been maintained by flow from the Colorado River at a time when it discharged into the Salton Trough rather than the Gulf of California.

Stanley (1963) has presented what he considered evidence for several levels of Lake Cahuilla, the highest of which is 160 feet above sea level. He considered the 42–45-foot shoreline the last stage of Lake Cahuilla and from charcoal found interstratified in lagoonal silts behind gravel bars of this stage, dated it at about 3 centuries ago. He believed it likely that the higher shorelines are late Pleistocene in age.

*Origin of Salton Sea.*    The present Salton Sea was formed by floodings from the Colorado River

FIG. 24.21    Lake Cahuilla shoreline southwest of Indio, California.    (*Photo by John S. Shelton.*)

between 1904 and 1907. From a maximum elevation of 195 feet below sea level in 1907 the level of Salton Sea gradually fell until in the 1940's it became stabilized around 240 feet below sea level. Beginning about 1948, the level of the lake began to rise, as more land was brought under irrigation. This caused considerable alarm to the farmers who occupied the flat shoreland areas; but recently its surface has stabilized again, at about 235 feet below sea level, giving the lake a surface area of approximately 350 square miles. Any tendency to expand in area is offset by the increased evaporation from a greater area of lake surface.

## Mexican Highland Section

Lying east of the Sonoran Desert section and south of the Colorado Plateau province, the Mexican Highland section is an extension into the United States of a geomorphic unit which has its maximum development in Mexico. It resembles the Great Basin section somewhat more than the Sonoran Desert section in that the ratio between mountain and basin is approximately equal, but the geology and structure are somewhat more variable than in the Great Basin. Fault block ranges are present here, but in a somewhat more disordered fashion than in the Great Basin section; particularly at the east are several graben-like troughs, included in what is known as the Rio Grande depression. Although the Mexican Highland section is characterized by semi-arid to arid climate, drainage to the sea is proportionately greater than in the Great Basin section. On the west, tributaries of the Colorado River such as the Gila, Salt, Williams, and Verde rivers provide outlets to the sea, and on the east the Rio Grande and its tributaries furnish a drainage outlet for a considerable area.

Fault block mountains are the most common type found in the section; some mountains, such as the Tres Hermanos Mountains of southwestern New Mexico, are built of granite prophyry intruded into Carboniferous limestone (Lindgren et al., 1910); others are laccolithic in nature; still others display folded structures not unlike those of the Appalachians.

*Intermontane Basins of Texas and New Mexico.* Probably the part of the Mexican Highland section that least fits the conventional picture of basin-range structure is the Marathon Basin region in Brewster County, western Texas (King, 1937). The Marathon topographic basin is only 30 or 40 miles in diameter, but it displays a type of geology and structure that is typically Appalachian in nature. Rocks ranging in age from Cambrian to Pennsylvanian are strongly folded and similar to those found in the Ouachita Mountains of Arkansas and Oklahoma. This similarity even extends so far as to have in the Caballos novaculite a correlative in lithology and age of the Arkansas novaculite (see p. 282). Folds trend northeast and are overturned to the northwest; many of the folds are broken by thrust faults, and one such fault shows a displacement of at least 6 miles. The Marathon Basin is an erosional basin developed on a broad dome of Cretaceous rocks in which the central part has been stripped of its Cretaceous cover, resulting in exposure of Paleozoic rocks at its center. All of the rocks of the dome have been broken by normal faults of probable Tertiary age.

The several mountain ranges at the eastern side of the section in New Mexico and Texas trend in a general north-south direction and more or less enclose a number of sizeable basins, chief among which are the Tularosa and Hueco basins, the Jornada del Muerto, the Plains of San Augustin, and the Rio Grande depression. The mountains are mainly fault blocks, and the basins are grabens. The eastermost of the basins are the Hueco Basin, in the extreme northwest corner of Texas, and, north of it in New Mexico and separated from it by a low divide, the Tularosa Basin. The Rio Grande crosses the Hueco Basin, but the Tularosa Basin lacks external drainage. The Tularosa Basin slopes southward from an altitude of about 4500 feet at the north to 3500 feet at the south. Drainage is centripetal and about midway north-south, and west of its center line is a salt flat which has been the source of the famous white gypsum sands of White Sands National Monument. The gypsum comes from ribs or low ridges of rocks of early Permian age (Herrick, 1900); weathering breaks the exposed gypsum crystals into small grains, which are then carried by the wind and built into dunes. At the northern end of the Tularosa Basin is a maturely developed pediment similar to those found throughout much of the Mexican Highland section (Fenneman, 1931). Another feature found in this basin that is common in the Mexican Highland section is a fresh basalt lava flow which is several miles wide and over 40 miles long.

Lying west of the Tularosa Basin and separated from it by the San Andres Mountains is the Jornado del Muerto, a downwarped trough similar to the Tularosa Basin. Actually the Jornado del Muerto is a series of small basins, several of which contain shallow, ephemeral lakes. Its general slope is to the south, and this fact has partly been responsible for the belief held by some geologists that the Rio Grande once flowed through it. Tight (1905), without giving any reasons for thinking so, dogmatically stated that the "Jornado del Muerto . . . is undoubtedly the old valley of the Rio Grande." Lee (1907) arrived at the same conclusion but gave some reasons for believing this. He thought that the topographic form of the Jornado del Muerto, its geographic position, its surface elevations, and its surface gradient suggested that it had once been the route of the Rio Grande. He believed that the Rio Grande had occupied the Jornado del Muerto as recently as late Pliocene or early Pleistocene time and that it was diverted to its present course by the San Marcial lava flow at the north end of the Jornado del Muerto.

Lying somewhat west and north of the above-mentioned basins is a large bolson or basin which extends in a northeast-southwest direction and is known as the Plains of San Augustin. This basin is about 60 miles long and 6 to 20 miles wide. No permanent streams enter it but ephemeral streams produce sporadic floods over its floor. This basin was the site during late Pleistocene time and early postglacial time of Lake San Augustin. This lake at its maximum was about 165 feet deep and covered some 155 square miles (Powers, 1939). Its shores are marked by beaches, bars, spits, and wave-cut cliffs. As many as nine or ten lake levels are recognizable. Lake San Augustin occupied only the southwestern three-fifths of the Plains of San Augustin, and low hills separate its lacustrine plain from two playas at the northesat end of the basin.

*Rio Grande Depression.* The "Rio Grande depression," as it was called by Bryan (1938), extends for 450 miles from Poncha Pass at the head of the San Luis Valley in Colorado to near El Paso in Texas. It consists of a series of grabens arranged en echelon along the course of the Rio Grande (Kelley, 1952). Altitudes along this structural belt range from about 8000 feet at the north to 3500 feet at the south. It divides the southern end of the Rocky Mountains into two prongs, the Sangre De Cristo Mountains on the east and the Conejos and Jemez Mountains on the west. Development of this structural depression probably began in late Miocene time and culminated late in Pliocene time. The present Rio Grande Valley is a system of connected basins partially filled with sediments from the adjoining uplands in which there is a high proportion of volcanic debris. These basin-fill sediments are known as the Santa Fe formation or group, the age of which has been variously considered as Miocene to Pleistocene.

*Origin of Rio Grande.* It is uncertain when the Rio Grande became integrated into a through stream. Bryan (1938) argued for its existence as a through stream as early as Pliocene time from the presence within the Santa Fe formation of both local basin-bajada type of sediments and floodplain gravels of throughgoing streams. Kelley (1952), however, thought that development as a through stream may have taken place as recently as Pleistocene time. Integration appears to have taken place as early as the development of the late stages of the Ortiz pediment surface along it, but the age of this pediment can not be determined with certainty. Kottlowski (1958) concluded that the Rio Grande was probably born in middle Pleistocene time as a consequence of increased rainfall in the San Juan and Sangre de Cristo mountains accompanying epeirogenic updoming of these mountains. Thus he felt that although the course of the Rio Grande appears to be structurally controlled, its initiating cause was climatic.

The abrupt change in direction of the Rio Grande to southeast at El Paso has led to the belief that the present river was formed by the joining together of two earlier streams, one that flowed southward along the La Mesa depression into the basins of northern Mexico, where the drainage ended and evaporated, and the portion of the Rio Grande downstream from El Paso. This latter stream was supposed to have extended itself headward through El Paso Canyon and captured the present upper Rio Grande. Both Bryan (1938) and Kottlowski (1953, 1958) favored this view.

This idea has been challenged in recent years by Kelley and Silver (1952), who concluded that the great thickness of the Santa Fe beds and a history of continued subsidence along the Rio Grande depression west of the Caballo Mountains supported the view that the Rio Grande has followed its present route ever since it became a through-flowing stream. Ruhe (1962), after a detailed study, came to the conclusion that the river valley at a maximum is mid-Pleistocene in age and that it has held the same general position that it now has since its initiation.

*Topography along Rio Grande Valley.* The Rio Grande Valley proper, in contrast with the more extensive Rio Grande depression, is cut below a topographic surface known as the Jornado-La Mesa surface. According to Ruhe (1962), this surface is mid-Pleistocene in age and consists in part of pediments and in part piedmont alluvial fans. Below the Jornado-La Mesa surface are three valley-flanking pediments, the Tortugas surface at about 350 feet, the Picacho surface at 135 feet, and the Fort Selden surface at 25 feet above the present floodplain. Radiocarbon dating of the Fort Selden surface indicates an age of 2620 ± 200 years. Kottlowski (1958) described three similar surfaces below the La Mesa surface in the El Paso area at somewhat comparable heights above floodplain level. Bryan (1938) likewise described and named several erosion surfaces along the Rio Grande

in the Albuquerque area. Thus, although the terminology varies from place to place, it appears that there is rather general agreement that there is an upper surface that is regional in extent and not restricted to the Rio Grande Valley, the Ortiz-Jornada-La Mesa surface, and below it a sequence of valley-flanking pediments, all presumably of Pleistocene age.

*Sacramento Section*

*General Description.* Lying between the Rio Grande depression on the west and the Pecos Valley section of the Great Plains province on the east is a rather narrow north-south strip named the Sacramento section from the Sacramento Mountains at its western margin. Faulting is prevalent here, but not the strong tilting that characterizes much of the basin-range topography. The topography is related to the Mexican Highland section in the existence within the section of several prominent bolsons. The Estancia Valley at the north and the Salt Basin at the south are prominent examples.

The topography is more plateau-like than mountainous at the north, particularly at the extreme north, where the Glorietta Mesa forms the eastern boundary. Between Glorietta Mesa and the Perdenal Hills on the east and the Sandia and the Manzano Mountains on the west lies Estancia Valley, now mainly a group of salt basins and dunes. This bolson was the site during Pleistocene time of an extensive lake.

*Mountain Ranges.* Southeastward from Estancia Valley and the Pedernal Hills is a chain of mountainous uplifts which from north to south are the Gallinas, Jicarilla, Sierra Blanca, Sacramento, Guadalupe, and Delaware Mountains. At the south, lying between the Guadalupe and Delaware Mountains on the east and the Sierra Diablo or Diablo Plateau on the west, is the prominent bolson known as Salt Basin. Highest of these mountain ranges is the Sierra Blanca, which is, as its name suggests, high enough that some snow remains on it throughout the year.

The eastern chain of mountains consists of a series of tilted blocks bounded on the west by bold scarps and having on their east sides more gentle dip slopes, which extend eastward toward the Pecos Valley. The Diablo Plateau, on the west side of the Salt Basin, is tilted in an opposite direction and has its scarp side facing the Salt Basin to the east of it.

The Guadalupe and Delaware Mountains (King, 1948) form a great north-south tilt block 100 miles long and roughly 50 miles wide. The major difference between the two mountain ranges is that the Guadalupe Mountains are composed mainly of limestones, whereas sandstones predominate in the Delaware Mountains. Forming the southeast side of the Guadalupe Mountains is the bold Reef Escarpment, the boundary in this area between the Basin and Range and Great Plains provinces. Here is the type area of the Capitan Reef, the youngest and best known of the Permian barrier reefs that are so excellently developed in this region (Adams and Frenzel, 1950). Forty-five miles of reef front are exposed in a stretch between Carlsbad, New Mexico, and El Capitan Peak, the bold southern headland of the Reef Escarpment. This, however, is only about one-tenth of the total length of this famous Permian reef.

Initially, the Guadalupe and Delaware Mountains formed a great tectonic arch which had its steepest dip on the west side. This structure was subsequently broken by numerous faults, particularly on the west. Here, along what is called the Border fault zone, strata have been dropped down 2000 to 4000 feet into the Salt Basin at the west. Arching of the mountains probably took place in Cretaceous time. The close correlation between existing topography and the fault blocks suggests that at least some of the faulting took place late in Cenozoic time. Probably more than one period of faulting was involved in uplift of the fault blocks. King (1948) came to the conclusion that the west-facing scarps of the two mountain ranges are fault scarps heightened somewhat by erosion, thus putting them in the class of scarps called composite scarps.

*Salt Basin.* Salt Basin, which lies between the Guadalupe-Delaware Mountains on the east and the Diablo Plateau on the west, is a large down-faulted block, whose floor, with an average altitude of around 3600 feet, lies nearly a mile

below Guadalupe Peak near the southern end of the Guadalupe Mountains. This basin has no outlet and is floored almost entirely by unconsolidated Cenozoic sediments; rock outcrops are limited largely to its margins. A broad bajada extends into the basin from the mountain base on the east, but the central part of the basin is covered with fine-grained sediments. Alkali flats, arranged in chains, like along the east and west sides of the depression and make up a considerable portion of the basin's surface. Dunes composed of both gypsum and quartz sand are common, but distinctly separate from each other. Beach ridges attest to the existence of a former lake. Two lake phases can be distinguished (King, 1948), an early one when the lake was about 40 feet deep and a later phase when it was 20 feet deep. Just when in Pleistocene time the lakes formed is uncertain.

*Summit Erosion Surface.* Even-crested summit areas in the Guadalupe Mountains that seem to be independent of geologic control suggest the presence of a summit erosion surface of uncertain age. King (1948) believed that the erosion surface rather than being Tertiary in age may have developed in Mesozoic time and may represent the surface on which the Cretaceous sediments that formerly extended across the mountain uplift were deposited. If this interpretation is correct, the erosion surface was exhumed, rather than developed during Tertiary time.

## COLORADO RIVER HISTORY

Various ideas as to the history of the Colorado River have been discussed in Chapter 22, and need not be repeated here; but since a considerable part of the Colorado River's course is across the Basin and Range province, certain relationships of its course to the ranges and basins of this province should be pointed out. Lee (1906) described the course of the Colorado River across the Basin and Range province as follows:

The Colorado River emerges from the Grand Canyon at the edge of the Colorado plateau and passes in succession across a debris-filled valley, the Grand Wash trough; through a rock gorge known as Iceberg Canyon; across a second debris-filled trough near Hualpai Wash; through a second rock canyon cutting the Virgin mountains; across the debris-filled Detrital-Sacramento Valley; through a third rock gorge—Boulder Canyon—cutting the Black Mountain range; across Las Vegas basin; through Black Canyon, and thence southward through a succession of less conspicuous rock canyons and detrital basins . . . . From casual observation it would seem to have chosen about the roughest course possible.

As Longwell (1946) has pointed out, the basins which the river crosses are floored with deposits that were laid down under conditions of interior drainage. Coarse debris near the mountain fronts grades basinward into finer clastics, which are intercalated with freshwater limestone and such evaporites as gypsum, and rock salt; nowhere are they mixed with pebbles that could have been deposited by a large stream with a distant source. The age of these basin-fill deposits is still uncertain. As stated in Chapter 22, the youngest interior basin deposit through which the Colorado River has cut its valley is the Muddy Creek formation of uncertain Miocene or Pliocene age. The oldest fluviatile deposits in the basins containing suites of minerals that indicate a provenance within the Colorado Plateau are likewise of uncertain age; they may be as old as Pliocene or as young as Pleistocene. Thus the date at which the Colorado River established a through course across the Basin and Range province remains in doubt until the age of the definitive formations has been more accurately determined.

## SUMMARY OF GEOMORPHIC HISTORY

The geomorphic history of the Basin and Range province can be summarized only in the most general terms. This is true of this province more than any other in the United States, to a large degree because the province consists of a large number of rather distinct structural and geomorphic units each of which has to some extent had its own geomorphic history. No erosional surface of regional scope such as those that have been described in the Rocky Moun-

tains and Appalachians exists or is expectable in an area that has been broken by faulting into a large number of separate structural and geomorphic units. It may well be that following the Mesozoic (presumably Jurassic) orogeny which produced the folds and thrust faults which are part of the internal structure of the mountain ranges the region was reduced to one of low relief. If such an erosional surface once existed, evidence of it has been largely destroyed by later diastrophism and erosion, except where preserved beneath Tertiary lava flows and ignimbrites. According to Misch (1960), such large volumes of rocks were removed from the area during late Mesozoic and early Tertiary time that external drainage must be presumed to have existed then. Van Houten (1956), pictured the Great Basin in early Cenozoic time as an area with warm temperate to subtropical climate, numerous lakes and swamps, and external drainage.

Some of the structural units may have begun to develop as early as Oligocene time, but the main block faulting came in late Tertiary time. Block faulting was accompanied by regional uplift and local accumulation of pyroclastic debris and lava flows. This late Tertiary faulting, combined with basin excavation, led to a period of maximum topographic relief for most of the province. Diastrophism has not ceased in the region, but apparently it has slowed down somewhat, and during Pleistocene time portions of the Basin and Range province experienced periods of sufficient crustal stability that local baselevels of erosion became expressed in the topography in the form of pediments flanking the mountains or along basins with through drainage.

## REFERENCES CITED

Adams, J. E., and H. N. Frenzel (1950). Capitan barrier reef, Texas and New Mexico, *Jour. Geol.*, **58**, 289–312.

Antevs, Ernst (1945). Correlation of Wisconsin glacial maxima, *Am. Jour. Sci.*, **243-A**, 1–39.

Blackwelder, Eliot (1928a). Origin of desert basins of southwest United States, *Geol. Soc. Am. Bull.*, **39**, 262–263 (abs.).

——— (1928b). The recognition of fault scarps, *Jour. Geol.*, **36**, 289–311.

—— (1931). Desert plains, *Jour. Geol.*, **39**, 133–140.

—— (1933). Lake Manly: an extinct lake of Death Valley, *Geog. Rev.*, **23**, 464–471.

—— (1954). Pleistocene lakes and drainage in the Mohave region, southern California, *Calif. Div. Mines Bull.* 170, Ch. 5, 35–40.

Blake W. P. (1907). Lake Cahuilla, the ancient lake of the Colorado Desert, *Nat. Geog. Mag.*, **18**, 830.

Broecker, W. C., and P. C. Orr (1958). Radiocarbon chronology of Lake Lahontan and Lake Bonneville, *Geol. Soc. Am. Bull.*, **69**, 1009–1032.

Brown, J. S. (1923). The Salton Sea region, California, *U. S. Geol. Survey Water-Supply Paper* 497, 292 pp.

Bryan, Kirk (1923). Erosion and sedimentation in the Papago country, Arizona, *U. S. Geol. Survey Bull.* 730, 19–90.

—— (1938). Geology and ground-water conditions of the Rio Grande depression in Colorado and New Mexico, in *Rio Grande Joint Investigation in the Upper Rio Grande Basin in Colorado, New Mexico, and Texas*, Nat. Resources Comm., Regional Planning, Pt. 6, 197–225.

Buwalda, J. P., and W. L. Stanton (1930). Geological events in the history of the Indio Hills and Salton Basin, southern California, *Science*, **71**, 104–106.

Clements, Thomas (1952). Lake Rogers, a Pleistocene lake in the north end of Death Valley, California, *Geol. Soc. Am. Bull.*, **63**, 1324 (abs.).

—— and Lydia Clements (1953). Evidence of Pleistocene man in Death Valley, California, *Geol. Soc. Am. Bull.*, **64**, 1189–1204.

Davis, W. M. (1903). The mountain ranges of the Great Basin, *Harvard Mus. Comp. Zoology Bull.*, **42**, 129–177.

—— (1905). The Wasatch, Canyon, and House Ranges, Utah, *Harvard Mus. Comp. Zoology Bull.*, **49**, 13–56.

—— (1930). The Peacock Range, Arizona, *Geol. Soc. Am. Bull.*, **41**, 293–313.

—— (1936). Geomorphology of mountainous deserts, *Rept. Intern. Geol. Congr.*, Pt. 2, 703–714.

Donath, F. A. (1962). Analysis of basin-range structure, southcentral Oregon, *Geol. Soc. Am. Bull.*, **73**, 1–16.

Droste, J. B. (1961). Clay minerals in sediments of Owens, China, Searles, Panamint, Cadiz, and Danby lake basins, *Geol. Soc. Am. Bull.*, **72**, 1713–1721.

Dutton, C. E. (1880). Geology of the High Plateaus of Utah, *U. S. Geog. and Geol. Survey Rocky Mountain Region (Powell)*, Govt. Printing Office, 307 pp.

Fenneman, N. M. (1931). *Physiography of Western United States*, McGraw-Hill Book Co., New York, 534 pp.

Feth, J. H., and Meyer Rubin (1957). Radiacarbon dating of wave-formed tufas from the Bonneville basin, *Geol. Soc. Am. Bull.*, **68**, 1827 (abs.).

Fitzsimmons, J. P. (1959). The structure and geo-

morphology of west-central New Mexico, N. M. Geol. Soc., *Guidebook, 10th Field Conference*, 112–116.

Flint, R. F. (1957). *Glacial and Pleistocene Geology*, John Wiley and Sons, New York, 553 pp.

—— and W. A. Gale (1958). Stratigraphy and radiocarbon dates at Searles Lake, California, *Am. Jour. Sci.*, **256**, 689–714.

Fuller, R. E. (1931). The geomorphology and volcanic sequence of Steens Mountain in southeastern Oregon, *Univ. Wash. Pub. Geol.*, **3**, 1–130.

—— and A. C. Waters (1929). The nature and origin of the horst and graben structure of southern Oregon, *Jour. Geol.*, **37**, 205–238.

Gale, H. S. (1915). Salines in the Owens, Searles, and Panamint basins, southeastern California, *U. S. Geol. Survey Bull.* 580, 251–324.

Gilbert, G. K. (1874). Preliminary geological report, expedition of 1872, *U. S. Geog. and Geol. Survey West of the One Hundredth Meridian (Wheeler) Progress Rept.*, 48–52.

—— (1875). Report on the geology of portions of Nevada, Utah, California, and Arizona examined in the years 1871 and 1872, *Rept. U. S. Geog. and Geol. Surveys West of the One Hundredth Meridian (Wheeler)*, **3**, 17–187.

—— (1890). Lake Bonneville, *U. S. Geol. Survey Mon.* 1, 438 pp.

Herrick, C. L. (1900). The geology of the white sands of New Mexico, *Jour. Geol.*, **8**, 112–128.

Hewett, D. F. (1931). Geology and ore deposits of the Goodsprings quadrangle, *U. S. Geol. Survey Profess. Paper* 162, 172 pp.

—— (1956). Geology and mineral resources of the Ivanpah quadrangle, California and Nevada, *U. S. Geol. Survey Profess. Paper* 275, 172 pp.

Hubbs, C. L., and R. R. Miller (1938). The Great Basin with emphasis on glacial and postglacial times, II, The zoological evidence, *Univ. Utah Bull.*, **38**, No. 20, 18–166.

Kelley, V. C. (1952). Tectonics of the Rio Grande depression of central New Mexico, N. M. Geol. Soc., *Guidebook, 3rd Field Conference*, 93–105.

—— and C. Silver (1952). Geology of the Caballo Mountains, *Univ. New Mexico Pub. Geol.*, No. 4, 286 pp.

Kesseli, J. E. (1947). Correlation of lake terraces and moraines at Mono Lake, California, *Geol. Soc. Am. Bull.*, **59**, 1375 (abs.).

Keyes, C. R. (1908). Rock-floor of intermont plains of arid regions, *Geol. Soc. Am. Bull.*, **19**, 63–92.

—— (1909). Erosional origin of the Great Basin ranges, *Jour. Geol.*, **17**, 31–37.

King, Clarence (1870). *Rept. U. S. Geol. Explor. 40th Parallel*, **3**, Govt. Printing Office, Washington, 451–473.

—— (1878). Systematic geology, *Rept. U. S. Geol. Explor. 40th Parallel*, **1**, Govt. Printing Office, Washington, 803 pp.

King, P. B. (1937). Geology of the Marathon region, Texas, *U. S. Geol. Survey Profess. Paper* 187, 148 pp.

—— (1948). Geology of the southern Guadalupe Mountains, Texas, *U. S. Geol. Survey Profess. Paper* 215, 183 pp.

—— (1959). *The Evolution of North America*, Princeton Univ. Press, Princeton, 190 pp.

Kottlowski, F. E. (1953). Tertiary-Quaternary sediments of the Rio Grande Valley in southern New Mexico, N. M. Geol. Soc., *Guidebook of Southwestern New Mexico*, 144–148.

—— (1958). Geologic history of the Rio Grande near El Paso, West Texas Geol. Soc., *Guidebook, 1958 Field Trip*, 46–54.

Lee, W. T. (1906). Geology of the lower Colorado River, *Geol. Soc. Am. Bull.*, 17, 275–284.

—— (1907). Water resources of the Rio Grande Valley in New Mexico, *U. S. Geol. Survey Water-Supply Paper* 188, 59 pp.

Lindgren, Waldemar, L. C. Graton, and C. H. Gordon (1910). The ore deposits of New Mexico, *U. S. Geol. Survey Profess. Paper* 68, 361 pp.

Longwell, C. R. (1928). Geology of the Muddy Mountains, Nevada, *U. S. Geol. Survey Bull.* 798, 152 pp.

—— (1945). Low-angle normal faults in the Basin and Range province, *Am. Geophys. Union Trans.*, 26, 107–118.

—— (1946). How old is the Colorado River? *Am. Jour. Sci.*, 244, 817–835.

—— (1952). Basin and Range geology west of the St. George Basin, Utah, Geol. and Min. Surv., *Guidebook to the Geology of Utah*, No. 7, 27–42.

Louderback, G. D. (1923). Basin Range structure in the Great Basin, *Univ. Calif. Pub. Geol. Sci.*, 14, 329–376.

McGee, W. J. (1897). Sheetflood erosion, *Geol. Soc. Am. Bull.*, 8, 87–112.

Mackin, J. H. (1960). Structural significance of Tertiary volcanic rocks in southwestern Utah, *Am. Jour. Sci.*, 258, 81–131.

Maxson, J. H. (1950). Physiographic features of the Panamint Range, California, *Geol. Soc. Am. Bull.*, 61, 99–114.

Means, T. H. (1932). Death Valley, *Sierra Club Bull.*, 17, 67–76.

Miller, R. R. (1946). Correlation between fish distribution and Pleistocene hydrography in eastern California and southwestern Nevada, *Jour. Geol.*, 54, 43–53.

Misch, Peter (1960). Regional structural reconnaissance in central-northeast Nevada and some adjacent areas; Observations and interpretations, Intermountain Assoc. Petroleum Geol., *Guidebook to the Geology of East Central Nevada*, 17–42.

Noble, L. F. (1926). Note on a colemanite deposit near Shasta, California, with a sketch of the Amargosa Valley, *U. S. Geol. Survey Bull.* 785, 63–75.

—— and L. A. Wright (1954). Geology of the central and southern Death Valley region, California, *Calif. Div. Mines Bull.* 170, Ch. 2, 143–160.

Nolan, T. B. (1943). The Basin and Range province in Utah, Nevada, and California, *U. S. Geol. Survey Profess. Paper* 197-D, 141–196.

Norris, R. M., and K. S. Norris (1961). Algodones dunes of southeastern California, *Geol. Soc. Am. Bull.*, 72, 605–629.

Powell, J. W. (1877). *Rept. Geog. and Geol. Survey Rocky Mt. Region*, Govt. Printing Office, Washington, 19 pp.

Powers, W. E. (1939). Basin and shore features of the extinct Lake Augustin, New Mexico, *Jour. Geomorph.*, 2, 345–356.

Putnam, W. C. (1949). Quaternary geology of the June Lake district, California, *Geol. Soc. Am. Bull.*, 60, 1281–1302.

—— (1950). Moraine and shoreline relationships at Mono Lake, California, *Geol. Soc. Am. Bull.*, 61, 115–122.

Ruhe, R. V. (1962). Age of the Rio Grande Valley in southern New Mexico, *Jour. Geol.*, 70, 151–167.

Russell, I. C. (1885). Geological history of Lake Lahontan, a Quaternary lake of northwestern Nevada, *U. S. Geol. Survey Mon.* 11, 288 pp.

Sharp, R. P. (1957). Geomorphology of Cima Dome, Mohave Desert, California, *Geol. Soc. Am. Bull.*, 68, 273–290.

Spurr, J. E. (1901). Origin and structure of the Basin Ranges, *Geol. Soc. Am. Bull.*, 12, 217–270.

Stanley, G. M. (1963). Prehistoric lakes in Salton Sea basin, *Geol. Soc. Am. Spec. Paper* 73, 249–250 (abs.).

Thompson, D. G. (1929). The Mohave Desert region, California, *U. S. Geol. Survey Water-Supply Paper* 578, 759 pp.

Threet, R. L. (1960). Geomorphology of east-central Nevada, Intermountain Assoc. Petroleum Geol.-Eastern Nevada Geol. Soc., *Guidebook to the Geology of East-Central Nevada, 11th Annual Field Conference*, 7–11.

Tight, W. G. (1905). Bolson plains of the southwest, *Am. Geologist*, 36, 271–284.

Van Houten, F. B. (1956). Reconnaissance of Cenozoic sedimentary rocks of Nevada, *Am. Assoc. Petroleum Geologists Bull.*, 40, 2801–2825.

Von Engeln, O. D. (1932). The Ubehebe craters and explosion breccias in Death Valley, *Jour. Geol.*, 40, 726–734.

ADDITIONAL REFERENCES

Bissell, H. J. (1963). Lake Bonneville: Geology of southern Utah Valley, Utah, *U. S. Geol. Survey Profess. Paper* 257-B, 101–130.

Blackwelder, Eliot (1931). Pleistocene glaciation of the Sierra Nevada and Basin Ranges, *Geol. Soc. Am. Bull.*, 42, 865–922.

—— (1933). Origin of the Colorado River, *Geol. Soc. Am. Bull.*, **45**, 551–566.

—— and E. W. Ellsworth (1936). Pleistocene lakes of the Afton Basin, California, *Am. Jour. Sci.*, **231**, 453–463.

Brown, W. H. (1939). Tucson Mountains, an Arizona Basin Range type, *Geol. Soc. Am. Bull.*, **50**, 687–759.

Davis, W. M. (1925). The Basin-Range problem, *Proc. Nat. Acad. Sci.*, **11**, 387–392.

Dibblee, T. W., Jr. (1952). Geology of the Imperial Valley region, California, *Calif. Div. Mines Bull.* 170, Ch. 2, 21–28.

Fitzsimmon, J. P. (1955). Geomorphology of south-central New Mexico, N. M. Geol. Soc., *Guidebook, 6th Field Conference*, 105–107.

Gilbert, G. K. (1928). Studies of basin-range structure, *U. S. Geol. Survey Profess. Paper* 153, 92 pp.

Gilluly, James (1928). Basin Range faulting along the Oquirrh Range, Utah, *Geol. Soc. Am. Bull.*, **39**, 1103–1130.

—— (1937). Physiography of the Ajo region, Arizona, *Geol. Soc. Am. Bull.*, **48**, 323–348.

Glock, W. S. (1929). Geology of the east-central part of the Spring Mountain Range, *Am. Jour. Sci.*, **217**, 326–341.

Hewett, D. F. (1954). General geology of the Mohave Desert region, California, *Calif. Div. Mines Bull.* 170, Ch. 2, 5–20.

Hinds, N. E. A. (1952). Evolution of the California landscape, *Calif. Div. Mines Bull.* 158, 240 pp.

Hopper, R. H. (1947). Geologic section from the Sierra Nevada to Death Valley, California, *Geol. Soc. Am. Bull.*, **58**, 393–432.

Hunt, C. B., H. D. Varnes, and H. E. Thomas (1953). Lake Bonneville: Geology of northern Utah Valley, Utah, *U. S. Geol. Survey Profess. Paper* 257-A, 99 pp.

Johnson, J. B., Jr. and K. L. Cook (1957). Regional gravity surveys of parts of Tooele, Juab, and Millard counties, Utah, *Geophysics*, **22**, 48–61.

Jones, D. J., and R. E. Marsell (1955). Pleistocene sediments of lower Utah Valley, Utah Geol. Soc., *Guidebook to the Geology of Utah*, No. 10, 85–112.

Longwell, C. R. (1949). Structure of the northern Muddy area, Nevada, *Geol. Soc. Am. Bull.*, **60**, 923–968.

—— (1954). History of the lower Colorado River and the Imperial depression, *Calif. Div. Mines Bull.* 170, Ch. 5, 53–56.

Louderback, G. D. (1924). Period of scarp production in the Great Basin, Univ. Calif. Publ., *Bull. Dept. Geol. Sci.*, **15**, 1–44.

Marsell, R. E., and D. J. Jones (1955). Pleistocene history of lower Jordan Valley, Utah Geol. Soc., *Guidebook to geology of Utah*, No. 10, 113–120.

Merriam, C. W., and C. A. Anderson (1942). Recon-naissance survey of the Roberts Mountains, Nevada, *Geol. Soc. Am. Bull.*, **53**, 1675–1728.

Morrison, R. B. (1961). New evidence on the history of Lake Bonneville from an area south of Salt Lake City, Utah, *U. S. Geol. Survey Profess. Paper* 424-D, D-125–D-127.

—— (1961). Lake Lahontan stratigraphy and history in the Carson Desert (Fallon) area, Nevada, *U. S. Geol. Survey Profess. Paper* 424-D, D-111–D-114.

Noble, L. F. (1941). Structural features of the Virgin Spring area, Death Valley, California, *Geol. Soc. Am. Bull.*, **52**, 941–1000.

Osmond, J. C. (1960). Tectonic history of the Basin and Range province in Utah and Nevada, *Mining Engineering*, **12**, 251–265.

Putnam, W. C. (1938). The Mono Craters, California, *Geog. Rev.*, **28**, 68–82.

—— (1960). Origin of Rock Creek and Owens River gorges, Mono County, California, *Univ. Calif. Pub. Geol. Sci.*, **34**, 221–280.

Reiche, Parry (1940). The origin of Kilbourne Hole, New Mexico, *Am. Jour. Sci.*, **238**, 212–225.

Richmond, G. M. (1952). Correlation of the late Quaternary deposits of the La Sal Mountains, Utah, and Lakes Bonneville and Lahontan by means of interstadial soils, *Geol. Soc. Am. Bull.*, **63**, 1369 (abs.).

—— (1961). New evidence of the age of Lake Bonneville from moraines in Little Cottonwood Canyon, Utah, *U. S. Geol. Survey Profess. Paper* 424-D, D 127–D 128.

Russell, R. J. (1928). Basin-range structure and stratigraphy of the Warner Range, northeastern California, Univ. Calif. Pub., *Bull. Dept. Geol. Sci.*, **17**, 387–496.

Sauer, Carl (1930). Basin and range forms in the Chiricahua area (Arizona and New Mexico), *Univ. Calif. Pub. Geog.*, **3**, 339–414.

Sharp, R. P. (1938). Pleistocene glaciation in the Ruby-East Humboldt Range, northeastern Nevada, *Jour. Geomorph.*, **1**, 296–323.

—— (1939). Basin-range structure of the Ruby-East Humboldt Range, northeastern Nevada, *Geol. Soc. Am. Bull.*, **50**, 881–919.

—— (1940). Geomorphology of the Ruby-East Humboldt Range, Nevada, *Geol. Soc. Am. Bull.*, **51**, 337–371.

Sykes, Godfrey (1937). The Colorado delta, *Am. Geog. Soc. Pub.* 19, 193 pp.

Tuan, Yi-fu (1959). Pediments in southeastern Arizona, *Univ. Calif. Pub. Geog.*, **13**, 140 pp.

Williams, J. S. (1962). Lake Bonneville: Geology of southern Cache Valley, Utah, *U. S. Geol. Survey Profess. Paper* 257-C, 131–152.

GENERAL DESCRIPTION

Recognizing the Sierra Nevada and Cascade Mountains as a single geomorphic province is largely a matter of convenience; in doing so we group together two mountain ranges that differ notably in their geology, topography, and geomorphic history. The chief justification for considering them a single geomorphic unit is that they form a more or less continuous barrier over 1000 miles long extending from southern Canada to the Mohave Desert in California. How formidable a barrier these mountain ranges are is indicated by the fact that along their entire length only two rivers, the Columbia and Pitt, flow through them.

Near its southern end in southern Oregon and northern California the Cascade Range breaks down and lacks a continuous crest, but individual peaks, such as Mt. Shasta, exceed 14,000 feet in altitude. Altitudes in the Sierra Nevada are highest in the Mt. Whitney area and decrease from here to the north and south. The Cascade Mountains are lowest at their southern end, and from here altitudes increase northward and attain their maximum near the Canadian border. A distinctive characteristic of the Cascade Mountains is that individual peaks may rise several thousand feet above the general level of the range crest. Range crest altitudes are as low as 5000 feet and rarely exceed 8000 feet, yet volcanic peaks attain altitudes ranging from 10,000 feet to over 14,000 feet on Mount Shasta and Mount Rainier.

The Sierra Nevada and Cascades differ from each other in the following significant respects:

about three-fourths of the Sierra Nevada rocks are granitic in type, whereas roughly the same proportion of the Cascade rocks are volcanics; faulting is much more significant in the Sierra Nevada than in the Cascades; average altitudes are greater in the Sierra Nevada than in the Cascades, although individual peaks may be as high in one range as in the other; the topography of the Sierra Nevada has been produced by erosional processes which have been in operation since early Tertiary time, whereas the topography of the Cascades is largely a product of constructional volcanism, modified only moderately by stream and glacial erosion.

SIERRA NEVADA SECTION

The Sierra Nevada is a massive fault block, 400 miles long and 40 to 80 miles wide, that is downtilted to the west. Its maximum width is at the north, where the Lake Tahoe Basin and the Carson Range east of it are included in the section. The Sierra Nevada uplift is generally considered as terminating at the south in the Tehachapi Mountains at the junction of the Garlock and San Andreas faults (see p. 538). Topographically the Tehachapi Mountains are a continuation of the Sierra Nevada, but in structure, geology, and mode of origin they are different (Buwalda, 1954). The Tehachapi Mountains did not originate as a block downtilted to the west but are more of the nature of a horst with complex internal structure. The northern end of the Sierra Nevada is abrupt and is where the older rocks of the Sierra Nevada disappear beneath the volcanic rocks of the southern Cascase Range and the Modoc Plateau.

## Geology and Structure

Rocks of the Sierra Nevada (Jenkins, 1943) are predominately plutonic rocks of the "Sierra Nevada batholith" of Mesozoic age. This so-called batholith, rather than consisting of a single great plutonic mass, is known to represent several intrusions of rocks of varying composition distributed over a moderately long period of geologic time (King, 1959). Particularly at the north are numerous small areas of meta-sedimentary and meta-igneous rocks of Paleozoic and Mesozoic age which form inclusions, roof pendants, and screens in the topography on the batholith. These features represent what is left of the rocks which were intruded by the batholith. Resting unconformably on the crystalline rocks, particularly in the western foothills, are scattered patches of Eocene fluviatile sediments, volcanic rocks of Miocene, Pilocene, and Quaternary age, and Quaternary glacial deposits and alluvial gravels.

The Paleozoic rocks consist mainly of slates, phyllites, graywackes, and other sedimentary types plus some lavas and tuffs. They are thought to be mainly Mississippian in age, but locally on the flanks of the Sierra Nevada rocks of Ordovician and Silurian age are found. The Mesozoic rocks are slates, graywackes, and volcanic rocks of Triassic and Jurassic age. These older rocks, which once extended across the site of the present Sierra Nevada, were metamorphosed during the Nevadan orogeny, in probable late Jurassic and early Cretaceous time, and compressed into a series of folded mountains similar in structure to those found in the Appalachian Highlands, with axes extending in a northwest-southeast direction. The remnants of Paleozoic rocks found in the western foothills and the scattered remains of Triassic and Jurassic rocks in the upland areas, particularly extensive at the northern part of the range, are the roots of these pre-batholithic fold mountains.

The Sierra Nevada displays a very asymmetric east-west profile with an abrupt and steep east front and a much longer and more gentle western backslope (see Figs. 25.1 and 25.2). Hinds (1952) has pointed out that the eastern front of the Sierra Nevada rises higher above its immediate surroundings than any other mountain front in the United States. In the Owens Valley area there is a difference of 11,000 feet between altitudes in the Sierra Nevada and Owens Valley. Two other areas in the United States where abrupt topographic rises exist are along the contact of the Rocky Mountains and Great Plains in Colorado and at the contact of the Teton Mountains and Jackson Hole. Along the Rocky Mountain front there is a difference between altitudes of 14,000 feet in the higher peaks and 5000 feet on the plains, for a maximum relief of 9000 feet; along the Teton front the relief is better than 6000 feet, the difference between altitudes of 12,000–13,000 feet in the higher peaks and about 6800 feet on the floor of Jackson Hole. It is rather generally agreed that the eastern front of the Sierra Nevada is a fault scarp and that the range exhibits basically a basin-range type of structure (Louderback, 1923). Justification for excluding it from the Basin and Range province can be found mainly in the fact that the Sierra Nevada is much larger, higher, and longer than the "typical" basin-range mountains and thus is of a magnitude that justifies recognition as a separate geomorphic unit. The advanced degree of glaciation on both the east and west sides is another reason why the range is hardly typical of the Basin and Range mountains.

Describing the east front of the Sierra Nevada as a fault scarp is not meant to imply that a single fault extends along its whole 400-mile length. Undoubtedly movement took place along a number of faults. Nor is it implied that the range front as now seen is the original scarp produced by faulting; that scarp has undergone a great deal of modification since it was formed. Putnam (1960a) has pointed out that many of the faults along the east margin of the Sierra Nevada have dips as great as 70 degrees, whereas the maximum slope of the Sierra Nevada frontal scarp rarely exceeds 30 degrees. This indicates that the original fault scarp has been modified appreciably by weathering, mass-wasting, and

FIG. 25.1    View of west slope of Sierra Nevada, looking toward Lake Tenaya from Yosemite.    (*Photo by Spence Air Photos.*)

erosion. The present scarp has apparently attained a slope angle which represents a condition of stability between existing rock types and the gradational processes now in operation on the scarp front. Foothills are notably lacking along the eastern margin of the Sierra Nevada, unless the Carson Range east of Lake Tahoe and Diamond and Grizzly Mountains farther north are considered such. Actually, these ranges are separate fault blocks tilted to the southwest like the Sierra Nevada block.

Lake Tahoe, which occupies the depressed block between the Sierra Nevada and the Carson Range, has an altitude of 6200 feet and a depth in excess of 1600 feet. Its basin is bounded on both the east and west sides by faults which are parallel to the boundary fault of the Sierra

Nevada. Sierra Valley, still farther north, has structural conditions similar to those of the Lake Tahoe basin. Lake Tahoe has a setting which for beauty and grandeur is equalled by few lakes in the United States.

*Contrast between Eastern and Western Slopes*

The western slope of the Sierra Nevada (see Fig. 25.1) across a belt 70 miles wide west of Lake Tahoe has an average gradient of only 100 feet per mile (Fenneman, 1931), or only slightly more than 1 degree. The average gradient for the whole western flank of the Sierra Nevada is of the order of 2 to 3 degrees. Despite the fact that the western slope is furrowed by numerous valleys, when viewed from a distance it gives the impression of a plateau-like surface of low relief.

The bold east front of the Sierra Nevada (see Fig. 25.2) displays a series of salients and re-entrants that seem to be controlled by the numerous faults that cut the bedrock. When viewed from a distance the face of the frontal escarpment appears to be a continuous slope, but when observed in detail it is seen to consist of a series of benches or shoulders separated from each other by steep risers which, as Putnam (1949) has noted, give it the appearance of a giant stairway. These benches probably reflect numerous faults that are present along the range front and seem to suggest that the range front was elevated as a series of successive fault slices which are now reflected in the benches. Large alluvial fans are notably lacking along the base of the east scarp of the Sierra Nevada.

This is probably due mainly to the lack of large streams on this side of the range as related to the lower precipitation here. Putnam (1960) thought, however, that another factor which may help to explain the scarcity of large streams is the great amount of frost-riven debris that mantles the upper slope of the escarpment; this material absorbs the melting snow in spring and releases it gradually to drainage lines.

### Geomorphic History

Although the western slope of the Sierra Nevada is less striking than its precipitous eastern front, this portion of the range throws more light on the geomorphic history of the Sierra Nevada than does the eastern slope, because here recognizable remnants of Tertiary erosion surfaces are preserved. Still present are even some remnants

FIG. 25.2  East front of Sierra Nevada, looking south; Mt. Whitney in the distance.  (*Photo by John S. Shelton.*)

of drainage lines dating back to the folded structures that developed in Jurassic time, long before the present Sierra Nevada was born. As Matthes (1960) has pointed out, the western slope of the Sierra Nevada is the only sizable elevated area west of the Rocky Mountains in which are preserved extensive topographic surfaces that date back into Tertiary time. This is particularly true of that portion of the western slope of the Sierra Nevada extending southward from the Tuolumne River to near the Kern River; the Kern Plateau south of Mt. Whitney is unequalled in this respect. North of the Tuolumne River volcanic agglomerates and lavas obscure the erosion surfaces, and south of the Kern River faulting has made difficult an interpretation of the early geomorphic history of the range.

Numerous papers have been published dealing with presumed erosion surfaces and cycles in the Sierra Nevada. Mainly these have dealt with two areas, the Kern River-Mount Whitney and the Yosemite Valley-San Joaquin Basin regions. Lawson (1904), in a discussion of the upper Kern Basin, was the first to give a detailed description of the topography of that area. He recognized three topographic zones, the High Mountain, High Valley, and Cañon zones. He thought that he saw evidence in the High Mountain zone of two topographic levels, which he called the Summit Upland and the Subsummit Plateau. The Summit Upland was supposedly represented by the higher peaks and the summit divide areas; the Subsummit Plateau, some 2500 feet lower, included a well-defined plateau area. The most prominent part of the High Valley zone is what is called the Chagoopa Plateau; below this is the 3000-foot-deep and 24-mile-long canyon of the Kern River. Lawson believed that the Summit Upland was a quasi-mature surface which came close to representing the unroofed top of the Sierra Nevada batholith; the Subsummit Plateau was viewed as an erosional surface that "must . . . be regarded . . . as the correlative of the late Tertiary peneplain of the western flank of the Sierra Nevada." Lawson thought that development of the Chagoopa Plateau and other areas of the High Valley zone

must have occupied most of Quaternary time; cutting of the Kern River canyon and glaciation were believed to have taken place very late in Quaternary time. It should be recognized, however, that at the time of publication of Lawson's paper evidence of multiple Pleistocene glaciation in the Sierra Nevada had not yet been recognized.

Knopf (1918), working on the eastern slope of the Sierra Nevada, saw what he considered evidence of two erosion surfaces which he called the Summit Upland and Subsummit Plateau surfaces. The gently sloping tops of such mountains as Mount Whitney, Mount Langley (see Fig. 25.3), Cirque Peak, and Mount Barnard were considered remnants of the Summit Upland surface, and fairly extensive portions of the Subsummit Plateau surface were thought to be preserved in the plateau tract below the higher peaks. Knopf did not agree with Lawson that the Subsummit surface might represent the undulating top surface of the Sierra Nevada batholith, but thought rather that it represented unreduced remnants of a once extensive upland erosion surface.

Matthes (1937), in a discussion of the erosion surfaces in the Mt. Whitney area, described what he called the Mt. Whitney, Cirque Peak, and Boreal Plateau surfaces; he later, in a posthumous paper (1950a) dealing with the Sequoia National Park area, added the Chagoopa Plateau surface to the list of erosion surfaces above the Kern River canyon. The Mt. Whitney and Cirque Peak surfaces, both of which were considered somewhat questionable, were believed to have formed during Eocene time; the Boreal Plateau (Subsummit) surface was considered Miocene in age and the Chagoopa surface, Pliocene; cutting of the Kern River canyon was supposed to have started at the beginning of the Pleistocene epoch.

Matthes (1930), in his treatment of the Yosemite Valley, recognized three cycles of erosion and designated them as the Broad Valley, Mountain Valley, and Canyon stages; in one posthumous paper (1950b) this same succession was restated, but in a later posthumous publication (1960), dealing with the geomorphology of the San Joaquin Basin, a cycle preceding the

FIG. 25.3   Remnants of erosion surfaces in Sierra Nevada as seen looking south toward Mount Whitney.   (*Photo by John S. Shelton.*)

Broad Valley cycle was added. This cycle, referred to as an "Eocene cycle," was supposedly represented by the tabular summits of such peaks as Mount Darwin and Mount Wallace. Matthes at no time attempted a correlation of the erosion surfaces in the Mount Whitney-Kern River area with those in the Yosemite-San Joaquin Basin region, because he did not feel that the topography in the Kern River region was fully typical of the Sierra Nevada.

As will be seen in Figure 25.4, the number of alleged erosion cycles represented in the two areas do not coincide. If it be considered likely that the questionable Mount Whitney and Cirque Peak erosion surfaces of the Kern River-Yosemite are not represented in the Yosemite region, a possible correlation could have the "Eocene surface" equivalent to the Boreal Plateau and the Broad Valley surface correlative with the Chagoopa Plateau surface. This leaves the Mountain Valley stage without an equivalent at the south. Possibly this apparent anomaly may be explained by the view of Axelrod and Ting (1961) that the Mountain Valley stage was merely an early local phase of the Canyon stage and was not significant regionally.

*Glaciation.* Both the east and west sides of the Sierra Nevada have been severely glaciated, and here some of the pioneer studies of mountain glaciation in North America were made. In the area between Lake Tahoe and Mount Whitney local mountain icecaps developed, and valley glaciers many miles long originated in these icecaps. The mountain icecap in the Yosemite area reached down to an altitude of around 5000 feet. The combined Merced-Yosemite glacier extended more than 15 miles beyond the ice field in which it originated, and a glacier in Yuba Valley, in the northern Sierra Nevada, during

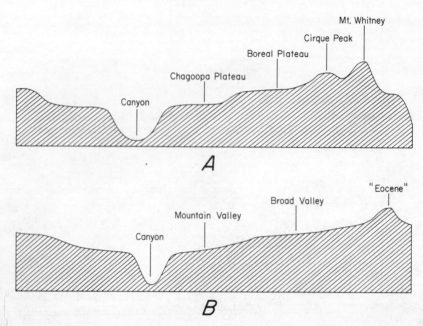

FIG. 25.4   Diagrams suggesting relationships of erosion surfaces in the (*A*) Kern River-Mt. Whitney area and (*B*) Yosemite-San Joaquin area.   (*After G. B. Dalrymple, Geol. Soc. Am. Bull., 74.*)

the maximum glaciation, was as much as 24 miles long.

U. S. Geological Survey Professional Paper 160, by Francois Matthes, "The Geologic History of Yosemite Valley," has become a sort of semiclassic in American geology. The deep, 7-mile-long glacial trough and associated hanging valleys and granite monoliths of Yosemite Valley are so familiar to American geologists that they need no description here. However, a seismological survey (Gutenberg, Buwalda, and Sharp, 1956) showed that during the earliest of the glaciations in Yosemite Valley the bedrock floor of the valley was excavated to a depth as much as 2000 feet below the present floor of the valley. Glacial outwash and interglacial and postglacial deltaic and lacustrine deposits have filled the trough to the level of its present bottom.

Glaciation in the Yosemite region followed or perhaps accompanied what has been designated as the Canyon stage in the geomorphic evolution of the present-day topography. Matthes recognized evidence of three ages of glaciation in the Yosemite Valley, the Glacier Point, El Portal, and Wisconsin glaciations. The Glacier

Point glaciation was believed to have occurred in either Nebraskan or Kansan time, and the El Portal in Kansan or Illinoian time. Matthes' classification of mountain glaciation on the western slope of the Sierra Nevada has not been followed much in recent years. In more common use is the classification proposed by Blackwelder (1931) for glacial ages on the eastern slope of the Sierra Nevada. Blackwelder saw here what he considered evidence for four ages of mountain glaciation, named by him, from oldest to youngest, the McGee, Sherwin, Tahoe, and Tioga (see Fig. 25.5). The McGee glaciation was believed to be of Nebraskan, the Sherwin of Kansan, the Tahoe of early Wisconsin, and the Tioga of late Wisconsin age.

Undoubtedly the Tahoe and Tioga glaciations are Wisconsin in age, but difference of opinion exists as to the age of the McGee and Sherwin tills. Axelrod and Ting (1960, 1961) and Axelrod (1962), from a study of pollen floras found in the Sierra Nevada and adjacent areas, concluded that the McGee till is Kansan in age and the Sherwin is Illinoian. Putnam (1960b, 1962), accepting the conclusion of Axelrod and Ting that the principal uplift of the Sierra Nevada occurred in Pleistocene time, concluded that the Sierra Nevada did not stand high enough in early Pleistocene time to produce extensive glaciation and that therefore the Nebraskan glaciation was missing. He therefore believed the McGee and Sherwin tills to be Kansan and Illinoian in age respectively.

If the potassium-argon dates obtained by Dalyrmple (1931) on the age of basalt flows resting on various erosion surfaces in the Sierra Nevada (see p. 514) are correct, serious doubt must exist as to the accuracy of the conclusion reached by Axelrod and Ting. Furthermore, if Putnam's (1960a) conclusion that the Bishop tuff is younger than the Sherwin till is correct, the

Illinoian age of the Sherwin till is doubtful, for a $K^{40}$-$A^{40}$ age of over 800,000 years has been obtained for this tuff (Evernden et al., 1957), and no existing chronology places the Illinoian glaciation that far back in Pleistocene time.

Sharp and Birman (1963) have presented what they considered evidence for a glaciation between the Sherwin and Tahoe that may possibly be of Illinoian age; this glaciation they designated as the Mono Lake. They also recognized a glacial substage between the Tahoe and Tioga, which they named the Tenaya.

Correlation of mountain glaciations with those of the Central Lowlands, particularly for an area as remote from the Central Lowlands as the Sierra Nevada, is at best speculative. It may

FIG. 25.5    Tioga, Tahoe, and Sherwin moraines below Convict Lake, eastern Sierra Nevada. (*Photo by John S. Shelton.*)

be reasonable to presume that glaciations in the mountains were equivalent in time and number to those in the lowlands, but there is no existing proof that this is so. With the present state of knowledge regarding glaciation in the Sierra Nevada, about the only safe conclusion that we may reach is that there is evidence of two and perhaps three pre-Wisconsin glaciations, but it is still uncertain how they correlate with glacial ages and subages recognized in the central and eastern United States.

A highly tenuous correlation of Sierra Nevada glaciations with those in the Rocky Mountains would make the Sherwin contemporaneous with the Buffalo glaciation, the Tahoe correlative with the Bull Lake glaciation, and the Tioga glaciation the same age as the Pinedale. However, if the proposed Mono Lake glaciation should prove to be a reality and of age rank, it might correlate with the Buffalo glaciation of the Rocky Mountains. Such correlations as this are exceedingly uncertain, for it has not been established yet that the glacial histories of all western mountains are the same.

*Time of Uplift of Sierra Nevada.* Early workers on the geomorphic history of the Sierra Nevada attributed an early to mid-Tertiary age to the erosion surfaces now preserved above the mountain canyons. This meant that uplift of the Sierra Nevada had to have begun in mid-Tertiary time, and thus only a small part of the tilting could be considered as recent as the Pleistocene. In recent years some geologists have been inclined to assign much younger dates to the erosion surfaces and the time of major uplift of the Sierra Nevada.

It will be recalled that the erosion surface variously called Eocene, Subsummit, and Boreal was long considered to be of early Tertiary age, and the surface called the High Valley, Broad Valley, or Chagoopa was thought to have been developed in Miocene or Pliocene time. Only the Canyon stage was dated as recent as Pleistocene. Approximately 2500 feet of uplift took place between development of the Eocene or Subsummit surface and the completion of the Broad Valley surface, and the Broad Valley

surface is trenched by canyons 3000 feet deep. Thus 5500 feet of uplift has taken place in the Kern Canyon region since the Subsummit surface developed.

Hudson (1960) accepted the idea of three stages of topographic development separated by two major periods of uplift and tilting, but he thought that these events took place much later than envisioned by Matthes. He considered the Broad Valley surface to be no older than late Pliocene and possibly as young as Pleistocene. This conclusion was arrived at from his belief that the Broad Valley-Chagoopa surface is developed across andesitic deposits known as the Mehrten formation whose age he considered to be early or middle Pliocene. Dalrymple (1963) differed with this conclusion as to the age of the Broad Valley-Chagoopa surface because a basalt flow filling a canyon cut into the Chagoopa surface from potassium-argon dating gave an age of 3.5 million years. This, according to Dalrymple, indicates that the Chagoopa surface is at least as old as early Pliocene, as originally suggested by Matthes.

Hudson further concluded that uplift of the Sierra Nevada was not, as Matthes believed, as a single block which was dislocated and tilted southwestward without appreciable deformation during the two successive uplifts, but rather the uplift was differential, being greater in the Merced River region than it was farther north. He further believed that the altitude of the Sierra Nevada in the Yosemite region was about 9000 feet at the time of the Broad Valley stage and that subsequent uplift of approximately 4000 feet took place during two episodes, one in early Pleistocene time and another in late middle Pleistocene time. The latter uplift, which he dated as post-Mountain Valley, was believed to have produced about two-thirds of the 4000 feet of uplift.

Axelrod and Ting (1961), from a study of spore-pollen floras in lacustrine sediments on the Boreal and Chagoopa erosion surfaces, concluded that the Boreal surface was late Pliocene in age and the Chagoopa surface early Pleistocene (see Fig. 25.6). There is, however, a degree of uncertainty to this type of dating of erosion surfaces,

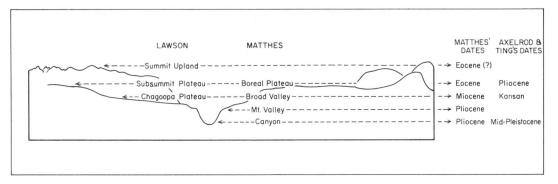

FIG. 25.6 Diagrammatic profile of upland erosion surfaces of Sierra Nevada with estimates of their ages. (*After W. C. Putnam, Univ. Calif. Pub. Geol. Sci.,* **40.**)

because it cannot be demonstrated that the sediments from which the fossil floras were obtained are of approximately the same age as the surfaces on which they rest. Axelrod (1962) agreed with Hudson that the Broad Valley or Chagoopa surface truncates beds of Pliocene age and is probably early Pleistocene in age, but he did not believe that this surface was developed at altitudes as high as 9000 feet. Fossil floras found in the lacustrine deposits on the Broad Valley or Chagoopa surfaces are of such a nature as to suggest that the region was one of low altitude during Oligocene, Miocene, and Pliocene time. The Miocene floras are similar to those found now in areas of low relief at altitudes of less than 2000 feet. Similarly, late Pliocene and early Pleistocene floras now at altitudes of 9000 to 10,000 feet on the Chagoopa surface are similar to present floras at moderate altitudes. Axelrod thus concluded that the fossil floras of the Mt. Whitney region indicate a post-Pliocene uplift in that area of around 9000 feet, 6000 feet of which took place in post-Kansan time. The entire fossil flora fails to show any evidence that the Sierra Nevada in Tertiary time was high enough to produce enough rain shadow effect to cause marked differences in the vegetation in California and in the Basin and Range area in Nevada.

Putnam (1960b, 1962) thought that there had been at least 4000 feet of uplift of the Sierra Nevada after deposition of the McGee till. This conclusion was reached from his belief that the

McGee till had been elevated that much as a result of faulting and warping since its deposition. He considered the upfaulted surface on which the McGee till rests to be the equivalent of the Boreal erosion surface of the Kern Canyon area or the Eocene stage of Matthes in the Yosemite and upper San Joaquin Valley regions and believed that it was cut in late Pliocene time. This differs markedly from Dalrymple's belief that the even younger Chagoopa (Broad Valley) surface is at least as old as early Pliocene.

The preceding discussion makes it apparent that there is marked divergence of opinion as to the number and ages of erosion surfaces in the Sierra Nevada. There does seem to be, however, agreement among a considerable number of workers that remnants of former erosion surfaces do exist, attesting to intermittent standstill and uplift of the Sierra Nevada during Tertiary and Quaternary time, but how many such cycles there were and when they occurred are still debatable. The crux of the argument lies in whether greater credence is to be given to potassium-argon dating or to the ages arrived at from interpretation of paleobotanical and glacial evidence.

*Buried Tertiary Valleys.* Work on the gold placers of the Sierra Nevada has resulted in an appreciation of some interesting relationships between Tertiary valley systems and present-day ones. Their description, originally by Lindgren (1911) and more recently by Jenkins and Wright

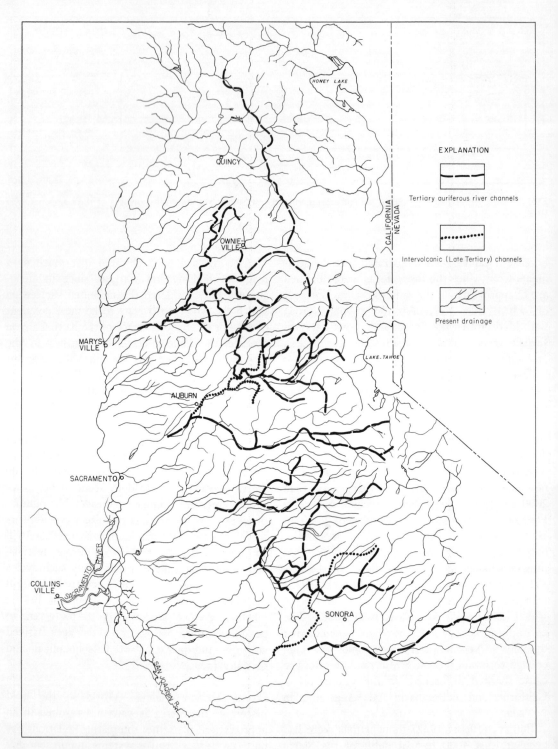

FIG. 25.7  Map showing relationships between Tertiary river channels and present valley systems.    (*After Waldemar Lindgren, U. S. Geol. Survey Profess. Paper 73.*)

(Jenkins, 1935; Jenkins and Wright, 1934) provides an interesting study in paleogeomorphology. Three sets of valley systems may be distinguished in the Sierra Nevada, the *prevolcanic valleys* of early Tertiary or Eocene age, the *intervolcanic valleys* of Miocene and Pliocene age, and the *postvolcanic valleys* of Quaternary age (see Fig. 25.7). The gold placers are found mainly in the early Tertiary prevolcanic valley systems; hence there is need to distinguish these from the later Miocene-Pliocene valleys. Following development of the Miocene-Pliocene valleys lava flows filled many of them, and today along some of the valleys, as at Table Mountain near Sonora, California, the lava flows have formed lava-capped ridges, interesting examples of inversion of topography.

## CASCADE RANGE

### General Description

Scattered patches of volcanic rocks in the northern Sierra Nevada make the boundary between this section and the southern Cascade section a transitional one. However, a very noticeable change in geology takes place about the 40th parallel, just north of where the Feather River flows out of the Sierra Nevada. Here, instead of the metamorphosed and faulted Paleozoic and Mesozoic rocks with their granitic intrusions which characterize the northern Sierra Nevada, volcanic rocks become predominant; not far north of here they bury all other types. Volcanic rocks characterize the Cascades until the latitude of Seattle is reached, where granitic rocks again make an appearance. The Cascade Range terminates a short distance north of the Canadian border.

Although the Cascade Range is largely a great pile of volcanic rocks, its present height was not attained entirely by the piling up of lavas, for it has undergone considerable regional uplift. The volcanic rocks of the Cascade Mountains, instead of having been poured out mainly as flows, as in the adjacent Columbia Intermontane Plateaus, were to an equal degree, at least, the product of explosive volcanism from central vents. Thus a large amount of pyroclastic material is found among the rocks of the Cascade Range. The most striking topographic feature of the Cascades is the line of volcanoes which represents the most recent phase of volcanic activity; these volcanoes rise several thousand feet above the general level of the Cascade Range (see Fig. 25.8).

The Cascade Mountains have been divided into three sections (Fenneman, 1931). The Southern Cascade section extends northward from about latitude 40 north for approximately 150 miles to the latitude of North Klamath Lake; the Middle Cascade section, which is by far the largest of the three sections, reaches northward to a line connecting Seattle and Ellensburg, Washington; and the Northern Cascade section extends from here to the end of the Cascade Range, a short distance north of the Canadian boundary.

### Southern Cascade Mountains

The southern Cascades hardly merit being called a mountain range, for they consist primarily of a line of volcanoes with valleys, sags, and basins between them. It is in this section that the Pitt River manages to find its way from the Basin and Range province through the Cascades into the Great Valley of California.

*Lassen Peak.* Hundreds of individual volcanic cones can be counted in the southern Cascade section, but by all odds the two which dominate the topography are Lassen Peak and Mount Shasta. Lassen Peak (see Fig. 25.9) is of interest on two accounts. Strictly speaking it is not a volcanic cone but is a plug dome built up by extrusion of viscous lava in the crater of a badly shattered former volcano called Mt. Brokeoff (Williams, 1932a; see Fig. 25.10). This plug dome stands about 2500 feet above the floor of the original crater and is about $1\frac{1}{2}$ miles in diameter. Lassen Peak is of further interest because it is the only volcano in conterminous United States which may be considered active, as it became mildly active in 1914 and continues to emit gases.

FIG. 25.8 View of southern Cascade Range showing line of volcanic peaks. The area covered extends from the Three Sisters in the foreground to Mount Rainier in the far background, a distance of approximately 225 miles. (*Air Force photo.*)

*Mount Shasta.* Eighty miles northwest of Lassen Peak is Mount Shasta, one of the most striking of the Cascade volcanoes (see Fig. 25.11). It is a typical strato-volcano composed of andesite and basalt lavas with minor amounts of dacite (Williams, 1932b). It exceeds 14,000 feet in altitude and is about 17 miles in diameter at its base. It is reported to have been active as recently as 1786. When it had nearly attained its present height, two fissures opened on its flanks; eruptions along the north-south fissure produced a line of cinder cones and plug domes; along the east-west fissure rose the large parasitic cone known as Shastina. Black Butte, a plug dome at the west base of Mount Shasta, may

also have developed during this period of activity. At the west the Mount Shasta lavas abut against the sedimentary and intrusive rocks of the Klamath Mountains, and on the east they merge with the lava beds of the Modoc Plateau.

### Northern Cascade Mountains

The Northern Cascade Mountains section will be treated before the Middle Cascade section because the Middle Cascade section partakes somewhat of the character of the sections to the south and north of it and can be better understood after these sections have been discussed.

*Geology and Topography.* A change in geology from that found at the south takes place at the southern margin of the Northern Cascade Mountains section. The rocks, instead of being dominantly volcanics, are Paleozoic and Mesozoic sedimentary and metamorphic rocks which have been intruded by numerous small batholiths and stocks. The majority of the peaks are the result of gradational processes rather than having been built by volcanic eruptions. Glacier Peak (10,436) and Mount Baker (10,750) are volcanic cones, but the other peaks in the section are composed of granitic rocks. The topography is rugged despite the fact that the summit surface is plateau-like in nature; many valleys 2000 to 3000 feet deep dissect the area.

In their overall aspects the Northern Cascades resemble more the Sierra Nevada than other parts of the Cascade Mountains. This similarity can be noted in the presence of: ancient Paleozoic and Mesozoic metamorphosed sediments intruded by batholiths; a plateau-like upland surface which may represent a former erosion surface; numerous granitic peaks which rise above the general level of the plateau surface; and marked effects of glaciation, in the form of innumerable cirques and, on the east side particularly, deep glacial troughs.

*Effects of Glaciation.* The effects of glaciation are manifest in Cascade topography, which is not surprising in view of the heavy snowfall that the area receives today. Several hundred small glaciers remain in the area, and glacial cirques

FIG. 25.9   Lassen Peak plug dome, viewed from Lake Helen.   (*Photo by National Park Service.*)

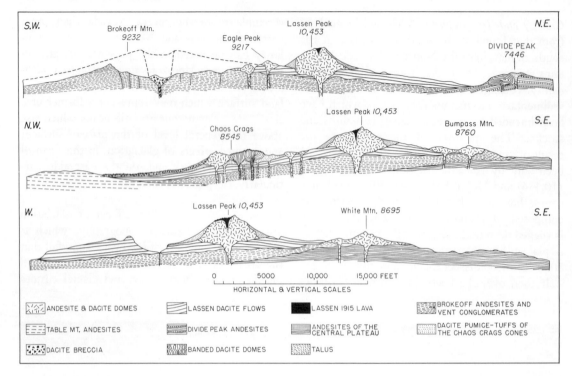

FIG. 25.10   Cross-section through Lassen Peak, showing relations of volcanic plug domes to surrounding rocks. (*After Howel Williams, Univ. Calif. Pub. Geol. Sci.,* **21**.)

are ubiquitous. Numerous glaciers are present in the Middle Cascades, but they are confined to the volcanic peaks. The effects here of glacial erosion do not extend much beyond the peaks, but in the Northern Cascades the topographic effects of glaciation may be seen along numerous valleys down to low altitudes. Some striking glacial troughs have developed on the east side of the Northern Cascade Range. Lake Chelan occupies a U-shaped trough that is 60 miles long and 1500 feet deep, which means that the trough bottom at its maximum depth is close to 400 feet below sea level. The portion of the glacial trough above Lake Chelan is now drained by the Stehekin River, and if this part of the trough is added to the Lake Chelan portion we have evidence of a Pleistocene glacier over 80 miles long. The glacier which occupied this trough was probably 5000 feet thick. The glacier in the valley to the north of Lake Chelan, the Methow Valley, at the time of its maximum

extent joined with the ice of the continental Okanogan lobe to form an almost continuous ice cover in this part of the Cascades. Then only the highest peaks projected above the ice (Barksdale, 1941), but a true ice stream occupied the valley during later phases of glaciation and built prominent end moraines in the valley.

*Middle Cascade Mountains*

South of the Seattle-Ellensburg line referred to above the Cascades are made up almost entirely of extrusive igneous rocks. A fairly uniform plateau summit similar to that in the Northern Cascades persists and in general decreases in altitude southward, but rising several thousand feet above the plateau level are the summits of a large number of the striking volcanic cones that are the characteristic features of the Cascade Range as a whole (see Fig. 25.8). Mount Rainier (14,408), Mount Adams (12,307),

Mount Hood (11,225), Mount Jefferson (11,225) and the Three Sisters (10,354; see Fig. 25.12) are among the better known of this great array of volcanic cones. All have been active in either late Pleistocene or Recent time, and all are distinctly younger than the plateau surface on which they stand.

*Geology.* It was believed originally that the volcanic rocks of the Cascades were Miocene in age and thus contemporaneous with the major part of the lavas in the Columbia Intermontane Plateau province. It is now recognized that they, like the rocks of the Columbia Intermontane Plateau province, span most of Tertiary time. The lavas range in age from Eocene to Pleistocene, if the volcanic cones are included. Volcanic rocks of Eocene, Oligocene, Miocene, and Pliocene age are present beneath the plateau surface. Rocks at the west side of the plateau are the oldest and are commonly referred to as the "western Cascade andesites," from a distinction shown by Callaghan (1933) to exist between the older, more altered, and more highly eroded volcanic rocks on the west side of the range and the younger andesites and basalts farther east and higher up in the range. The older sequence, on the western slope of the Cascades, consists of warped, faulted, and altered flows and pyroclastic rocks of late Eocene to late Miocene age (Peck, 1960) and averages about 12,000 feet in thickness. The younger rocks, of the high Cascades and the eastern slope, are mainly unaltered andesites and basalts of Pliocene to Recent age which were derived from the shield and stratovolcanoes which rise above the crest of the volcanic plateau. The Columbia River flows extend into the Cascades on the east and actually through them along the Columbia River gorge. On the west side of the Cascades these

FIG. 25.11  View of Mount Shasta, looking southeast. Haystack and Lava Park show in the foreground. (*From Geology Illustrated, by John S. Shelton, copyright by W. H. Freeman and Company.*)

FIG. 25.12    The Three Sisters, near Bend, Oregon, looking west.    (*Photo courtesy Oregon State Highway Commission.*)

lavas are interstratified with marine Miocene beds.

The present height of the Cascade Mountains, although to a considerable degree a result of the piling up of a succession of Tertiary volcanic flows and pyroclastics, is in part a result of epeirogenic uplift which came after the outpouring of the Miocene basalts. Lowry and Baldwin (1952) thought that as much as 2700 feet of the range's height could be attributed to uplift. They considered the uplift to have been differential, being greatest near the axis of the range and less on the eastern and western flanks. Evidence of this uplift can be seen in the upwarped lava flows along the Columbia River gorge.

*Crater Lake.* Crater Lake, in Oregon, near the southern end of the Middle Cascades section, is a well-known feature (see Fig. 25.13). This lake, whose surface is somewhat above 6000 feet in altitude, occupies a caldera that averages above 5½ miles in diameter and whose rim rises from 500 to 2000 feet above the surface of the lake. Crater Lake covers some 20 square miles and is as much as 2000 feet deep. A Pleistocene volcano known as Mount Mazama formerly occupied the site of the lake. This volcano had a height sufficiently great to nourish a number of glaciers, as evidenced by the presence on the flanks of the caldera of interbedded volcanic ejecta, fluvioglacial materials, and glacial till. Difference of opinion exists as to whether the caldera in which Crater Lake lies was produced by an explosion which blew off the top of Mount Mazama or was the result of subsidence. Preponderance of opinion at the present time seems to favor the subsidence theory, largely because of the absence of sufficient pyroclastic material adjacent to Crater Lake to fill the caldera (Williams, 1941, 1942). The caldera probably formed near the close of the Pleistocene epoch, and after a period of dormancy volcanic activity was resumed on a mild scale to produce Wizard Island and two other small cinder cones on the caldera floor.

*Columbia River Gorge.* The history of the Columbia River course through the Cascade Mountains (see Fig. 25.14) is even more problematical than that of its course east of the Cascades (see p. 464). Lowry and Baldwin (1952) considered the Columbia River an antecedent stream through the Cascades, as well as through the Coast Range. It was presumed to have taken its present route through the range soon after extrusion of the Columbia basalts in Mio-

cene time and to have maintained this course despite uplift of the Cascade Range athwart it. In support of their contention that the river presently follows approximately its ancestral course they cited the greater thickness of the basalts in the Columbia gorge than elsewhere and considered this evidence of a pre-existing valley through the ancestral Cascade Range along approximately the same route as that of the present Columbia River.

Hodge (1938) maintained, however, that the ancestral Columbia River course through the Cascades lies somewhat south of its present route (see Fig. 25.15). He believed that damming and ponding of the river by lavas from Mount Hood caused it to overflow and establish its present course. According to this interpretation the present route is a consequent one, since it was believed by Hodge to have been deter-

FIG. 25.13 Crater Lake and Wizard Island. (*Photo courtesy Oregon State Highway Commission.*)

FIG. 25.14    Columbia River gorge, looking east from Vista House on Crown Point.    (*Photo courtesy Union Pacific Railway.*)

mined by existing sags and downfaulted tracts in the Cascades.

When it is realized how obscure the evidence is regarding possible former routes of the Columbia River, it becomes evident that it is next to impossible to pass judgment on the soundness of the various theories. Such valleys as did exist are so deeply buried beneath volcanic materials that they are difficult to recognize; even if a section of one is exposed, it is hard to say whether it was part of the ancestral Columbia valley, a tributary to it, or another unrelated valley.

### Geomorphic History of Cascade Range

Many details of the geomorphic history of the Cascade Range remain to be filled in, but enough information is available that a broad picture of

the geomorphic history can be painted.[1] The pre-Tertiary history need not be considered here, but the major events of Tertiary time can be fairly clearly outlined. The area now occupied by the Northern Cascade Range in Eocene time was a low plain underlain by a great thickness of sediments intermixed with which were beds of coal. Numerous interbedded layers of volcanic ash and basalt flows give evidence of the first episode of volcanism during the evolution of the Cascade landscape.

Oligocene time saw the growth of a folded mountain range where formerly a low-lying plain had existed. Evidence for this orogeny is found in the presence beneath Miocene lavas of the

---

[1] The geomorphic history here outlined is largely based on unpublished material made available to the writer by Professor J. Hoover Mackin.

eroded roots of these mountains and in certain anamalous drainage relationships. Although the Cascade Range extends in a north-south direction, many of its streams flow northwestward or southeastward, reflecting the influence of the Oligocene fold mountains, whose axes extended in a northwest-southeast direction. Associated with the growth of the Oligocene mountains was eruptive activity during which extensive andesitic lava flows and pyroclastic materials were spread over the region. Remnants of these volcanic rocks are found today particularly in the central and southern parts of the Cascades of Washington.

Next came the great outpouring of Miocene lavas known as the Columbia River basalts; in extent and volume this dwarfed all previous and later volcanic eruptions in the Pacific Northwest. Whether the Oligocene mountains had been largely destroyed by erosion prior to the outpouring of the Miocene lavas is uncertain. Local peaks may have remained, but it seems likely that the mountains had at least been reduced to low relief, for the Miocene lavas spread over the area where the mountains once stood, and by the time the eruptions ceased a vast lava plain extended across the site of the present Cascades. Some of the older volcanic rocks may have projected as peaks through this lava plain, and perhaps a few volcanoes rose above it.

The next major gologic event in Cascade history was initiation of the uplift which produced the present Cascade Range. This upwarping and folding took place during Pliocene time. In addition to broad regional upwarping there was localized folding of the Miocene basalts into anticlinal and synclinal folds such as those so excellently displayed in the Yakima folds on the eastern flank of the range. The amount of uplift involved in this orogeny varied from perhaps 3000 feet to as much as 6000 feet.

Accompanying the Pliocene upwarping of the Cascades was the birth of a new generation of volcanoes, the spectacular line of volcanoes which

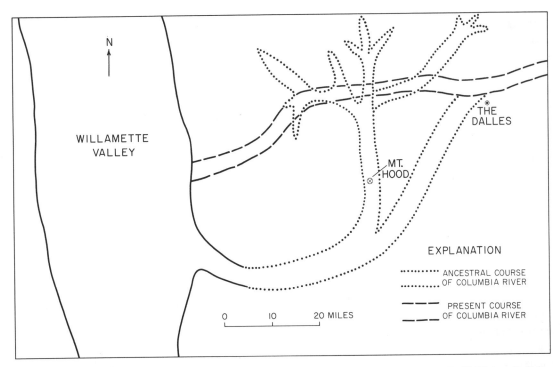

FIG. 25.15  Possible course of ancestral Columbia River through Cascade Range.  (*After E. T. Hodge, Geol. Soc. Am. Bull.*, **49**.)

is the crowning glory of the Cascade Range. The cones are composed mainly of andesitic lavas and pyroclastic materials, in contrast to the basalt flows above which they rise. The volcanoes must have attained essentially their present proportions before the beginning of Pleistocene glaciation and thus stood several thousand feet above the crest of the Cascade Range.

There is topographic evidence to suggest that the uplift of the Cascade Range was not a continuous one, but rather that after one-half to two-thirds of the uplift had taken place there was a pronounced slowing down or even cessation of uplift. The basis for this conclusion lies in the existence in the Cascades of two distinct phases of valley development, consisting of upper broad open valley profiles within which are narrow, deep canyon profiles. The open valley stage apparently developed during a pause in uplift and the inner gorge portions of the valleys after renewal of uplift, during the later part of Pleistocene time. The amount of Pleistocene uplift varies from a few hundred feet around the outer margins of the range to as much as a few thousand feet along the axis of the range.

Pleistocene mountain glaciers formed on the volcanic peaks and extended down the valleys many miles; at the north, in particular, practically the entire range summit was covered by ice. It is interesting to note that the nonvolcanic peaks in the Northern Cascades show the effects of glacial sculpturing more strikingly than do the volcanic cones. This suggests that volcanic eruptions continued through the Pleistocene and thereby "repaired" the damage done to the volcanic cones by glacial erosion.

The above outline of geomorphic history applies particularly to the northern part of the Cascades, in Washington, but there seems to be little reason to doubt that in its broad outlines it may be applicable to the more southerly parts of the range.

It is not surprising that the rather uniform summit surface of the Cascade Range has been interpreted by some as a peneplain surface. Such a possibility is only worth considering for the Northern Cascades, for elsewhere the summit surface of the Cascade range is constructional in origin. In the Northern Cascades, where igneous and metamorphic rocks crop out extensively, the possibility of the preservation of an erosional surface exists. Russell (1900) considered the range summit an erosional surface which he called the Cascade peneplain, and a few years later Willis (1903) referred to it as the Methow peneplain. In addition to the Methow peneplain Willis thought he saw evidence of two other cycles of erosion of pre-Pleistocene age. He believed that following development of the Methow surface the region was eroded to a mature stage which he called the Entiat matureland, following which there was a period of canyon cutting designated as the Twisp canyon stage.

Waters (1939) denied the existence of the Methow peneplain and thought that all the areas designated by Willis as remnants of this erosion surface could be accounted for as structural surfaces controlled by the Columbia River basalts. He did accept the reality of the Entiat matureland surface and thought that it could be recognized beneath the basalts and in extensive remnants in the areas of granodiorite and gneiss, but only in a very fragmentary fashion on other rock types.

## REFERENCES CITED

Axelrod, D. I. (1962). Post-Pliocene uplift of the Sierra Nevada, California, *Geol. Soc. Am. Bull.*, **73,** 183–198.

——— and W. S. Ting (1960). Late Pliocene floras east of the Sierra Nevada, *Univ. Calif. Pub. Geol. Sci.*, **39,** 1–118.

——— (1961). Early Pleistocene floras from the Chagoopa surface, southern Sierra Nevada, *Univ. Calif. Pub. Geol. Sci.*, **39,** 119–194.

Barksdale, J. D. (1941). Glaciation of the Methow Valley, Washington, *Jour. Geol.*, **49,** 721–737.

Blackwelder, Eliot (1931). Pleistocene glaciation in the Sierra Nevada and Basin Ranges, *Geol. Soc. Am. Bull.*, **42,** 865–922.

Buwalda, J. P. (1954). Geology of the Tehachapi Mountains, California, *Calif. Div. Mines Bull.* 170, Ch. 2, Pt. 9, 131–142.

Callaghan, Eugene (1933). Some features of the volcanic sequence in the Cascade Range in Oregon, *Am. Geophys. Union Trans.*, **14,** 243–249.

Dalrymple, G. B. (1963). Potassium-argon dates of some Cenozoic rocks of the Sierra Nevada, California, *Geol. Soc. Am. Bull.*, **74,** 379–390.

Evernden, J. F., G. H. Curtis, and R. Kistler (1957). Potassium-argon dating of Pleistocene volcanics, *Quaternaria*, **4,** 13–17.

Fenneman, N. M. (1931). *Physiography of Western United States*, McGraw-Hill Book Company, New York, 534 pp.

Gutenberg, Beno, J. P. Buwalda, and R. P. Sharp (1956). Seismic explorations on the floor of Yosemite Valley, *Geol. Soc. Am. Bull.*, **67**, 1051–1078.

Hinds, N. E. A. (1952). Evolution of the California landscape, *Calif. Div. Mines Bull.* 158, 240 pp.

Hodge, E. T. (1938). Geology of the lower Columbia River, *Geol. Soc. Am. Bull.*, **49**, 831–930.

Hudson, F. S. (1960). Post-Pliocene uplift of the Sierra Nevada, *Geol. Soc. Am. Bull.*, **71**, 1547–1574.

Jenkins, O. P. (1935). New technique applicable to the study of placers, *Calif. Jour. Mines and Geol.*, **31**, 143–200.

—— (1943). Geomorphic provinces of California, *Calif. Div. Mines Bull.* 118, 83–88.

—— and W. Q. Wright (1934). California's gold-bearing Tertiary gravels, *Eng. Mining Jour.*, **135**, 497–502.

King, P. B. (1959). *The Evolution of North America*, Princeton Univ. Press, Princeton, 190 pp.

Knopf, Adolph (1918). A geologic reconnaissance of the Inyo Range and the eastern slope of the southern Sierra Nevada, California, *U. S. Geol. Survey Profess. Paper* 110, 130 pp.

Lawson, A. C. (1904). Geomorphogeny of the upper Kern basin, *Univ. Calif. Pub. Geol.*, **3**, 291–376.

Lindgren, Waldemar (1911). The Tertiary gravels of the Sierra Nevada, *U. S. Geol. Survey Profess. Paper* 73, 9–81.

Louderback, G. D. (1923). Basin Range structure in the Great Basin, *Calif. Univ. Dept. Geol. Sci. Bull.*, **14**, 329–376.

Lowry, W. D., and E. M. Baldwin (1952). Late Cenozoic geology of the lower Columbia River Valley, Oregon and Washington, *Geol. Soc. Am. Bull.*, **63**, 1–24.

Matthes, F. E. (1930). Geologic history of the Yosemite Valley, *U. S. Geol. Survey Profess. Paper* 160, 137 pp.

—— (1937). The geologic history of Mount Whitney, *Sierra Club Bull.*, **22**, 1–18.

—— (1950a). *Sequoia National Park, A Geological Album*, edited by Fritiof Fryxell, Univ. Calif. Press, 136 pp.

—— (1950b). *The Incomparable Valley, A Geologic Interpretation of the Yosemite*, edited by Fritiof Fryxell, Univ. Calif. Press, 160 pp.

—— (1960). Reconnaissance of the geomorphology and glacial geology of the San Joaquin Basin, Sierra Nevada, California, *U. S. Geol. Survey Profess. Paper* 329, 62 pp.

Peck, D. L. (1960). Cenozoic volcanism in the Oregon Cascades, *U. S. Geol. Survey Profess. Paper* 400-B, B308–B310.

Putnam, W. C. (1949). Quaternary geology of the June Lake district, California, *Geol. Soc. Am. Bull.*, **60**, 1281–1302.

—— (1960a). Origin of Rock Creek and Owens River gorges, Mono County, California, *Univ. Calif. Pub. Geol. Sci.*, **34**, 221–280.

—— (1960b). Faulting and Pleistocene glaciation in the east-central Sierra Nevada of California, U. S. A., *Rept. 21st Internat. Geol. Cong.*, Pt. 21, 270–274.

—— (1962). Late Cenozoic geology of McGee Mountain, Mono County, California, *Univ. Calif. Pub. Geol. Sci.*, **40**, 181–218.

Russell, I. C. (1900). Geology of the Cascade Mountains in northern Washington, *U. S. Geol. Survey 20th Ann. Rept.*, Pt. 2, 83–210.

Sharp, R. P., and J. H. Birman (1963). Additions to classical sequence of Pleistocene glaciations, Sierra Nevada, California, *Geol. Soc. Am. Bull.*, **74**, 1079–1086.

Waters, A. C. (1939). Resurrected erosion surface in central Washington, *Geol. Soc. Am. Bull.*, **50**, 635–659.

Williams, Howel (1932a). Geology of the Lassen Volcanic National Park, California, *Univ. Calif. Pub. Geol. Sci.*, **21**, 195–386.

—— (1932b). Mount Shasta, a Cascade volcano, *Jour. Geol.*, **40**, 417–429.

—— (1941). Calderas and their origin, Univ. Calif. Pubs., *Dept. Geol. Sci. Bull.*, **25**, 239–346.

—— (1942). Volcanoes of the Three Sisters region, Oregon Cascades, Univ. Calif. Pub., *Dept. Geol. Sci. Bull.*, **27**, 37–63.

Willis, Bailey (1903). Physiography and deformation of the Wenatchee-Chelan district, Cascade Range, *U. S. Geol. Survey Profess. Paper* 19, 49–97.

## ADDITIONAL REFERENCES

Atwood, W. W., Jr. (1935). The glacial history of an extinct volcano, Crater Lake National Park, *Jour. Geol.*, **43**, 142–168.

Kesseli, J. E. (1941). Glacial land forms in the Sierra Nevada south of Lake Tahoe, *Univ. Calif. Pub. Geog.*, **3**, 137–157.

Mackin, J. H. (1941). Glacial geology of the Snoqualmie-Cedar area, Washington, *Jour. Geol.*, **49**, 449–481.

Page, B. M. (1939). Multiple alpine glaciation in the Leavenworth area, Washington, *Jour. Geol.*, **47**, 785–815.

Putnam, W. C. (1950). Moraine and shoreline relationships at Mono Lake, California, *Geol. Soc. Am. Bull.*, **61**, 115–122.

Reid, J. A. (1911). The geomorphogeny of the Sierra Nevada northeast of Lake Tahoe, Univ. Calif. Pub., *Dept. Geol. Sci. Bull.*, **6**, 89–161.

Smith, W. D., and C. R. Swartzlow (1936). Mount Mazama; explosion versus collapse, *Geol. Soc. Am. Bull.*, **47**, 1809–1830.

Webb, R. W. (1946). Geomorphology of the middle Kern River basin, southern Sierra Nevada, *Geol. Soc. Am. Bull.*, **57**, 355–362.

# 26

# Pacific Border Province

## GENERAL DESCRIPTION

The broad regional plan of the Pacific Border province is fairly simple. It consists of a line of mountains along the coast and a chain of troughs or lowlands, commonly called "valleys," east of the mountain ranges. This arrangement breaks down at two places, in the Klamath Mountains and the Transverse Ranges. The Klamath Mountains in southern Oregon and northern California are a sprawling mountain mass that extends eastward to the Cascade Mountains and divides the lowland tract east of the Coast Ranges into northern and southern parts. Likewise the east-west-trending Transverse Ranges in southern California separate the Valley of California from the series of basins and valleys that lies north of the Gulf of California.

The mountains along the western side of the province are generally called the Coast Ranges, although this is not true for the Olympic Mountains at the extreme north. Vancouver Island and the Queen Charlotte Islands in Canada are a continuation of the northern belt of coastal mountains that is separated from the mainland of Canada by sounds produced by recent submergence. The linear Coast Ranges of Oregon extend south to the Klamath Mountains. The California Coast Ranges reach as far south as the San Rafael Mountains, the northwesternmost member of the group of ranges known as the Transverse Ranges. The Transverse Ranges have a general east-west trend in contrast to the north-south-trending coastal mountains. South of the Transverse Ranges the pattern becomes more complicated, and the Peninusular Ranges

lie back from the coast far enough that they are not commonly thought of as coastal ranges. Although the Oregon and California coastal ranges share a common geographic relationship they are notably different in geology and topography; the rocks and structures of the Oregon Coast Ranges are relatively simple compared with those of the California Coast Ranges.

Although the lowlands east of the Coast Ranges are commonly called "valleys," and even though axial streams are present in them, they are in no sense the products of stream erosion but rather are structural troughs. These troughs are being filled with waste brought by streams from the adjacent highlands rather than being deepened by stream erosion. The northernmost of these troughs includes the Willamette Valley of Oregon, the Cowlitz Valley and upper Chehalis Valley of Washington, and the Puget Sound Trough at the extreme north. This trough continues northward beyond the internation boundary in the sounds which lie between Vancouver and Queen Charlotte Islands and the Canadian mainland. The boundaries of the northern lowland are drawn at the foothills of the Olympic Mountains and Coast Ranges on the west and at the base of the Cascade Mountains on the east.

The California trough lies between the California Coast Ranges and the Sierra Nevada and southern Cascade Mountains. It is commonly known as the Great Valley of California. The portion north of the latitude of San Francisco is known as the Sacramento Valley and the part south of there as the San Joaquin Valley.

It will be readily seen that if the major mountains and lowlands of the Pacific Border province are taken along with the mountains of the Sierra Nevada-Cascade province, their broad plan is a crude letter H with the Klamath Mountains at the center of the H. The mountains form northward and southward projecting prongs from this central mountain mass that enclose the two lowlands.

## Olympic Section

The Olympic section consists mainly of a northward-projecting peninsula bounded on the east by Puget Sound, on the north by the Straits of Juan de Fuca, on the west by the Pacific Ocean, and on the south by the Chehalis River. Although the section includes narrow strips of lowland, the Olympic Mountains make up its major part.

*Topography.* The Olympic Mountains are the highest and most beautiful of any of the coastal ranges. Although they contain no towering volcanic cones or rugged granite peaks such as are found in the Cascades and Sierra Nevada, their topography is rugged and includes many steep-sided, jagged ridges (Danner, 1955). Mount Olympus, the highest peak, has a maximum altitude of 7954 feet and several other peaks exceed 7000 feet in altitude.

*Geology.* The oldest rocks in the Olympic Mountains belong to the lower Cretaceous Soleduck formation and consist of metamorphosed sedimentary and volcanic rocks that are now argillites, slates, phyllites, and greenstones. These rocks underlie the greater part of the mountain mass. Rocks of Eocene and Oligocene age crop out around the margin of the uplift. Several of the peaks are composed of the Lower Eocene Metchosen formation, which consists of basalts, volcanic tuffs and breccias, and inter-bedded marine beds. The youngest rocks in the

FIG. 26.1  Seven Lakes Basin in the Olympic Mountains, looking west.  (*Photo courtesy National Park Service.*)

Olympic Mountains are Oligocene marine sediments. Uplift of the mountains began in late Cretaceous or early Tertiary time and culminated during the Pliocene-Pleistocene (Cascadian) orogeny, which raised the Cascade Mountains and depressed Puget Trough.

*Glaciation.* The Olympic Mountains have in them some fifty glaciers, the longest of which has a length slightly less than 4 miles. Pleistocene glaciers were numerous, and their topographic effects are very conspicuous (see Fig. 26.1). Although no granitic rocks crop out in the Olympic Mountains, granite boulders are found on the north side of the mountains up to altitudes of 3000 feet. They apparently were carried by a lobe of ice in the Puget Sound lowland that pushed westward through the Straits of Juan de Fuca and extended onto the flanks of the Olympics, bringing with it granite erratics from the mountains of western British Columbia.

*Puget Trough Section*

The Puget Trough section, or what is more commonly referred to as the Willamette-Puget

Lowland, is close to 400 miles long and averages about 50 miles in width. It extends southward between the Cascade Mountains and the Coast Ranges to the latitude of Eugene, Oregon. This section can be divided into four parts. These are, from north to south, Puget Sound and adjacent lowland, the Chehalis-Cowlitz valleys, the lower Columbia Valley, and the Willamette Valley at the extreme south.

Two things distinguish the Puget Sound area, the fact that it has been glaciated and that it has not yet recovered from its depression under the ice load. As a consequence of postglacial rise of sea level the former valley system that drained through the Straits of Juan de Fuca has been drowned, giving rise to a complex of inlets and "canals," as they are called in this region (see Fig. 26.2). Many parts of Puget Sound are as much as 600 feet deep and one area is nearly 1000 feet deep.

*Effects of Glaciation.* Numerous mountain glaciers from the mainland of British Columbia entered the depression between Vancouver Island and the mainland and formed a large tongue of

FIG. 26.2    Inlets or "canals" in Puget Sound trough, near Tacoma, Washington. (*Photo by Fairchild Aerial Surveys, Inc.*)

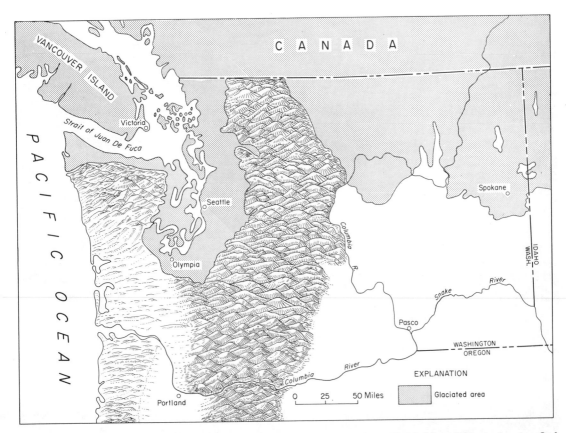

FIG. 26.3   Map showing extent of glaciation in Puget Sound area.   (*After Glacial Map of North America, Geol. Soc. Am.*)

ice that extended southward into the Puget Sound trough. This mass of ice split into two lobes, one that moved westward through the Straits of Juan de Fuca and against the Olympic Range on the south and another that moved southward in the Puget Trough to about 10 miles south of Olympia, Washington (see Fig. 26.3). Willis (1898) early recognized evidence of two glaciations, the older Admiralty and younger Vashon, separated by what he called the Puyallup interglacial. More recent work in this area by Crandell, Mullineaux, and Waldron (1958) has produced evidence of four glaciations and three interglacials. The stratigraphic sequence recognized by them is as follows:

7. Vashon drift: possibly Tazewell in age
6. Erosion interval: nonglacial
5. Salmon Springs drift: pre-Wisconsin, middle to late Pleistocene

4. Puyallup formation: nonglacial in nature
3. Stuck glacial drift: early to middle Pleistocene
2. Alderton formation: nonglacial
1. Orting drift: early Pleistocene

The Puget Sound ice lobe moved against the base of the Cascades on the east and built there a prominent end moraine. Drumlinoid hills veneered with till of Vashon age are common in the area. The cores of these hills beneath the veneer of Vashon till consist of beds of gravels, sands, and clay with intercalated beds of peat and till of pre-Vashon age. Several glacial lakes, such as Lake Washington in Seattle, Sammanish, and Whatcom, are also present. As shown by Mackin (1941) the valley glaciers on the west side of the Cascade Mountains were small and did not reach into the Puget Sound lowland. Rather, the Puget Sound glacier pushed against the Cascades, blocked the mountain valleys, and

FIG. 26.4   Mima mounds of southwest Washington.   (*Photo by A. M. Ritchie.*)

formed numerous lakes in these valleys. Several such lakes are shown on the Sultan and Cedar Lake, Washington, quadrangles.

*Chehalis-Cowlitz Valleys.* Occupying a position between Puget Sound and the lower Columbia River Valley are the valleys of the Chehalis and Cowlitz rivers. Bedrock hills mixed with gravel terraces on glacial outwash characterize this area. Several valley trains lead southward from the area of the Vashon glaciation to the Chehalis River. The terraces produced by dissection of the valley trains are locally known as "prairies," and on several of these "prairies" are found the much-discussed Mima Mounds (see Fig. 26.4).

*Mima Mounds.* Earth mounds of one origin or another are present in various parts of the United States. Those of the Coastal Plain province have already been discussed (see p. 66). Earth mounds are numerous in the Columbia Intermontane province between the John Day and Deschutes Rivers, in California, Arizona, and Alaska, to mention only some of the areas where such features exist. The Mima mounds are from 1 to 7 feet in height and 8 to 50 feet in diameter and are composed of gravel and silt. At least a dozen theories have been proposed to account for them, but none has proven quite satisfactory. Among those that seem more probable are that they are: periglacial phenomena (Péwé, 1948; Newcomb, 1952), the work of the pocket gopher *Thomomys talpoides* (Dalquest and Scheffer, 1942), or features produced on partially thawed silts possessing a polygonal pattern (Ritchie, 1953).

*Lower Columbia River History.*   The history of the Columbia River through the Cascade Mountains and east of them has been discussed in previous chapters (see pp. 523 and 464).   The history of the lower Columbia River remains to be discussed.   After emerging from the Cascade Range the Columbia River flows for about 40 miles in a general northwest course across the Willamette-Puget Lowland and then cuts through the Coast Range to the sea.   Throughout this stretch the Columbia River is essentially a drowned valley, for tides extend up the Columbia as far as the Cascade Mountains, a distance of 140 miles.

The route of the lower Columbia River ap-parently postdates the Columbia River basalts and was established on these basalts.   The present valley, however, is cut through formations of Pliocene and Pleistocene age.   Following out-pouring of the Columbia River basalts the region was depressed below sea level, and the sediments of the Pliocene Troutdale forma-tion were deposited over the area (Lowry and Baldwin, 1952).   The Troutdale formation con-sists mainly of sands and gravels except for an upper silty member known as the Portland Hills silt.   Above the Troutdale formation is a Pleis-tocene formation known as the Portland gravels, or what was at one time called the "Portland delta gravels."   A backwater phase of the Port-land gravels in the Willamette Valley is known as the Willamette silts.   The amount of deforma-tion that the region has undergone since Troutdale time is indicated by the fact that the Troutdale sediments vary in altitude from 1400 feet below

FIG. 26.5   Willamette Valley as viewed from Bunker Hill, southwest of Salem, Oregon.   (*Photo courtesy Oregon State Highway Commission.*)

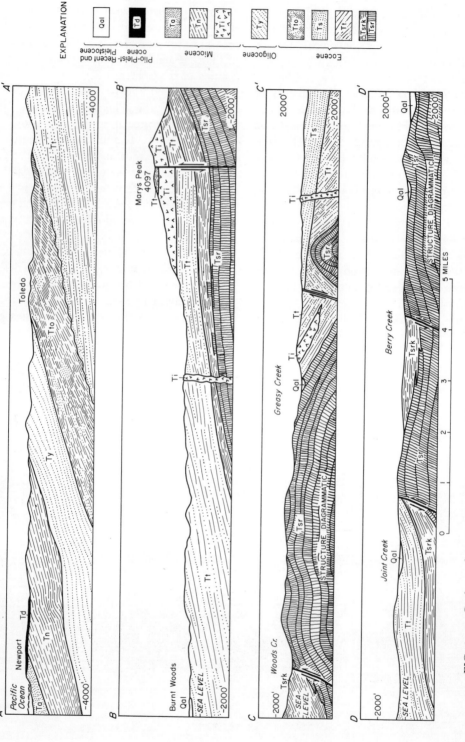

FIG. 26.6   Geology of the Oregon Coast Range.   (*After W. D. Wilkinson and others, Oregon Dept. Geol. Min. Resources Bull. 50.*)

sea level in the Portland Basin to 2700 feet above sea level on the south side of the Columbia River gorge near Wyeth, Oregon.

Lowry and Baldwin (1952) have suggested the following phases in the history of the lower Columbia Valley:

1. Outpouring of the Columbia River basalts into the area west of the Cascade Range.
2. Establishment of the Columbia River's course on these basalts.
3. The beginning of Pliocene folding and down-warping with initiation of deposition of the Troutdale sediments in local downwarps.
4. Continued downwarping, with accompanying rise of sea level, bringing about submergence of the whole lower Columbia Valley as well as tributary valleys such as the Willamette.
5. Lowering of sea level in early Wisconsin time to allow the cutting of valleys several hundred feet deep in the previously deposited Troutdale fill, as well as the development of several marine terraces along the coast.
6. Rise of sea level with another submergence and deposition of the Portland gravels in previously cut valleys.
7. Late Wisconsin uplift accompanied by the cutting in the Portland gravels of a series of terraces that reaches as high as 400 feet above sea level.

*Willamette Valley.* The 125 mile long Willamette Valley or Lowland (see Fig. 26.5) is only 20 to 30 miles wide and is mostly alluvial-filled. Northward through it flows the extremely sluggish and meandering Willamette River. The Salem, Waldo, Eola, and Amity Hills in the valley are capped with basalt or sandstone and rise above the general level of the lowland. The Willamette Valley terminates at the south near Eugene, Oregon.

### Oregon Coast Range Section

What is commonly called the Oregon Coast Range, although the range actually begins in Washington at the Chehalis River, extends southward some 250 miles to the Coquille River, in

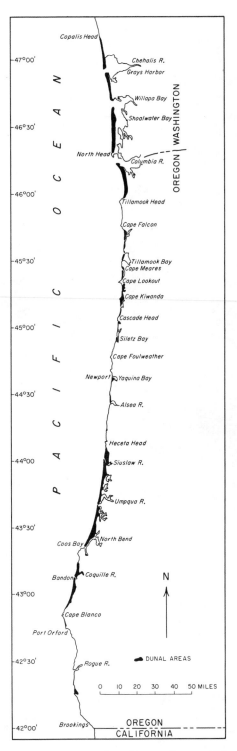

FIG. 26.7 Dune areas along Oregon Coast. (*After W. S. Cooper, Geol. Soc. Am. Memoir 72.*)

FIG. 26.8   Lakes back of dunes along Oregon coast between Sea Lion Point and Coos Bay.   (*Photo courtesy Oregon State Highway Commission.*)

Oregon. This range averages about 50 miles in width and is nowhere lofty. Marys Peak, the highest peak in the Coast Range, is only 4097 feet high. The Washington portion of the range is known as the Willapa Hills and is mainly below 2000 feet in height, although one peak exceeds 3000 feet. The bedrock of the Coastal Range (see Fig. 26.6) consists primarily of flat to slightly deformed sedimentary rocks of Tertiary age and some lava flows and intrusive igenous rocks (Wilkinson, 1959). In many respects the Coast Range is more plateau-like in nature than mountainous. In contrast to the Olympic Mountains at the north and the Klamath Mountains to the south, the Coast Range displays a certain degree of north-south parallelism in its component ridges and valleys in response to the moderate folding which its rocks have undergone. Major streams, such as the Chehalis, Columbia, and Willapa, are transverse to the structure. Most of the streams which cross the Coast Range are drowned in their lower portions.

A narrow strip of coastal plain borders the Coast Range on the west and along this coastal plain strip is one of the most extensive dunal belts (Cooper, 1958) along the whole Pacific coast (see Fig. 26.7). Growth of the dunes has resulted in the damming of several of the tidal rivers to form a series of lakes back of the coast (see Fig. 26.8).

# GEOMORPHIC REGIONS OF CALIFORNIA

## General Description

Undoubtedly California has within its borders a greater variety of landscapes than any state in conterminus United States and perhaps within the entire fifty states. Four geomorphic provinces, according to the Fenneman classification, are represented in California and although Virginia contains parts of five geomorphic provinces it does not have as great variety of topography as does California.

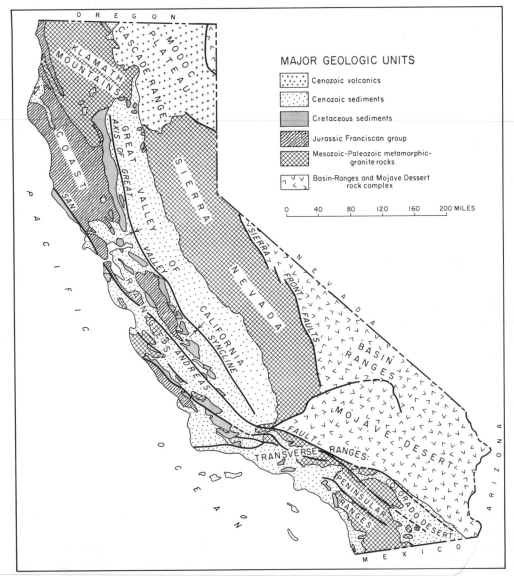

FIG. 26.9 Geologic map of California showing geomorphic regions. (*After N. E. A. Hinds, Calif. Div. Mines Bull. 158.*)

The latest treatment of California land forms (Hinds, 1952) recognized eleven geomorphic regions in the state, the Modoc Plateau, Cascade Range, Klamath Mountains, Coast Ranges, Valley of California, Sierra Nevada, Basin-Ranges, Mohave Desert, Transverse Ranges, Colorado Desert, and Peninsular Ranges (see Fig. 26.9). For the part of the Pacific Border province in California we shall follow Hinds' classification but shall not discuss those regions which have been previously described in other chapters.

California is to a large degree a state of strongly contrasting geomorphic regions because of the juxtaposition by faulting of numerous earth blocks having dissimilar rock types, structures, and geologic histories. Hundreds of fault scarps, scarplets, or fault-line scarps may be seen in the state. In addition, there are fault-controlled valleys, trenches, and troughs; closed depressions or sag ponds mark the courses of faults; and offset drainage lines mark the position of some faults. The faults are of various types, but the one most distinctive type found here is the transcurrent fault, in which major movement has been strike-slip.

## Influence of Faults on Topography

Two major fault patterns are recognizable in California (see Fig. 26.10), one trending north-northwest and another east-northeast. The north-northwest-trending belt includes such faults as the San Andreas, San Jacinto, and Elsinore at the south and the Hayward and Calaveras faults at the north. The east-northeast-trending belt includes the Garlock, Big Pine, San Gabriel, Cucamonga, and White Wolf faults.

*San Andreas Fault.* Most famous of the California faults is the San Andreas (Noble, 1927) which is really a fault zone rather than a single fault. This fault can be traced at the surface (see Fig. 26.11) for over 500 miles from Point Arena north of San Francisco to where it disappears at the south beneath the sediments of the Imperial Valley at the head of the Gulf of California. Its actual length, as suggested by seismic data, is likely of the order of 700 miles. Displacement along the fault is right lateral, as evidenced by offset drainage lines and rock belts. There is, however, considerable disagreement as to the magnitude of the displacement that has taken place. Estimates of this vary from 15 miles (Higgins, 1961) to as much as 350 miles. Hill and Dibble (1953) suggested that there has been this latter amount of displacement since initiation of the fault in Jurassic time.

Topographically the San Andreas fault zone is marked by offset drainage, pressure ridges, sag ponds, and by one or several parallel trenches. Except in the San Andreas Valley, south of San Francisco, the fault is not followed by streams except for short distances where they cross it. Where the fault cuts across the Reyes Peninsula, north of San Francisco, it has produced a narrow fault valley which separates this peninsula from the main Marin Peninsula. Tomales Bay at the north (see Fig. 26.12) and Bolinas Bay at the south occupy this fault trench.

*Garlock Fault.* The Garlock fault, so-named by Hess (1910), in contrast to the San Andreas, displays left lateral displacement. It is about 150 miles long (Hill and Dibblee, 1953). Offsetting of drainage as much as one-half mile is observable along it. The Garlock fault marks the southern end of the Sierra Nevada and forms the boundary between the Basin-Ranges and Mohave Desert geomorphic regions of Hinds (see Figs. 26.9 and 26.10) and thus bounds unlike geomorphic and geologic units.

## Modoc Plateau

The Modoc Plateau of California (Peacock, 1931) is a part of the Basin and Range province and belongs with that portion of the Great Basin section in Oregon, Nevada, and California where volcanic rocks similar in age to those of the Columbia Intermontane province are widespread. This area, it will be recalled, was included in the Basin and Range province because extensive faulting has produced here a type of structure and topography more similar to that of the Basin and Range province than to that of the Columbia Intermontane province.

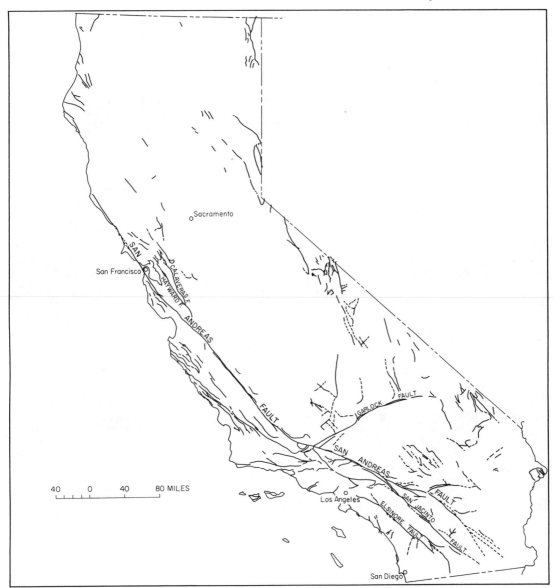

FIG. 26.10 Distribution of faults in California. *(After O. P. Jenkins, Calif. Div. Mines Bull. 158.)*

Altitudes in the Modoc Plateau average around 4500 feet, but numerous hills and peaks rise above this altitude. The rocks are largely basaltic and of Pleistocene age. The lava flows are broken by numerous faults, many of which are strikingly expressed in the topography as fault scarps (Hinds, 1952). Cinder cones and spatter cones mark the lines of many of the fissures along which the lavas rose.

## Klamath Mountains

The Klamath Mountains are a sprawling mountain mass that lies about as much in Oregon as in California. They are rugged mountains with numerous peaks over 6000 feet in altitude and a few near 9000 feet. Some of the peaks were high enough that Pleistocene glaciers formed on them. Klamath Mountain geology resembles more that

FIG. 26.11    Trace of San Andreas fault as seen looking southeast near Palmdale, California.    *(Photo courtesy Fairchild Aerial Surveys, Inc.)*

of the Sierra Nevada than that of the Coast Ranges; the bedrock ranges in age from Precambrian to Mesozoic and includes a predominance of metamorphosed Paleozoic rocks, some volcanic rocks, and many intrusive bodies. In contrast to the longitudinal valley systems of the Coast Ranges, there is a dendritic pattern in the Klamath Mountains. The Jurassic folding, faulting, and granitic intrusions of the Sierra Nevada may have extended into the Klamath Mountains; the ages and structures of many of the rocks are not known in detail.

Although they are much dissected, there is a marked uniformity of summit elevations in the

Klamath Mountains that suggested to early workers that the region had been peneplained. Diller (1902) thought he saw evidence for two peneplains in the Klamath Mountains; the higher surface he called the Klamath peneplain and the lower, the Sherwood peneplain. In recent years, however, considerable doubt has been expressed as to the reality of these erosion surfaces.

### California Coast Ranges

The California Coast Ranges form a linear system of nearly parallel ranges which trends north 30 to 40 degrees west. They extend from the Klamath Mountains on the north to the Transverse Ranges at the south, a distance of approximately 400 miles. In general they are not high mountains, and altitudes are commonly between 2000 and 4000 feet (see Fig. 26.13), but individual peaks may reach up to 6000 feet. The Great Valley of California lies to the east of the Coast Ranges and little or no coastal plain separates them from the Pacific Ocean. The Coast Ranges are commonly divided into northern (Irwin, 1960) and southern (Oakeshott, 1960) groups, with the separation being made at San Francisco Bay, a broad irregular downwarp of late Pliocene age that has been modified somewhat by middle Pleistocene faulting.

*Structure.* The Coast Ranges are essentially geosynclinal in structure, with the usual sub-

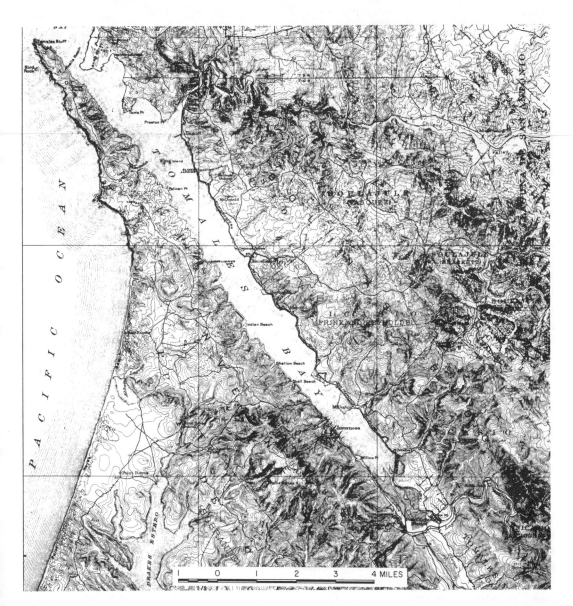

FIG. 26.12   Portion of Point Reyes, California, quadrangle showing influence of San Andreas fault upon configuration of Tomales Bay.

FIG. 26.13    Coast Range, Santa Barbara County, California, looking west along foothills south of Cuyama.    (*Photo by Spence Air Photos.*)

sequent folding and faulting.    The broad outlines of their topography are controlled by a series of longitudinal folds and faults.    The upfolds have been rather generally eroded away, with the exception of the Kettleman Hills, and even here much of the upfold has been removed.    The result is a group of nearly parallel mountains and intervening valleys trending northwest-southeast.

The detailed structure of the Coast Ranges is highly complex; the mostly sedimentary rock masses were closely folded in Miocene and later time, eroded considerably, and then broken into fault blocks with the present configuration; present heights were attained mostly in the Pleistocene.    Some mountain blocks have been uplifted without notable tilting; other blocks have been significantly tilted; still other blocks have been warped.    Similar diversity of structure is true of the depressed blocks.    An interesting aspect of some of the faults is that they will follow particular mountain-valley boundaries for a short distance and then cut obliquely across the topography to adjacent mountain fronts.    The San Andreas fault displays this pattern excellently.

It cuts obliquely across the Santa Cruz Mountains on the San Francisco Peninsula, then across the northeast end of the Gabilan Range, and follows its eastern boundary for a considerable distance before transecting the Temblor Range (Oakeshott, 1960).

*Rock Types.*    The Tertiary rocks of the Coast Ranges rest on a basement of Mesozoic and older rocks (Weaver, 1949).    The oldest rocks are the metamorphic rocks of the Sur series, of uncertain age.    Very abundant in the Coast Ranges are the rocks of the Franciscan-Knoxville groups which are thought to range in age from late Jurassic to late Cretaceous (Oakeshott, 1960).    Intrusive granites, which radioactive dating suggests are early late Cretaceous in age, are also present.    Rocks belonging to all periods of the Tertiary are present, but largely in scattered patches.    However, Miocene strata are the most widespread.

*Drainage Pattern.*    Most of the drainage parallels the structure, but the Russian River at the north cuts across it.    In several areas a fault-trellis drainage pattern has developed. This pattern is particularly well displayed on the San Francisco peninsula (see the San Mateo, California, topographic sheet).

*Coastline Features.* Because the California coastline has a slightly more northerly trend than the structures and topography of the Coast Ranges, the coast intersects the structures at a slight angle. As a consequence of this, structures and rocks are strikingly displayed along the coast. A further result of this relationship is an interesting alternation along the coast of rugged projecting headlands, where the mountain ranges intersect the coast, with inlets or indentations, where the valleys meet the coast.

At numerous localities the seaward sides of the Coast Ranges are notched by wave-cut terraces. In the San Francisco Bay area there is a series of terraces (Howard, 1951) the highest of which is better than 1500 feet above sea level; here some of the better preserved terrace treads are as much as a mile or two wide. Bradley (1956) has described several marine terraces in the vicinity of Santa Cruz, the lowest of which, at about 100 feet above sea level, has a radiocarbon date of older than 39,000 years. These numerous terraces show how restive the coast of California has been in recent geologic time; most, if not all of them, are Pleistocene in age.

*Geomorphic History.* The geomorphic history of the Coast Ranges has been a very complex one and is not yet well understood. It is probably true, as in the Transverse Ranges of southern California, that each range has had to a certain degree an independent history and needs to be considered separately. Thus it may be questionable whether any regional pattern exists which would make possible a synthesis of the geomorphic history of the Coast Ranges and correlation of it with geomorphic events in the Sierra Nevada. Howard (1951) has attempted an interpretation of geomorphic history of the northern Coast Ranges along with that of the adjacent Valley of California, but his postulated sequence of events is based on such scanty and scattered evidence that it may be asked whether it has more than local application.

## Valley of California

*Description.* The Valley of California, 400 miles long and 50 miles wide on the average, is one of the major structural depressions of the world. It is bordered by the Sierra Nevada on the east, the Tehachapi Mountains on the south, the Coast Ranges on the west, and the Klamath Mountains on the north; its northern part is known as the Sacramento Valley and its southern part as the San Joaquin Valley. There is a single outlet to the sea, Carquinez Strait, through which the combined Sacramento-San Joaquin Rivers flow into San Francisco Bay.

*Structure.* The Valley of California trough is asymmetrical in form, with a steep western flank and a more gently inclined eastern flank. The eastern border of the downwarp is a continuation of the western slope of the Sierra Nevada tilt block, and at the center of the trough it is buried beneath a maximum of perhaps 25,000 or 30,000 feet of upper Cretaceous and Cenozoic sediments. The Valley of California downwarp probably has existed since the folding which elevated the Sierra Nevada and Klamath Mountains in Jurassic time. During Cretaceous and much of Cenozoic time it was a large geosynclinal tract that extended westward over the site of the present Coast Ranges and may have received sediments from the west from the often-postulated ancient land mass of Cascadia, and from the Sierra Nevada on the east. It was not until the late Pliocene development of the Coast Ranges that the trough was practically cut off from the sea and came to have essentially its present outline.

*Sacramento Valley.* The Sacramento Valley is only a little more than half as long as the San Joaquin Valley. In most of it the relief is low and the highest parts are only a few hundred feet above sea level. The so-called "red lands," the name given to belts of hilly or undulating topography developed largely on Pleistocene alluvium that stand terrace-like above the present valley flats, are about the only land that is not flood-plain, natural levee, islands, or flood basins.

FIG. 26.14    The Marysville Buttes, looking northwest.    (*Photo by John S. Shelton.*)

*Marysville Buttes.* The most notable departure from the low relief of the Sacramento Valley is found in the Marysville Buttes (see Fig. 26.14), which lie in the center of the valley about 20 miles northwest of the city of Marysville. These hills are about 10 miles in diameter and exceed 2000 feet in altitude. They are a mass of igneous rocks consisting of an earlier laccolithic intrusion (Williams, 1928) and a later mushroom-shaped rhyolitic plug dome (Williams, 1932), from which the former sedimentary cover has been eroded.

*San Joaquin Valley.* The San Joaquin Valley (see Fig. 26.15) differs from the Sacramento Valley in four significant respects: (1) it is longer and wider, (2) altitudes and relief of the neighboring mountains are greater, (3) it is more arid, and (4) the southern one-third lacks external drainage.

The streams that drain into the San Joaquin Valley from the high Sierra Nevada are much larger and more permanent than those that drain from the much lower Coast Ranges on the west. The larger Sierra Nevada streams are heavily loaded with sediment; as they enter the drier lower slopes they lose volume, and as a result have built more extensive alluvial fans into the San Joaquin Valley than have the smaller streams from the Coast Ranges. The result has been a displacement of the drainage axis to the west of the center of the structural trough. This drainage asymmetry does not exist in the Sacramento Valley because here there is a much less marked contrast in the amount of rainfall in the mountains on its two sides.

South of the Kings River, the San Joaquin Valley has internal drainage. The topography in this arid part of the San Joaquin Valley consists mainly of a series of alluvial fans with playa-type basins between them. Two major playa basins exist here, the Tulare at the north and the Buena Vista at the south. They are separated from each other by the extension across the valley of the large, flat alluvial fan of the Kern River.

Greatest relief in the San Joaquin Valley is found in the Kettleman Hills, which lie close to the eastern base of the Coast Ranges in the southern third of the valley (Woodring, Stewart, and Richards, 1940). Altitudes at the northern end of these hills exceed 1300 feet. The Kettleman Hills are developed on three elongated anticlines known as South, Middle, and North domes. They cover an area about 30 miles long and 5 miles wide. Although the folding which produced these structures did not take place until Pleistocene time, the folds have been dissected to such an extent that there is a close adjustment of topography to structure. An old erosion surface, near El Prado at the north end of the Kettleman Hills, suggests that the region may have been reduced to baselevel before the doming took place.

The lower or northern part of the San Joaquin Valley is not significantly different from the Sacramento Valley in its topographic characteristics and consists largely of dissected uplands, low alluvial fans and plains, and floodplains across which the streams flow in multiple channels that split the lowlands into numerous island-like tracts.

### Transverse Ranges

The Transverse Ranges region of California gets its name from a line of ranges, called the Transverse Ranges, whose general east-west

FIG. 26.15 San Joaquin Valley, looking northeast. Wheeler Ridge with its prominent wind and water gaps is in foreground. Background area extends from Bakersfield at left to Bear Mountain at right. (*Photo by John S. Shelton.*)

trend is nearly at right angles to the major structural trends in California. This region consists of a complex chain of mountain ranges and enclosed valleys or basins including also, at the west, the offshore islands of Santa Cruz, Santa Rosa, and San Miguel (Bailey and Jahns, 1954). From west to east the mountain ranges are the Santa Ynez, Santa Monica, San Gabriel, San Bernardino, Little San Bernardino, Orocopia, and Chuckwalla. These mountain ranges, along with the Peninsular Ranges to the south, have batholithic cores and are part of one continuous, though complex, line of intrusive granitic bodies extending from the Klamath Mountains through the Sierra Nevada southward into Baja California. The most puzzling features in this lengthy chain of plutons are the east-west trending Transverse Ranges. Their east-west structures apparently extend back into Precambrian time, but there is no apparent explanation of why they depart in alignment from other structures in California.

*Rocks and Structure.* The geology of this region is highly complex. Rocks range in age from Precambrian to Quaternary; particularly thick Cenozoic sections are present around the margins of the mountains and in the basins at the west. Structurally the mountain ranges consist of steep-sided folds which have been broken by innumerable faults, some of which are normal, some thrust, and some strike-slip or transcurrent. The result is that each range comprises several sub-blocks which may differ notably in their lithology. Metamorphic and igneous rocks predominate in the range cores. At one time the intrusive bodies were all considered to be Mesozoic in age, but it has been demonstrated by radioactive dating that some are Precambrian and one is as recent as Oligocene or Miocene.

According to Jahns (1954a), the ranges and hills at the western end of the Transverse region are in their simplest analysis elongate folds that have been ruptured along their axes and faulted on their flanks. Ranges such as the San Gabriel and San Bernardino are large upthrown blocks bounded in part by steeply dipping faults that may have strike-slip components of movement.

Bailey (1943) has presented paleontologic,

stratigraphic, and structural evidence which indicates that the principal orogeny which produced the Transverse Ranges occurred in middle or late Pleistocene time, and judging from the present seismic activity in the region this orogeny is apparently still in progress.

*San Gabriel Range.* Typical of the eastern Transverse Ranges is the San Gabriel Range. This range is largely fault bounded; the transcurrent San Andreas fault bounds it on the northeast, and the practically vertical, probably dip-slip Sierra Madre and Cucamonga faults on the south. A major east-west-trending fault, the San Gabriel, runs through the heart of the range. In addition, numerous other faults lie in or marginal to the range. The main mass of the San Gabriel Range consists of gneisses, schists, and anorthosites of probable Precambrian age; limestones and quartzites of probable Paleozoic age; and intrusive granites, quartz monzonites, and quartz diorites that are probably of three ages, Precambrian, Cretaceous, and mid-Tertiary. Along both the north and south margins Cenozoic sediments and volcanics are extensive.

The San Gabriel Range presents a bold front to the south, and sloping southward from its base is an extensive alluvial plain (Eckis, 1928) or bajada built from debris that the mountain range has been shedding into the sinking Los Angeles Basin since mid-Miocene time. Mount Baldy, the highest peak in the range, has an altitude of 10,080 feet. There is some suggestion of an erosional summit level in the western part of the range of probable Pleistocene age. This surface is developed at an altitude around 5000 feet in the area northeast of Pasedena but is not recognizable in the eastern part of the range, possibly because of the numerous faults here.

### Peninsular Ranges

*General Description.* That portion of California south of the Transverse Ranges is known locally as the Peninsular Ranges (Hinds, 1951; Jahns, 1954b). In Fenneman's classification it would include essentially the Los Angeles Range section of the Pacific Border province. In addition to a number of mountain ranges, this area includes several basins and valleys, the most important of which is the South Coastal (Los Angeles) Basin. Actually the greater part of this geomorphic unit lies in Mexico, and as it extends southward to include the Baja California Peninsula it has a total length of around 900 miles. The section as a whole is characterized by elongate ranges and intermontane valleys whose trends are controlled by various faults which branch from or are approximately parallel to the San Andreas fault. The ranges and intermontane valleys terminate at the north at the Transverse Ranges, but included in the region are the partially submerged mountains that are now Santa Catalina, Santa Barbara, San Nicolas, and San Clemente islands. The Palos Verde Hills, northwest of Long Beach, although now attached to the mainland, were once members of this island group.

*South Coastal Basin.* At the northern end of the Peninsular Ranges is a sizeable area that lacks mountains, although it has within it several belts of low hills. This hydrographic area and geomorphic lowland includes the coastal Los Angeles structural basin and the irregularly shaped lowland to the east (Eckis, 1934). It consists of three rather distinct parts, a coastal plain strip on the west, an intermediate belt of hills or low mountains, and three more or less enclosed basins known as the San Fernando Valley and the San Gabriel and Upper Santa Ana basins.

The coastal plain strip is about 50 miles long and 10 to 30 miles wide. It is the flat surface developed on top of 25,000 or more feet of mostly marine Cretaceous and Cenozoic sediments by stream erosion and deposition during Pleistocene and Recent time. The latest sediments were brought from the north and east, mainly by the Los Angeles, San Gabriel, and Santa Ana rivers.

The most conspicuous hills that rise above the coastal plain are the Palos Verde (formerly called San Pedro Hills), northwest of Long Beach; these hills stand out conspicuously, for they attain altitudes of 1500 feet. Other low hills such as famous Signal Hill, the Baldwin Hills, and the Dominguez Hills, all topographic expressions of anticlinal or domal uplifts, add relief.

Farther east the Puente Hills, the northern end of the Santa Ana Mountains, separate the San Gabriel and upper Santa Ana basins on the east from the Los Angeles Basin at the west. The bajada at the southern base of the San Gabriel Mountains extends through the Whittier Narrows in the Puente Hills to the coastal plain. The San Jose Hills separate the San Gabriel Basin from the upper Santa Ana Basin to the east. The latter basin is about 40 miles long and 20 miles wide at its western edge and is filled with debris brought from the San Bernardino Mountains by the Santa Ana River. This river leaves the Santa Ana Basin through a gorge in the Santa Ana Mountains, which is an excellent example of an antecedent stream course.

*Structure and Topography of Peninsular Ranges.* The Peninsular Ranges represent a mountainous tract that extends about 100 miles northward into California from Baja California. Most important of the individual ranges are the Santa Ana, San Jacinto, and Santa Rosa. Taken as a whole (Jahns, 1954), "the entire province can be regarded as an uplifted and westward-tilted plateau that has been broken into several large, elongate subparallel blocks by major faults that trend northwest." The faults are largely responsible for the lineation in the topography. Individual faults have been active intermittently during much of late Cenozoic time, but rather independently of each other, so that the numerous fault blocks have had rather distinctly individual histories. Within the ranges are numerous basins and valleys, most of which are developed on grabens between the mountain ranges. The topography becomes somewhat more subdued to the west and southwest, but even here there are still prominent ridges and peaks along with fault-controlled valleys and basins.

*Rocks.* The rocks of the Peninsular Ranges are largely igneous, meta-sedimentary, and meta-igenous rocks of Mesozoic and Paleozoic (?) age, but upper Cretaceous and Cenozoic marine and nonmarine sedimentary rocks are present along the ocean and elsewhere. Despite the exceedingly complex geology of the Peninsular Ranges, in simple analysis they may be thought of as a

FIG. 26.16   View of Linda Vista terrace, north of San Diego, California.   (*Photo by Fairchild Aerial Surveys, Inc.*)

large Cretaceous batholithic mass, now badly broken by faults, that was intruded into a series of slightly older metamorphosed sedimentary and volcanic rocks.

*Marine Terraces.*   On the western side of the Peninsular Ranges is a narrow strip of coastal lowland.   At several places along this lowland are sets of marine terraces cut into the Cretaceous and Tertiary rocks.   The topography around La Jolla and San Diego is dominated by such terraces (Hanna, 1926).   Three terraces are recognized north of the San Diego River, the Poway, Linda Vista, and La Jolla, named from highest to lowest.   The highest of these terraces, the Poway, attains altitudes as high as 1200 feet.   The Linda Vista terrace (see Fig. 26.16), which

is best displayed in the area back of La Jolla, extends inland for 10 miles and rises from 300 feet on its seaward side to 500 feet inland.   The general evenness of its surface is broken by several beach ridges.   South of the San Diego River a more complex set of marine terraces is present (Hertlein and Grant, 1954).   Here the seven following topographic levels have been identified:

| Name of Terrace | Altitude Range |
|---|---|
| Otay | 430–525 |
| Sub-Otay | 425 (approximately) |
| Avondale | 200–250 |
| Chula Vista | 100–130 |
| Nestor | 25–100 |
| Tijuana | 20–50 |
| Modern coastal flats | 0–20 |

Marine terraces are also well displayed north of San Diego, in the area around Oceanside, but probably the best known and most striking marine terraces in southern California are those found on the west side of the Palos Verde Hills (Woodring, Bramlette, and Kew, 1946), where thirteen terraces are recognizable (see Fig. 26.17). The lowest terrace is 100 feet above sea level and the highest definitely identifiable terrace is at 1300 feet, but the possibility exists of a still higher one at 1425 feet. Intervals between the terraces vary from 50 to 200 feet. Offshore from the Palos Verde Hills on San Clemente and Santa Catalina islands (Smith, 1933) are similar sets of terraces. On Santa Catalina Island fourteen terraces are identifiable, and the highest reaches an altitude of 1700 feet.

It seems evident that terraces as high as 1300 and 1700 feet do not represent former high sea levels; rather they were cut at lower altitudes and raised to their present altitudes. Attempts to correlate the terraces of one area with those of other localities have met with little success, for they are not present everywhere in the same number and at comparable altitudes. This indicates that the California coast has not been elevated as a whole but as individual segments which have moved independently of each other. So far few specific age determinations of the terraces have been made. It seems unlikely that they are all Wisconsin in age, but how far back in the Pleistocene they date is not known.

*Possible Erosion Surfaces.* In an area as diastrophically active as southern California has been during Tertiary and Recent time it is hardly expectable that anything approaching regional peneplanation could have taken place. Over most of the area there is little suggestion of former baselevels of erosion, but in a few localities what have been considered remnants of former erosion surfaces have been described. One such

FIG. 26.17 Marine terraces on west side of Palos Verde Hills, California. (*Photo by R. C. Frampton and John S. Shelton.*)

area is that called the Perris block. This is a structural unit south of the San Bernardino Mountains which is bounded by the San Jacinto fault on the northeast and the Elsinore graben on the southwest. Here two old-age surfaces have been described (Dudley, 1936), the Perris surface, at an average altitude of around 1700 feet, and the Gavilan-Lakeview surface, at about 2100 feet. Dudley considered the Perris surface, although lower than the Gavilan-Lakeview surface, to be the older and explained this unusual topographic relationship by assuming that the Perris surface was buried and later exhumed after the development of the Gavilan-Lakeview erosion surface. Another possible interpretation of the Gavilan-Lakewood surface is that it is a local surface controlled by hard rock. What may possibly represent erosion surfaces correlative with the Perris surface are found in the foothills of the San Gabriel Range and in the Puente Hills to the west of the Perris block.

Sauer (1929) considered the Mesa Grande and Julian Mesa in the Peninsular Ranges examples of summit surfaces of the type called by Penck primärrumpfe, and regarding them he stated: "We have here not, in so far as is known, a surface once worn down to a low level and then uplifted, but an assemblage of forms, which although at summit position, is in the process of reduction in relief . . . In so far as we known the area has been subject to sub-aerial denudation indefinitely, perhaps since Mesozoic time. It long ago became detached by uplift from any base-level of erosion extraneous to the local block, if such connection once existed."

Jahns (1954a) believed that remnants of erosion surfaces existed in southern California at numerous levels, most of which were no older than Quaternary, although he recognized the possibility that some might be more ancient surfaces that had been exhumed from beneath sedimentary or volcanic cover masses. It is extremely difficult to determine whether apparently multiple surfaces are of different age or whether they represent parts of a once continuous erosion surface that have been dismembered and differentially uplifted by faulting.

It is not surprising that many California geologists regard peneplains and erosion cycles with considerable skepticism. In an area that has been as active diastrophically as California has been during Tertiary, Pleistocene, and Recent time there has been little opportunity for baseleveling to take place except very locally, and even possible former local erosion surfaces have become disjointed by late Pleistocene and Recent diastrophism. Under such conditions the kind of geomorphic interpretation that may have validity in the eastern United States does not work too well.

REFERENCES CITED

Bailey, T. L. (1934). Late Pleistocene Coast Range orogenesis in southern California, *Geol. Soc. Am. Bull.*, **54**, 1549–1568.
—— and R. H. Jahns (1954). Geology of the Transverse Range province, southern California, *Calif. Div. Mines Bull.*, **170**, II, Pt. 6, 83–106.
Bradley, W. C. (1956). Carbon-14 date for marine terraces at Santa Cruz, California, *Geol. Soc. Am. Bull.*, **67**, 675–677.
Cooper, W. S. (1958). Coastal sand dunes of Oregon and Washington, *Geol. Soc. Am. Memoir* 72, 169 pp.
Crandell, D. R., D. R. Mullineaux, and H. H. Waldron (1958). Pleistocene sequence in southeastern part of the Puget Sound Lowland, Washington, *Am. Jour. Sci.*, **256**, 384–397.
Dalquest, W. W., and V. B. Scheffer (1942). The origin of the Mima mounds of western Washington, *Jour. Geol.*, **50**, 68–84.
Danner, W. R. (1955). *Geology of Olympic National Park*, Univ. Wash. Press, Seattle, 68 pp.
Diller, J. S. (1902). Topographic development of the Klamath Mountains, *U. S. Geol. Survey Bull.* 196, 69 pp.
Dudley, P. H. (1936). Physiographic history of a portion of the Perris block, southern California, *Jour. Geol.*, **44**, 358–378.
Eckis, Rollin (1928). Alluvial fans in the Cucamonga district, southern California, *Jour. Geol.*, **36**, 224–247.
—— (1934). South coastal-basin investigation; Geology and ground-water storage capacity of valley fill, *Calif. Dept. Pub. Works, Water Resources Div., Bull.* 45, 279 pp.
Hess, F. L. (1910). Gold mining in the Randsburg quadrangle, California, *U. S. Geol. Survey Bull.* 430, 23–47.
Higgins, C. G. (1961). San Andreas fault north of San Francisco, California, *Geol. Soc. Am. Bull.*, **72**, 51–68.
Hill, M. L., and T. W. Dibblee, Jr. (1953). San Andreas, Garlock, and Big Pine faults, California, *Geol. Soc. Am. Bull.*, **64**, 443–458.

Hinds, N. E. A. (1952). Evolution of the California landscape, *Calif. Div. Mines Bull.* 158, 240 pp.

Howard, A. D. (1951). Development of the landscape of the San Francisco Bay counties, *Calif. Div. Mines Bull.* 154, 95–106.

Irwin, W. P. (1960). Geologic reconnaissance of the northern Coast Ranges and Klamath Mountains, California, with a summary of the mineral resources, *Calif. Div. Mines Bull.* 179, 80 pp.

Jahns, R. H. (1954a). Investigations and problems of southern California geology, *Calif. Div. Mines Bull.* 170, Ch. 1, Pt. 1, 5–29.

——— (1954b). Geology of the Peninsular Range province, southern California and Baja California, *Calif. Div. Mines Bull.* 170, Ch. II, Pt. 3, 29–52.

Lowry, W. D., and E. M. Baldwin (1952). Late Cenozoic geology of the lower Columbia River Valley, Oregon and Washington, *Geol. Soc. Am. Bull.*, 63, 1–24.

Mackin, J. H. (1941). Glacial geology of the Snoqualmie-Cedar area, Washington, *Jour. Geol.*, 49, 449–481.

Newcomb, R. C. (1952). Origin of Mima mounds, Thurston County region, Washington, *Jour. Geol.*, 60, 461–472.

Noble, L. F. (1927). The San Andreas rift and some other active faults in the desert region of southeastern California, *Seismological Soc. Am. Bull.*, 17, 25–39.

Oakeshott, G. B. (1960. Geologic sketch of the southern Coast Ranges, *Calif. Div. Mines, Mineral Information Service*, 17, 1–13.

Peacock, M. A. (1931). The Modoc lava field, north California, *Geog. Rev.*, 21, 259–275.

Péwé, T. L. (1948). Origin of the Mima mounds, *Sci. Monthly*, 66, 293–296.

Ritchie, A. M. (1953). The erosional origin of the Mima mounds of southwest Washington, *Jour. Geol.*, 61, 41–50.

Sauer, Carl (1929). Land forms in the Peninsular Range of California, as developed about Warner's Hot Springs and Mesa Grande, *Univ. Calif. Pub. Geog.*, 3, 199–290.

Smith, W. S. T. (1933). Marine terraces on Santa Catalina Island, *Am. Jour. Sci.*, 225, 123–136.

Weaver, C. E. (1949). Geology of the Coast Ranges immediately north of the San Francisco Bay region, California, *Geol. Soc. Am. Memoir* 35, 242 pp.

Wilkinson, W. D. (1959). Field Guidebook, College teachers conference in geology, *Oregon Dept. Geol. Min. Resources Bull.* 50, 148 pp.

Williams, Howel (1948). Geology of the Marysville Buttes, California, *Univ. Calif. Pub. Geol. Sci.*, 18, 103–220.

——— (1943). The history and character of volcanic domes, *Univ. Calif. Pub. Geol. Sci.*, 21, 51–146.

Willis, Bailey (1898). Drift phenomena of Puget Sound, *Geol. Soc. Am. Bull.*, 9, 111–162.

Woodring, W. P., Ralph Stewart, and R. W. Richards (1940). Geology of the Kettleman Hills oil field, California, *U. S. Geol. Survey Profess. Paper* 195, 170 pp.

——— M. N. Bramlette, and W. S. Kew (1946). Geology and paleontology of Palos Verde Hills, California, *U. S. Geol. Survey Profess. Paper* 207, 145 pp.

ADDITIONAL REFERENCES

Alexander, C. S. (1953). The marine and stream terraces of the Capitola-Watsonville area, *Univ. Calif. Pub. Geog.*, 10, 1–44.

Allen, C. R. (1957). San Andreas fault zone in San Gorgonio Pass, southern California. *Geol. Soc. Am. Bull.*, 68, 315–350.

Bretz, J H. (1913). Glaciation of the Puget Sound region, *Wash. Geol. Surv. Bull.* 8, 244 pp.

——— (1919). Late Pleistocene submergence in the Columbia Valley of Oregon and Washington, *Jour. Geol.*, 27, 489–506.

Crowell, J. C. (1952). Probable large lateral displacement on San Gabriel fault, southern California, *Am. Assoc. Petroleum Geologists Bull.*, 36, 2026–2035.

——— (1962). Displacement along San Andreas fault, California, *Geol. Soc. Am. Spec. Paper* 71, 61 pp.

Driver, H. L. (1948). Genesis and evolution of Los Angeles basin, California, *Am. Assoc. Petroleum Geologists Bull.*, 32, 109–125.

Hill, M. L. (1954). Tectonics of faulting in southern California, *Calif. Div. Mines Bull.* 170, Ch. IV, Pt. 1, pp. 5–13.

Hoots, H. W., T. L. Bear, and W. D. Kleinpell (1954). Geological summary of the San Joaquin Valley, California, *Calif. Div. Mines Bull.* 170, Ch. II, Pt. 8, 113–129.

Louderback, G. D. (1951). Geologic history of San Francisco Bay, *Calif. Div. Mines Bull.* 154, 75–94.

Miller, W. J. (1935). Geomorphology of the southern Peninsular Range of California, *Geol. Soc. Am. Bull.*, 46, 1535–1561.

Putnam, W. C. (1942). Geomorphology of the Ventura region, California, *Geol. Soc. Am. Bull.*, 53, 691–754.

Reed, R. D. (1933). *Geology of California*, Am. Assoc. Petroleum Geol., Tulsa, 355 pp. Republished in 1951.

——— and J. S. Hollister (1936). *The Structural Evolution of Southern California*, Am. Assoc. Petroleum Geol., Tulsa, 157 pp. Republished in 1951.

Russell, R. J. (1932). Land forms of San Gorgonio Pass, southern California, *Univ. Calif. Pub. Geog.*, 6, 23–121.

Sharp, R. P. (1954a). Some physiographic aspects of southern California, *Calif. Div. Mines Bull.* 170, Ch. V, Pt. 1, 5–10.

——— (1954b). Physiographic features of faulting in southern California, *Calif. Div. Mines Bull.* 170. Ch. I, Pt. 3, 21–28.

Taliaferro, N. L. (1943). Geologic history and structure of the central Coast Ranges of California, *Calif. Div. Mines Bull.* 118, 119–163.

—— (1951). Geology of the San Francisco Bay counties, *Calif. Div. Mines Bull.* 154, 117–150.

Upson, J. E. (1951). Former marine shorelines of the Gaviota quadrangle, Santa Barbara County, California, *Jour. Geol.*, **59**, 415–446.

Weaver, C. E. (1945). Geology of Oregon and Washington and its relation to occurrence of oil and gas, *Am. Assoc. Petroleum Geologists Bull.*, **29**, 1377–1415

Willis, Bailey, (1938). San Andreas rift, California, *Jour. Geol.*, **46**, 793–827.

Willis, Robin (1925). Physiography of the California Coast Ranges, *Geol. Soc. Am. Bull.*, **36**, 641–678.

# 27

# *Hawaiian Islands*

## GENERAL DESCRIPTION

The Hawaiian archipelago consists of a group of islands, atolls, and shoals which lie near the center of the North Pacific Ocean between the approximate longitudes of 154° 40′ and 178° west and latitudes of 18° 54′ and 28° 15′ north. The islands stretch for 1600 miles from the island of Ocean (Kure), northwest of Midway, to the Island of Hawaii at the southeast. The major islands are at the southeast end of the archipelago and are, in order from northwest to southeast, Niihau, Kauai, Oahu, Molokai, Lanai, Kahoolawe, Maui, and Hawaii (see Fig. 27.1). Northwest of these 8 islands are 26 islets, atolls, and shoals known collectively as the Leeward Islands. The islands of the Leeward group are the summits of submarine volcanoes; the visible parts of those at the extreme northwest are entirely organic limestone or calcareous sands, but those at the southeast have volcanic rocks projecting through the limy organic reefs.

TABLE 27.1 Areas and Maximum Altitudes of Main Group of Hawaiian Islands. (After Stearns, 1946.)

| Name of Island | Approximate Area in Square Miles | Maximum Altitude |
|---|---|---|
| Hawaii | 4,030 | 13,784 |
| Maui | 728 | 10,025 |
| Oahu | 604 | 4,025 |
| Kauai | 555 | 5,170 |
| Molokai | 260 | 4,970 |
| Lanai | 141 | 3,370 |
| Niihau | 72 | 1,281 |
| Kahoolawe | 45 | 1,477 |

Members of the main group of Hawaiian Islands vary notably in size and altitude. These variations are indicated in Table 27.1.

## STRUCTURE OF HAWAIIAN ISLANDS

The Hawaiian Islands are part of a ridge of volcanic cones superposed on a broad, low rise in the ocean floor known as the Hawaiian Swell; this swell is over 600 miles across (Dietz and Menard, 1953). Along the base of the Hawaiian Ridge is a depressed area known as the Hawaiian Deep. This deep is particularly prominent along the northeast side and at the southeast end of the Hawaiian Ridge. Outside (northeast) of the deep is the Hawaiian Arch, which is more than 200 miles across and as much as 600 miles long. Relief on the arch typically varies from 1800 to 2400 feet and in one area is as great as 3600 feet (Hamilton, 1957). The Hawaiian Ridge displays the greatest continuous relief from ocean floor to mountain summit (about 32,000 feet) found anywhere in the world.

## VOLCANIC ACTIVITY

Only on the Island of Hawaii are there presently active volcanoes. This island has been formed by the joining together of five volcanic cones, Kohala at the north, Mauna Kea at the northeast, Hualalai at the west, Mauna Loa near its center, and Kilauea at the southeast (see Fig. 27.2). Only Mauna Loa and Kilauea volcanoes are presently active. Mauna Loa, the most prolific producer of lava in the world, has aver-

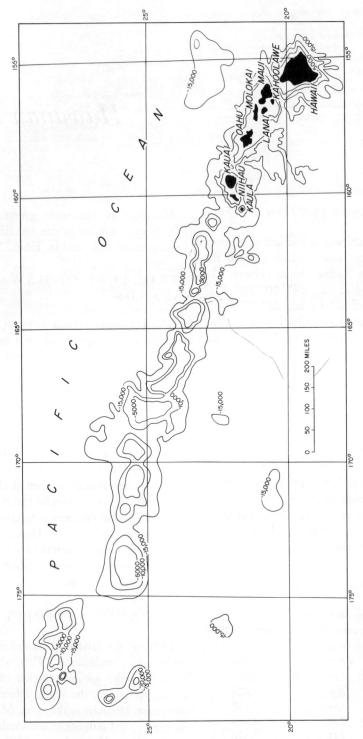

FIG. 27.1 Map of the volcanic ridge which forms the Hawaiian archipelago, with water depths shown by submarine contours. (*After H. T. Stearns, Hawaii Div. Hydrog. Bull. 8.*)

aged an outbreak of lava in its caldera once every 3⅓ years and has produced a lava flow on the average of once every 6 years (see Fig. 27.3). Kilauea has produced 12 lava flows outside its caldera since A.D. 1800; Hualalai erupted in A.D. 1801. Mauna Kea has not been active since the Hawaiians discovered Hawaii, but it has erupted since its summit was covered with a small ice cap during the latest glaciation. Kohala was the first of the five volcanoes to become

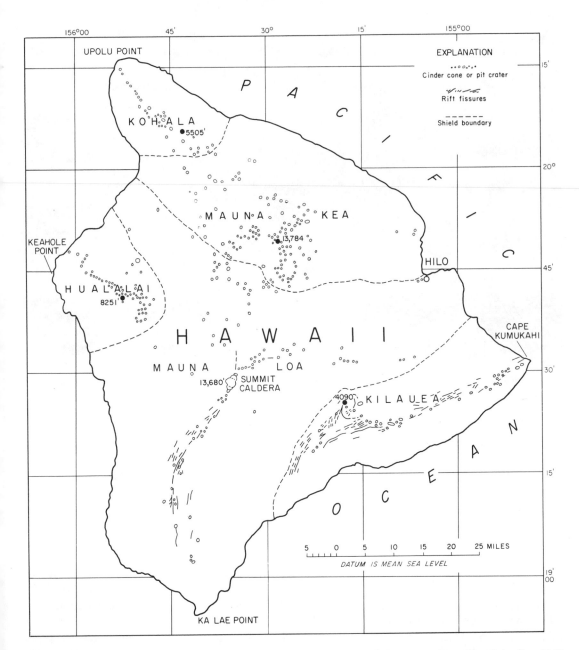

FIG. 27.2   Map of Island of Hawaii showing cinder cones, pit craters, rift fissures, and margins of the five shield volcanoes which form the island.   (*After C. K. Wentworth and G. A. Macdonald, U. S. Geol. Survey Bull.* 994.)

FIG. 27.3    Mauna Loa volcano with lava flow in foreground.    (*Photo courtesy Hawaii Visitors Bureau.*)

inactive, but no record is available as to when this occurred.

Mauna Kea is slightly higher than Mauna Loa, 25 miles to the north, and is the highest point in the Pacific Ocean, but it is not so large a volcano as Mauna Loa. Mauna Loa, which is 60 miles long and 30 miles wide, is the world's largest active volcano. Its summit (13,680 feet) rises about 30,000 feet above its base on the ocean floor. The base of Mauna Loa at sea level covers approximately 2000 square miles, but its submarine base extends over 5000 square miles (Wentworth and Macdonald, 1953). The volume of Mauna Loa above its sea floor base is around 10,000 cubic miles, as compared with a volume of 80 cubic miles for Mount Shasta above its 4500-foot base.

Hawaiian volcanoes are the broad shield type, with slopes that typically range between 4 and 10 degrees except where fault scarps produce much steeper slopes. The volcanoes are arranged in definite groups and there has been a merging of adjacent volcanoes by interfingering of their lava flows around their peripheries to form what have been called *volcanic shield clusters* (Wentworth and Macdonald, 1953). Pyroclastic materials make up less than 5 per cent of their volumes and their lavas are about equally aa and pahoehoe types. In composition the lavas are predominantly olivine basalt, but some of the younger lavas, as on Mauna Kea, are andesitic in nature (Macdonald, 1949). A few bulbous domes and one large pumice cone of trachyte are associated with the short, thick flows on the north slope of Kualalai (Stearns, 1946). Nepheline basalts characterize the valley-filling younger flows on Oahu and Kauai.

## AGES OF VOLCANOES

The fact that the northwest end of the Hawaiian island chain is marked by atolls and inactive volcanoes must mean that either this end is older than the southeast part or that volcanic activity persisted longer at the southeast. Emery (1955) thought that both the geomorphic and structural evidence suggested that the center of volcanic activity had shifted slowly from northwest to southeast. If this is true, it might be suspected that still younger centers of volcanism may in time appear on the sea floor southeast of the Island of Hawaii that will in time become new islands. Hydrographic surveys showed the existence of five sea mounts southeast of Hawaii, and these may represent centers from which new volcanic islands will eventually emerge.

Neither the date at which the Hawaiian Islands began their growth on the sea floor nor the time when they emerged above sea level is known with certainty. Macdonald and associates (1960) thought that their growth began some time during the later part of the Tertiary period, probably in Pliocene time, and Wentworth (1927) thought that the geologic evidence indicated that none of the islands emerged above sea level prior to late Tertiary time. Hinds (1931), however, thought that the islands became emergent in early Tertiary time. A trachyte in the lower part of the Waianae lava series in Mauna Kuwale Ridge on the Island of Oahu has been dated by the potassium-argon method as $8.4 \pm 0.2$ million years old (McDougall, 1963). This would suggest an early or middle Pliocene age.

Macdonald and associates (1960) have outlined what they considered the probable geologic history of the island of Kauai, one of the oldest islands of the Hawaiian group, and its history may be considered typical of the other islands.

At some time in the later part of the Tertiary period, probably in Pliocene time, a large fissure opened on the floor of the Pacific Ocean and volcanic activity began. Because of high water pressures the activity at first was nonexplosive and remained so until the volcano had built its summit into rather shallow water. Finally the volcano rose above sea level and began a period of eruptive activity similar to that now displayed by Mauna Loa and Kilauea. Using the rate at which Mauna Loa is pouring out lava as a guide, it was estimated that the shield of Kauai could have been built in as short a time as 175,000 years. However, it was thought probable that outpouring of lava was accompanied by subsidence of the ocean floor; if this is taken into account the time required for emergence of the volcano may well have been twice as great.

Following emergence of the volcanic shield of Kauai there ensued periods of activity and quiesence during which the volcanic pile was alternately added to and eroded. Finally, probably rather late in Pliocene time, volcanic activity ceased, and since then fluvial and marine erosion have been the dominant processes.

## CLIMATE OF HAWAIIAN ISLANDS

Although the effect of climate on landscape characteristics may be recognized to some degree in all parts of the United States, it is particularly evident in the Hawaiian Islands. Their tropical location produces temperatures that are notably different from most of conterminous United States, and location in the belt of the northeast trade winds, along with mountanious topography, makes for sharp contrasts in the amount of rainfall. The outstanding features of the climate of the Hawaiian Islands (Feldwisch, 1941) are marked differences in rainfall within short distances, continuing moderately high temperatures, and persistent control of the trade winds on the daily weather.

Temperature and rainfall conditions are intimately related to two major topographic controls, altitude and exposure to the northeast trade winds. Approximately one-fourth of the islands lies at altitudes below 650 feet, about one-half below 1950 feet, and one-fourth above 4500 feet. Practically year-round summer-like temperatures prevail in the lowlands, and such conditions combined with heavy rainfall promote rapid rock weathering. Rapid chemical weathering produces deep lateritic soils which reduce surface permeability of the volcanic rocks and lead to the development of numerous surface streams. Frost rarely occurs below altitudes of 4000 feet, but in winter temperatures are cold enough at higher levels for the summits of Mauna Loa and Mauna Kea on Hawaii and Haleakala on Maui to be covered with snow, and perennial ice is found in crevices atop these peaks.

Rainfall contrasts are very pronounced between the windward northeast sides of the islands and the leeward southwest sides. This contrast is well illustrated on the island of Kauai: near the summit of Mount Waialeale, at an altitude of slightly over 5000 feet, the annual rainfall is over 450 inches, whereas on the leeward southwest side of the island the annual rainfall is less than 20 inches. At levels of maximum rainfall the climate is like that of the tropical rainforest areas. On the leeward sides of the islands the climates vary from a savanna type at intermediate levels to arid near sea level. No permanent streams exist on the low semi-arid domes of West Molokai, Lanai, Kahoolawe, and Niihau (Hinds, 1931).

## FACTORS INFLUENCING DEGREE OF EROSION

Commonly the northeast sides of the islands will be characterized by deeply incised canyons as compared with lesser valleys on the leeward sides, but this relationship does not always prevail, for another factor affecting the degree of erosion is the relative age of the different parts of an island. The leeward side of the Waianae Range on the Island of Oahu is more eroded than the windward slope because the rocks on the leeward side are older than those on the windward side and thus have been exposed longer to the erosional processes. Thus three factors, altitude, amount of rainfall, and age of the island surface,

are reflected in the magnitude of erosion displayed in various parts of the islands. Wentworth (1927) concluded that the islands of Kauai and Oahu show the most advanced stages of erosion and Hawaii the least. These differences were explained mainly by their age differences. Maui and Molokai display depths of erosion intermediate in amount between Oahu and Hawaii; the other islands are not deeply eroded, mainly because of their low altitudes and consequent low rainfall rather than because of their youthfulness.

## MAJOR TOPOGRAPHIC FEATURES

### Land Forms of Volcanic Origin

The Hawaiian shield volcanoes have been built mainly by the eruption of many thousand thin lava flows through lines of fractures called rift zones. The rift zones vary in width from a few hundred feet to better than 2 miles (Wentworth and Macdonald, 1953) and are found mainly on the flanks of the volcanoes (see Fig. 27.2). Collapse graben and fault scarps are common along the rift zones. Surface erosion has exposed hundreds of individual dikes and numerous dike complexes formed by the rise of lava along fractures in the rift zones. Numerous other volcanic forms such as pit craters, spatter and cinder cones, or even open fissures mark the position of the rift zones. One open fissure, the Great Crack on Kilauea volcano, is more than 8 miles long, 30 to 40 feet wide, and as much as 50 feet deep.

Most of the volcano summits are indented with collapse caldera and pit craters. The Mokuaweoweo caldera on top of Mauna Loa is 3 miles long, $1\frac{1}{2}$ miles wide, and as much as 600 feet deep. The walls of the caldera consist of a series of step-fault scarps. The summit caldera on Kilauea is about $2\frac{1}{2}$ miles long and 2 miles wide. Near its southwest edge is a depression known as Halemaumau (the Fire Pit), which is the focus of Kilauea's eruptive activity (Macdonald and Hubbard, 1961). Stearns (1946) thought that some of the calderas on the older islands might originally have been larger than those on the Island of Hawaii. He believed that the one on East Molokai was as much as 4 miles long and the one on Kauai as much as 10 miles across.

The pit craters are not only much smaller than the calderas, but they differ from them in that they never throw out lava (Wentworth and Macdonald, 1953). In some, however, lava has broken through their walls or the talus piles at the bases of their walls, as in 1959 and 1963. Pit craters range in size from less than 100 feet to more than ½ mile in diameter; they range in depth from 50 feet to as much as 800 feet. The largest one is the Napau crater along the eastern rift zone of Kilauea volcano, which is 0.7 mile long and 0.6 mile wide. The pit craters are collapse features due possibly in part to the stoping effect of rising magma (Stearns and Clark, 1930).

Although pyroclastic debris makes up a very small part of the total eruptive mass of the Hawaiian Islands, locally material of this sort has been built into cinder and tuff cones. Diamond Head near Honolulu is probably the best known example of a tuff cone, but other examples are Koko Crater (see Fig. 27.4), on the Island of Oahu, Molokini, near the Island of Maui, and Lehau and Kaula, near the Island of Kauai. All the tuff cones lie near the coast or offshore, whereas cinder cones are found at various altitudes. The tuff cones are saucer-shaped, with out-dipping and in-dipping beds in their rims. They are usually highest at their southwest sides, because of greater transport of ash in this direction by the prevailing northeast trade winds. They consist mainly of palagonitic tuff, an indurated form of glassy basalt. All the tuff cones are the result of phreatomagmatic explosions consequent on magma's coming in contact

FIG. 27.4  Koko Head tuff ring on Island of Oahu, Hawaii.  (*Photo courtesy Hawaii Vistors Bureau.*)

FIG. 27.5 Waimea Canyon on the Island of Kauai, sometimes called the Grand Canyon of the Pacific. (*Photo courtesy Hawaii Visitors Bureau.*)

with groundwater or sea water (Stearns and Vaksvik, 1935).

### Land Forms Resulting from Subaerial Erosion

Stream erosion and associated subaerial processes rather than marine erosion are dominant on the Hawaiian Islands. Wentworth (1927) estimated that fluvial processes exceeded marine processes here in the ratio of at least 7 to 1. The effects of stream erosion vary notably for reasons stated above (see p. 558). In areas of maximum erosion many deep canyons exist (see Fig. 27.5), as well as many lesser valleys. A somewhat unique aspect of fluvial erosion is the development of numerous closely spaced ravines which give to the slopes in which they are cut a fluted or corrugated effect that has been described as "washboard topography." These closely spaced ravines have extremely steep gradients; some at Waimalolo, on the Island of Oahu, extend nearly vertically as much as 1600

to 1700 feet. Palmer (1927a) considered the flutings a form of lapiés resulting from solution of the basalts.

The heads of many Hawaiian valleys have a pronounced amphitheatre shape. Since valley heads of this sort are particularly well developed on the Island of Oahu they have been called "Oahu valleys" (Cotton, 1943). According to Cotton, this type of valley head seems to develop particularly under conditions of rapid tropical weathering and heavy rainfall. Wentworth attributed the Oahu type of valley head to normal erosional processes wherein rapid chemical weathering near the level of the water table predominated. Stearns and Vaksvik (1935) questioned, however, the importance of chemical weathering, because the valley heads are well above the low water table level in the porous basalts. They considered landslides, plunge-pool recession, and piracy as more significant in the production of the amphitheatre-shaped valley heads. Stearns (1942) has presented evidence which indicates that the scenic "caldera" on the summit of Haleakala volcano, Island of Maui, is the result of the recession of two amphitheatre-headed valleys, a hypothesis advanced earlier by Cross (1915).

A distinctive topographic form found on some of the Hawaiian islands is what is known by the local name of *pali* (Hawaiian word for precipice). These are steep rockwalls that have considerable linear extent. One of the most striking examples is the great cliff that extends along the crest of the Koolau Range on the Island of Oahu (see Fig. 27.6). This great cliff varies in height from 500 to 2500 feet (Stearns and Vaksvik, 1935).

Various ideas have been expressed as to the origin of the palis. They have been considered fault scarps (Dana, 1849; Davis, 1928), the result of foundering of part of an island (Palmer, 1927b), a product of faulting accompanied by marine erosion (Hinds, 1931), and a product of normal stream erosion (Dutton, 1884). Stearns and Vaksvik (1935) have restated the erosional theory of Dutton with slight modification. They believed the palis to be the product of a long period of erosion during which numerous amphitheatre-shaped valley heads resulted in narrowing of the ridges between adjacent valleys; the narrow ridges were believed then to have been cut away near the coast by marine abrasion and greatly reduced in height by submergence and alluviation of the valleys during high glacio-eustatic stands of the sea.

The topographic diversity of the Hawaiian Islands is indicated by the fact that Wentworth (1936), making use of the nature of the original volcanic forms and their degree of modification by gradational processes, devised a classification for the land forms of the Island of Hawaii that divided the island into 30 geomorphic units. If such a detailed classification of land forms were applied to all the islands, probably even more land form types would be recognized. Although Wentworth's classification is too detailed for our particular purpose, it does point up the fact that the topography of the Hawaiian Islands exhibits more variety than may be commonly recognized.

## Land Forms Produced by Marine Erosion

The Hawaiian Islands have experienced many relative changes in level of land and sea, and features associated with both emergence and submergence are widespread. Stearns (1935) recognized that such phenomena could be explained as the result of: alternate uplift and subsidence of the land, with sea level remaining essentially fixed in position; the land's remaining stable, with the sea fluctuating in level; or unstable land along with a fluctuating sea level. It seems very probable that the third condition prevailed most of the time and that preglacial eustatic and glacio-eustatic fluctuations of sea level were superposed on a slowly subsiding island chain.

*Features Associated with Submergence.* Evidence of submergence consists of such phenomena as drowned valleys, buried soils, submerged valley fills of basalt, submerged lithified dunes, erosional

FIG. 27.6   The Nuuanu Pali, which forms the northeast cliff of the Koolau Range on the Island of Oahu, Hawaii. (*Photo courtesy Hawaii Visitors Bureau.*)

unconformities recognized in well borings, submerged organic materials in tuffs, and submerged wave-cut benches or platforms. Lualualei Valley, on the island of Oahu, apparently was cut when sea level was at least 1200 feet lower than now, for wells in this valley failed to encounter bedrock within this depth (Stearns, 1935). Coast and Geodetic Survey profiles of West Lanai, Molokai, and Oahu suggest the presence off these islands on an extensive submerged platform at a depth of about 1800 feet. Stearns thought it likely that this platform was cut at the time that the presently submerged Lualualei Valley was eroded.

*Features Indicative of Emergence.* The presence above sea level of wave-cut benches and platforms, wave-cut nips in dunes, marine terraces in sediments at valley mouths, emergent reef limestones, and loose marine detritus give evidence of coastal emergence. The highest former shoreline so far reported is at 1069 feet above sea level on the Island of Lanai (Stearns, 1936). At times sea level remained stable long enough for fairly extensive marine platforms to be cut. Extending around the Island of Oahu is a narrow coastal plain that emerged during Pleistocene time; in places this marine platform is as much as 6 miles wide (Stearns, 1935).

Wentworth and Palmer (1925) were impressed with the existence of a wave-cut bench at 4 to 12 feet above sea level which they found around all the islands. This bench is commonly 10 to 30 feet wide, but it may be as much as 120 to 150 feet wide. They believed that it represented a negative change of sea level of 12 to 15 feet but were unable to determine its age. The possibility exists, however, that this platform may have been cut by storm waves.

Although former shorelines have been described on most of the islands, the most complicated sequence of sea level changes so far proposed is that which Stearns (1935) postulated for the islands of Oahu and Maui. In addition to the evidence for submergence of at least 1200 feet, as mentioned above, he presented evidence on these islands for sea level stands at 300 and 60 feet below present sea level and at 55, 95, 70,

40, and 25 feet above present sea level. Subsequently Stearns (1961) described what he considered evidence for additional shorelines at 2, 5, and 12 feet above sea level.

## Glacial Features

In view of the fact that at the present time snow accumulates on the higher Hawaiian terrain, it is not surprising that there is evidence that the Island of Hawaii experienced Pleistocene glaciation. Daly (1910) apparently was the first geologist to recognize evidence for glaciation there. Later, Wentworth and Powers (1941) described what they thought was extensive glacial drift above an altitude of about 11,000 feet. They described what they considered four glacial drifts on Mauna Kea which they correlated with the Wisconsin, Illinoian, Kansan, and Nebraskan drifts of midwestern United States. Stearns (1945), however, disagreed with this interpretation of the glacial deposits of Mauna Kea. He accepted the younger of the so-called drifts as being of glacial origin and of Wisconsin age, but he interpreted the other "drifts" as either material produced by paroxysmal explosions or fanglomerate deposits.

The icecap on Mauna Kea was several hundred feet thick and apparently covered an area between 26 and 28 square miles. Stearns thought that the absence of early Pleistocene glacial deposits could be reasonably explained by the assumption that the volcanoes had not yet reached a height great enough to nourish glaciers. An alternative hypothesis would be that older drifts do exist on the island but lie buried beneath lavas erupted after their deposition. This hypothesis is rendered somewhat dubious, however, by the fact that the lavas in the upper part of the mountain are so fresh that it seems doubtful that they date very far back into the Pleistocene.

## REFERENCES CITED

Cotton, C. A. (1943). Oahu valley sculpture: a composite review, *Geol. Mag.*, **80**, 237–243.

Cross, Whitman (1915). Lavas of Hawaii and their relations, *U. S. Geol. Survey Profess. Paper* 88, 97 pp.

Daly, R. A. (1910). Pleistocene glaciation and the coral reef problem, *Am. Jour. Sci.*, **180**, 297–308.

Dana, J. D. (1849). *Report United States Exploring Expedition during the Years 1838 to 1842*, **10**, Philadelphia, 756 pp.

Davis, W. M. (1928). *The Coral Reef Problem*, Am. Geog. Soc., Spec. Pub. 9, New York, 596 pp.

Dietz, R. S., and H. W. Menard, Jr. (1953). Hawaiian swell, deep, and arch and the subsidence of the Hawaiian Islands, *Jour. Geol.*, **61**, 99–113.

Dutton, C. E. (1884). Hawaiian volcanoes, *U. S. Geol. Survey 4th Ann. Rept.*, 75–219.

Emery, K. O. (1955). Submarine topography south of Hawaii, *Pacific Science*, **9**, 286–291.

Feldwisch, W. F. (1941). Climate of Hawaiian Islands, in *Climate and Man*, Yearbook of Agriculture, Dept. Agriculture, 1216–1221.

Hamilton, E. L. (1957). Marine geology of the southern Hawaiian ridge, *Geol. Soc. Am. Bull.*, **68**, 1011–1026.

Hinds, N. E. A. (1929). Wave-cut platforms in Hawaii, *Jour. Geol.*, **37**, 603–610.

—— (1931). The relative ages of the Hawaiian landscapes, *Univ. Calif. Pub. Geol. Sci.*, **20**, 143–260.

Macdonald, G. A. (1949). Petrography of the island of Hawaii, *U. S. Geol. Survey Profess. Paper* 214-D, 96 pp.

——, D. A. Davis, and D. C. Cox (1960). Geology and groundwater resources of the island of Kauai, Hawaii, *Hawaii Div. Hydrography Bull.* 13, 212 pp.

—— and D. H. Hubbard (1961). *Volcanoes of the National Parks in Hawaii*, 2nd edit., Hawaii, Nat. Hist. Assoc., 41 pp.

McDougall, Ian (1963). Potassium-argon ages from western Oahu, Hawaii, *Nature*, **197**, 344–345.

Palmer, H. S. (1927a). Lapiés in Hawaiian basalts, *Geog. Rev.*, **17**, 627–631.

—— (1927b). *The Geology of the Honolulu Artesian System*, supplement to report Honolulu Sewer and Water Comm. to legislature of Territory of Hawaii, 68 pp.

Stearns, H. T. (1935). Pleistocene shorelines on the islands of Oahu and Maui, Hawaii, *Geol. Soc. Am. Bull.*, **46**, 1927–1956.

—— (1936). High shorelines on the Island of Lanai, Hawaii, *Geol. Soc. Am. Proc. for 1936*, 105 (abs.).

—— (1942). Origin of Haleakala Crater, Island of Maui, Hawaii, *Geol. Soc. Am. Bull.*, **53**, 1–14.

—— (1945). Glaciation of Mauna Kea, Hawaii, *Geol. Soc. Am. Bull.*, **56**, 267–274.

—— (1946). Geology of the Hawaiian Islands, *Hawaii Div. Hydrography Bull.* 8, 106 pp.

—— (1961). Eustatic shorelines on Pacific Islands, *Zeitschrift für Geomorphologie*, Supplementband 3, 3–16.

—— and W. O. Clark (1930). Geology and water resources of the Kau district, Hawaii, *U. S. Geol. Survey Water-Supply Paper* 616, 29–191.

—— and K. N. Vaksvik (1935). Geology and groundwater resources of the Island of Oahu, Hawaii, *Hawaii Div. Hydrography Bull.* 1, 479 pp.

Wentworth, C. K. (1927). Estimates of marine and fluvial erosion in Hawaii, *Jour. Geol.* **35**, 117–133.

—— (1928). Principles of stream erosion in Hawaii, *Jour. Geol.*, **36**, 385–410.

—— (1936). Geomorphic divisions of the island of Hawaii, *Univ. Hawaii Bull.*, **16**, No. 8, 15 pp.

—— (1943). Soil avalanches on Oahu, Hawaii, *Geol. Soc. Am. Bull.*, **54**, 53–54.

—— and H. S. Palmer (1925). Eustatic bench of islands of the North Pacific, *Geol. Soc. Am. Bull.*, **36**, 521–544.

—— and W. E. Powers (1941). Multiple glaciation of Mauna Kea, Hawaii, *Geol. Soc. Am. Bull.*, **52**, 1193–1218.

—— and G. A. Macdonald (1953). Structures and forms of basaltic rocks in Hawaii *U. S. Geol. Survey Bull.* 994, 98 pp.

## ADDITIONAL REFERENCES

Betz, F., and H. H. Hess (1942). The floor of the North Pacific Ocean, *Geog. Rev.*, **32**, 99–116.

Cotton, C. A. (1944). *Volcanoes as Landscape Forms*, Whitcombe and Tombs, Ltd. Christchurch, 416 pp.

Dana, J. D. (1890). *Characteristics of Volcanoes*, Dodd, Mead and Company, New York, 399 pp.

Jones, S. B. (1938). Geomorphology of the Hawaiian Islands, *Jour. Geomorph.*, **1**, 55–61.

Macdonald, G. A. (1949). Hawaiian petrographic province, *Geol. Soc. Am. Bull.*, **60**, 1541–1596.

Palmer, H. S. (1955). Geomorphic contrasts within the Koolau Range of Oahu, Hawaii, *Pacific Science*, **9**, 304–317.

Stearns, H. T. (1940). Geology and ground-water resources of the islands of Lanai and Kahoolawe, Hawaii, *Hawaii Div. Hydrography Bull.* 6, 177 pp.

—— and G. A. Macdonald (1942). Geology and ground-water resources of the Island of Maui, Hawaii, *Hawaii Div. Hydrography Bull.* 7, 344 pp.

—— (1946). Geology and ground-water resources of the Island of Hawaii, *Hawaii Div. Hydrography Bull.* 9, 363 pp.

—— (1947a). Geology and ground-water resources of the Island of Molokai, Hawaii, *Hawaii Div. Hydrography Bull.* 11, 113 pp.

—— (1947b). Geology and ground-water resources of the Island of Niihaua, Hawaii, *Hawaii Div. Hydrography Bull.* 12, Pt. 1, 1–38.

Woollard, G. P. (1951). A gravity reconnaissance of the Island of Oahu, *Am. Geophys. Union Trans.*, **32**, 358–368.

$$28$$

*Alaska*

## GENERAL DESCRIPTION

Alaska has an area of nearly 600,000 square miles and thus is about one-fifth as large as conterminous United States. It extends through approximately 57 degrees of longitude, a distance equal to that across conterminous United States in the latitude of Los Angeles. Alaska extends in latitude through a distance equal to that between the Mexico-New Mexico boundary and the Canada-North Dakota boundary (Brooks, 1906).

If Alaska were divided into geomorphic provinces on a basis comparable to that used by the Fenneman committee for conterminous United States, at least four and probably six provinces would have to be recognized. Two attempts have been made to divide Alaska into geomorphic units. One classification (see Fig. 28.1) recognizes four major units or provinces with 14 sections (Williams et al., 1958), and the other (Wahrhaftig, 1960) divides the area into 12 provinces with 60 sections (see Fig. 28.2). Probably the first classification comes nearer to being comparable in magnitude of divisions with the Fenneman classification of conterminous United States.

The topography of Alaska is so varied and complex that a brief chapter like the present one can do little more than point out a few of the major geomorphic features of this vast state. To do justice to the geomorphology of Alaska would require a book in itself.

Alaska has three westward-extending peninsulas of considerable size, the Alaska, Kenai, and Seward peninsulas. The Alaska Peninsula ex-

tends southwestward, and its continuation, the Aleutian Islands, stretches for 1200 miles toward Siberia. The Kenai Peninsula, south of the Alaska Peninsula across Cook Inlet, is a much smaller peninsula; it too has a detached southwest extension, Kodiak Island. The Seward Peninsula extends westward from central Alaska, and its tip represents the westernmost point of continental North America.

In their broad aspects the major topographic features of Alaska can be correlated with similar features in western Canada and conterminous United States. The ranges of southeastern Alaska are the geologic and topographic equivalents of the Coastal Ranges of British Columbia, Washington, and Oregon. The Alaska Range and its southwestward extension, the Aleutian Range, along with such associated smaller ranges as the Nutzotin, Talkeetna, and Wrangell (see Fig. 28.1) correlate with the Sierra Nevada-Cascade province. The region between the Brooks Range and the Alaska Range, including the Seward Peninsula, is in some respects comparable to the Basin and Range and Colorado Plateau provinces. The Brooks Range is essentially a continuation of Rocky Mountain geology and topography, and the Arctic Coastal Plain is the geological equivalent of the Great Plains, even though its topography may be somewhat different because of the abundance of features resulting from the existence of continuous permafrost.

Mountain systems form the major framework of Alaska and outline its major geomorphic regions. The broad cordillera which extends northwestward across conterminous United States

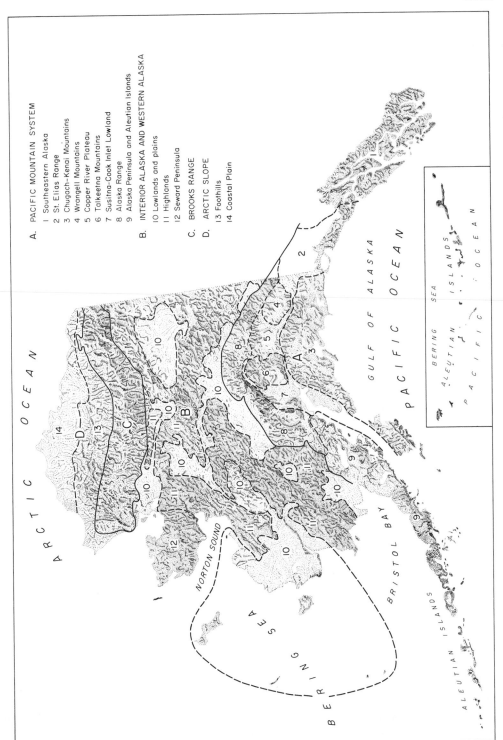

A. PACIFIC MOUNTAIN SYSTEM
  1 Southeastern Alaska
  2 St. Elias Range
  3 Chugach–Kenai Mountains
  4 Wrangell Mountains
  5 Copper River Plateau
  6 Talkeetna Mountains
  7 Susitna-Cook Inlet Lowland
  8 Alaska Range
  9 Alaska Peninsula and Aleutian Islands
B. INTERIOR ALASKA AND WESTERN ALASKA
  10 Lowlands and plains
  11 Highlands
  12 Seward Peninsula
C. BROOKS RANGE
D. ARCTIC SLOPE
  13 Foothills
  14 Coastal Plain

FIG .28.1  Geomorphic regions of Alaska.   (*After map in Landscapes of Alaska, Howel Williams, Editor, by permission of Univ. Calif. Press.*)

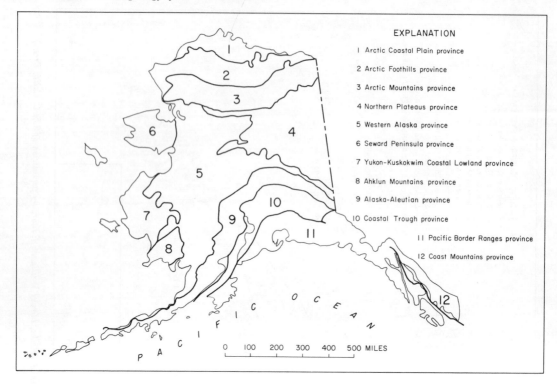

FIG. 28.2   Geomorphic regions of Alaska.   (*After Clyde Wahrhaftig and others, U. S. Geol. Survey open file report, The Physiographic Provinces of Alaska.*)

and Canada bends to the west-southwest in Alaska and gives to the Alaskan mountain ranges an arcuate pattern which is particularly well displayed in the Pacific Mountain System around the Gulf of Alaska.   The tectonic framework of Alaska (Gryc, 1961) is marked by a number of arcuate synclinal and anticlinal belts which, except for the Brooks Range at the north, roughly parallel the southern coast.

## GEOLOGY

The topography of Alaska is complex, mainly because great variety and complexity of rock types and structures exist within the state. Rocks belonging to practically all the periods of geologic time are present. Among the sedimentary rocks are some of late Precambrian age; all periods of the Paleozoic are represented, as is true of the Mesozoic and Cenozoic eras.   Metamorphic rocks are mainly

of early Precambrian and early Paleozoic age, but some are believed to be of Mesozoic age. Igneous intrusive rocks are of Devonian, Jurassic, Cretaceous, and Tertiary age, and volcanic rocks of Devonian, Mississippian, Permian, Pennsylvanian, Triassic, Jurassic, Cretaceous, Tertiary, and Quaternary age are present (Dutro and Payne, 1954).

Geologic structures vary from the relatively simple homoclinal structures of the Arctic Coastal Plain to intricate folds and faults in the mountainous areas.   All of the mountain belts have been subjected to uplift and deformation several times, including diastrophism as recent as Quaternary.   The oldest of the present-day mountains are believed to have originated in Jurassic time.   Mertie (1930) concluded that there is evidence that the southern coastal ranges experienced uplift and deformation in early Jurassic, late Jurassic, Eocene, Pliocene, and Quaternary time and that the Brooks Range had undergone uplift and deformation in Jurassic, Cretaceous, Eocene, late Tertiary, and Quaternary time. The mountains owe their present heights mainly to late Tertiary and Quaternary uplift, but many of their structures date back to earlier periods of diastrophism. Mountain uplift apparently had attained sufficient magnitude by Pliocene time in the mountain ranges back of the Gulf of Alaska that glaciation had already begun in this area (Brooks, 1906; Miller, 1958). That uplift has continued into Recent time is indicated by the deformation of Pleistocene outwash terraces in the Alaska Range (Wahrhaftig, 1958a).

## CLIMATE AND ITS GEOMORPHIC EFFECTS

Both temperatures and precipitation vary markedly over Alaska. Four major climatic zones may be recognized (*Climatography of the United States,* 1959): (1) a zone in southern, southeast, and southwest Alaska with a dominant maritime influence, (2) a zone of extreme continental climate in the interior of Alaska, (3) a zone between these two areas where the climate is transitional from maritime to continental climatic conditions, and (4) a zone of dominant Arctic influence at the north. Extreme southeast, south, and southwest Alaska have relatively mild and equable temperatures. At Sitka, Alaska, the average monthly temperatures for January and August are approximately 28° and 50° Fahrenheit respectively, giving to the station an annual temperature range of only 22°.

In interior Alaska temperatures exceeding 100° may occur during the summer, and extremely low winter temperatures are recorded; Fort Yukon has recorded a maximum temperature of 100° and a record low of −75°. The record low for all Alaska up to 1959 (*Climatography of the United States,* 1959) was a temperature of −76° recorded at Tanana, in 1886; the absolute maximum temperature for this same station is 98°. Although winter temperatures are severe in the Arctic portion of Alaska, they are not so extreme as in the interior. Absolute minimum temperatures in the Arctic region commonly range between −45° and −60°. The number of days with minimum temperatures of zero or lower is a fairly good clue to the severity of a climate. At Sitka on the average only 2 such days in a period of 20 years occur, whereas Fort Yukon, in the interior, has an average of more than 130 such days per year, and at Barrow, on the north coast, as many as 170 such days may occur annually.

Variations in annual precipitation are as marked as those of temperature. Precipitation is heaviest along the southern coastal area, and for numerous stations it exceeds 150 inches a year. Little Port Walter, with the greatest amount, has an annual precipitation slightly over 221 inches. Annual precipitation decreases rapidly inland to only 4 to 10 inches in the Arctic region. Snowfall varies from maxima of 240 to 260 inches in southeastern Alaska to 40 or 50 inches in interior Alaska and less than 40 inches in Arctic Alaska

The severe continental climates over much of Alaska are reflected geomorphically in the widespread occurrence of frozen ground and the various phenomena which are associated with a marked importance of frost-riving, solifluction, and the other processes encompassed under the general term cryoplanation (Bryan, 1946). Extensive areas are covered with rock rubble produced by the effects of the temperatures which exist under periglacial or "frost-climate" conditions.

## GLACIATION IN ALASKA

### *Present-Day Glaciers*

At the present time about 20,000 square miles, or 3 per cent, of Alaska are covered by glaciers (Field, 1958). Present-day glaciers are largely confined to the Coastal Mountains, Wrangell Mountains, and Alaska Range, mainly because their great heights and exposure to winds off the ocean produce heavy snowfall. There is meager development of glaciers in the Brooks Range because of the much lower snowfall in these mountains.

## Pleistocene Glaciers

*Distribution.* In the main, the distribution of Pleistocene glaciers was similar to that at present, except that then there were a few glaciers in the interior of Alaska, on the Seward Peninsula, and extension of glaciers from the Brooks Range onto the Arctic Coastal Plain, all areas where today glaciers are lacking except for a few small glaciers in the Kigluaik Mountains on the Seward Peninsula (Field, 1958). The great ice mass that existed in southern and southeastern Alaska apparently was connected at the east with the main continental ice in Canada, but it was completely independent as to its supply area, directions of movement, and persistence (Capps, 1932). The icecap in southeastern Alaska consisted of ice of local origin, and its movement was controlled by the mountain topography. The icecap in the Brooks Range was likewise independent of the continental ice sheet as to supply and movement, although it may have been connected with it near the mouth of the MacKenzie River.

*Multiple Glaciation.* Evidence of multiple glaciation has been recognized in various parts of Alaska, but so far most of the surficial glacial deposits recognized appear to belong to the Wisconsin age. Four glaciations have been recognized in the northern part of the Alaska Peninsula; three glaciations in the Kilbuck Mountains; at least four glaciations in the Cook Inlet area; three and possibly more in the Kenai Peninsula; four in the Nenana Valley; four on the Seward Peninsula; at least three in the Big Delta area; and four in the Brooks Range (Péwé et al., 1953).

The evidence is sufficiently alike in the various areas to suggest that they all experienced essentially similar glacial histories. In each area there is found:

1. Evidence of a minor glacial advance within the last few centuries.
2. Fresh moraines that indicate major advances during Wisconsin time.
3. Moraines of an older and more extensive glaciation thought to be Illinoian in age.

4. Scattered evidence of what is believed to represent a pre-Illinoian glaciation.

## PERMAFROST IN ALASKA

Over much of Alaska some type of permafrost exists (see Fig. 28.3). Only in southeastern Alaska is it largely lacking, but even here it is present in the mountains. Regional variations in temperatures result in a transition from continuous permafrost in the Arctic Coastal Plain, Brooks Range, and Seward Peninsula, through discontinuous permafrost in interior Alaska, through continuous permafrost in the Alaska, Aleutian, Wrangell, and associated mountain ranges and probably sporadic permafrost in their adjacent foothills and lowlands, to no permafrost along the southern margin of Alaska. Differences in lithology, topography, and drainage produce marked local variations in the character and distribution of the permafrost which to some extent obscure the regional distribution pattern.

Permafrost in Alaska is a product of both present and Pleisotocene climatic conditions. Relict masses of Pleistocene frozen ground are found mainly in areas of impermeable soils and rocks, and they are often found overlain by permeable layers that have been thawed by circulating groundwater. Most of the ancient permafrost is thawing differentially at the present, but at the same time in some areas, such as the Chugach Range, new permafrost is forming.

The intensive frost action found in areas of perennially frozen ground results in distinctive microrelief patterns, although patterned ground is not restricted to areas of permafrost. Two broad categories of polygonal patterns can be recognized (Hopkins et al., 1955): (1) frost-stirred or sorted polygons, including such forms as stone polygons, vegetation polygons, and related striped forms, and (2) constructional or tensional polygons such as ice-wedge polygons. Other features commonly encountered in areas of frozen ground are pingos, thaw lakes, and beaded drainage (a series of small ponds connected by short stream courses).

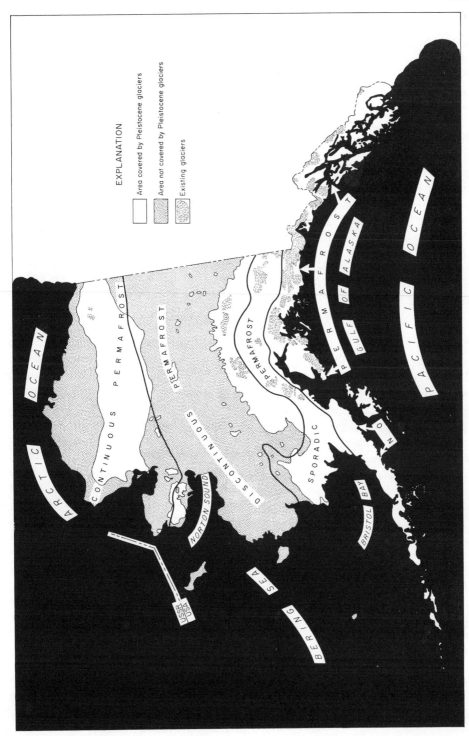

FIG. 28.3   Glacial and permafrost map of Alaska; compiled by U. S. Geol. Survey.   (*From Landscapes of Alaska, Howel Williams, Editor, by permission of Univ. Calif. Press.*)

# PACIFIC MOUNTAIN SYSTEM

The Pacific Mountain System consists mainly of a broad belt of ranges which are essentially parallel to the southern coast of Alaska and form a curved belt concave to the south. The mountain system is broadest in the area where the mountain belt has its maximum curvature and narrows from here to both the southwest and southeast. Included in the Pacific Mountain System are two sizeable nonmountainous areas, the Susitna-Cook Inlet Lowland and the Copper River Plateau. Major mountain ranges are the Coast Range of southeastern Alaska, the St. Elias Mountains, the Chugach-Kenai Mountains, the Alaska Range, and the Aleutian Range with its southwestward continuation into the Aleutian Islands. Somewhat less extensive ranges are the Wrangell and Talkeetna.

## Coast Range of Southeast Alaska

The Coast Range of Alaska, like the Coastal Range of British Columbia, has a core of granitic rocks belonging to the great Jurassic-Cretaceous batholith. Offshore from the Coast Range are the many islands of the Alexander Archipelago, which are separated from the mainland by a number of fiords and drowned counterparts of the lowlands on the mainland.

Lineation is well displayed in the topography of the Alaska Panhandle, particularly in the northwest-southeast alignment of the major topographic features. This lineation is related to such structural controls as rock schistosity, shear zones, and faults (Twenhofel and Sainsbury, 1958). Most striking of the structurally controlled features is the great fiord which includes Lynn Canal and Chatham Strait. This feature is at least 250 miles long and is controlled in its position by a major fault zone which cuts rocks ranging in age from Paleozoic to Cretaceous, including the Coast Range batholith.

## St. Elias Mountains

The Alaskan "panhandle" is joined to the main part of Alaska by high coastal mountains known as the St. Elias Range, which is probably the most spectacular mountain range in North America. This range, which lies partly in Alaska and partly in Canada, is about 300 miles long and has a maximum width of about 100 miles. The St. Elias Mountains are the highest coastal mountains to be found anywhere in the world (Miller, 1958). From Cross Sound to the Copper River, the St. Elias Range, along with the Chugach Mountains, presents a formidable barrier. Mount Logan (19,850 feet) and Mount St. Elias (18,008 feet) are the second and fourth highest peaks on the continent of North America; these two peaks and twelve others in this range exceed in altitude Mount Whitney, the highest peak in conterminous United States.

So rugged and difficult of access are the St. Elias Mountains that their geology is known only in a fragmentary way. Reconnaissance investigations indicate that the range consists mainly of sedimentary rocks of Paleozoic and Mesozoic age that have been intensely folded and faulted. The ruggedness and height of the range are to a large degree results of uplift that has taken place along a system of northwest-southeast-trending faults. The St. Elias Range, along with the Chugach and Kenai Mountains to the west, has in it some of the most extensive valley glacier systems to be found in North America. The Hubbard Glacier in the St. Elias Range is probably the longest valley glacier in Alaska (Field, 1958). It is believed to be more than 90 miles long and at several places is as much as 10 miles wide. On the seaward side of the range most of the large glaciers descend to altitudes of less than 500 feet above sea level, and many reach the sea. The area along the north side of Yakutat Bay especially is marked by a number of glaciers which reach the sea. It might be expected logically that extensive shelf ice would have developed in the adjacent Gulf of Alaska during times of glacial maximum, but the geological evidence seems to indicate that for some unexplained reason this did not happen.

The largest and probably the best known of the present-day Alaskan glaciers is the Malaspina Glacier (see Fig. 28.4). This ice sheet covers about 850 square miles on the coastal plain of southern Alaska along the north shore of the

FIG. 28.4 View of Malaspina Glacier with Mount St. Elias in background. (*Photo by Bradford Washburn.*)

Gulf of Alaska (Sharp, 1958). The glacier extends from the open sea near Sitkagi Bluffs inland for 28 miles to the base of the St. Elias Range and for 40 miles west from Yakutat Bay to Icy Bay. Seismic data indicate that it is as much as 2000 feet thick and lies in a basin that extends 800 to 1000 feet below sea level. Altitudes on the glacier range from 75 feet, at its outer margin, to near 2500 feet, where the Seward Glacier debouches into it. Nearly 70 per cent of the mass of the glacier is supplied by the Seward Glacier from the St. Elias Range. The remaining ice comes from several small glaciers from the same range.

### Chugach-Kenai Mountains

Westward and southwestward extensions from the St. Elias Range are known as the Chugach and Kenai Mountains respectively. They form a 450-mile-long mountain chain which borders the Gulf of Alaska and extends from the St. Elias Mountains on the east to the tip of the Kenai Peninsula. These two ranges are similar geologically and structurally, but they are given separate names because two glacial fiords and a low mountain pass form a depression which separates them.

Altitudes in general decrease to the west in these mountains, and the highest peak in the Kenai Mountains has an altitude of only 6800 feet. Although the Chugach-Kenai Mountains are not so high as the St. Elias Range, they are still rugged mountains, largely because of the intense glacial erosion which they have experienced. Kodiak and adjacent islands are geologically, structurally, and topographically a southwestward continuation of the Kenai Mountains, although they are noticeably lower in altitude. The arcuate form of the Chugach-Kenai-Kodiak mountain chain is controlled by the structure and outcrop pattern of the bedrock (Miller, 1958). Movement along major faults has contributed to the rugged relief. Meta-sedimentary and volcanic rocks of late Paleozoic and Mesozoic age predominate in the ranges, but rocks of Tertiary age occur in the foothills. Diastrophism during Jurassic and Cretaceous time established the structural framework, but present heights are largely a result of late Tertiary and Pleistocene uplift. Wave-cut terraces on the southern flanks of the mountains occur up to altitudes as high as 1600 feet and attest to the recent and intermittent uplift that the region has experienced.

## Wrangell Mountains

The Wrangell Range occupies an elliptical area between the Chugach Range at the south and the Alaska Range at the north. The Wrangell Range is a cluster of volcanic mountains resting on a base of meta-sedimentary and meta-igneous rocks. Eruptions of basaltic and andesitic lavas began in Tertiary time and continued into Recent time. Mount Wrangell has erupted within the last century (Black 1958a). The Wrangell Range rises conspicuously above the Copper River Plateau to the south, and more than a dozen peaks in the range exceed 12,000 feet in altitude; Mount Blackburn, the highest peak, has an altitude of 16,523 feet. The Wrangell Mountains are among the most striking of the Alaskan ranges because of their rugged peaks and extensive snowfields and glaciers. The Nabesna Blacier, which originates in the large icecap which covers the crest of the Wrangell Range, is at least 45 miles long (Field, 1958).

## The Alaska Range

The Alaska Range (see Fig. 28.5) is one of the youngest and most striking mountain ranges in Alaska; in it is Mount McKinley (20,300 feet), the highest peak in North America. The Alaska Range extends in an arcuate pattern for nearly

600 miles; it is only some 30 miles wide at the Canadian border but widens westward until in the vicinity of Mount McKinley it is about 120 miles wide (Wahrhaftig, 1958b). The range is nearly concentric with the Coast Range but of slightly shorter radius. The range separates the series of mountains and lowlands south of it, which drain to the Pacific Ocean, from the lowlands and highlands of interior Alaska, which drain to the Bering Sea.

The great height of Mount McKinley is somewhat exceptional, for there are fewer than 20 peaks in the Alaska Range which exceed 10,000 feet in altitude. The relief in the Wrangell Mountains is actually greater than that in the Alaska Range. East of Mount McKinley altitudes decrease, and the range eventually loses its identity as it merges with the Coast Ranges north of Mount St. Elias (Moffit, 1954).

The Alaska Range is extensively glaciated, but the glaciers on its south side are much longer than those on the north.

One anomalous feature is the fact that although the Alaska Range forms the great topographic barrier between the Pacific Coast and the interior of Alaska, only southwest from Mount McKinley does it serve as the drainage divide. East of Mount McKinley six rivers, the Nenana, Delta, Nabesna, Chusana, Beaver, and White, flow northward through the range to the Yukon River. The implication of this unusual drainage distribution is discussed on page 580. On the south side of the Alaska Range is a foothill belt 25 to 30 miles wide in which altitudes gradually rise to those of the higher peaks; however, the foothill belt on the north side of the range is much narrower, and here the range rises rather abruptly from the interior lowlands.

Rocks of the Alaska Range are varied in character and represent most of the geologic periods. They have been subjected to repeated deformation, and as a consequence their structure is highly complex. In a general sense the Alaska Range may be thought of as a great synclinorium in which the youngest rocks lie near the center of the range and the oldest rocks along its flanks (Wahrhaftig, 1958b). This syncline is cut by several great longitudinal faults that are marked

FIG. 28.5   View of Alaska Range, looking south and showing Mount Hayes and head of Delta Creek.   (*Photo by Bradford Washburn.*)

by lines of valleys and passes. Tertiary rocks underlie many of the logitudinal lowlands. Numerous nearly oval granitoid stocks and batholiths are responsible for the higher mountainous tracts (Wahrhaftig, 1960).

The great mountain wall which the Alaska Range presents toward the Tanana-Kuskokwim lowland, on the north, is largely controlled by an extended fault which runs through the Alaska Range from Bering Sea past Mount McKinley into southeastern Alaska. This fault is known as the Denali fault and was thought by St. Amand (1957) to connect with the fault in Lynn Canal and Chatham Strait (see p. 570) in southeast Alaska. A trough along this fault separates the largely glacier-free lower foothills belt from the high ice-clad mountains to the south. A striking pattern of parallel east-west ridges separated by long narrow valleys is displayed by the Alaska Range east of Mount McKinley (Wahrhaftig, 1958b). Strangely the drainage does not follow these valleys but instead cuts across them in a dendritic pattern, which suggests that the present drainage is not structurally controlled but rather was inherited from an earlier topography whose drainage was independent of structure.

### Alaska Peninsula and Aleutian Islands

The name Aleutian Range is commonly applied to the narrow belt of east-west-trending ridges which extends from Mount Spurr, west of Anchorage, to Attu Island at the extreme western tip of the Aleutian island chain. This line of ridges is surmounted at intervals ranging from

5 to 85 miles by volcanic peaks 4500 to 8500 feet high (Wahrhaftig, 1960). The range has been extensively glaciated, but most of the volcanoes attained their present proportions after the glaciation of the range. The term Aleutian Arc has also been applied to this belt (Coats, 1950; St. Amand, 1957) because of its similarity to the so-called arcs in the circum-Pacific ring of tectonic activity. The entire arc has a length of about 1600 miles and includes in addition to the Aleutian Islands an extension onto the mainland through the Alaska Peninsula. About 80 major volcanoes lie in this arc, and at least 36 of them have been active since 1760 (Coats, 1950). Some 20 large caldera are also present within this volcanic belt; those above sea level range in diameter from 1½ to 8 miles, but the submarine Buldir caldera between the islands of Kiska and Buldir measures 27 by 13 miles (Powers, 1958) and is apparently the world's largest caldera.

Probably the most famous of the Alaskan calderas is that of Katmai on the Alaska Peninsula north of Kodiak island. This caldera, along with the adjacent Valley of Ten Thousand Smokes, came into existence as the result of a series of spectacular eruptions in 1912. Ash flows of nuée ardente origin as much as 700 feet thick accumlated during the eruptions, and it has been estimated that more than 7 cubic miles of pyroclastic materials were hurled into the atmosphere (Powers, 1958). The eruptions came mainly from nearby Novarupta volcano. At about the same time that the nuée ardentes were discharging from Novarupta, the entire top of Mount Katmai volcano, 6 miles to the east, collapsed, giving rise to a caldera nearly 3 miles long and 2 miles wide. It is of interest that a glacier now occupies the caldera.

In general, the Aleutian volcanoes are superposed on a basement of Tertiary and older extrusive and intrusive igneous rocks plus some sedimentaries. The present line of volcanoes is built of rocks ranging in composition from olivine basalt to rhyolite, but andesite is probably the most common rock type. In this respect the volcanoes resemble their contemporaries in the Cascade Range.

# INTERIOR AND WESTERN ALASKA

Between the Pacific Mountain System on the south and the Brooks Range on the north is an extensive area of diverse topography that extends from the Bering Sea on the west to beyond the international boundary at the east. Except for the Seward Peninsula area at the northwest this region is drained by the Yukon and Kuskokwim Rivers. The topography

consists of an irregular assemblage of intricately dissected uplands and broad alluvium-floored lowland basins. The floors of most of the basins average less than 600 feet in altitude. The hill and ridge tops of uplands in the western part of the region average 2,000 to 3,000 feet in altitude and those of uplands to the east in the Yukon-Tanana region average 4,000 to 5,000 feet. Surmounting most of the upland areas are scattered mountains that rise 1,000 to 2,000 feet above the surrounding hilltops and commonly are composed of resistant intrusive igneous bodies. (Miller et al., 1959.)

## Highland Areas

Three hilly or low mountainous areas are distinguishable at the west, the Seward Peninsula Highlands, the Norton Sound Highlands between Norton Sound and the Yukon Valley, and the Kuskokwim Highlands or Mountains east of the Yukon. The Kuskokwim Mountains are the dominant topography features of this region, and they extend eastward as far as central Alaska. Except for the Brooks and Alaska Ranges, the Kuskokwim Mountains and Seward Peninsula represent the largest glaciated areas north of the Coast Range. The southern third of these mountains was glaciated during Pleistocene time, and a few small glaciers persist there today, as they do in the Kilbuck Mountains to the southwest (Hoare, 1958; Field, 1958). Most of the ridge crests in the western highlands are relatively barren of vegetation, and features produced by frost action and solifluction are widespread. Upland summit surfaces suggest the preservation of remnants of two former erosion surfaces (see p. 580). Numerous striking elongate piedmont lakes are found at the extreme south in what are known locally as the Tilchik and Wood River Mountains; these lakes occupy fiord-like glacial troughs that have been cut well below sea level.

The interior highlands of eastern Alaska vary in nature from rolling hills covered with vegetation to high, rugged mountains that reach above timber line (Miller et al., 1959; Chapman, 1958). The highest terrain lies in a belt extending westward from the Canadian boundary between the Yukon and Tanana Rivers. Mertie (1937) described the topography of this area as follows:

> The region lying between the Yukon and Tanana Rivers, which is part of the central plateau [technically not plateau] province of interior Alaska, is a country of diversified topography and drainage. This province has no continuous chains of mountains, similar to the various ranges of the Rocky Mountains [Brooks Range], but instead is a rolling upland characterized by discontinuous groups of higher mountains that diversify an otherwise monotonous skyline produced by ridge crests of more or less uniform height. The valleys likewise lack uniformity. Some of the headwater streams have narrow, canyonlike valleys; some flow in wide open valleys that are disproportionately large in comparison with the streams that now occupy them; and some flow across aggraded headwater plains . . . . This marked topographic diversity is the result of a long and complex geomorphic history, which dates back to the Tertiary period.

Loessial silts mantle the upland slopes and ridges throughout much of central Alaska (Péwé, 1955). The loess attains its maximum thickness along the north side of the Tanana Valley. Around Fairbanks, where the loess is well exposed, its maximum thickness ranges from 200 feet on hilltops to 300 feet in valley bottoms.

## Lowland Areas

Numerous lowlands and plains are scattered throughout interior Alaska. Just north of the Alaska Range is an almost continuous lowland extending from the Canadian border to the Bering Sea. It seems likely that this lowland reflects a depressed structural belt that parallels the Alaska Range. In some respects the Alaska Range resembles one of the Pacific structural arcs, and it was suggested by St. Amand (1957) that possibly the Tanana Valley is analogous to the ocean deeps which commonly parallel the Pacific arcs. The existence of the Denali fault zone along the east part of this lowland adds further credence to the probability that the lowland may be as much a product of diastrophism as of degradation. Bedrock in the lowland is actually below sea level.

Surficial materials in the interior lowlands are largely Quaternary clays, silts, sands, and gravels, mainly of glacial and eolian origin (Williams, 1962; Black, 1958b). Glaciers advanced into the lowlands repeatedly or at least sent outwash into them.

The Yukon Valley is the major erosional lowland across interior Alaska. The Yukon River, with its tributaries, forms one of the world's great drainage systems. It heads in the northwest corner of British Columbia and drains the southwestern part of the Yukon Territory as well as most of central Alaska. In central Alaska it receives two major tributaries, the Porcupine from the northeast and the Tanana from the southeast. In the area known as the Great Bend of the Yukon is one of the larger lowland areas of central Alaska; here is Yukon Flats, one of several troughs and basins in interior Alaska that were areas of sedimentation during Tertiary and Quaternary time (Williams, 1962). Yukon Flats are about 200 miles long and 40 to 100 miles wide and cover approximately 9000 square miles. Crossing this lowland the Yukon River meanders across a valley flat as much as 50 miles wide. The continental deposits of Yukon Flats represent either remnants of formerly more extensive sediments that have been preserved by post-Eocene downfaulting or deposits that accumulated as the troughs and basins that were initiated during the Laramide orogeny in interior Alaska continued to subside. A Pleistocene lake may have existed in the area, but not so many of the sediments are lacustrine as was once thought. A similar depressed area in the Kuskokwin drainage basin is known as Kuskokwin Flats.

## BROOKS RANGE

The Brooks Range includes a group of mountain masses with individual names which extends from the Canadian border most of the way across Alaska. The mountains are rugged and were severely glaciated, but they are not so high as several other Alaskan ranges, as the highest peaks are only slightly more than 9000 feet in altitude. Despite their modest altitudes the Brooks Range represents the highest mountains to be found anywhere within the Arctic Circle.

The geology of the Brooks Range is not yet known in detail, but the core of the range consists of limestones, quartzites, and other metamorphic rocks ranging in age from Silurian to Mississippian (Gryc, 1958a). Younger rocks around the flanks of the range are sandstones, shales, conglomerates, and limestones of Permian to Cretaceous age. Uplift of the Brooks Range began in Jurassic time and continued throughout the Cretaceous and into the Tertiary. The range apparently was strongly deformed during early Tertiary time but was subsequently reduced to low relief. The present range was elevated in late Tertiary time, and its topographic detail is largely a product of fluvial and glacial erosion since then. Structurally the Brooks Range is a large geanticline which has been compressed into numerous tight folds and broken by numerous faults. The northern part of the range consists of a number of plates that have been thrust northward in imbricate fashion (Payne et al., 1951).

Because the Brooks Range largely lacks a forest cover, its geology and complex structures are clearly displayed. Although some of the topography is covered with frost-riven rubble, bedrock exposures are abundant. Many small glaciers still exist, and large glacial cirques and troughs attest to former much more extensive glaciation. Pleistocene glaciers were not so extensive in the Brooks Range as in the Alaska and Coastal Ranges because of the lesser amount of snowfall. Evidence has been presented for what were believed to be four major glacial advances (Holmes and Lewis, 1961) in the Franklin Mountains in the northeastern part of the Brooks Range. These were, from oldest to youngest, the pre-Illinoian Weller and Chamberlin, the Illinoian Schrader, and Wisconsin Peters glacial advances. The Weller glaciation extended into the foothills as a piedmont glaciation. In addition there is evidence for two recent fluctuations in the glaciers. Deposits belonging to four glaciations have also been recognized on the south side of the Brooks Range adjacent to the Yukon Flats region (Williams, 1962).

## ARCTIC SLOPE

The so-called Arctic Slope is a region of frozen tundra, the only such area under the American flag. The area is more than 600 miles long, east-west, and from 100 to 200 miles wide, north-south, and comprises about one-seventh of the area of Alaska. The Arctic Slope is divisible into two distinct geologic and topographic parts, the Foothills Belt at the south and the Coastal Plain at the north. The structure of the Arctic Slope taken as a whole consists of a great downfold or trough consisting of a complex structural belt in the foothills north of the Brooks Range which merges northward into more gentle structures paralleling the axis of the trough and still farther north into the nearly flat-lying beds of the Coastal Plain (Gryc, 1958b).

### Foothills Belt

The Foothills Belt between the Brooks Range and the Coastal Plain consists of rolling plateaus and low linear mountains. It can be divided into southern and northern parts, which differ notably in their geologic structure and topography. The southern foothills have more the structural complexity of the Brooks Range, but differ from this range in that they are composed of weaker rocks (Payne et al., 1951). The rocks here are shales, limestones, cherts, sandstones, and conglomerates of Triassic, Jurassic, and Cretaceous age, tightly folded along east-west axes. As a consequence of their complex structure the topography of the southern foothills belt is very irregular. Altitudes in the southern foothills descend from about 3500 feet adjacent to the Brooks Range to about 1200 at their northern margin, and local relief may be as much as 2500 feet. The topography is characterized by irregular east-trending buttes, mesas, and ridges separated from each other by undulating tundra plains (Wahrhaftig, 1960).

In the northern foothills are sedimentary rocks of Devonian to Cretaceous age with some mafic intrusions. They are less complexly folded than those to the south; the folds here are open, and the rocks have a recognizable regional northward dip. Structures are not unlike those commonly designated as an Appalachian type; a few thrust faults are present. The more simple structures of the northern foothills are reflected in a greater regularity of topography with aligned east-west ridges of nearly accordant altitudes (Payne et al., 1951).

Hummocky glacial moraines are present along most of the valleys that extend from the Brooks Range onto the Coastal Plain (Wahrhaftig, 1960), and at one place glacial materials were recognized 40 miles north of the mountain front (Péwé et al., 1953). Evidence for six glacial advances has been described (Detterman et al., 1958), of which two were believed to be pre-Wisconsin, two early Wisconsin, one late Wisconsin, and one Recent. Outwash terraces extend seaward from the end moraines. Loessial silts are relatively thin in this area, and to a considerable degree are mixed with the rock rubble which overlies the bedrock of much of the area.

## Arctic Coastal Plain

Northward from the foothill belts stretches the vast, monotonous Arctic Coastal Plain. Its surface is marked by thousands of lakes and swamps and by numerous meandering streams. Locally lakes exceed land in area, and for the region as a whole they represent about one-fifth of the total area. Permafrost underlies most of the Coastal Plain. Surficial materials are the unconsolidated clays, silts, sands, and gravels of the mainly marine Pleistocene Gubik formation, which is as much as 250 feet thick. West of the Colville River the bedrock is of late Cretaceous age; east of this river rocks of Tertiary age are found.

*Permafrost Features.* The presence beneath most of the Coastal Plain of perennially frozen ground results in the development here of extensive permafrost phenomena. A network of ice-wedge polygons covers the Coastal Plain (see Fig. 28.6), some of which are as much as 300 feet in diameter (Black, 1952). Pingoes, which are ice-cored mounds 20 to over 200 feet in height, are locally so abundant as to produce an undulatory skyline (Wahrhaftig, 1960). Thaw sinks are common, and probably the most striking features of the coastal plain are the numerous oriented lakes (see Fig. 28.7). Lakes of this type occur over an area of some 25,000 square miles (Black and Barksdale, 1949). Their orientation ranges through about 30 degrees, from north to north 30° west; their average range of orientation is about 12 degrees, from north 9° west to north 21° west (Carson and Hussey, 1962). Their remarkable orientation is equalled only by the Carolina Bays. The lakes range in length from a few feet to more than 9 miles, and they may be as much as 3 miles wide. Both large and small lakes are found together. Their shapes may be elliptical, ovoid, egg-shaped, rectangular, triangular, or irregular. As with the Carolina Bays, many theories have been advanced to explain their remarkable orientation, but none has been completely successful in doing so.

## GEOMORPHIC HISTORY OF ALASKA

### Evidence of Former Erosion Surfaces

Not enough detailed geomorphic studies have been made in Alaska to give a very clear picture of the pre-Pleistocene history of the region, and even the details of Pleistocene events remain to be worked out. Remnants of former peneplains have been postulated for several areas in Alaska, but some were proposed at a time when the peneplain concept was new and peneplains were being described from rather meager evidence. Spencer (1903) believed that the summits of the Coastal Range in both British Columbia and Alaska represent the remnants of a former

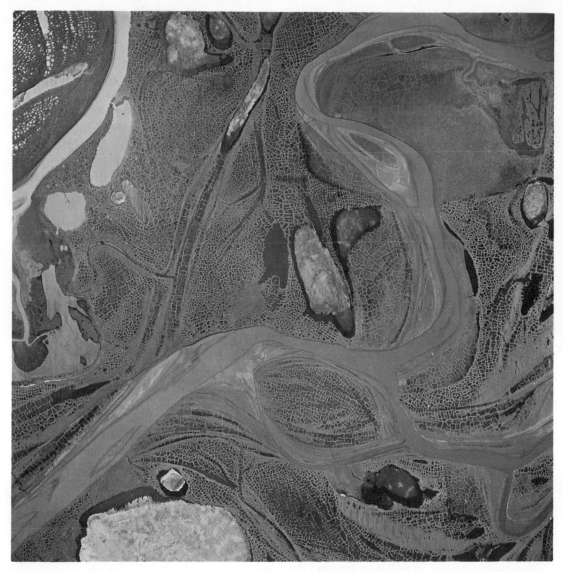

FIG. 28.6    Vertical photograph of patterned ground near Barrow, Alaska.    (*U. S. Navy Photo, courtesy R. F. Black.*)

peneplain.    He also interpreted the summits of the Chugach Range and the surface of the Yukon Plateau as erosion surfaces equivalent in age to that in the Coast Ranges.    He believed their age to be late Mesozoic or early Tertiary, most probably Eocene.    The anomalous drainage of the eastern Alaska Range, wherein six rivers have their sources south of the range crest and flow northward through the range to the Yukon River, was believed by Spencer to be antecedent to the

uplift of the Alaska Range and inherited from the postulated Eocene peneplain.

Schrader (1904), from a reconnaissance of northern Alaska, described what he believed to be three peneplain levels in that part of Alaska. The highest peneplain was thought to be represented by levels in the Endicott Mountains, a mountain group in the central part of the Brooks Range, at altitudes around 6000 feet. An intermediate level was described in the Yukon

Plateau at about 3000 feet, and a still lower erosion surface was postulated in the Koyukuk Plateau at altitudes near 1200 feet. Brooks (1906) thought, however, that the then available reconnaissance topographic maps did not bear out Schrader's contention that the Koyukuk surface was separate and distinct from the Yukon surface.

Mertie (1937), in a discussion of the area between the Yukon and Tanana Rivers, pointed out that if the ridge crests in this area were joined the result would be a nearly flat dome with its greatest height in the east-central part. This would represent what many geologists would call a peneplain, but Mertie considered this a questionable interpretation and believed that the former erosion surface was better described as a mature than as an old age surface. He recognized that many of the ridge tops were very nearly flat, and he attributed their low relief to the operation of such processes as nivation, solifluc-

FIG. 28.7   Oriented lakes on Artic Coastal Plain south of Wainwright, Alaska.   (*Air Force photo, courtesy R. F. Black.*)

tion, and other processes encompassed under the term cryoplanation.

Cockfield (1921), from a study of the Yukon Plateau in Canada and adjacent Alaska, concluded that is an area that was "extensively planated during a long period of crustal stability and reduced to a slightly undulating plain." Remnants of the former erosion surface are now found in flat-topped ridges whose surfaces display no evidence of structural control. Cockfield was uncertain as to the time of uplift of the erosion surface except that it occurred after deposition of early Tertiary beds.

Cady and others (1955), in their discussion of the Kuskokwim Mountain area in southwestern Alaska, described two topographic levels which they thought had regional extent. The older of these two surfaces was designated the Georgetown summit level and the younger the Sleetmute. The Georgetown surface characteristically occurs at altitudes between altitudes of 2000 and 2200 feet and may be traced for 125 miles southeast beyond the Kuskokwim region. Thus the Georgetown erosion surface was believed to have had hardly more than 200 feet of relief. Its age was believed to be late Tertiary (Miocene or Pliocene), and it was correlated with similar summit levels in the Yukon region in east-central Alaska and the Yukon Territory of Canada.

The Sleetmute surface was thought to have been nearly as extensive as the Georgetown surface above it; it was described as a late mature upland surface with altitudes ranging from 1000 to 2000 feet. The Sleetmute surface was interpreted as primarily a product of processes associated with intensive frost action. Its slopes are almost completely free of streams, but soil stripes and other types of patterned ground radiate from its surface toward the valleys which have been cut below it. Movement of rock debris into the major valleys is mainly by creep and solifluction. High points on the Sleetmute surface attain essentially the level of the Georgetown surface. Development of the Sleetmute surface was believed to have begun in Tertiary time and to be continuing at the present.

Wahrhaftig (1958a), in a discussion of the Nenana Valley and northern foothill belt of the Alaska Range, cited the existence of numerous flat-topped mountains as evidence of a former erosion surface that once extended across the deformed Tertiary and pre-Tertiary rocks of this region. Not all of the flat-topped mountain surfaces were correlated with this erosion surface, however, for some were believed to represent exhumed portions of an erosion surface on which the Tertiary rocks were deposited. Wahrhaftig thought it likely that once a relatively smooth plain with northward slope existed in the area. Present altitudes of the erosion remnants range from 3000 to 7000 feet and they have a northward gradient of about 90 feet per mile. If it is assumed that the old erosion surface had gradients no greater than present stream gradients, altitudes on the erosion surface would have been between 1000 and 2000 feet. Thus between 5000 and 6000 feet of uplift is suggested following development of the erosion surface, much of which apparently took place during Pleistocene time.

*Anomalous Drainage in Alaska Range.* Strong support for the existence of a former erosion surface in the Alaska Range is found in the drainage relationships here. There is a discordance between drainage and topography which can be explained most logically by assuming that the present drainage was inherited from a former erosion surface. The present northward-flowing streams form a dendritic pattern which extends at right angles to and across the east-west range structure. This suggests existence of an earlier drainage system that bore little resemblance to the present topography of the Alaska Range. The fact previously mentioned (see p. 572) that six rivers head south of the Alaska Range crest and flow northward through the range seems to lend further support to the belief that the present drainage was inherited from an old age surface that existed prior to the uplift of the present range.

Wahrhaftig (1950), in an earlier attempt to interpret the geomorphic history of southern Alaska, postulated the following succession of events:

1. Deposition of a discontinuous cover of early Tertiary sediments on a postmature topography.
2. Folding and faulting of the early Tertiary rocks during a mid-Tertiary orogeny, accompanied by contemporaneous deposition of several thousand feet of gravels in subsiding intramountain basins.
3. Development of an erosion surface of low relief, with drainage well adjusted to structure where the surface cut across hard pre-Tertiary rocks and with little structural control where the drainage was across Tertiary rocks.
4. Warping and minor faulting in late Tertiary and Quaternary time, resulting in major streams' being controlled in their courses by troughs produced by this deformation, except in areas of pre-Tertiary rocks where the new cycle of erosion inherited a well-adjusted drainage system from the erosion cycle during which the region was reduced to low relief.
5. Addition of the topographic details to the landscape by glacial and periglacial processes.

*Conclusions.* There seem to be considerable grounds for believing that various parts of Alaska have experienced periods during which the topography was reduced to a condition of low relief. Not enough information is available, however, to make very firm correlations between erosion surfaces in various parts of the state. Whether the ancient topographic surfaces were products of the processes commonly inferred by the term peneplanation is uncertain. If the present is any clue to the past, we must conclude that for much of Alaska cryoplanation processes may have been as significant as the fluviatile processes.

## REFERENCES CITED

Black, R. F. (1958a). Wrangell Mountains, in *Landscapes of Alaska*, Howel Williams, Editor, Univ. Calif. Press, 30–33.

―――― (1958b). Lowlands and plains of interior and western Alaska, in *Landscapes of Alaska*, Howel Williams, Editor, Univ. Calif. Press, 76–81.

―――― (1952). Polygonal patterns and ground conditions from aerial photographs, *Photogram. Engineering*, **18**, 123–134.

―――― and W. L. Barksdale (1949). Oriented lakes of northern Alaska, *Jour. Geol.*, **57**, 105–118.

Brooks, A. H. (1906). The geography and geology of Alaska, *U. S. Geol. Survey Profess. Paper* 45, 327 pp.

Bryan, Kirk (1946). Cryopedology—The study of frozen ground and intensive frost action with suggestions of nomenclature, *Am. Jour. Sci.*, **244**, 622–642.

Cady, W. M., R. E. Wallace, J. M. Hoare, and E. J. Webber (1955). The central Kuskokwim region, Alska, *U. S. Geol. Survey Profess. Paper* 268, 132 pp.

Capps, S. R. (1932). Glaciation in Alaska, *U. S. Geol. Survey Profess. Paper* 170-A, 1–8.

Carson, C. E., and K. M. Hussey (1962). The oriented lakes of Arctic Alaska, *Jour. Geol.*, **70**, 417–439.

Chapman, R. M. (1958). Interior highlands of eastern Alaska, in *Landscapes of Alaska*, Howel Williams, Editor, Univ. Calif. Press, 88–103.

*Climatography of the United States*, Climates of the States, Alaska (1959). U. S. Dept. Commerce, Weather Bureau, No. 60-49.

Coats, R. P. (1950). Volcanic activity in the Aleutian arc, *U. S. Geol. Survey Bull.* 974-B, 35–49.

Cockfield, W. E. (1921). Sixtymile and Ladue rivers area, Yukon, *Canadian Geol. Survey Memoir* 123, 60 pp.

Detterman, R. L., A. L. Bowsher, and J. T. Dutro, Jr. (1958). Glaciation on the Arctic slope of the Brooks Range, northern Alaska, *Arctic*, **11**, 43–61.

Dutro, J. T., Jr., and T. G. Payne (1957). *Geologic Map of Alaska*, U. S. Geol. Survey, Washington.

Field, W. O., Jr. (1958). *Geographic Study of Mountain Glaciation in the Northern Hemisphere*, Pt. 2-A, Alaska and adjoining parts of Canada, Amer. Geog. Soc., Dept of Exploration and Field Research, New York.

Gryc, George, (1958a). Brooks Range, in *Landscapes of Alaska*, Howel Williams, Editor, Univ. Calif. Press, 111–118.

―――― (1958b). Arctic Slope, in *Landscapes of Alaska*, Howel Williams, Editor, Univ. Calif. Press, 119–127.

―――― (1961). Progress report: A study of tectonics of Alaska, in *Geology of the Arctic*, G. O. Rasch, Editor, Univ. Toronto Press, 596.

Hoare, J. M. (1958). Interior highlands of western Alaska, in *Landscapes of Alaska*, Howel Williams, Editor, Univ. Calif. Press, 82–87.

Holmes, C. W., and C. R. Lewis (1961). Glacial geology of the Mount Chamberlin area, Brooks Range, Alaska, in *Geology of the Arctic*, G. O. Rasch, Editor, Univ. Toronto Press, 848–864.

Hopkins, D. M., T. N. V. Karlstrom, and others (1955). Permafrost and groundwater in Alaska, *U. S. Geol. Survey Profess. Paper* 264-F, 113–146.

Mertie, J. B., Jr. (1930). Mountain building in Alaska, *Am. Jour. Sci.*, **220**, 101–124.

—— (1937). The Yukon-Tanana region, Alaska, *U. S. Geol. Survey Bull.* 872, 276 pp.

Miller, D. J. (1958). Gulf of Alaska area, in *Landscapes of Alaska*, Howel Williams, Editor, Univ. Calif. Press, 19–29.

—— T. G. Payne, and George Gryc (1959). Geology of possible petroleum provinces in Alaska, *U. S. Geol. Survey Bull.* 1094, 131 pp.

Moffit, F. H. (1954). Geology of the eastern part of the Alaska Range and adjacent area, *U. S. Geol. Survey Bull.* 989-D, 63–218.

Payne, T. G., et al. (1951). Geology of the Arctic slope of Alaska, *U. S. Geol. Survey Oil and Gas Investigations Map* 126, Sheet 1.

Péwé, T. L. (1955). Origin of the upland silt near Fairbanks, Alaska, *Geol. Soc. Am. Bull.*, **66,** 699–724.

—— et al. (1953). Multiple glaciation in Alaska, *U. S. Geol. Survey Circular* 289, 13 pp.

Powers, H. A. (1958). Alaska Peninsula-Aleutian Islands, in *Landscapes of Alaska*, Howel Williams, Editor, Univ. Calif. Press, 61–75.

Reed, J. C. (1958). Exploration of naval petroleum reserve No. 4 and adjacent area, northern Alaska, 1944–1953, Part 1, History of exploration, *U. S. Geol. Survey Profess. Paper* 301, 192 pp.

Schrader, F. C. (1904). A reconnaissance in northern Alaska in 1901, *U. S. Geol. Survey Profess. Paper* 20, 139 pp.

Sharp, R. P. (1958). Malaspina Glacier, Alaska, *Geol. Soc. Am. Bull.*, **69,** 617–646.

Spencer, A. C. (1903). Pacific mountain system in British Columbia and Alaska, *Geol. Soc. Am. Bull.*, **14,** 117–132.

St. Amand, Pierre (1957). Geological and geophysical synthesis of the tectonics of portions of British Columbia, the Yukon Territory, and Alaska, *Geol. Soc. Am. Bull.*, **68,** 1343–1370.

Twenhofel, W. S., and C. L. Sainsbury (1958). Fault patterns in southeastern Alaska, *Geol. Soc. Am. Bull.*, **69,** 1431–1442.

Wahrhaftig, Clyde (1950). Physiographic history of southern Alaska: A hypothesis, *Geol. Soc. Am. Bull.*, **61,** 1532 (abs.).

—— (1958a). Quaternary geology of the Nenana River Valley and adjacent parts of the Alaska Range, *U. S. Geol. Survey Profess. Paper* 293-A, 1–68.

—— (1958b). The Alaska Range, in *Landscapes of Alaska*, Howel Williams, Editor, Univ. Calif. Press, 48–60.

—— (1960). The physiographic provinces of Alaska, *U. S. Geol. Survey Open File Report*, 76 pp.

Williams, J. R. (1962). Geologic reconnaissance of the Yukon Flats district, Alaska, *U. S. Geol. Survey Bull.* 1111-H, 289–331.

ADDITIONAL REFERENCES

Capps, S. R. (1940). Geology of the Alaska railroad region, *U. S. Geol. Survey Bull.* 907, 201 pp.

Fernald, A. T. (1960). Geomorphology of the upper Kuskokwin region, Alaska, *U. S. Geol. Survey Bull.* 1071-G, 191–279.

Hopkins, D. M. (1949). Thaw lakes and thaw sinks in the Imurik Lake area, Seward Peninsula, Alaska, *Jour. Geol.*, **57,** 119–131.

—— F. S. MacNeil, and E. B. Leopold (1960). The coastal plain at Nome, Alaska: A late Cenozoic type section for the Bering Strait region, *Rept. 21st Internat. Geol. Congr.*, Part IV, 46–57.

Karlstrom, T. N. V. (1960). Surficial deposits of Alaska, *U. S. Geol. Survey Profess. Paper* 400-B, B333–B335.

Lachenbruch, A. H. (1962). Mechanics of thermal contraction cracks and ice-wedge polygons in permafrost, *Geol. Soc. Amer. Spec. Paper* 70, 69 pp.

Leffingwell, E. DeK. (1919). The Canning River region, northern Alaska, *U. S. Geol. Survey Profess. Paper*, 109, 251 pp.

Miller, R. D., and Ernest Debrovolny (1959). Surficial geology of Anchorage and vicinity, Alaska, *U. S. Geol. Survey Bull.* 1093, 127 pp.

Payne, T. G. (1951). Geologic history of the Arctic slope, *U. S. Geol. Survey Oil and Gas Investigations Map* 126, Sheet 3.

Péwé, T. L. (1958). Geologic map of the Fairbanks quadrangle, Alaska, *U. S. Geol. Survey, Map* GQ-110.

Reed, J. C., Jr. (1961). Geology of the Mount McKinley quadrangle, Alaska, *U. S. Geol. Survey Bull.* 1108-A, 1–36.

Trainer, F. W. (1961). Eolian deposits of the Matanuska Valley agricultural region, Alaska, *U. S. Geol. Survey Bull.* 1121-C, 35 pp.

Wahrhaftig, Clyde (1954). Tectonic history of the central Alaska Range, *Geol. Soc. Am. Bull.*, **65,** 1317 (abs.).

—— and Allan Cox (1959). Rock glaciers in the Alaska Range, *Geol. Soc. Amer. Bull.*, **70,** 383–436.

# Author Index

# Subject Index